| General Information | 1 |
| Functional Index | 2 |
| Field-Programmable Logic | 3 |
| PROMs | 4 |
| RAMs and Memory-Based Code Converters | 5 |
| Designing with Texas Instruments Field-Programmable Logic | 6 |
| Mechanical Data | 7 |

# The TTL Data Book
# Volume 3

## TEXAS INSTRUMENTS

**IMPORTANT NOTICE**

Texas Instruments (TI) reserves the right to make changes in the devices or the device specifications identified in this publication without notice. TI advises its customers to obtain the latest version of device specifications to verify, before placing orders, that the information being relied upon by the customer is current.

TI warrants performance of its semiconductor products, including SNJ and SMJ devices, to current specifications in accordance with TI's standard warranty. Testing and other quality control techniques are utilized to the extent TI deems such testing necessary to support this warranty. Unless mandated by government requirements, specific testing of all parameters of each device is not necessarily performed.

In the absence of written agreement to the contrary, TI assumes no liability for TI applications assistance, customer's product design, or infringement of patents or copyrights of third parties by or arising from use of semiconductor devices described herein. Nor does TI warrant or represent that any license, either express or implied, is granted under any patent right, copyright, or other intellectual property right of TI covering or relating to any combination, machine, or process in which such semiconductor devices might be or are used.

Specifications contained in this data book supersede all data for these products published by TI in the US before January 1985.

General Information

Functional Index

Field Programmable Logic

PROM

RAMs and Memory-Based
Code Converters

Designing with Texas Instruments
Field Programmable Logic

Mechanical Data

# INTRODUCTION

In this volume, Texas Instruments presents technical information on field-programmable logic and memory devices, including Programmable Array Logic (PAL®) circuits, Field-Programmable Logic Array (FPLA) devices, and Schottky[†] TTL memories (PROMs, RAMs, and memory-based code converters).

TI's line of programmable array logic products includes high-speed leadership circuits as well as standard PALs which are pin-compatible and functionally equivalent with other programmable logic array devices available. This volume includes specifications on existing and future products including:

- High-performance IMPACT PALs and low-power IMPACT PALs with leadership speed at 12 ns and 25 ns (max), respectively
- 20-Pin and 24-pin standard and half-power PALs
- High-complexity Latched and Registered input PALs and Exclusive-OR arrays
- Simple PALs

Each of these offer the designer significant reductions in "custom" design cycle time, as well as savings in board space by reducing SSI/MSI package count by as much as 5 to 1.

Specifications for TI's two high-performance field-programmable logic arrays, TIFPLA839 and '840, are also detailed. Designed with both programmable AND and programmable OR arrays, these functions contain 32 product terms and six sum terms. Each of the sum-of-products output functions can be programmed either active high (true) or active low (true). They provide high-speed, data-path logic replacement where several conventional SSI functions can be implemented with a single FPLA package. Product preview information on six field programmable logic sequencers (FPLS) has been included.

TI's family of high-performance Schottky TTL memories offers a wide variety of organizations providing efficient solutions for virtually any size microcontrol or program memory application. This volume contains information on TI's standard PROMs and new high-speed Series 3 IMPACT PROMs, including:

- 256-Bit, 1K, and 2K PROMs suitable for logic replacement
- Standard and low-power 512 × 8, 4K PROM, and 1024 × 8, 8K PROM
- Series 3 PROMs:
  High-speed, 15ns, 32 × 8, 256-Bit PROM
  1K, 2K, 8K IMPACT PROMs in 4- or 8-Bit word width configurations
  2K × 8 and 4K × 4, 16K IMPACT PROMs, in both high-speed and low-power options

Series 3 PROMs feature high-speed access times and dependable titanium-tungsten fuse link programming elements in both low-density configurations for logic replacement, and high density configurations for high-performance memory application. Package options for these PROMs will include plastic and ceramic chip carriers as well as the standard DIPs. To achieve significant reductions in board space, TI offers the 16K, 2K × 8 Series 3 PROMs in a 300-mil, 24-pin DIP, and 28-pin chip carrier packages.

TI's leadership PAL ICs and Series 3 PROMs utilize our new advanced bipolar technology, IMPACT (IMPlanted Advanced Composed Technology). This unique innovation offers performance advantages in speed, power, and circuit density over preceding bipolar technologies and includes such features as:

- 2-$\mu$m Feature size
- 7-$\mu$ Metal pitch
- Walled emitter
- Ion implant
- Oxide isolation
- Composed masks

PAL is a registered trademark of Monolithic Memories Inc.
[†]Integrated Schottky-Barrier diode-clamped transistor is patented by Texas Instruments, U.S. Patent Number 3,463,975.

A new Field Programmable Logic Application Report has been incorporated in this data book as a reference tool. It provides the first-time user of field-programmable logic with a basic understanding of this powerful semicustom logic.

Also included in this volume is a Functional Index to all bipolar digital device types available or under development. All logic technologies (TTL, S, LS, ALS, AS), field-programmable logic, programmable read-only memories, and bipolar complex LSI are also included. Logic symbols and pin assignments for all bipolar devices are shown in the Product Guide section of Volume 1 with typical performance data and chip carrier information.

While this volume offers design and specification data for bipolar programmable logic and memory components, complete technical data for any TI semiconductor product is available from your nearest TI field sales office, local authorized TI distributor, or by calling Texas Instruments at 1-800-232-3200, ext. 951.

General Information

1

# ALPHANUMERIC INDEX

**1**

**General Information**

# GLOSSARY

**General Information** | **1**

## INTRODUCTION

These symbols, terms and definitions are in accordance with those currently agreed upon by the JEDEC Council of the Electronic Industries Association (EIA) for use in the USA and by the International Electrotechnical Commission (IEC) for international use.

## PART I — GENERAL CONCEPTS AND CLASSIFICATIONS OF CIRCUIT COMPLEXITY

**Chip-Enable Input**

A control input that when active permits operation of the integrated circuit for input, internal transfer, manipulation, refreshing, and/or output of data and when inactive causes the integrated circuit to be in reduced-power standby mode.
NOTE: See "chip-select input".

**Chip-Select Input**

A gating input that when inactive prevents input or output of data to or from an integrated circuit.
NOTE: See "chip-enable input".

**Field-Programmable Logic Array (FPLA)**

A user-programmable integrated circuit whose basic logic structure consists of a programmable AND array and whose outputs feed a programmable OR array.

**Gate Equivalent Circuit**

A basic unit-of-measure of relative digital-circuit complexity. The number of gate equivalent circuits is that number of individual logic gates that would have to be interconnected to perform the same function.

**Large-Scale Integration (LSI)**

A concept whereby a complete major subsystem or system function is fabricated as a single microcircuit. In this context a major subsystem or system, whether digital or linear, is considered to be one that contains 100 or more equivalent gates or circuitry of similar complexity.

**Mask-Programmed Read-Only Memory**

A read-only memory in which the data content of each cell is determined during manufacture by the use of a mask, the data content thereafter being unalterable.

**Medium-Scale Integration (MSI)**

A concept whereby a complete subsystem or system function is fabricated as a single microcircuit. The subsystem or system is smaller than for LSI, but whether digital or linear, is considered to be one that contains 12 or more equivalent gates or circuitry of similar complexity.

**Memory Cell**

The smallest subdivision of a memory into which a unit of data has been or can be entered, in which it is or can be stored, and from which it can be retrieved.

**Memory Integrated Circuit**

An integrated circuit consisting of memory cells and usually including associated circuits such as those for address selection, amplifiers, etc.

# GLOSSARY

**Output-Enable Input**

A gating input that when active permits the integrated circuit to output data and when inactive causes the integrated circuit output(s) to be at a high impedance (off).

**Programmable Array Logic (PAL)**

A user-programmable integrated circuit which utilizes proven fuse link technology to implement logic functions. Implements sum of products logic by using a programmable AND array whose outputs feed a fixed OR array.

**Programmable Read-Only Memory (PROM)**

A read-only memory that after being manufactured can have the data content of each memory cell altered once only.

**Random-Access Memory (RAM)**

A memory that permits access to any of its address locations in any desired sequence with similar access time for each location.
NOTE: The term RAM, as commonly used, denotes a read/write memory.

**Read/Write Memory**

A memory in which each cell may be selected by applying appropriate electronic input signals and the stored data may be either (a) sensed at appropriate output terminals, or (b) changed in response to other similar electronic input signals.

**Small-Scale Integration (SSI)**

Integrated circuits of less complexity than medium-scale integration (MSI).

**Typical (TYP)**

A calculated value representative of the specified parameter at nominal operating conditions ($V_{CC} = 5$ V, $T_A = 25°C$), based on the measured value of devices processed, to emulate the process distribution.

**Very-Large-Scale Integration (VLSI)**

A concept whereby a complete system function is fabricated as a single microcircuit. In this context, a system, whether digital or linear, is considered to be one that contains 3000 or more gates or circuitry of similar complexity.

**Volatile memory**

A memory the data content of which is lost when power is removed.

## PART 2 — OPERATING CONDITIONS AND CHARACTERISTICS (IN SEQUENCE BY LETTER SYMBOLS)

$f_{max}$     **Maximum clock frequency**
The highest rate at which the clock input of a bistable circuit can be driven through its required sequence while maintaining stable transitions of logic level at the output with input conditions established that should cause changes of output logic level in accordance with the specification.

$I_{CC}$     **Supply current**
The current into* the $V_{CC}$ supply terminal of an integrated circuit.

$I_{CCH}$     **Supply current, outputs high**
The current into* the $V_{CC}$ supply terminal of an integrated circuit when all (or a specified number) of the outputs are at the high level.

$I_{CCL}$     **Supply current, outputs low**
The current into* the $V_{CC}$ supply terminal of an integrated circuit when all (or a specified number) of the outputs are at the low level.

$I_{IH}$     **High-level input current**
The current into* an input when a high-level voltage is applied to that input.

$I_{IL}$     **Low-level input current**
The current into* an input when a low-level voltage is applied to that input.

$I_{OH}$     **High-level output current**
The current into* an output with input conditions applied that, according to the product specification, will establish a high level at the output.

$I_{OL}$     **Low-level output current**
The current into* an output with input conditions applied that, according to the product specification, will establish a low level at the output.

$I_{OS}$ ($I_O$)     **Short-circuit output current**
The current into* an output when that output is short-circuited to ground (or other specified potential) with input conditions applied to establish the output logic level farthest from ground potential (or other specified potential).

$I_{OZH}$     **Off-state (high-impedance-state) output current (of a three-state output) with high-level voltage applied**
The current flowing into* an output having three-state capability with input conditions established that, according to the product specification, will establish the high-impedance state at the output and with a high-level voltage applied to the output.
NOTE: This parameter is measured with other input conditions established that would cause the output to be at a low level if it were enabled.

$I_{OZL}$     **Off-state (high-Impedance-state) output current (of a three-state output) with low-level voltage applied**
The current flowing into* an output having three-state capability with input conditions established that, according to the product specification, will establish the high-impedance state at the output and with a low-level voltage applied to the output.
NOTE: This parameter is measured with other input conditions established that would cause the output to be at a high level if it were enabled.

*Current out of a terminal is given as a negative value.

# GLOSSARY

**V$_{IH}$**   **High-level input voltage**
An input voltage within the more positive (less negative) of the two ranges of values used to represent the binary variables.
NOTE: A minimum is specified that is the least-positive value of high-level input voltage for which operation of the logic element within specification limits is guaranteed.

**V$_{IK}$**   **Input clamp voltage**
An input voltage in a region of relatively low differential resistance that serves to limit the input voltage swing.

**V$_{IL}$**   **Low-level input voltage**
An input voltage level within the less positive (more negative) of the two ranges of values used to represent the binary variables.
NOTE: A maximum is specified that is the most-positive value of low-level input voltage for which operation of the logic element within specification limits is guaranteed.

**V$_{OH}$**   **High-level output voltage**
The voltage at an output terminal with input conditions applied that, according to the product specification, will establish a high level at the output.

**V$_{OL}$**   **Low-level output voltage**
The voltage at an output terminal with input conditions applied that, according to the product specification, will establish a low level at the output.

**t$_a$**   **Access time**
The time interval between the application of a specific input pulse and the availability of valid signals at an output.

**t$_{dis}$**   **Disable time (of a three-state output)**
The time interval between the specified reference points on the input and output voltage waveforms, with the three-state output changing from either of the defined active levels (high or low) to a high-impedance (off) state. (t$_{dis}$ = t$_{PHZ}$ or t$_{PLZ}$).

**t$_{en}$**   **Enable time (of a three-state output)**
The time interval between the specified reference points on the input and output voltage waveforms, with the three-state output changing from a high-impedance (off) state to either of the defined active levels (high or low). (t$_{en}$ = t$_{PZH}$ or t$_{PZL}$).

**t$_h$**   **Hold time**
The time interval during which a signal is retained at a specified input terminal after an active transition occurs at another specified input terminal.
NOTES: 1. The hold time is the actual time interval between two signal events and is determined by the system in which the digital circuit operates. A minimum value is specified that is the shortest interval for which correct operation of the digital circuit is guaranteed.
2. The hold time may have a negative value in which case the minimum limit defines the longest interval (between the release of the signal and the active transition) for which correct operation of the digital circuit is guaranteed.

**t$_{pd}$**   **Propagation delay time**
The time between the specified reference points on the input and output voltage waveforms with the output changing from one defined level (high or low) to the other defined level. (t$_{pd}$ = t$_{PHL}$ or t$_{PLH}$).

TEXAS
INSTRUMENTS

**t$_{PHL}$**     **Propagation delay time, high-to-low level output**
The time between the specified reference points on the input and output voltage waveforms with the output changing from the defined high level to the defined low level.

**t$_{PHZ}$**     **Disable time (of a three-state output) from high level**
The time interval between the specified reference points on the input and output voltage waveforms with the three-state output changing from the defined high level to a high-impedance (off) state.

**t$_{PLH}$**     **Propagation delay time, low-to-high-level output**
The time between the specified reference points on the input and output voltage waveforms with the output changing from the defined low level to the defined high level.

**t$_{PLZ}$**     **Disable time (of a three-state output) from low level**
The time interval between the specified reference points on the input and output voltage waveforms with the three-state output changing from the defined low level to a high-impedance (off) state.

**t$_{PZH}$**     **Enable time (of a three-state output) to high level**
The time interval between the specified reference points on the input and output voltage waveforms with the three-state output changing from a high-impedance (off) state to the defined high level.

**t$_{PZL}$**     **Enable time (of a three-state output) to low level**
The time interval between the specified reference points on the input and output voltage waveforms with the three-state output changing from a high-impedance (off) state to the defined low level.

**t$_{sr}$**     **Sense recovery time**
The time interval needed to switch a memory from a write mode to a read mode and to obtain valid data signals at the output.

**t$_{su}$**     **Setup time**
The time interval between the application of a signal at a specified input terminal and a subsequent active transition at another specified input terminal.
NOTES:  1.  The setup time is the actual time interval between two signal events and is determined by the system in which the digital circuit operates. A minimum value is specified that is the shortest interval for which correct operation of the digital circuit is guaranteed.
        2.  The setup time may have a negative value in which case the minimum limit defines the longest interval (between the active transition and the application of the other signal) for which correct operation of the digital circuit is guaranteed.

**t$_{w}$**     **Pulse duration (width)**
The time interval between specified reference points on the leading and trailing edges of the pulse waveform.

General Information

1

# EXPLANATION OF FUNCTION TABLES

The following symbols are used in function tables on TI data sheets:

| | | |
|---|---|---|
| H | = | high level (steady state) |
| L | = | low level (steady state) |
| ↑ | = | transition from low to high level |
| ↓ | = | transition from high to low level |
| → | = | value/level or resulting value/level is routed to indicated destination |
| ∩ | = | value/level is re-entered |
| X | = | irrelevant (any input, including transitions) |
| Z | = | off (high-impedance) state of a 3-state-output |
| a..h | = | the level of steady-state inputs at inputs A through H respectively |
| $Q_0$ | = | level of Q before the indicated steady-state input conditions were established |
| $\overline{Q}_0$ | = | complement of $Q_0$ or level of $\overline{Q}$ before the indicated steady-state input conditions were established |
| $Q_n$ | = | level of Q before the most recent active transition indicated by ↓ or ↑ |
| ⊓ | = | one high-level pulse |
| ⊔ | = | one low-level pulse |
| TOGGLE | = | each output changes to the complement of its previous level on each transition indicated by ↓ or ↑. |

If, in the input columns, a row contains only the symbols H, L, and/or X, this means the indicated output is valid whenever the input configuration is achieved and regardless of the sequence in which it is achieved. The output persists so long as the input configuration is maintained.

If, in the input columns, a row contains H, L, and/or X together with ↑ and/or ↓, this means the output is valid whenever the input configuration is achieved but the transition(s) must occur following the achievement of the steady-state levels. If the output is shown as a level (H, L, $Q_0$, or $\overline{Q}_0$), it persists so long as the steady-state input levels and the levels that terminate indicated transitions are maintained. Unless otherwise indicated, input transitions in the opposite direction to those shown have no effect at the output. (If the output is shown as a pulse, ⊓ or ⊔, the pulse follows the indicated input transition and persists for an interval dependent on the circuit.)

TEXAS
INSTRUMENTS

## PARAMETER MEASUREMENT INFORMATION

**FOR THREE-STATE OUTPUTS AND BI-STATE TOTEM-POLE OUTPUTS**

**FOR OPEN-COLLECTOR OUTPUTS**

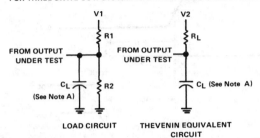

LOAD CIRCUIT    THEVENIN EQUIVALENT CIRCUIT

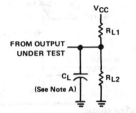

TEST CIRCUIT FOR USE WHEN R$_{L1}$ AND R$_{L2}$ ARE SPECIFIED

### VOLTAGE VALUES

| MEASUREMENTS | V$_{CC}$ | V1 | V2 |
|---|---|---|---|
| t$_{PLH}$ and t$_{PHL}$ | 5.5 V | 5.5 V | 3.7 V |
| | 5.25 V | 5.25 V | 3.5 V |
| | 4.75 V | 4.75 V | 3.2 V |
| | 4.5 V | 4.5 V | 3 V |
| t$_{PHZ}$ and t$_{PZH}$ | ALL | 0 V | 0 V |
| t$_{PLZ}$ and t$_{PZL}$ | ALL | 5 V | 3.3 V |

### RESISTOR VALUES

| I$_{OL}$MAX$^†$ | R1 | R2 | R$_L$ |
|---|---|---|---|
| 24 mA | 200 Ω | 400 Ω | 133 Ω |
| 20 mA | 240 Ω | 480 Ω | 160 Ω |
| 16 mA | 300 Ω | 600 Ω | 200 Ω |
| 12 mA | 400 Ω | 800 Ω | 267 Ω |
| 8 mA | 600 Ω | 1.2 kΩ | 400 Ω |

$^†$See Recommended Operating Conditions.

NOTE A: C$_L$ includes probe and jig capacitance.

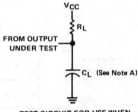

TEST CIRCUIT FOR USE WHEN SINGLE R$_L$ IS SPECIFIED

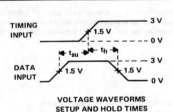

VOLTAGE WAVEFORMS
SETUP AND HOLD TIMES

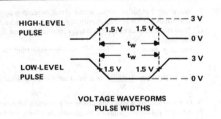

VOLTAGE WAVEFORMS
PULSE WIDTHS

General Information

## PARAMETER MEASUREMENT INFORMATION

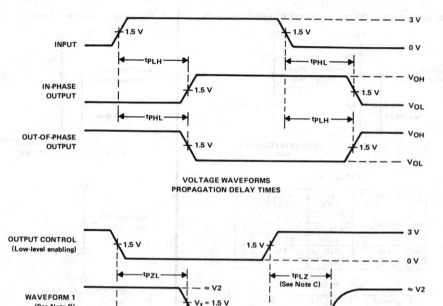

**VOLTAGE WAVEFORMS**
**PROPAGATION DELAY TIMES**

**VOLTAGE WAVEFORMS**
**ENABLE AND DISABLE TIMES, THREE-STATE OUTPUTS**

NOTES: B. Waveform 1 is for an output with internal conditions such that the output is low except when disabled by the output control.
Waveform 2 is for an output with internal conditions such that the output is high except when disabled by the output control.

C. TI normally measures $t_{PLZ}$ and $t_{PHZ}$ by reading at the 1.5-volt ($V_t$) point on the waveform and subtracting the RC time from the reading.

For $t_{PLZ}$, RCin $\dfrac{V2 - V_{OL}\ max}{V2 - V_t}$ is subtracted from the reading.

For $t_{PHZ}$, RCin $\dfrac{V_{OH}min}{V_t}$ is subtracted from the reading.

D. In the examples above, the phase relationships between inputs and outputs have been chosen arbitrarily.

E. All input pulses are supplied by generators having the following characteristics: PRR $\leq$ 1 MHz, $Z_{out} \approx$ 50 $\Omega$, $t_r \leq$ 2.5 ns, $t_f \leq$ 2.5 ns.

**1**

**General Information**

## PARAMETER MEASUREMENT INFORMATION

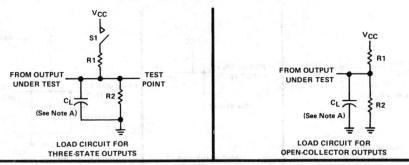

LOAD CIRCUIT FOR
THREE-STATE OUTPUTS

LOAD CIRCUIT FOR
OPEN-COLLECTOR OUTPUTS

### RESISTOR VALUES

| $I_{OL}$ MAX† | R1* | R2* |
|---|---|---|
| 24 mA | 200 Ω | 400 Ω |
| 20 mA | 240 Ω | 480 Ω |
| 16 mA | 300 Ω | 600 Ω |
| 12 mA | 400 Ω | 800 Ω |
| 8 mA | 600 Ω | 1.2 kΩ |

†See Recommended Operating Conditions.
*Unless otherwise specified.

NOTE A: $C_L$ includes probe and jig capacitance.

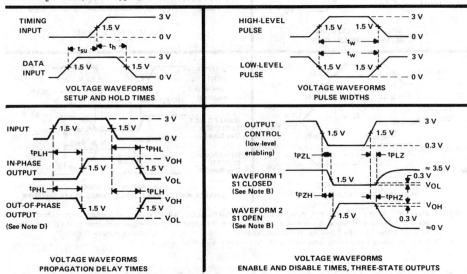

VOLTAGE WAVEFORMS
SETUP AND HOLD TIMES

VOLTAGE WAVEFORMS
PULSE WIDTHS

VOLTAGE WAVEFORMS
PROPAGATION DELAY TIMES

VOLTAGE WAVEFORMS
ENABLE AND DISABLE TIMES, THREE-STATE OUTPUTS

NOTES: B. Waveform 1 is for an output with internal conditions such that the output is low except when disabled by the output control.
Waveform 2 is for an output with internal conditions such that the output is high except when disabled by the output control.
C. All input pulses have the following characteristics: PRR ≤ 1 MHz, $t_r$ = $t_f$ = 2 ns, duty cycle = 50%.
D. When measuring propagation delay times of 3-state outputs, switch S1 is closed.

TEXAS
INSTRUMENTS

General Information

1

**General Information**

## PARAMETER MEASUREMENT INFORMATION

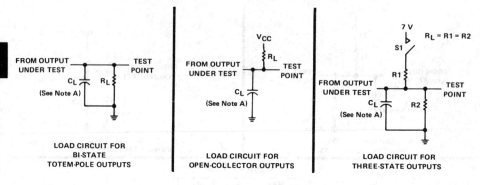

LOAD CIRCUIT FOR
BI-STATE
TOTEM-POLE OUTPUTS

LOAD CIRCUIT FOR
OPEN-COLLECTOR OUTPUTS

LOAD CIRCUIT FOR
THREE-STATE OUTPUTS

NOTE A: $C_L$ includes probe and jig capacitance.

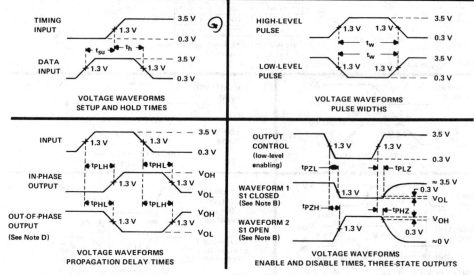

VOLTAGE WAVEFORMS
SETUP AND HOLD TIMES

VOLTAGE WAVEFORMS
PULSE WIDTHS

VOLTAGE WAVEFORMS
PROPAGATION DELAY TIMES

VOLTAGE WAVEFORMS
ENABLE AND DISABLE TIMES, THREE-STATE OUTPUTS

NOTES: B. Waveform 1 is for an output with internal conditions such that the output is low except when disabled by the output control.
Waveform 2 is for an output with internal conditions such that the output is high except when disabled by the output control.
C. All input pulses have the following characteristics: PRR $\leq$ 1 MHz, $t_r = t_f = 2$ ns, duty cycle = 50%.
D. When measuring propagation delay times of 3-state outputs, switch S1 is closed.

**TEXAS INSTRUMENTS**

### RAM AND MEMORY-BASED CODE CONVERTERS NUMBERING SYSTEM
### AND ORDERING INSTRUCTIONS

Electrical characteristics presented in this data book, unless otherwise noted, apply for circuit type(s) listed in the page heading regardless of package. the availability of a circuit function in a particular package is denoted by an alphabetical reference above the pin-connection diagram(s). These alphabetical references refer to mechanical outline drawings shown in this section.

Factor orders for circuits described in this catalog should include a four-part type number as explained in the following example.

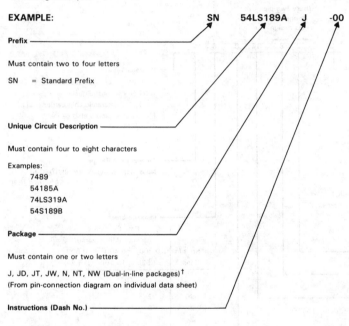

**EXAMPLE:**      SN    54LS189A   J    -00

**Prefix**

Must contain two to four letters

SN    = Standard Prefix

**Unique Circuit Description**

Must contain four to eight characters

Examples:
> 7489
> 54185A
> 74LS319A
> 54S189B

**Package**

Must contain one or two letters

J, JD, JT, JW, N, NT, NW (Dual-in-line packages)[†]
(From pin-connection diagram on individual data sheet)

**Instructions (Dash No.)**

Must contain two numbers

— 00 No special instructions
— 10 Solder-dipped leads (N and NT packages only)

[†]These circuits in dual-in-line packages are shipped in one of the carriers shown below. Unless a specific method of shipment is specified by the customer (with possible additional costs), circuits will be shipped in the most practical carrier. Please contact your TI sales representative for the method that will best suit your particular needs.

Dual-in-line (J, JD, JT, JW, N, NT, NW)

— Slide Magazines
— A-Channel Plastic Tubing
— Barnes Carrier (N only)
— Sectioned Cardboard Box
— Individual Plastic Box

**1**

### PROM NUMBERING SYSTEM AND ORDERING INSTRUCTIONS

To complement Texas Instruments continually expanding line of bipolar PROMs, a new numbering system is being implemented. This system provides the user with information regarding the generic programming family, bit density, organization, temperature range, and the size and type of package without the necessity of looking up this information in tables. Below is a guide for use of this new numbering system.

Factory orders for PROMs described in this book should include a type number as explained in the following example.

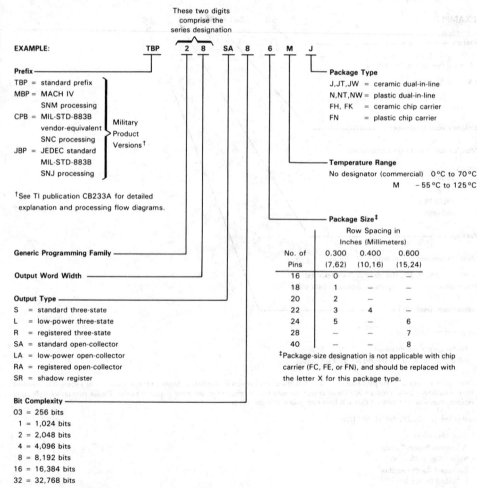

These two digits comprise the series designation

EXAMPLE:  TBP  2  8  SA  8  6  M  J

**Prefix**
TBP = standard prefix
MBP = MACH IV
   SNM processing
CPB = MIL-STD-883B
   vendor-equivalent
   SNC processing
JBP = JEDEC standard
   MIL-STD-883B
   SNJ processing
} Military Product Versions[†]

[†]See TI publication CB233A for detailed explanation and processing flow diagrams.

**Generic Programming Family**

**Output Word Width**

**Output Type**
S = standard three-state
L = low-power three-state
R = registered three-state
SA = standard open-collector
LA = low-power open-collector
RA = registered open-collector
SR = shadow register

**Bit Complexity**
03 = 256 bits
 1 = 1,024 bits
 2 = 2,048 bits
 4 = 4,096 bits
 8 = 8,192 bits
16 = 16,384 bits
32 = 32,768 bits

**Package Type**
J,JT,JW = ceramic dual-in-line
N,NT,NW = plastic dual-in-line
FH, FK = ceramic chip carrier
FN  = plastic chip carrier

**Temperature Range**
No designator (commercial) 0 °C to 70 °C
       M  −55 °C to 125 °C

**Package Size[‡]**

| No. of Pins | Row Spacing in Inches (Millimeters) | | |
| --- | --- | --- | --- |
| | 0.300 (7,62) | 0.400 (10,16) | 0.600 (15,24) |
| 16 | 0 | — | — |
| 18 | 1 | — | — |
| 20 | 2 | — | — |
| 22 | 3 | 4 | — |
| 24 | 5 | — | 6 |
| 28 | — | — | 7 |
| 40 | — | — | 8 |

[‡]Package-size designation is not applicable with chip carrier (FC, FE, or FN), and should be replaced with the letter X for this package type.

**TEXAS INSTRUMENTS**

## PAL® NUMBERING SYSTEM AND ORDERING INSTRUCTIONS

Factory orders for leadership PAL® circuits described in this catalog should include a nine-part type number as explained in the example below. Exclude the prefix when ordering standard PALs.

**EXAMPLE:**  TIB  PAL  16  R  8  −15  C  N

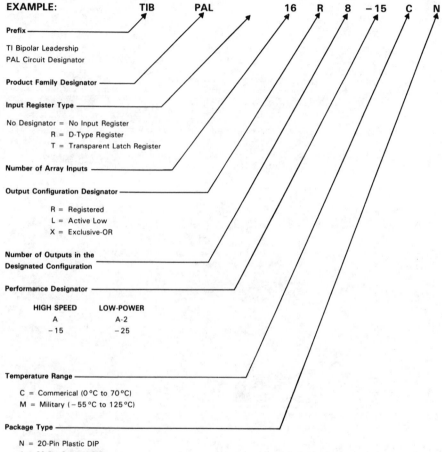

**Prefix**

TI Bipolar Leadership
PAL Circuit Designator

**Product Family Designator**

**Input Register Type**

No Designator = No Input Register
R = D-Type Register
T = Transparent Latch Register

**Number of Array Inputs**

**Output Configuration Designator**

R = Registered
L = Active Low
X = Exclusive-OR

**Number of Outputs in the
Designated Configuration**

**Performance Designator**

| HIGH SPEED | LOW-POWER |
|---|---|
| A | A-2 |
| −15 | −25 |

**Temperature Range**

C = Commerical (0 °C to 70 °C)
M = Military (−55 °C to 125 °C)

**Package Type**

N = 20-Pin Plastic DIP
J = 20-Pin Ceramic DIP
NT = 24-Pin, 300-mil Plastic DIP
JT = 24-Pin, 300-mil Ceramic Dip
JW = 24-Pin, 600-mil Ceramic DIP
NW = 24-Pin, 600-mil Plastic DIP
FN = Plastic Chip Carrier
FH, FK = Ceramic Chip Carrier

PAL is a registered trademark of Monolithic Memories Inc.

TEXAS
INSTRUMENTS

General Information

---

### ADDRESS FOR PAL AND FPLA PROGRAMMING AND SOFTWARE MANUFACTURERS*

## HARDWARE MANUFACTURERS

Citel
3060 Raymond St.
Santa Clara, CA 95050
(408) 727-6562

Structured Design
1700 Wyatt Dr., Suite 7
Santa Clara, CA 95054
(408) 988-0725

DATA I/O
10525 Willows Rd.
Redmond, WA 98052
(206) 881-6444

Sunrise Electronics
524 S. Vermont Avenue
Glendora, CA 91740
(213) 914-1926

DIGITAL MEDIA
3178 Gibralter Ave.
Costa Mesa, CA 92626
(714) 751-1373

Valley Data Sciences
2426 Charleston Rd.
Mountain View, CA 94043
(415) 968-2900

Kontron Electronics
630 Price Avenue
Redwood City, CA 94063
(415) 361-1012

Varix
1210 Campbell Rd.
Richardson, TX 75081
(214) 437-0777

Stag Micro Systems
528-5 Weddell Drive
Sunnyvale, CA 94086
(408) 745-1991

Wavetec/Digelec
586 Weddel Dr. Suite 1
Sunnyvale, CA 94089
(408) 745-0722

Storey Systems
3201 N. Hwy 67, Suite H
Mesquite, TX 75150
(214) 270-4135

## SOFTWARE MANUFACTURERS

Assisted Technologies (CUPL)
2381 Zanker Road, Suite 150
Santa Clara, CA 95050
(408) 942-8787

Monolithic Memories Inc. (PALASM)
2175 Mission College Blvd.
Santa Clara, CA 95050
(408) 970-9700

DATA I/O (ABEL)
10525 Willows Rd.
Redmond, WA 98052
(206) 881-6444

*Texas Instruments does not endorse or warrant the suppliers referenced. Presently, Texas Instruments has certified DATA I/O, Sunrise, Structured Design and Digital Media. Other programmers are now in the certification process. For a current list of certified programmers, please contact your local TI sales representative.

General Information

1

## ADDRESS FOR PROM PROGRAMMING AND SOFTWARE MANUFACTURERS*

### HARDWARE MANUFACTURERS

Citel
3060 Raymond St.
Santa Clara, CA 95050
(408) 727-6562

DATA I/O
10525 Willows Rd.
Redmond, WA 98052
(206) 881-6444

DIGITAL MEDIA
3178 Gibralter Ave.
Costa Mesa, CA 92626
(714) 751-1373

Kontron Electronics
630 Price Avenue
Redwood City, CA 94063
(415) 361-1012

Stag Micro Systems
528-5 Weddell Drive
Sunnyvale, CA 94086
(408) 745-1991

Sunrise Electronics
524 S. Vermont Avenue
Glendora, CA 91740
(213) 914-1926

Valley Data Sciences
2426 Charleston Rd.
Mountain View, CA 94043
(415) 968-2900

Varix
1210 Campbell Rd.
Richardson, TX 75081
(214) 437-0777

Wavetec/Digelec
586 Weddel Dr., Suite 1
Sunnyvale, CA 94089
(408) 745-0722

### SOFTWARE MANUFACTURERS

Assisted Technologies (CUPL)
2381 Zanker Road, Suite 150
Santa Clara, CA 95050
(408) 942-8787

DATA I/O (ABEL), (PROMLINK)
10525 Willows Rd.
Redmond, WA 98052
(206) 881-6444

Monolithic Memories Inc. (PLEASM)
2175 Mission College Blvd.
Santa Clara, CA 95050
(408) 970-9700

*Texas Instruments does not endorse or warrant the suppliers referenced. Presently, Texas Instruments has certified DATA I/O. Other programmers are now in the certification process. For a current list of certified programmers, please contact your local TI sales representative.

# GATES AND INVERTERS

## POSITIVE-NAND GATES AND INVERTERS

| DESCRIPTION | TYPE | STD TTL | ALS | AS | H | L | LS | S | VOLUME |
|---|---|---|---|---|---|---|---|---|---|
| Hex 2-Input Gates | '804 | | A | B | | | | | 3 |
| Hex Inverters | '04 | ● | | | ● | ● | ● | ● | 2 |
| | | | A | ● | | | | | 3 |
| | '1004 | | ● | ● | | | | | 3 |
| Quadruple 2-Input Gates | '00 | ● | | | ● | ● | ● | ● | 2 |
| | | | A | ● | | | | | 3 |
| | '1000 | | A | A | | | | | 3 |
| Triple 3-Input Gates | '10 | ● | | | ● | ● | ● | ● | 2 |
| | | | A | ● | | | | | 3 |
| | '1010 | | A | | | | | | 3 |
| Dual 4-Input Gates | '20 | ● | | | ● | ● | ● | ● | 2 |
| | | | A | ● | | | | | 3 |
| | '1020 | | A | | | | | | 3 |
| 8-Input Gates | '30 | ● | | | ● | ● | ● | ● | 2 |
| | | | A | ● | | | | | 3 |
| 13-Input Gates | '133 | | | | | | | ● | 2 |
| | | | ● | | | | | | 3 |
| Dual 2-Input Gates | '8003 | | ● | | | | | | 3 |

## POSITIVE-NAND GATES AND INVERTERS WITH OPEN-COLLECTOR OUTPUTS

| DESCRIPTION | TYPE | STD TTL | ALS | AS | H | L | LS | S | VOLUME |
|---|---|---|---|---|---|---|---|---|---|
| Hex Inverters | '05 | ● | | | ● | | ● | ● | 2 |
| | | | A | | | | | | 3 |
| | '1005 | | ● | | | | | | 3 |
| Quadruple 2-Input Gates | '01 | ● | | | ● | | ● | | 2 |
| | | | ● | | | | | | 3 |
| | '03 | ● | | | | ● | ● | | 2 |
| | | | | B | | | | | |
| | '1003 | | A | | | | | | 3 |
| Triple 3-Input Gates | '12 | ● | | | | | ● | | 2 |
| | | | A | | | | | | 3 |
| Dual 4-Input Gates | '22 | ● | | | ● | | ● | ● | 2 |
| | | | | B | | | | | 3 |

## POSITIVE-AND GATES

| DESCRIPTION | TYPE | STD TTL | ALS | AS | H | LS | S | VOLUME |
|---|---|---|---|---|---|---|---|---|
| Hex 2-Input Gates | '808 | | A | B | | | | 3 |
| Quadruple 2-Input Gates | '08 | ● | | | | ● | ● | 2 |
| | | | ● | ● | | | | 3 |
| | '1008 | | A | ● | | | | 3 |
| Triple 3-Input Gates | '11 | ● | | | ● | ● | ● | 2 |
| | | | A | ● | | | | 3 |
| | '1011 | | A | | | | | 3 |
| Dual 4-Input Gates | '21 | | | | ● | ● | | 2 |
| | | | ● | ● | | | | 3 |
| Triple 4-Input AND/NAND | '800 | | ▲ | | | | | 3 |

## POSITIVE-AND GATES WITH OPEN-COLLECTOR OUTPUTS

| DESCRIPTION | TYPE | STD TTL | ALS | AS | H | LS | S | VOLUME |
|---|---|---|---|---|---|---|---|---|
| Quadruple 2-Input Gates | '09 | ● | | | | ● | ● | 2 |
| | | | ● | | | | | 3 |
| Triple 3-Input Gates | '15 | | | | ● | ● | ● | 2 |
| | | | A | | | | | 3 |

## POSITIVE-OR GATES

| DESCRIPTION | TYPE | STD TTL | ALS | AS | LS | S | VOLUME |
|---|---|---|---|---|---|---|---|
| Hex 2-Input Gates | '832 | | A | B | | | 3 |
| Quadruple 2-Input Gates | '32 | ● | | | ● | ● | 2 |
| | | | ● | ● | | | |
| | '1032 | | A | ● | | | 3 |
| Triple 4-Input OR/NOR | '802 | | ▲ | | | | 3 |

## POSITIVE-NOR GATES

| DESCRIPTION | TYPE | STD TTL | ALS | AS | L | LS | S | VOLUME |
|---|---|---|---|---|---|---|---|---|
| Hex 2-Input Gates | '805 | | A | B | | | | 3 |
| Quadruple 2-Input Gates | '02 | ● | | | ● | ● | ● | 2 |
| | | | ● | ● | | | | |
| | '1002 | | A | | | | | 3 |
| Triple 3-Input Gates | '27 | ● | | | | ● | | 2 |
| | | | ● | ● | | | | 3 |
| Dual 4-Input Gates with Strobe | '25 | ● | | | | | | 2 |
| Dual 5-Input Gates | '260 | | | | | | ● | 2 |

## SCHMITT-TRIGGER POSITIVE-NAND GATES AND INVERTERS

| DESCRIPTION | TYPE | STD TTL | ALS | AS | LS | S | VOLUME |
|---|---|---|---|---|---|---|---|
| Hex Inverters | '14 | ● | | | ● | | |
| | '19 | | | | ● | | |
| Octal Inverters | '619 | | | | ● | | |
| Dual 4-Input Positive-NAND | '13 | ● | | | ● | | 2 |
| | '18 | | | | ● | | |
| Triple 4-Input Positive-NAND | '618 | | | | ● | | |
| Quadruple 2-Input Positive-NAND | '24 | | | | ● | | |
| | '132 | ● | | | ● | ● | |

## CURRENT-SENSING GATES

| DESCRIPTION | TYPE | ALS | AS | LS | VOLUME |
|---|---|---|---|---|---|
| Hex | '63 | | | ● | 2 |

## DELAY ELEMENTS

| DESCRIPTION | TYP | ALS | AS | LS | VOLUME |
|---|---|---|---|---|---|
| Inverting and Noninverting Elements, 2-Input NAND Buffers | '31 | | | ● | 2 |

● Denotes available technology.
▲ Denotes planned new products.
A Denotes "A" suffix version available in the technology indicated.
B Denotes "B" suffix version available in the technology indicated.

**2**

Functional Index

TEXAS INSTRUMENTS

## GATES, EXPANDERS, BUFFERS, DRIVERS, AND TRANSCEIVERS

### AND-OR-INVERT GATES

| DESCRIPTION | TYPE | STD TTL | ALS | AS | H | L | LS | S | VOLUME |
|---|---|---|---|---|---|---|---|---|---|
| 2-Wide 4-Input | '55 | | | | • | • | • | | |
| 4-Wide 2-2-3-2 Input | '64 | | | | | | | • | |
| 4-Wide 2-2-3-2 Input | '54 | | | | • | | | | 2 |
| 4-Wide 2-Input | '54 | • | | | | | | | |
| 4-Wide 2-3-3-2 Input | '54 | | | | | • | • | | |
| Dual 2-Wide 2-Input | '51 | • | | | • | • | • | • | |

### AND-OR-INVERT GATES WITH OPEN-COLLECTOR OUTPUTS

| DESCRIPTION | TYPE | STD TTL | ALS | AS | S | VOLUME |
|---|---|---|---|---|---|---|
| 4-Wide 2-2-3-2 Input | '65 | | | | • | 2 |

### EXPANDABLE GATES

| DESCRIPTION | TYPE | STD TTL | ALS | AS | H | L | LS | VOLUME |
|---|---|---|---|---|---|---|---|---|
| Dual 4-Input Positive-NOR with Strobe | '23 | • | | | | | | |
| 4-Wide AND-OR | '52 | | | | • | | | |
| 4-Wide AND-OR-INVERT | '53 | • | | | • | | | 2 |
| 2-Wide AND-OR-INVERT | '55 | | | | • | • | • | |
| Dual 2-Wide AND-OR-INVERT | '50 | • | | | • | | | |

### EXPANDERS

| DESCRIPTION | TYPE | STD TTL | ALS | AS | H | VOLUME |
|---|---|---|---|---|---|---|
| Dual 4-Input | '60 | • | | | • | |
| Triple 3-Input | '61 | | | | • | 2 |
| 3-2-2-3 Input AND-OR | '62 | | | | • | |

### BUFFER AND INTERFACE GATES WITH OPEN-COLLECTOR OUTPUTS

| DESCRIPTION | TYPE | STD TTL | ALS | AS | LS | S | VOLUME |
|---|---|---|---|---|---|---|---|
| Hex | '07 | • | | | | | 2 |
| | '17 | • | | | | | |
| | '35 | | • | | | | 3 |
| | '1035 | | • | | | | 3 |
| Hex Inverter | '06 | • | | | | | 2 |
| | '16 | • | | | | | |
| | '1005 | | • | | | | 3 |
| Quad 2-Input Positive-NAND | '26 | • | | | • | | 2 |
| | '38 | | A | | • | • | 3 |
| | '39 | • | | | • | | 2 |
| | '1003 | | A | | | | 3 |
| Quad 2-Input Positive-NOR | '33 | • | | | • | | 2 |
| | | | A | | | | 3 |

### BUFFERS, DRIVERS, AND BUS TRANSCEIVERS WITH OPEN-COLLECTOR OUTPUTS

| DESCRIPTION | TYPE | STD TTL | ALS | AS | LS | S | VOLUME |
|---|---|---|---|---|---|---|---|
| Noninverting Octal Buffers/Drivers | '743 | | A | | | | |
| | '757 | | • | • | | | |
| | '760 | | | • | | | |
| Inverting Octal Buffers/Drivers | '742 | | A | | | | |
| | '756 | | | • | | | 3 |
| | '763 | | • | • | | | |
| Inverting and Noninverting Octal Buffers/Drivers | '762 | | • | • | | | |
| Noninverting Quad Transceivers | '759 | | | • | | | |
| Inverting Quad Transceivers | '758 | | | • | | | |

• Denotes available technology.

▲ Denotes planned new products.

A Denotes ''A'' suffix version available in the technology indicated.

TEXAS INSTRUMENTS

## GATES, EXPANDERS, BUFFERS, DRIVERS, AND TRANSCEIVERS

**GATES, BUFFERS, DRIVERS, AND BUS TRANSCEIVERS WITH 3-STATE OUTPUTS**

| DESCRIPTION | TYPE | STD TTL | ALS | AS | LS | S | VOLUME |
|---|---|---|---|---|---|---|---|
| Noninverting 10-Bit Buffers Drivers | '29827 | | ▲ | | | | |
| Inverting 10-Bit Buffers Drivers | '29828 | | ▲ | | | | |
| Noninverting 10-Bit Transceivers | '29861 | | ▲ | | | | |
| Inverting 10-Bit Transceivers | '29862 | | ▲ | | | | LSI |
| Noninverting 9-Bit Transceivers | '29863 | | ▲ | | | | |
| Inverting 9-Bit Transceivers | '29864 | | ▲ | | | | |
| | '241 | | | | ● | ● | 2 |
| | | | A | ● | | | 3 |
| | '244 | | | | ● | ● | 2 |
| | | | A | ● | | | 3 |
| Noninverting | '465 | | | | ● | | 2 |
| Octal Buffers/Drivers | | | A | | | | 3 |
| | '467 | | | | ● | | 2 |
| | | | A | | | | 3 |
| | '541 | | | | ● | | 2 |
| | | | ● | | | | |
| | '1241ᶜ | | | ▲ | | | 3 |
| | '1244ᶜ | | A | | | | |
| | '231 | | | | ● | ● | |
| | '240 | | | | ● | ● | 2 |
| | | | A | ● | | | 3 |
| Inverting Octal | '466 | | | | ● | | 2 |
| Buffers/Drivers | | | A | | | | 3 |
| | '468 | | | | ● | | 2 |
| | | | A | | | | 3 |
| | '540 | | | | ● | | 2 |
| | | | ● | | | | 3 |
| | '1240ᶜ | | | ● | | | |
| Inverting and Noninverting | '230 | | | ● | | | 3 |
| Octal Buffers/Drivers | | | | | | | |
| | '245 | | | | ● | | 2 |
| Octal Transceivers | | | A | ● | | | 3 |
| | '1245 | | | A | | | |
| | '365 | A | | | A | | 2 |
| Noninverting | | | ● | | | | 3 |
| Hex Buffers/Drivers | '367 | A | | | A | | 2 |
| | | | ● | | | | 3 |
| Inverting | '366 | A | | | A | | 2 |
| | | | ▲ | | | | 3 |
| Hex Buffers/Drivers | '368 | A | | | A | | 2 |
| | | | ▲ | | | | 3 |
| Quad Buffers/Drivers | '125 | ● | | | A | | |
| with Independent | '126 | ● | | | A | | |
| | '425 | ● | | | | | 2 |
| Output Controls | '426 | ● | | | | | |
| Noninverting | '243 | | | | ● | | |
| Quad Transceivers | | | A | ● | | | 3 |
| | '1243ᶜ | | ▲ | | | | |
| Inverting | '242 | | | | ● | | 2 |
| Quad Transceivers | | | A | ● | | | 3 |
| | '1242ᶜ | | ● | | | | |
| Quad Transceivers with Storage | '226 | | | | | ● | 2 |
| 12-Input NAND Gate | '134 | | | | | ● | |

**50-OHM/75-OHM LINE DRIVERS**

| DESCRIPTION | TYPE | STD TTL | ALS | AS | S | VOLUME |
|---|---|---|---|---|---|---|
| Hex 2-Input Positive-NAND | '804 | | A | B | | |
| Hex 2-Input Positive-NOR | '805 | | A | B | | |
| Hex 2-Input Positive-AND | '808 | | A | B | | 3 |
| Hex 2-Input Positive-OR | '832 | | A | B | | |
| Quad 2-Input Positive-NOR | '128 | ● | | | | 2 |
| Dual 4-Input Positive-NAND | '140 | | | | ● | |

● Denotes available technology.
▲ Denotes planned new products.
ᶜ Denotes very low power.
A Denotes "A" suffix version available in the technology indicated.
B Denotes "B" suffix version available in the technology indicated.

**2** Functional Index

# BUFFERS, DRIVERS, TRANSCEIVERS, AND CLOCK GENERATORS

## BUFFERS, CLOCK/MEMORY DRIVERS

| DESCRIPTION | TYPE | STD TTL | ALS | AS | H | LS | S | VOLUME |
|---|---|---|---|---|---|---|---|---|
| Hex 2-Input Positive-NAND | '804 | | A | B | | | | |
| Hex 2-Input Positive-NOR | '805 | | A | B | | | | |
| Hex 2-Input Positive-AND | '808 | | A | B | | | | |
| Hex 2-Input Positive-OR | '832 | | A | B | | | | 3 |
| Hex Inverter | '1004 | | • | • | | | | |
| Hex Buffer | '34 | | • | • | | | | |
| | '1034 | | • | A | | | | |
| Quad 2-Input Positive-NAND | '37 | • | | | | • | • | 2 |
| | '1000 | | A | • | | | | 3 |
| Quad 2-Input Positive-NOR | '28 | • | | | | • | | 2 |
| | '1002 | | A | | | | | |
| | '1036 | | | A | | | | |
| Quad 2-Input Positive-AND | '1008 | | A | • | | | | |
| Quad 2-Input Positive-OR | '1032 | | A | • | | | | 3 |
| Triple 3-Input Positive-NAND | '1010 | | A | | | | | |
| Triple 3-Input Positive-AND | '1011 | | A | | | | | |
| Triple 4-Input AND-NAND | '800 | | ▲ | | | | | |
| Triple 4-Input OR-NOR | '802 | | ▲ | | | | | |
| Dual 4-Input Positive-NAND | '40 | • | | | • | • | • | 2 |
| | '1020 | | A | | | | | 3 |
| Line Driver/Memory Driver with Series Damping Resistor | '436 | | | | | • | | 2 |
| Line Driver/Memory Driver | '437 | | | | | | • | |

## BI-/TRI-DIRECTIONAL BUS TRANSCEIVERS AND DRIVERS

| DESCRIPTION | TYPE OF OUTPUT | TYPE | ALS | AS | LS | S | VOLUME |
|---|---|---|---|---|---|---|---|
| Quad with Bit Direction | 3-State | '446 | | | • | | |
| Controls | 3-State | '449 | | | • | | |
| | OC | '440 | | | • | | |
| | OC | '441 | | | • | | |
| Quad Tridirection | 3-State | '442 | | | • | | 2 |
| | 3-State | '443 | | | • | | |
| | 3-State | '444 | | | • | | |
| | OC | '448 | | | • | | |
| 4-Bit with Storage | 3-State | '226 | | | | • | |

## OCTAL BUS TRANSCEIVERS/MOS DRIVERS

| DESCRIPTION | TYPE | STD TTL | ALS | AS | LS | S | VOLUME |
|---|---|---|---|---|---|---|---|
| Inverting Outputs, 3-State | '2620 | | | • | | | |
| | '2640 | | | • | | | |
| True Outputs, 3-State | '2623 | | | • | | | 3 |
| | '2645 | | | • | | | |

## OCTAL BUFFERS AND LINE DRIVERS WITH INPUT/OUTPUT RESISTORS

| DESCRIPTION | | TYPE | STD TTL | ALS | AS | LS | S | VOLUME |
|---|---|---|---|---|---|---|---|---|
| Input Resistors | Inverting Outputs | '746 | | • | | | | |
| | Noninverting Outputs | '747 | | • | | | | |
| Output Resistors | Inverting Outputs | '2540 | | • | | | | 3 |
| | Noninverting Outputs | '2541 | | • | | | | |

## OCTAL BI-/TRI-DIRECTIONAL BUS TRANSCEIVERS

| DESCRIPTION | TYPE OF OUTPUT | TYPE | ALS | AS | LS | VOLUME |
|---|---|---|---|---|---|---|
| 12 mA 24 mA 48 mA 64 mA Sink, True Outputs — Low Power | 3-State | '245 | A | • | | 3 |
| | | | | | • | 2 |
| | OC | '621 | A | • | | 3 |
| | | | | | • | 2 |
| | 3-State | '623 | A | • | | 3 |
| | | | | | • | 2 |
| | OC, 3-State | '639 | A | • | | 3 |
| | | | | | • | 2 |
| | 3-State | '652 | • | • | | 3 & LSI |
| | | | | | • | 2 |
| | OC, 3-State | '654 | ▲ | | | 3 |
| | | | | | • | 2 |
| Very Low Power | OC | '1621 | ▲ | | | |
| | 3-State | '1623 | ▲ | | | 3 |
| | OC, 3-State | '1639 | ▲ | | | |
| 12 mA 24 mA 48 mA 64 mA Sink, Inverting Outputs — Low Power | 3-State | '620 | A | • | | 3 |
| | | | | | • | 2 |
| | OC | '622 | A | • | | 3 |
| | | | | | • | 2 |
| | OC, 3-State | '638 | A | • | | 3 |
| | | | | | • | 2 |
| | 3-State | '651 | • | • | | 3 & LSI |
| | | | | | • | 2 |
| | OC, 3-State | '653 | ▲ | | | 3 |
| | | | | | • | 2 |
| Very Low Power | 3-State | '1620 | ▲ | | | |
| | OC | '1622 | ▲ | | | 3 |
| | OC, 3-State | '1638 | ▲ | | | |
| 12 mA 24 mA 48 mA 64 mA Sink, True Outputs — Low Power | OC | '641 | A | • | | 2 |
| | 3-State | '645 | A | • | | 3 |
| | | | | | • | 2 |
| Very Low Power | OC | '1641 | ▲ | | | |
| | 3-State | '1645 | ▲ | | | 3 |
| 12 mA 24 mA 48 mA 64 mA Sink, Inverting Outputs — Low Power | 3-State | '640 | A | • | | 2 |
| | OC | '642 | A | • | | 3 |
| | | | | | • | 2 |
| Very Low Power | 3-State | '1640 | ▲ | | | |
| | OC | '1642 | ▲ | | | 3 |
| 12 mA 24 mA 48 mA 64 mA Sink, True and Inverting Outputs — Low Power | 3-State | '643 | A | • | | 2 |
| | OC | '644 | A | • | | 3 |
| | | | | | • | 2 |
| Very Low Power | 3-State | '1643 | ▲ | | | |
| | OC | '1644 | ▲ | | | 3 |
| Registered with Multiplex 12 mA 24 mA 48 mA 64 mA True Outputs | 3-State | '646 | • | • | | 3 & LSI |
| | | | | | • | 2 |
| | OC | '647 | | • | | 3 |
| | | | | | • | 2 |
| Registered with Multiplexed 12 mA 24 mA 48 mA 64 mA Inverting Outputs | 3-State | '648 | • | • | | 3 & LSI |
| | | | | | • | 2 |
| | OC | '649 | | • | | 3 & LSI |
| | | | | | • | 2 |
| Universal Transceiver Port Controllers | | '877 | | • | | |
| | 3-State | '852 | | • | | 3 & LSI |
| | | '856 | | • | | |

• Denotes available technology.
▲ Denotes planned new products.
A Denotes "A" suffix version available in the technology indicated.
B Denotes "B" suffix version available in the technology indicated.

TEXAS INSTRUMENTS

## FLIP-FLOPS

**DUAL AND SINGLE FLIP-FLOPS**

| DESCRIPTION | TYPE | TECHNOLOGY | | | | | | | VOLUME |
| | | STD TTL | ALS | AS | H | L | LS | S | |
|---|---|---|---|---|---|---|---|---|---|
| Dual J-K Edge-Triggered | '73 | • | | | • | • | A | | 2 |
| | '76 | | | | | | A | | |
| | '78 | | | | • | • | A | | |
| | '103 | | | | • | | | | |
| | '106 | | | | • | | | | |
| | '107 | • | | | | | A | | |
| | '108 | | | | • | | | | |
| | '109 | • | | | | | A | | |
| | | | A | • | | | | | 3 |
| | '112 | | | | | | A | • | 2 |
| | | | A | ▲ | | | | | 3 |
| | '113 | | | | | | A | • | 2 |
| | | | A | ▲ | | | | | 3 |
| | '114 | | | | | | A | • | 2 |
| | | | A | ▲ | | | | | 3 |
| Single J-K Edge-Triggered | '70 | • | | | | | | | |
| | '101 | | | | • | | | | |
| | '102 | | | | • | | | | |
| Dual Pulse-Triggered | '73 | • | | | • | • | | | |
| | '76 | • | | | • | • | | | |
| | '78 | • | | | • | • | | | |
| | '107 | • | | | • | | | | |
| Single Pulse-Triggered | '71 | | | | • | • | | | 2 |
| | '72 | • | | | • | • | | | |
| | '104 | • | | | | | | | |
| | '105 | • | | | | | | | |
| Dual J-K with Data Lockout | '111 | • | | | | | | | |
| Single J-K with Data Lockout | '110 | • | | | | | | | |
| Dual D-Type | '74 | • | | | • | • | A | • | |
| | | | A | • | | | | | 3 |

**QUAD AND HEX FLIP-FLOPS**

| DESCRIPTION | NO. OF FFs | OUTPUTS | TYPE | TECHNOLOGY | | | | | VOLUME |
| | | | | STD TTL | ALS | AS | LS | S | |
|---|---|---|---|---|---|---|---|---|---|
| D Type | 6 | Q | '174 | • | | | • | • | 2 |
| | | | '378 | | • | • | • | | 3 |
| | 4 | Q, $\overline{Q}$ | '171 | | | | • | | 2 |
| | | | '175 | • | | | • | • | |
| | | | '379 | | • | • | | | 3 |
| J-K | 4 | Q | '276 | • | | | | | 2 |
| | | | '376 | • | | | | | |

**OCTAL, 9-BIT, AND 10-BIT D-TYPE FLIP-FLOPS**

| DESCRIPTION | NO. OF BITS | OUTPUT | TYPE | TECHNOLOGY | | | | | VOLUME |
| | | | | STD TTL | ALS | AS | LS | S | |
|---|---|---|---|---|---|---|---|---|---|
| True Data | Octal | 3-State | '374 | | • | • | | | 3 |
| | | 3-State | '574 | | | | • | • | 2 |
| True Data with Clear | Octal | 2-State | '273 | B | • | | | | 3 |
| | | 3-State | '575 | • | • | | • | | 2 |
| | | 3-State | '874 | • | • | | | | 3 |
| | | 3-State | '878 | • | • | | | | |
| True with Enable | Octal | 2-State | '377 | | | | • | | 2 |
| Inverting | Octal | 3-State | '534 | • | • | | | | 3 |
| | | 3-State | '564 | A | | | | | |
| | | 3-State | '576 | A | • | | | | |
| Inverting with Clear | Octal | 3-State | '577 | A | • | | | | |
| | | 3-State | '879 | A | • | | | | |
| Inverting with Preset | Octal | 3-State | '876 | A | • | | | | |
| True | Octal | 3-State | '825 | | • | | | | |
| Inverting | Octal | 3-State | '826 | | • | | | | |
| True | 9-Bit | 3-State | '823 | | • | | | | |
| Inverting | 9-Bit | 3-State | '824 | | • | | | | |
| True | 10-Bit | 3-State | '821 | | • | | | | |
| Inverting | 10-Bit | 3-State | '822 | | • | | | | 3 & LSI |
| True | Octal | 3-State | '29825 | ▲ | | | | | |
| Inverting | Octal | 3-State | '29826 | ▲ | | | | | |
| True | 9-Bit | 3-State | '29823 | ▲ | | | | | |
| Inverting | 9-Bit | 3-State | '29824 | ▲ | | | | | |
| True | 10-Bit | 3-State | '29821 | ▲ | | | | | |
| Inverting | 10-Bit | 3-State | '29822 | ▲ | | | | | |

**2**

**Functional Index**

• Denotes available technology.
▲ Denotes planned new products.
A Denotes "A" suffix version available in the technology indicated.
B Denotes "B" suffix version available in the technology indicated.

# LATCHES AND MULTIVIBRATORS

**QUAD LATCHES**

| DESCRIPTION | OUTPUT | TYPE | STD TTL | ALS | AS | L | LS | VOLUME |
|---|---|---|---|---|---|---|---|---|
| Dual 2-Bit Transparent | 2-State | '75 | • | | | • | • | 2 |
| | 2-State | '77 | • | | | • | • | |
| | 2-State | '375 | | | | | • | |
| S-R | 2-State | '279 | • | | | | A | A |

**RETRIGGERABLE MONOSTABLE MULTIVIBRATORS**

| DESCRIPTION | TYPE | STD TTL | ALS | AS | LS | L | VOLUME |
|---|---|---|---|---|---|---|---|
| Single | '122 | • | | | • | • | 2 |
| | '130 | • | | | | | |
| | '422 | | | | • | | |
| Dual | '123 | • | | | • | • | |
| | '423 | | | | • | | |

**D-TYPE**
**OCTAL, 9-BIT, AND 10-BIT READ-BACK LATCHES**

| DESCRIPTION | NO. OF BITS | TYPE | STD TTL | ALS | AS | LS | S | VOLUME |
|---|---|---|---|---|---|---|---|---|
| Edge-Triggered Inverting and Noninverting | Octal | '996 | | ▲ | | | | |
| Transparent True | Octal | '990 | | • | | | | |
| | 9-Bit | '992 | | • | | | | |
| | 10-Bit | '994 | | • | | | | |
| Transparent Noninverting | Octal | '991 | | • | | | | 3 & LSI |
| | 9-Bit | '992 | | • | | | | |
| | 10-Bit | '994 | | • | | | | |
| Transparent with Clear True Outputs | Octal | '666 | | • | | | | |
| Transparent with Clear Inverting Outputs | Octal | '667 | | • | | | | |

**OCTAL, 9-BIT, AND 10-BIT LATCHES**

| DESCRIPTION | NO. OF BITS | OUTPUT | TYPE | STD TTL | ALS | AS | LS | S | VOLUME |
|---|---|---|---|---|---|---|---|---|---|
| Transparent | Octal | 3-State | '268 | | | | | • | 2 |
| | | 3-State | '373 | | | | • | • | |
| | | 3-State | '573 | | • | • | | | 3 |
| Dual 4-Bit Transparent | Octal | 2-State | '100 | • | | | | | 2 |
| | | 2-State | '116 | • | | | | | |
| | | 3-State | '873 | | B | • | | | |
| Inverting Transparent | Octal | 3-State | '533 | | • | • | | | 3 |
| | | 3-State | '563 | | A | | | | |
| | | 3-State | '580 | | A | • | | | |
| Dual 4-Bit Inverting Transparent | Octal | 3-State | '880 | | A | • | | | |
| 2-Input Multiplexed | Octal | 3-State | '604 | | | | • | | 2 |
| | | OC | '605 | | | | • | | |
| | | 3-State | '606 | | | | • | | |
| | | OC | '607 | | | | • | | |
| Addressable | Octal | 2-State | '259 | • | | | • | | 3 |
| Multi-Mode Buffered | Octal | 3-State | '412 | | | | | • | 2 |
| True | Octal | 3-State | '845 | | • | • | | | |
| Inverting | Octal | 3-State | '846 | | ▲ | • | | | |
| True | 9-Bit | 3-State | '843 | | • | • | | | 3 & LSI |
| Inverting | 9-Bit | 3-State | '844 | | • | • | | | |
| True | 10-Bit | 3-State | '841 | | • | • | | | |
| Inverting | 10-Bit | 3-State | '842 | | • | • | | | |

**MONOSTABLE MULTIVIBRATORS WITH SCHMITT-TRIGGER INPUTS**

| DESCRIPTION | TYPE | STD TTL | ALS | AS | LS | S | L | VOLUME |
|---|---|---|---|---|---|---|---|---|
| Single | '121 | • | | | | | • | 2 |
| Dual | '221 | • | | | • | | | |

● Denotes available technology.
▲ Denotes planned new products.
A Denotes "A" suffix version available in the technology indicated.
B Denotes "B" suffix version available in the technology indicated.

TEXAS INSTRUMENTS

**2**
**Functional Index**

# REGISTERS

**SHIFT REGISTERS**

| DESCRIPTION | NO. OF BITS | S-R | S-L | LOAD | HOLD | TYPE | STD TTL | ALS | AS | L | LS | S | VOLUME |
|---|---|---|---|---|---|---|---|---|---|---|---|---|---|
| Sign-Protected | | X | | X | X | '322 | | | | A | | | |
| Parallel-In, Parallel-Out, Bidirectional | 8 | X | X | X | X | '198 | ● | | | | | | 2 |
| | | X | X | X | X | '299 | | | ● | ▲ | | | 3 |
| | | X | X | X | X | '323 | | | | | ● | | 2 |
| | | | | | | | | | ▲ | | | | 3 |
| | 4 | X | X | X | X | '194 | ● | | | A | | ● | 2 |
| | | | | | | | | | ▲ | | | | 3 |
| Parallel-In, Parallel-Out, Registered Outputs | 4 | X | X | X | X | '671 | | | | | ● | | |
| | | X | X | X | X | '672 | | | | | ● | | 2 |
| Parallel-In, Parallel-Out | 8 | X | | X | X | '199 | ● | | | | | | |
| | 5 | X | | X | | '96 | ● | | | | ● | ● | 2 |
| | | X | | X | | '95 | A | | | | ● | B | 2 |
| | | | | | | | | | ● | | | | 3 |
| | 4 | X | | X | | '99 | ● | | | | ● | | |
| | | X | | X | X | '178 | ● | | | | | | 2 |
| | | X | | X | X | '179 | ● | | | | | | |
| | | X | | X | | '195 | ● | | | A | | ● | 2 |
| | | | | | | | | | ▲ | | | | 3 |
| | | X | | X | | '295 | | | | B | | | 2 |
| | | X | | X | | '395 | | | | A | | | 2 |
| | | | | | | | | | ▲ | | | | 3 |
| Serial-In, Parallel-Out | 16 | X | | X | X | '673 | | | | | ● | | 2 |
| | 8 | X | | | | '164 | ● | | | ● | ● | | 2 |
| | | | | | | | | | ▲ | | | | 3 |
| Parallel-In, Serial-Out | 16 | X | | X | X | '674 | | | | | ● | | 2 |
| | 8 | X | | X | X | '165 | ● | | | | | A | 3 |
| | | X | | X | X | '166 | ● | | | | | A | 2 |
| | | | | | | | | | ▲ | | | | 3 |
| Serial-In, Serial-Out | 8 | X | | | | '91 | A | | | | ● | ● | 2 |
| | 4 | X | | X | | '94 | ● | | | | | | |

**SIGN-PROTECTED REGISTERS**

| DESCRIPTION | NO. OF BITS | S-R | S-L | LOAD | HOLD | TYPE | ALS | AS | LS | VOLUME |
|---|---|---|---|---|---|---|---|---|---|---|
| Sign-Protected Register | 8 | X | | X | X | '322 | | | A | 2 |

**REGISTER FILES**

| DESCRIPTION | OUTPUT | TYPE | STD TTL | ALS | AS | LS | VOLUME |
|---|---|---|---|---|---|---|---|
| 8 Words × 2 Bits | 3-State | '172 | ● | | | | |
| 4 Words × 4 Bits | OC | '170 | ● | | | ● | 2 |
| | 3-State | '670 | | | | ● | |
| Dual 16 Words × 4 Bits | 3-State | '870 | | | ● | | 3 & LSI |
| | 3-State | '871 | | | ● | | |
| 64 Words × 40 Bits | 3-State | '8834 | | ▲ | | | LSI |

**OTHER REGISTERS**

| DESCRIPTION | TYPE | STD TTL | ALS | AS | L | LS | S | VOLUME |
|---|---|---|---|---|---|---|---|---|
| Quadruple Multiplexers with Storage | '98 | | | | ● | | | 2 |
| | '298 | ● | | | | ● | | 3 |
| | '398 | | | | ● | | | 2 |
| | '399 | | | | ● | | | |
| 8-Bit Universal Shift Registers | '299 | | ● | ▲ | | ● | ● | 3 |
| Quadruple Bus-Buffer Registers | '173 | ● | | | A | | | 2 |
| Octal Storage Register | '396 | | | | | ● | | |
| Dual-Rank 8-Bit Shift Registers | '963 | | ▲ | | | | | 3 & LSI |
| | '964 | | ▲ | | | | | |
| 8-Bit Diagnostics Pipeline Registers | '29818 | | ▲ | | | | | |
| | '29819 | | ▲ | | | | | |

**SHIFT REGISTERS WITH LATCHES**

| DESCRIPTION | NO. OF BITS | OUTPUTS | TYPE | ALS | AS | LS | VOLUME |
|---|---|---|---|---|---|---|---|
| Parallel-In, Parallel-Out with Output Latches | 4 | 3-State | '671 | | | ● | |
| | | 3-State | '672 | | | ● | |
| Serial-In, Parallel-Out with Output Latches | 16 | 2-State | '673 | | | ● | |
| | 8 | Buffered | '594 | | | ● | |
| | | 3-State | '595 | | | ● | |
| | | OC | '596 | | | ● | 2 |
| | | OC | '599 | | | ● | |
| Parallel-In, Serial-Out, with Input Latches | 8 | 2-State | '597 | | | ● | |
| | | 3-State | '589 | | | ● | |
| Parallel I/O Ports with Input Latches, Multiplexed Serial Inputs | 8 | 3-State | '598 | | | ● | |

**2**

Functional Index

● Denotes available technology.
▲ Denotes planned new products.
A Denotes "A" suffix version available in the technology indicated.
B Denotes "B" suffix version available in the technology indicated.

## COUNTERS

### SYNCHRONOUS COUNTERS – POSITIVE-EDGE TRIGGERED

| DESCRIPTION | PARALLEL LOAD | TYPE | STD TTL | ALS | AS | L | LS | S | VOLUME |
|---|---|---|---|---|---|---|---|---|---|
| Decade | Sync | '160 | • | | | | A | | 2 |
| | | | | B | • | | | | 3 |
| | Sync | '162 | • | | | | A | • | 2 |
| | | | | B | • | | | | 3 |
| | Sync | '560 | | A | | | | | |
| | Sync | '668 | | | | | • | | |
| | Sync | '690 | | | | | • | | 2 |
| | Sync | '692 | | | | | • | | |
| Decade Up/Down | Sync | '168 | | | | | B | • | |
| | | | | B | • | | | | 3 |
| | Async | '190 | • | | | | • | | 2 |
| | | | | | • | | | | 3 |
| | Async | '192 | • | | | • | • | | 2 |
| | | | | | • | | | | 3 |
| | Sync | '568 | | A | | | | | |
| | Sync | '696 | | | | | • | | |
| | Sync | '698 | | | | | • | | 2 |
| Decade Rate Multiplier, 1/N10 | Async Set-to-9 | '167 | • | | | | | | 2 |
| 4-Bit Binary | Sync | '161 | • | | | | A | | |
| | | | | B | • | | | | 3 |
| | Sync | '163 | • | | | | A | • | 2 |
| | | | | B | • | | | | 3 |
| | Sync | '561 | | A | | | | | |
| | Sync | '669 | | | | | • | | |
| | Sync | '691 | | | | | • | | 2 |
| | Sync | '693 | | | | | • | | |
| 4-Bit Binary Up/Down | Sync | '169 | | | | | B | • | |
| | | | | B | • | | | | 3 |
| | Async | '191 | • | | | | • | | 2 |
| | | | | | • | | | | 3 |
| | Async | '193 | • | | | • | • | | 2 |
| | | | | | • | | | | 3 |
| | Sync | '569 | | A | | | | | |
| | Sync | '697 | | | | | • | | |
| | Sync | '699 | | | | | • | | 2 |
| 6-Bit Binary Rate Multiplier, 1/N2 | | '97 | • | | | | | | |
| 8-Bit Up/Down | Async CLR | '867 | | | • | | | | 3 & LSI |
| | Sync CLR | '869 | | | • | | | | |

### ASYNCHRONOUS COUNTERS (RIPPLE CLOCK) – NEGATIVE-EDGE TRIGGERED

| DESCRIPTION | PARALLEL LOAD | TYPE | STD TTL | ALS | AS | L | LS | S | VOLUME |
|---|---|---|---|---|---|---|---|---|---|
| Decade | Set-to-9 | '90 | A | | | • | • | | |
| | | '68 | | | • | | | | |
| | Yes | '176 | • | | | | | | |
| | Yes | '196 | • | | | | • | • | |
| | Set-to-9 | '290 | • | | | | • | | |
| 4-Bit Binary | None | '93 | A | | | • | • | | |
| | | '69 | | | • | | | | 2 |
| | Yes | '177 | • | | | | | | |
| | Yes | '197 | • | | | | • | • | |
| | None | '293 | • | | | | • | | |
| Divide-by-12 | None | '92 | A | | | | • | | |
| Dual Decade | None | '390 | • | | | | • | | |
| | Set-to-9 | '490 | • | | | | • | | |
| Dual 4-Bit Binary | None | '393 | • | | | | • | | |

### 8-BIT BINARY COUNTERS WITH REGISTERS

| DESCRIPTION | TYPE OF OUTPUT | TYPE | ALS | AS | LS | VOLUME |
|---|---|---|---|---|---|---|
| Parallel Register | 3-State | '590 | | | • | |
| Outputs | OC | '591 | | | • | 2 |
| Parallel Register Inputs | 2-State | '592 | | | • | |
| Parallel I/O | 3-State | '593 | | | • | |

### FREQUENCY DIVIDERS, RATE MULTIPLIERS

| DESCRIPTION | TYPE | STD TTL | ALS | AS | LS | VOLUME |
|---|---|---|---|---|---|---|
| 50-to-1 Frequency Divider | '56 | | | | • | |
| 60-to-1 Frequency Divider | '57 | | | | • | 2 |
| 60-Bit Binary Rate Multiplier | '97 | • | | | | |
| Decade Rate Multiplier | '167 | • | | | | |

• Denotes available technology.
A Denotes "A" suffix version available in the technology indicated.
B Denotes "B" suffix version available in the technology indicated.

2 Functional Index

## DECODERS, ENCODERS, DATA SELECTORS/MULTIPLEXERS AND SHIFTERS

### DATA SELECTORS/MULTIPLEXERS

| DESCRIPTION | TYPE OF OUTPUT | TYPE | STD TTL | ALS | AS | L | LS | S | VOLUME |
|---|---|---|---|---|---|---|---|---|---|
| 16-to-1 | 2-State | '150 | • | | | | | | 2 |
| | 3-State | '250 | | | • | | | | |
| | 3-State | '850 | | | • | | | | 3 & LSI |
| | 3-State | '851 | | | • | | | | |
| Dual 8-to-1 | 3-State | '351 | • | | | | | | 2 |
| 8-to-1 | 2-State | '151 | A | | | • | • | | 2 |
| | | | | • | • | | | | 3 |
| | 2-State | '152 | A | | | | • | | 2 |
| | 3-State | '251 | • | | | | • | • | |
| | | | | • | ▲ | | | | 3 |
| | 3-State | '354 | | | • | | | | |
| | 2-State | '355 | | | • | | | | |
| | 3-State | '356 | | | • | | | | 2 |
| | OC | '357 | | | • | | | | |
| Dual 4-to-1 | 2-State | '153 | • | | | • | • | • | |
| | | | | • | • | | | | 3 |
| | 3-State | '253 | | | | | • | • | 2 |
| | | | | • | • | | | | 3 |
| | 2-State | '352 | | | | | • | | 2 |
| | | | | • | • | | | | 3 |
| | 3-State | '353 | | | | | • | | 2 |
| | | | | • | • | | | | 3 |
| Octal 2-to-1 with Storage | 3-State | '604 | | | • | | | | |
| | OC | '605 | | | • | | | | |
| | 3-State | '606 | | | • | | | | 2 |
| | OC | '607 | | | • | | | | |
| Quad 2-to-1 with Storage | 2-State | '98 | | | | • | | | |
| | 2-State | '298 | • | | | | • | | 2 |
| | | | | | • | | | | 3 |
| | 2-State | '398 | | | | | • | | 2 |
| | 2-State | '399 | | | | | • | | |
| Quad 2-to-1 | 2-State | '157 | • | | | • | • | • | |
| | | | | • | • | | | | 3 |
| | 2-State | '158 | | | | | • | • | 2 |
| | | | | • | • | | | | 3 |
| | 3-State | '257 | | | | | B | • | 2 |
| | | | | A | • | | | | 3 |
| | 3-State | '258 | | | | | B | • | 2 |
| | | | | A | • | | | | 3 |
| 6-to-1 Universal Multiplexer | 3-State | '857 | | • | • | | | | 3 |

### DECODERS/DEMULTIPLEXERS

| DESCRIPTION | TYPE OF OUTPUT | TYPE | STD TTL | ALS | AS | L | LS | S | VOLUME |
|---|---|---|---|---|---|---|---|---|---|
| 4-to-16 | 3-State | '154 | • | | | | • | | 2 |
| | OC | '159 | • | | | | | | |
| 4-to-10 BCD-to-Decimal | 2-State | '42 | A | | | • | • | | |
| 4-to-10 Excess 3-to-Decimal | 2-State | '43 | A | | | • | | | 2 |
| 4-to-10 Excess 3-Gray-to-Decimal | 2-State | '44 | A | | | • | | | |
| 3-to-8 with Address Latches | | '131 | | • | ▲ | | | | 3 |
| | 2-State | '137 | | • | ▲ | | • | | 2 |
| 3-to-8 | 2-State | '138 | | • | ▲ | | | | 3 |
| | | | | | | | • | • | 2 |
| | 3-State | '538 | | ▲ | | | | | 3 |
| Dual 2-to-4 | 2-State | '139 | | ▲ | • | | | | |
| | | | | | | | A | • | 3 |
| | 2-State | '155 | • | | | | A | | 2 |
| | OC | '156 | • | | | | • | | |
| Dual 1-to-4 Decoders | 3-State | '539 | ▲ | | | | | | 3 |

### CODE CONVERTERS

| DESCRIPTION | TYPE | STD TTL | S | VOLUME |
|---|---|---|---|---|
| 6-Line-BCD to 6-Line Binary, or 4-Line to 4-Line BCD 9's/BCD 10's Converters | '184 | • | | 2 |
| 6-Bit-Binary to 6-Bit BCD Converters | '185 | A | | |
| BCD-to-Binary Converters | '484 | | A | 4 |
| Binary-to-BCD Converters | '485 | | A | |

### PRIORITY ENCODERS/REGISTERS

| DESCRIPTION | TYPE | STD TTL | ALS | AS | LS | VOLUME |
|---|---|---|---|---|---|---|
| Full BCD | '147 | • | | | • | |
| Cascadable Octal | '148 | • | | | • | 2 |
| Cascadable Octal with 3-State Outputs | '348 | | | | • | |
| 4-Bit Cascadable with Registers | '278 | • | | | | |

### SHIFTERS

| DESCRIPTION | OUTPUT | TYPE | STD TTL | ALS | AS | L | LS | S | VOLUME |
|---|---|---|---|---|---|---|---|---|---|
| 4-Bit Shifter | 3-State | '350 | | | | | | • | 2 |
| Parallel 16-Bit Multi-Mode Barrel Shifter | 3-State | '897 | | | • | | | | LSI |
| 32-Bit Barrel Shifter | 3-State | '8838 | | | ▲ | | | | |

• Denotes available technology.
▲ Denotes planned new products.
A Denotes "A" suffix version available in the technology indicated.
B Denotes "B" suffix version available in the technology indicated.

TEXAS INSTRUMENTS

**2**

Functional Index

## DISPLAY DECODERS/DRIVERS, MEMORY/MICROPROCESSOR CONTROLLERS, AND VOLTAGE-CONTROLLED OSCILLATORS

### OPEN-COLLECTOR DISPLAY DECODERS/DRIVERS

| DESCRIPTION | OFF-STATE OUTPUT VOLTAGE | TYPE | STD TTL | ALS | AS | L | LS | VOLUME |
|---|---|---|---|---|---|---|---|---|
| BCD-to-Decimal | 30 V | '45 | • | | | | | |
| | 60 V | '141 | • | | | | | |
| | 15 V | '145 | | | | | • | |
| | 7 V | '445 | | | | | • | |
| BCD-to-Seven-Segment | 30 V | '46 | | | | A | | 2 |
| | 15 V | '47 | | | | A | • | |
| | 5.5 V | '48 | | | | | • | |
| | 5.5 V | '49 | | | | | • | |
| | 30 V | '246 | • | | | | | |
| | 15 V | '247 | • | | | | | |
| | 7 V | '347 | | | | | • | |
| | 7 V | '447 | | | | | • | |
| | 5.5 V | '248 | | | | | • | |
| | 5.5 V | '249 | • | | | | | |

### OPEN COLLECTOR DISPLAY DECODERS/DRIVERS WITH COUNTERS/LATCH

| DESCRIPTION | TYPE | STD TTL | ALS | AS | VOLUME |
|---|---|---|---|---|---|
| BCD Counter/4-Bit Latch/BCD-to-Decimal Decoder/Driver | '142 | • | | | |
| BCD Counter/4-Bit Latch/BCD-to-Seven-Segment Decoder/LED Driver | '143 | • | | | 2 |
| BCD Counter/4-Bit Latch/BCD-to-Seven-Segment Decoder/Lamp Driver | '144 | • | | | |

### VOLTAGE-CONTROLLED OSCILLATORS

| No. VCOs | COMP'L $Z_{OUT}$ | ENABLE | RANGE INPUT | $R_{ext}$ | $f_{max}$ MHz | TYPE | LS | S | VOLUME |
|---|---|---|---|---|---|---|---|---|---|
| Single | Yes | Yes | Yes | No | 20 | '624 | • | | |
| Single | Yes | Yes | Yes | Yes | 20 | '628 | • | | |
| Dual | No | Yes | Yes | No | 60 | '124 | | • | |
| Dual | Yes | Yes | No | No | 20 | '626 | • | | 2 |
| Dual | No | No | No | No | 20 | '627 | • | | |
| Dual | No | Yes | Yes | No | 20 | '629 | • | | |

### MEMORY/MICROPROCESSOR CONTROLLERS

| DESCRIPTION | | TYPE | ALS | AS | LS | S | VOLUME |
|---|---|---|---|---|---|---|---|
| System Controllers (Universal or for '888) | | '890 | | • | | | LSI |
| Memory Refresh Controllers | Transparent. 4K, 16K | '600 | | | A | | |
| | Burst Modes 64K | '601 | | | A | | |
| | Cycle Steal. 4K, 16K | '602 | | | A | | 2 |
| | Burst Modes 64K | '603 | | | A | | |
| Memory Cycle Controller | | '608 | | | • | | |
| Memory Mappers | 3-State | '612 | | | • | | |
| | OC | '613 | | | • | | LSI |
| Memory Mappers with Output Latches | 3-State | '610 | | | • | | |
| | OC | '611 | | | • | | |
| Multi-Mode Latches (8080A Applications) | | '412 | | | | • | 2 |
| Dynamic Memory Controllers | 16K, 64K | 2967 | ▲ | | | | |
| | 256K | 2968 | ▲ | | | | LSI |
| | 16K, 64K | 6301 | ▲ | | | | |
| | 256K, 1 MEG | 6302 | ▲ | | | | |

### CLOCK GENERATOR CIRCUITS

| DESCRIPTION | TYPE | STD TTL | ALS | AS | LS | S | VOLUME |
|---|---|---|---|---|---|---|---|
| Quadruple Complementary-Output Logic Elements | '265 | • | | | | | |
| Dual Pulse Synchronizers/Drivers | '120 | • | | | | | |
| Crystal-Controlled Oscillators | '320 | | | | • | | |
| | '321 | | | | • | | 2 |
| Digital Phase-Lock Loop | '297 | | | | • | | |
| Programmable Frequency Dividers/Digital Timers | '292 | | | | • | | |
| | '294 | | | | • | | |
| Triple 4-Input AND/NAND Drivers | '800 | | | ▲ | | | 3 |
| Triple 4-Input OR/NOR Drivers | '802 | | | ▲ | | | |
| Dual VCO | '124 | | | | | • | 2 |

**RESULTANT DISPLAYS USING '46A, '47A, '48, '49, 'L46, 'L47, 'LS47, 'LS48, 'LS49, 'LS347**

**RESULTANT DISPLAYS USING '246, '247, '248, '249, 'LS247, 'LS248, 'LS249, 'LS447**

**RESULTANT DISPLAYS USING '143, '144**

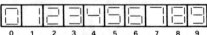

• Denotes available technology.
▲ Denotes planned new products.
A Denotes "A" suffix version available in the technology indicated.

TEXAS INSTRUMENTS

## COMPARATORS AND ERROR DETECTION CIRCUITS

### 4-BIT COMPARATORS

| DESCRIPTION | | | | | TYPE | TECHNOLOGY | | | | | | VOLUME |
| P=Q | P>Q | P<Q | OUTPUT | OUTPUT ENABLE | | STD TTL | ALS | AS | L | LS | S | |
|---|---|---|---|---|---|---|---|---|---|---|---|---|
| Yes | Yes | No | 2 State | No | '85 | • | | | • | • | • | 2 |

### 8-BIT COMPARATORS

| INPUTS | P=Q | P̄=Q̄ | P>Q | P̄>Q̄ | P<Q | OUTPUT | OUTPUT ENABLE | TYPE | ALS | AS | LS | VOLUME |
|---|---|---|---|---|---|---|---|---|---|---|---|---|
| 20 kΩ Pull Up | Yes | No | No | No | No | OC | Yes | 518 | • | | | 3 |
| | No | Yes | No | No | No | 2-S | Yes | 520 | • | | | |
| | No | Yes | No | No | No | OC | Yes | 522 | • | | | |
| | No | Yes | No | Yes | No | 2-S | No | 682 | | | • | 2 |
| | No | Yes | No | Yes | No | OC | No | 683 | | | • | |
| Standard | Yes | No | No | No | No | OC | Yes | 519 | • | | | 3 |
| | No | Yes | No | No | No | 2-S | Yes | 521 | • | | | |
| | No | Yes | No | Yes | No | 2-S | No | 684 | | | • | |
| | No | Yes | No | Yes | No | OC | No | 685 | | | • | 2 |
| | No | Yes | No | Yes | No | 2-S | Yes | 686 | | | • | |
| | No | Yes | No | Yes | No | OC | Yes | 687 | | | • | |
| | No | Yes | No | No | No | 2-S | Yes | '688 | | • | • | 3 / 2 |
| | No | Yes | No | No | No | OC | Yes | '689 | | • | • | 3 / 2 |
| Latched P Logic & Arith | No | No | Yes | No | Yes | 2-S | Yes | '885 | | • | | 3 & LSI |
| Latched P&Q Logic & Arith | Yes | No | Yes | No | Yes | Latched | Yes | '866 | | | • | 3 |

### ADDRESS COMPARATORS

| DESCRIPTION | OUTPUT ENABLE | LATCHED OUTPUT | TYPE | ALS | AS | VOLUME |
|---|---|---|---|---|---|---|
| 16-Bit to 4-Bit | Yes | | '677 | • | | 3 |
| | | Yes | '678 | • | | |
| 12-Bit to 4-Bit | Yes | | '679 | • | | |
| | | Yes | '680 | • | | |

### PARITY GENERATORS/CHECKERS, ERROR DETECTION AND CORRECTION CIRCUITS

| DESCRIPTION | | NO. OF BITS | TYPE | STD TTL | ALS | AS | LS | S | VOLUME |
|---|---|---|---|---|---|---|---|---|---|
| Odd/Even Parity Generators/Checkers | | 8 | '180 | • | | | | | 2 |
| | | 9 | '280 | | • | • | | | |
| | | 9 | '286 | | | • | | | 3 & LSI |
| Parallel Error Detection/Correction Circuits | 3-State | 8 | '636 | | | | • | | 2 |
| | OC | 8 | '637 | | | | • | | |
| | 3-State | 16 | '616 | | • | | | | 3 & LSI |
| | OC | 16 | '617 | | ▲ | | | | |
| | 3-State | 16 | '630 | | | | • | | 2 |
| | OC | 16 | '631 | | | | • | | |
| | 3-State | 16 | '8400 | | ▲ | | | | LSI |
| | 3-State | 32 | '632 | | A | ▲ | | | 3 & LSI |
| | OC | 32 | '633 | | • | ▲ | | | |
| | 3-State | 32 | '634 | | ▲ | ▲ | | | |
| | OC | 32 | '635 | | ▲ | ▲ | | | |

### FUSE-PROGRAMMABLE COMPARATORS

| DESCRIPTION | TYPE | STD TTL | ALS | AS | LS | S | VOLUME |
|---|---|---|---|---|---|---|---|
| 16-Bit Identity Comparator | '526 | | • | | | | |
| 12-Bit Identity Comparator | '528 | | • | | | | 3 |
| 8-Bit Identity Comparator and 4-Bit Comparator | '527 | | • | | | | |

• Denotes available technology.
▲ Denotes planned new products.
A Denotes "A" suffix version available in the technology indicated.

2

Functional Index

2

Functional Index

## ARITHMETIC CIRCUITS AND PROCESSOR ELEMENTS

### PARALLEL BINARY ADDERS

| DESCRIPTION | TYPE | STD TTL | ALS | AS | H | LS | S | VOLUME |
|---|---|---|---|---|---|---|---|---|
| 1-Bit Gated | '80 | ● | | | | | | |
| 2-Bit | '82 | ● | | | | | | |
| 4-Bit | '83 | A | | | | A | | 2 |
| | '283 | ● | | | | ● | ● | |
| Dual 1-Bit Carry-Save | '183 | | | | | ● | ● | |

### ACCUMULATORS, ARITHMETIC LOGIC UNITS, LOOK-AHEAD CARRY GENERATORS

| DESCRIPTION | TYPE | STD TTL | ALS | AS | LS | S | VOLUME |
|---|---|---|---|---|---|---|---|
| 4-Bit Parallel Binary Accumulators | '281 | | | | | ● | 2 |
| | '681 | | | | ● | ● | |
| 4 Bit Arithmetic Logic Units Function Generators | '181 | ● | | A | ● | ● | 3 & LSI |
| | '1181 | | ● | | | | |
| | '381 | | | A | | ● | 2 |
| | '881 | | | A | | | 3 & LSI |
| 4 Bit Arithmetic Logic Unit with Ripple Carry | '382 | | | | ● | | 2 |
| Look Ahead Carry Generators | 16 Bit | '182 | ● | | | | ● | 2 |
| | '282 | | | ▲ | | | 3 |
| 32 Bit | '882 | | | A | | | 3 & LSI |
| Quad Serial Adder Subtractor | '385 | | | | ● | | 2 |

### MULTIPLIERS

| DESCRIPTION | TYPE | STD TTL | ALS | AS | LS | S | VOLUME |
|---|---|---|---|---|---|---|---|
| 2-Bit-by-4-Bit Parallel Binary Multipliers | '261 | | | | | ● | |
| 4-Bit-by-4-Bit Parallel Binary Multipliers | '284 | ● | | | | | 2 |
| | '285 | ● | | | | | |
| 25-MHz 6-Bit Binary Rate Multipliers | '97 | ● | | | | | |
| 25-MHz Decade Rate Multipliers | '167 | ● | | | | | |
| 8-Bit × 1-Bit 2's Complement Multipliers | '384 | | | | ● | | |

### OTHER ARITHMETIC OPERATORS

| DESCRIPTION | TYPE | STD TTL | ALS | AS | H | L | LS | S | VOLUME |
|---|---|---|---|---|---|---|---|---|---|
| Quad 2-Input Exclusive-OR Gates with Totem-Pole Outputs | '86 | ● | | | ● | A | | ● | 2 |
| | '386 | | ● | | | | A | | 3 |
| Quad 2-Input Exclusive-OR Gates with Open-Collector Outputs | '136 | ● | | | | | | ● | 2 |
| | | | ● | | | | | | 3 |
| Quad 2-Input Exclusive NOR Gates | '266 | | | | | | ● | | 2 |
| | '810 | | ● | ▲ | | | | | 3 |
| Quad 2-Input Exclusive-NOR Gates with Open-Collector Outputs | '811 | | ● | ▲ | | | | | 3 |
| Quad Exclusive OR/NOR Gates | '135 | | | | | | | ● | 2 |
| 4-Bit True/Complement Element | '87 | | | | ● | | | | 2 |

### BIPOLAR BIT-SLICE PROCESSOR ELEMENTS

| DESCRIPTION | CASCADABLE TO N-BITS | TYPE | ALS | AS | LS | S | VOLUME |
|---|---|---|---|---|---|---|---|
| 8-Bit Slice | No | '887 | | ● | | | LSI |
| | Yes | '888 | | ● | | | |
| | Yes | '895 | ▲ | | | | |

● Denotes available technology.

▲ Denotes planned new products.

A Denotes "A" suffix version available in the technology indicated.

TEXAS INSTRUMENTS

## MEMORIES

### USER-PROGRAMMABLE READ-ONLY MEMORIES (PROMs)
#### STANDARD PROMs

| DESCRIPTION | TYPE | ORGANIZATION | TYPE OUTPUT | S | VOLUME |
|---|---|---|---|---|---|
| 16K-Bit Arrays | TBP28S166 | 2048W × 8B | 3-State | ● | |
| | TBP38S165 | 2048W × 8B | 3-State | ● | |
| | TBP38S166 | 2048W × 8B | 3-State | ● | |
| | TBP38SA165 | 2048W × 8B | OC | ● | |
| | TBP38SA166 | 2048W × 8B | OC | ● | |
| | TBP34S162 | 4096W × 4B | 3-State | ● | |
| | TBP34SA162 | 4096W × 4B | OC | ● | |
| 8K-Bit Arrays | TBP24S81 | 2048W × 4B | 3-State | ● | |
| | TBP24SA81 | 2048W × 4B | OC | ● | |
| | TBP28S85A | 1024W × 8B | 3-State | ▲ | |
| | TBP28S86A | 1024W × 8B | 3-State | ▲ | |
| | TBP28SA86A | 1024W × 8B | OC | ▲ | |
| | TBP38S85 | 1024W × 8B | 3-State | ▲ | |
| | TBP38SA85 | 1024W × 8B | OC | ▲ | |
| | TBP38S86 | 1024W × 8B | 3-State | ▲ | |
| | TBP38SA86 | 1024W × 8B | OC | ▲ | 4 |
| 4K-Bit Arrays | TBP24S41 | 1024W × 4B | 3-State | ● | |
| | TBP24SA41 | 1024W × 4B | OC | ● | |
| | TBP28S42 | 512W × 8B | 3-State | ● | |
| | TBP28SA42 | 512W × 8B | OC | ● | |
| | TBP28S46 | 512W × 8B | 3-State | ● | |
| | TBP28SA46 | 512W × 8B | OC | ● | |
| 2K-Bit Arrays | TBP38S22 | 256W × 8B | 3-State | ● | |
| | TBP38SA22 | 256W × 8B | OC | ● | |
| 1K-Bit Arrays | TBP24S10 | 256W × 4B | 3-State | ● | |
| | TBP24SA10 | 256W × 4B | OC | ● | |
| | TBP34S10 | 256W × 4B | 3-State | ● | |
| | TBP34SA10 | 256W × 4B | OC | ● | |
| 256-Bit Arrays | TBP18S030 | 32W × 8B | 3-State | ● | |
| | TBP18SA030 | 32W × 8B | OC | ● | |
| | TBP38S030 | 32W × 8B | 3-State | ● | |
| | TBP38SA030 | 32W × 8B | OC | ● | |

#### LOW-POWER PROMs

| DESCRIPTION | TYPE | ORGANIZATION | TYPE OUTPUT | S | VOLUME |
|---|---|---|---|---|---|
| 16K-Bit Arrays | TBP28L166 | 2048W × 8B | 3-State | ● | |
| | TBP38L165 | 2048W × 8B | 3-State | ● | |
| | TBP38L166 | 2048W × 8B | 3-State | ● | |
| | TBP34L162 | 4096W × 4B | 3-State | ● | |
| 8K-Bit Arrays | TBP28L85A | 1024W × 8B | 3-State | ▲ | |
| | TBP28L86A | 1024W × 8B | 3-State | ▲ | |
| | TBP38L85 | 1024W × 8B | 3-State | ▲ | |
| | TBP38L86 | 1024W × 8B | 3-State | ▲ | 4 |
| 4K-Bit Arrays | TBP28L42 | 512W × 8B | 3-State | ● | |
| | TBP28L46 | 512W × 8B | 3-State | ● | |
| 2K-Bit Arrays | TBP28L22 | 256W × 8B | 3-State | ● | |
| | TBP28LA22 | 256W × 8B | OC | ● | |
| | TBP38L22 | 256W × 8B | 3-State | ● | |
| 1K-Bit Arrays | TBP34L10 | 256W × 4B | 3-State | ● | |
| 256-Bit Arrays | TBP38L030 | 32W × 8B | 3-State | ● | |

### REGISTERED PROMs

| DESCRIPTION | TYPE | ORGANIZATION | TYPE OUTPUT | S | VOLUME |
|---|---|---|---|---|---|
| 16K-Bit Arrays | TBP34R162 | 4096W × 4B | 3-State | ● | |
| | TBP34SR165 | 4096W × 4B | 3-State | ● | 4 |
| | TBP38R165 | 2048W × 8B | 3-State | ● | |

### RANDOM-ACCESS READ-WRITE MEMORIES (RAMs)

| DESCRIPTION | ORGANIZATION | TYPE OF OUTPUT | TYPE | STD TTL | ALS | AS | LS | S | VOLUME |
|---|---|---|---|---|---|---|---|---|---|
| 256-Bit Arrays | 256 × 1 | 3-State | '201 | | | | | ● | |
| | | OC | '301 | | | | | ● | |
| 64-Bit Arrays | 16 × 4 | OC | '89 | ● | | | | | 4 |
| | | 3-State | '189 | | | | A | B | |
| | | 3-State | '219 | | | | A | | |
| | | OC | '289 | | | | A | B | |
| | | OC | '319 | | | | A | | |
| 16-Bit Multiple-Port Register File | 8 × 2 | 3-State | '172 | ● | | | | | 2 |
| 16-Bit Register File | 4 × 4 | OC | '170 | ● | | | ● | | |
| | | 3-State | '670 | | | | ● | | |
| Dual 64-Bit Register Files | 16 × 4 | 3-State | '870 | | | ● | | | 3 |
| | | | '871 | | | ● | | | |

### FIRST-IN FIRST-OUT MEMORIES (FIFOs)

| DESCRIPTION | TYPE OF OUTPUT | TYPE | ALS | AS | LS | S | VOLUME |
|---|---|---|---|---|---|---|---|
| 16 × 4 | 3-State | 222 | | | ● | | LSI |
| | 3-State | 224 | | | ● | | |
| | 3-State | 227 | | | ● | | |
| | 3-State | 228 | | | ● | | |
| | 3-State | 232 | A | | | | 3 & LSI |
| 16 × 5 | 3-State | 225 | | | ● | ● | LSI |
| | 3-State | 229 | A | | | | 3 & LSI |
| | 3-State | 233 | A | | | | |

● Denotes available technology.
▲ Denotes planned new products.
A Denotes "A" suffix version available in the technology indicated.
B Denotes "B" suffix version available in the technology indicated.

2

Functional Index

● Denotes available technology.
▲ Denotes planned new products.
A Denotes "A" suffix version available in the technology indicated.
B Denotes "B" suffix version available in the technology indicated.

TEXAS INSTRUMENTS

## PROGRAMMABLE LOGIC ARRAYS

PROGRAMMABLE LOGIC ARRAYS

| DESCRIPTION | INPUTS | OUTPUTS | | TYPE | ALS | IMP | NO. OF | VOLUME |
| | | NO. | TYPE | NO | | | PINS | |
|---|---|---|---|---|---|---|---|---|
| High-Performance PAL^ | 16 | 8 | Active-Low | 'PAL16L8A | • | | | |
| | | 4 | | 'PAL16R4A | • | | 20 | |
| | | 6 | Registered | 'PAL16R6A | • | | | |
| | | 8 | | 'PAL16R8A | • | | | |
| Half-Power PAL^ | 16 | 8 | Active-Low | 'PAL16L8A-2 | • | | | |
| | | 4 | | 'PAL16R4A-2 | • | | 20 | |
| | | 6 | Registered | 'PAL16R6A-2 | • | | | |
| | | 8 | | 'PAL16R8A-2 | • | | | |
| High-Performance PAL^ | 20 | 8 | Active-Low | 'PAL20L8A | • | | | |
| | | 4 | | 'PAL20R4A | • | | 24 | |
| | | 6 | Registered | 'PAL20R6A | • | | | |
| | | 8 | | 'PAL20R8A | • | | | |
| Half-Power PAL^ | 20 | 8 | Active-Low | 'PAL20L8A-2 | • | | | |
| | | 4 | | 'PAL20R4A-2 | • | | 24 | |
| | | 6 | Registered | 'PAL20R6A-2 | • | | | |
| | | 8 | | 'PAL20R8A-2 | • | | | |
| Impact PAL^ | 16 | 8 | Active-Low | 'TIBPAL16L8-12 | | • | | |
| | | 4 | | 'TIBPAL16R4-12 | | • | 20 | |
| | | 6 | Registered | 'TIBPAL16R6-12 | | • | | |
| | | 8 | | 'TIBPAL16R8-12 | | • | | |
| Impact PAL^ | 16 | 8 | Active-Low | 'TIBPAL16L8-15 | | • | | |
| | | 4 | | 'TIBPAL16R4-15 | | • | 20 | |
| | | 6 | Registered | 'TIBPAL16R6-15 | | • | | |
| | | 8 | | 'TIBPAL16R8-15 | | • | | |
| Impact PAL^ | 20 | 8 | Active-Low | 'TIBPAL20L8-15 | | • | | |
| | | 4 | | 'TIBPAL20R4-15 | | • | 24 | |
| | | 6 | Registered | 'TIBPAL20R6-15 | | • | | |
| | | 8 | | 'TIBPAL20R8-15 | | • | | |
| Exclusive-OR PAL^ | 20 | 10 | Active-Low | 'TIBPAL20L10-20 | • | | | |
| | | 4 | | 'TIBPAL20X4-20 | • | | 24 | 4 |
| | | 8 | Registered | 'TIBPAL20X8-20 | • | | | |
| | | 10 | | 'TIBPAL20X10-20 | • | | | |
| Exclusive-OR PAL^ | 20 | 8 | Active-Low | 'TIBPAL20L10-35 | • | | | |
| | | 4 | | 'TIBPAL20X4-35 | • | | 24 | |
| | | 8 | Registered | 'TIBPAL20X8-35 | • | | | |
| | | 10 | | 'TIBPAL20X10-35 | • | | | |
| Registered-Input PAL^ | 19 | 8 | Active-Low | 'TIBPALR19L8 | • | | | |
| | | 4 | | 'TIBPALR19R4 | • | | 24 | |
| | | 6 | Registered | 'TIBPALR19R6 | • | | | |
| | | 8 | | 'TIBPALR19R8 | • | | | |
| Registered-Input PAL^® | 19 | 8 | Active-Low | 'TIBPALR19L8 | • | | | |
| | | 4 | | 'TIBPALR19R4 | • | | 24 | |
| | | 6 | Registered | 'TIBPALR19R6 | • | | | |
| | | 8 | | 'TIBPALR19R8 | • | | | |
| Latched-Input PAL^ | 19 | 8 | Active-Low | 'TIBPALT19L8 | • | | | |
| | | 4 | | 'TIBPALT19R4 | • | | 24 | |
| | | 6 | Registered | 'TIBPALT19R6 | • | | | |
| | | 8 | | 'TIBPALT19R8 | • | | | |
| Latched-Input PAL^ | 19 | 8 | Active-Low | 'TIBPALT19L8 | • | | | |
| | | 4 | | 'TIBPALT19R4 | • | | 24 | |
| | | 6 | Registered | 'TIBPALT19R6 | • | | | |
| | | 8 | | 'TIBPALT19R8 | • | | | |
| Field-Programmable 14 × 32 × 6 Logic Arrays | 14 | 6 | 3-State | 'TIFPLA839 | • | | 24 | |
| | | | OC | 'TIFPLA840 | • | | | |

^ PAL is a registered trademark of Monolithic Memories Incorporated.

• Denotes available technology.

TEXAS
INSTRUMENTS

**General Information** `1`

**Functional Index** `2`

**Field-Programmable Logic** `3`

**PROMs** `4`

**RAMs and Memory-Based Code Converters** `5`

**Designing with Texas Instruments Field-Programmable Logic** `6`

**Mechanical Data** `7`

- ● **Standard ECL 10KH PAL**

- ● **Programmable replacement for conventional ECL 10KH logic**

- ● **24 pin, 300 mil package**

- ● **Reliable titanium-tungsten fuses**

| DEVICE | INPUTS | REGISTERED Q OUTPUTS | I/O PORTS | STD OUTPUT |
|--------|--------|----------------------|-----------|------------|
| PAL16P8 | 12 | 0 | 4 | 4 |
| PAL16RP8 | 12 | 8 | 0 | 0 |

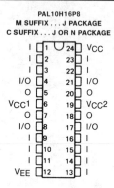

PAL10H16P8
M SUFFIX . . . J PACKAGE
C SUFFIX . . . J OR N PACKAGE

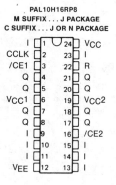

PAL10H16RP8
M SUFFIX . . . J PACKAGE
C SUFFIX . . . J OR N PACKAGE

## Description

These PAL devices combine the IMPACT (Implanted Advanced Composed Technology) with proven titanium-tungsten fuses. These devices provide reliable, high-performance substitutes for conventional ECL 10KH logic. Their easy programmability allows for quick design of "custom" functions and typically result in a more compact circuit board. In addition, chip carriers are available for further reduction in board space.

All devices in this series are provided with an output polarity fuse that, if removed, will allow an output to provide a logic low when the implemented equation is satisfied. When the output polarity fuse is intact, the output provides a logic true when the implemented equation is satisfied.

The output registers are D-type flip flops which store data on the low-to-high transition of the clock input. A separate clock enable is provided for each group of four registered outputs. A common clock is provided which controls all registered outputs. A master reset control pin clears all the registers and force all registered outputs to a low state. The master reset is asynchronous and overrides the clock inputs.

All devices in this series contain a security feature. A last fuse inhibits verification or programming when not intact. This prevents easy duplication.

PAL is a registered trademark of Monolithic Memories, Inc.

**3**

**Field-Programmable Logic**

FEBRUARY 1984 – REVISED JANUARY 1985

- Standard High-Speed (25 ns) PAL Family

- Choice of Operating Speeds
  HIGH SPEED, A Devices . . . 35 MHz
  HALF POWER, A-2 Devices . . . 18 MHz

- Choice of Input/Output Configuration

- Package Options Include Both Plastic and
  Ceramic Chip Carriers in Addition to Plastic
  and Ceramic DIPs

| DEVICE | INPUTS | 3-STATE O OUTPUTS | REGISTERED Q OUTPUTS | I/O PORTS |
|--------|--------|-------------------|----------------------|-----------|
| PAL16L8 | 10 | 2 | 0 | 6 |
| PAL16R4 | 8 | 0 | 4 (3-state) | 4 |
| PAL16R6 | 8 | 0 | 6 (3-state) | 2 |
| PAL16R8 | 8 | 0 | 8 (3-state) | 0 |

### description

These programmable array logic devices feature
high speed and a choice of either standard or
half-power devices. They combine Advanced
Low-Power Schottky[†] technology with proven
titanium-tungsten fuses. These devices will
provide reliable, high-performance substitutes
for conventional TTL logic. Their easy
programmability allows for quick design of
"custom" functions and typically result in a
more compact circuit board. In addition, chip
carriers are available for further reduction in
board space.

The Half-Power versions offer a choice of
operating frequency, switching speeds, and
power dissipation. In many cases, these Half-
Power devices can result in significant power
reduction from an overall system level.

The PAL16′ M series is characterized for
operation over the full military temperature range
of −55°C to 125°C. The PAL16′ C series is
characterized for operation from 0°C to 70°C.

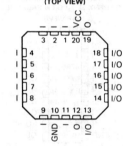

PAL16L8′
M SUFFIX . . . J PACKAGE
C SUFFIX . . . J OR N PACKAGE
(TOP VIEW)

PAL16L8′
M SUFFIX . . . FH OR FK PACKAGE
C SUFFIX . . . FN PACKAGE
(TOP VIEW)

Pin assignments in operating mode (pins 1 and 11 less positive than $V_{IHH}$)

[†]Integrated Schottky-Barrier diode-clamped transistor is patented
by Texas Instruments, U.S. Patent Number 3,463,975.

PAL is a registered trademark of Monolithic Memories Inc.

TEXAS
INSTRUMENTS

**3**

**Field-Programmable Logic**

# PAL16R4A, PAL16R6A, PAL16R8A
## STANDARD HIGH-SPEED PAL CIRCUITS

**PAL16R4'**
M SUFFIX . . . J PACKAGE
C SUFFIX . . . J OR N PACKAGE
(TOP VIEW)

| | | | |
|---|---|---|---|
| CLK | 1 | 20 | V_CC |
| I | 2 | 19 | I/O |
| I | 3 | 18 | I/O |
| I | 4 | 17 | Q |
| I | 5 | 16 | Q |
| I | 6 | 15 | Q |
| I | 7 | 14 | Q |
| I | 8 | 13 | I/O |
| I | 9 | 12 | I/O |
| GND | 10 | 11 | $\overline{OE}$ |

**PAL16R4'**
M SUFFIX . . . FH OR FK PACKAGE
C SUFFIX . . . FN PACKAGE
(TOP VIEW)

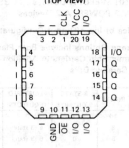

**PAL16R6'**
M SUFFIX . . . J PACKAGE
C SUFFIX . . . J OR N PACKAGE
(TOP VIEW)

| | | | |
|---|---|---|---|
| CLK | 1 | 20 | V_CC |
| I | 2 | 19 | I/O |
| I | 3 | 18 | Q |
| I | 4 | 17 | Q |
| I | 5 | 16 | Q |
| I | 6 | 15 | Q |
| I | 7 | 14 | Q |
| I | 8 | 13 | Q |
| I | 9 | 12 | I/O |
| GND | 10 | 11 | $\overline{OE}$ |

**PAL16R6'**
M SUFFIX . . . FH OR FK PACKAGE
C SUFFIX . . . FN PACKAGE
(TOP VIEW)

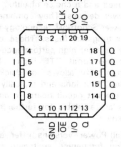

**PAL16R8'**
M SUFFIX . . . J PACKAGE
C SUFFIX . . . J OR N PACKAGE
(TOP VIEW)

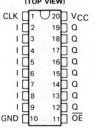

| | | | |
|---|---|---|---|
| CLK | 1 | 20 | V_CC |
| I | 2 | 19 | Q |
| I | 3 | 18 | Q |
| I | 4 | 17 | Q |
| I | 5 | 16 | Q |
| I | 6 | 15 | Q |
| I | 7 | 14 | Q |
| I | 8 | 13 | Q |
| I | 9 | 12 | Q |
| GND | 10 | 11 | $\overline{OE}$ |

**PAL16R8'**
M SUFFIX . . . FH OR FK PACKAGE
C SUFFIX FN PACKAGE
(TOP VIEW)

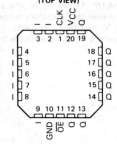

Pin assignments in operating mode (pins 1 and 11 less positive than $V_{IHH}$)

TEXAS
INSTRUMENTS

**functional block diagrams (positive logic)**

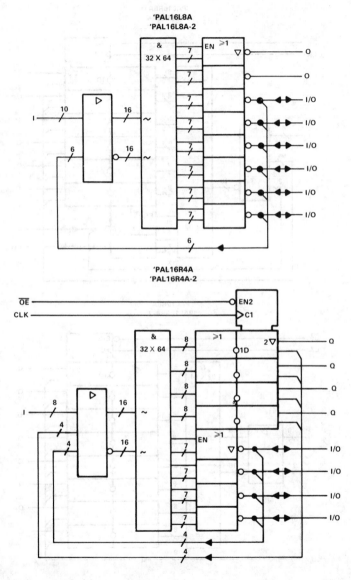

~ denotes fused inputs

Field-Programmable Logic

3

**functional block diagrams (positive logic)**

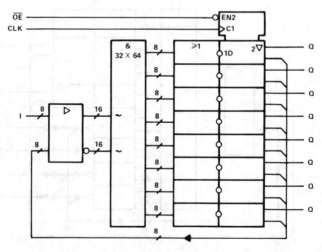

~ denotes fused inputs

TEXAS
INSTRUMENTS

## logic diagram

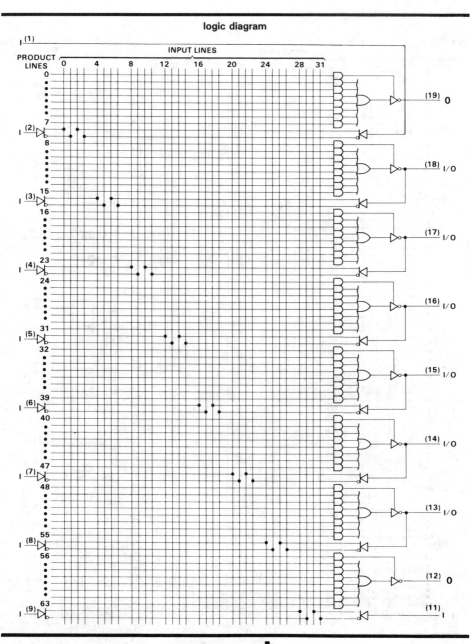

Field-Programmable Logic

3

## PAL16R4A
## STANDARD HIGH-SPEED PAL CIRCUITS

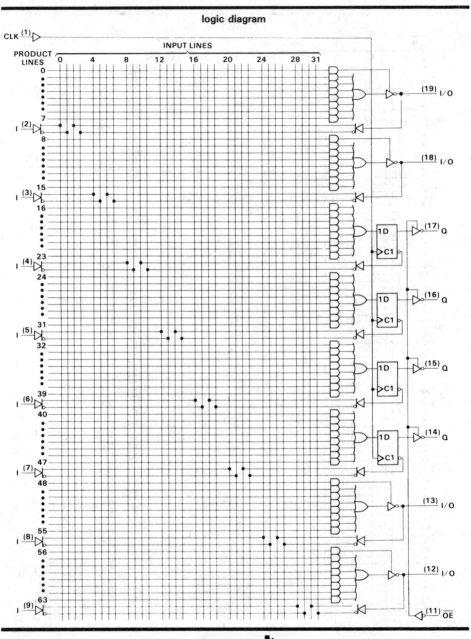

logic diagram

## logic diagram

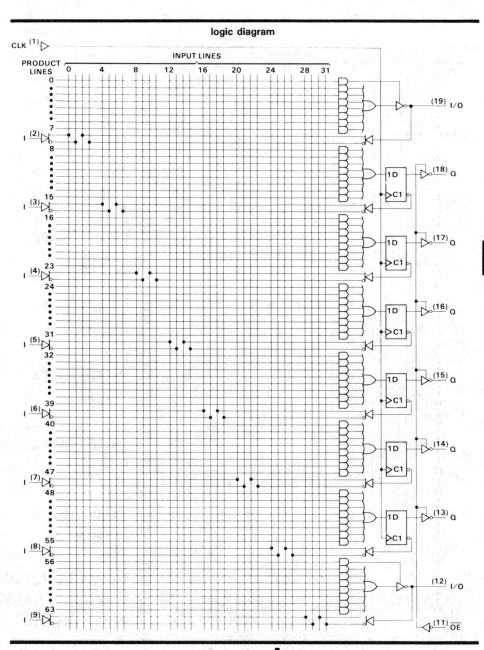

Field-Programmable Logic

3

### logic diagram

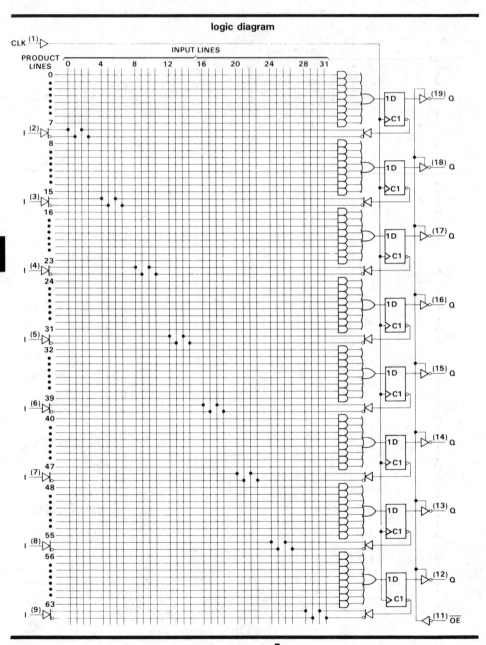

### absolute maximum ratings over operating free-air temperature range (unless otherwise noted)

Supply voltage, $V_{CC}$ (see Note 1) . . . . . . . . . . . . . . . . . . . . . . . . . . . . . . . . . . . . . . . . . . . . . 7 V
Input voltage (see Note 1) . . . . . . . . . . . . . . . . . . . . . . . . . . . . . . . . . . . . . . . . . . . . . . . . . . 5.5 V
Voltage applied to a disabled output (see Note 1) . . . . . . . . . . . . . . . . . . . . . . . . . . . . . . . 5.5 V
Operating free-air temperature range: M suffix . . . . . . . . . . . . . . . . . . . . . . . . . . . −55°C to 125°C
　　　　　　　　　　　　　　　　　　　C suffix . . . . . . . . . . . . . . . . . . . . . . . . . . . 0°C to 70°C
Storage temperature range . . . . . . . . . . . . . . . . . . . . . . . . . . . . . . . . . . . . . −65°C to 150°C

NOTE 1: These ratings apply except for programming pins during a programming cycle.

### recommended operating conditions

| PARAMETER | | M SUFFIX | | | C SUFFIX | | | UNIT |
|---|---|---|---|---|---|---|---|---|
| | | MIN | NOM | MAX | MIN | NOM | MAX | |
| $V_{CC}$ | Supply voltage | 4.5 | 5 | 5.5 | 4.75 | 5 | 5.25 | V |
| $V_{IH}$ | High-level input voltage — $\overline{OE}$ input | 2.4 | | 5.5 | 2 | | 5.5 | V |
| | High-level input voltage — All others | 2 | | 5.5 | 2 | | 5.5 | |
| $V_{IL}$ | Low-level input voltage | | | 0.8 | | | 0.8 | V |
| $I_{OH}$ | High-level output current | | | −2 | | | −3.2 | mA |
| $I_{OL}$ | Low-level output current | | | 12 | | | 24 | mA |
| $T_A$ | Operating free-air temperature | −55 | | 125 | 0 | | 70 | °C |

### programming parameters, $T_A = 25°C$

| | | MIN | NOM | MAX | UNIT |
|---|---|---|---|---|---|
| $V_{CC}$ | Verify-level supply voltage | 4.5 | 5.0 | 5.5 | V |
| $V_{IH}$ | High-level input voltage | 2 | | 5.5 | V |
| $V_{IL}$ | Low-level input voltage | | | 0.8 | V |
| $V_{IHH}$ | Program-pulse input voltage | 10.25 | 10.5 | 10.75 | V |
| $I_{IHH}$ | Program-pulse input current — PO | | 20 | 50 | mA |
| | Program-pulse input current — PGM ENABLE, L/R | | 10 | 25 | |
| | Program-pulse input current — PI, PA | | 1.5 | 5 | |
| | Program-pulse input current — $V_{CC}$ | | 250 | 400 | |
| $t_{w1}$ | Program-pulse duration at PO pins | 10 | | 50 | μs |
| $t_{w2}$ | Pulse duration at PGM VERIFY | 100 | | | ns |
| | Program-pulse duty cycle at PO pins | | | 25 | % |
| $t_{su}$ | Setup time | 100 | | | ns |
| $t_h$ | Hold time | 100 | | | ns |
| $t_{d1}$ | Delay time from $V_{CC}$ to 5 V to PGM VERIFY↑ | 100 | | | μs |
| $t_{d2}$ | Delay time from PGM VERIFY ↑ to valid output | 200 | | | ns |
| | Input voltage at pins 1 and 11 to open verify-protect (security) fuse | 20 | 21 | 22 | V |
| | Input current to open verify-protect (security) fuse | | | 400 | mA |
| $t_{w3}$ | Pulse duration to open verify-protect (security) fuse | 20 | | 50 | μs |
| | $V_{CC}$ value during security fuse programming | | 0 | 0.4 | V |

3

Field-Programmable Logic

### recommended operating conditions

| | | | M SUFFIX | | | C SUFFIX | | | UNIT |
|---|---|---|---|---|---|---|---|---|---|
| | | | MIN | TYP | MAX | MIN | TYP | MAX | |
| $f_{clock}$ | Clock frequency | | 0 | | 25 | 0 | | 35 | MHz |
| $t_w$ | Pulse duration, see Note 2 | Clock high | 15 | | | 12 | | | ns |
| | | Clock low | 20 | | | 16 | | | |
| $t_{su}$ | Setup time, input or feedback before CLK ↑ | | 25 | | | 20 | | | ns |
| $t_h$ | Hold time, input or feedback after CLK ↑ | | 0 | | | 0 | | | ns |

NOTE 2: The total clock period of clock high and clock low must not exceed clock frequency, $f_{clock}$. The minimum pulse durations specified are only for clock high or clock low, but not for both simultaneously.

### electrical characteristics over recommended operating free-air temperature range

| PARAMETER | | TEST CONDITIONS[†] | | M SUFFIX | | | C SUFFIX | | | UNIT |
|---|---|---|---|---|---|---|---|---|---|---|
| | | | | MIN | TYP[‡] | MAX | MIN | TYP[‡] | MAX | |
| $V_{IK}$ | | $V_{CC}$ = MIN, | $I_I$ = −18 mA | | | −1.5 | | | −1.5 | V |
| $V_{OH}$ | | $V_{CC}$ = MIN, | $I_{OH}$ = MAX | 2.4 | 3.2 | | 2.4 | 3.3 | | V |
| $V_{OL}$ | | $V_{CC}$ = MIN, | $I_{OL}$ = MAX | | 0.25 | 0.4 | | 0.35 | 0.5 | V |
| $I_{OZH}$ | Outputs | $V_{CC}$ = MAX, | $V_O$ = 2.7 V | | | 20 | | | 20 | μA |
| | I/O ports | | | | | 100 | | | 100 | |
| $I_{OZL}$ | Outputs | $V_{CC}$ = MAX, | $V_O$ = 0.4 V | | | −20 | | | −20 | μA |
| | I/O ports | | | | | −250 | | | −250 | |
| $I_I$ | | $V_{CC}$ = MAX, | $V_I$ = 5.5 V | | | 0.2 | | | 0.1 | mA |
| $I_{IH}$ | | $V_{CC}$ = MAX, | $V_I$ = 2.7 V | | | 25 | | | 20 | μA |
| $I_{IL}$ | | $V_{CC}$ = MAX, | $V_I$ = 0.4 V  OE INPUT | | | −0.25 | | | −0.4 | mA |
| | | | All others | | | −0.2 | | | −0.2 | |
| $I_O$ [§] | | $V_{CC}$ = MAX, | $V_O$ = 2.25 V | −30 | | −125 | −30 | | −125 | mA |
| $I_{CC}$ | | $V_{CC}$ = MAX, $V_I$ = 0 V | Outputs Open | | 140 | 185 | | 140 | 180 | mA |

[†]For conditions shown as MIN or MAX, use the appropriate value specified under recommended operating conditions.
[‡]All typical values are at $V_{CC}$ = 5 V, $T_A$ = 25 °C.
[§]The output conditions have been chosen to produce a current that closely approximates one half of the true short-circuit output current, $I_{OS}$.

### switching characteristics over recommended supply voltage and operating free-air temperature ranges (unless otherwise noted)

| PARAMETER | FROM | TO | TEST CONDITIONS | M SUFFIX | | | C SUFFIX | | | UNIT |
|---|---|---|---|---|---|---|---|---|---|---|
| | | | | MIN | TYP[‡] | MAX | MIN | TYP[‡] | MAX | |
| $f_{max}$ | | | | 25 | 45 | | 35 | 45 | | MHz |
| $t_{pd}$ | I, I/O, | O, I/O | | | 15 | 30 | | 15 | 25 | ns |
| $t_{pd}$ | CLK↑ | Q | $R_L$ = 500 Ω, | | 10 | 20 | | 10 | 15 | ns |
| $t_{en}$ | OE↓ | Q | $C_L$ = 50 pF, | | 15 | 25 | | 15 | 22 | ns |
| $t_{dis}$ | OE↑ | Q | See Note 3 | | 10 | 25 | | 10 | 15 | ns |
| $t_{en}$ | I, I/O | O, I/O | | | 14 | 30 | | 14 | 25 | ns |
| $t_{dis}$ | I, I/O | O, I/O | | | 13 | 30 | | 13 | 25 | ns |

[‡]All typical values are at $V_{CC}$ = 5 V, $T_A$ = 25 °C.
NOTE 3: Load circuits and voltage waveforms are shown in Section 1.

**TEXAS INSTRUMENTS**

### recommended operating conditions

| PARAMETER | | | M SUFFIX | | | C SUFFIX | | | UNIT |
|---|---|---|---|---|---|---|---|---|---|
| | | | MIN | TYP | MAX | MIN | TYP | MAX | |
| $f_{clock}$ | Clock frequency | | 0 | | 16 | 0 | | 18 | MHz |
| $t_w$ | Pulse duration, see Note 2 | Clock high | 28 | | | 25 | | | ns |
| | | Clock low | 28 | | | 25 | | | |
| $t_{su}$ | Setup time, input or feedback before CLK↑ | | 35 | | | 28 | | | ns |
| $t_h$ | Hold time, input or feedback after CLK↑ | | 0 | | | 0 | | | ns |

NOTE 2: The total clock period of clock high and clock low must not exceed clock frequency, $f_{clock}$. The minimum pulse durations specified are only for clock high or clock low, but not for both simultaneously.

### electrical characteristics over recommended operating free-air temperature range

| PARAMETER | | TEST CONDITIONS[†] | | M SUFFIX | | | C SUFFIX | | | UNIT |
|---|---|---|---|---|---|---|---|---|---|---|
| | | | | MIN | TYP[‡] | MAX | MIN | TYP[‡] | MAX | |
| $V_{IK}$ | | $V_{CC}$ = MIN, | $I_I$ = −18 mA | | | −1.5 | | | −1.5 | V |
| $V_{OH}$ | | $V_{CC}$ = MIN, | $I_{OH}$ = MAX | 2.4 | 3.2 | | 2.4 | 3.3 | | V |
| $V_{OL}$ | | $V_{CC}$ = MIN, | $I_{OL}$ = MAX | | 0.25 | 0.4 | | 0.35 | 0.5 | V |
| $I_{OZH}$ | Outputs | $V_{CC}$ = MAX, | $V_O$ = 2.7 V | | | 20 | | | 20 | μA |
| | I/O ports | | | | | 100 | | | 100 | |
| $I_{OZL}$ | Outputs | $V_{CC}$ = MAX, | $V_O$ = 0.4 V | | | −20 | | | −20 | μA |
| | I/O ports | | | | | −250 | | | −250 | |
| $I_I$ | | $V_{CC}$ = MAX, | $V_I$ = 5.5 V | | | 0.2 | | | 0.1 | mA |
| $I_{IH}$ | | $V_{CC}$ = MAX, | $V_I$ = 2.7 V | | | 25 | | | 20 | μA |
| $I_{IL}$ | | $V_{CC}$ = MAX, | $V_I$ = 0.4 V | $\overline{OE}$ INPUT | | −0.2 | | | −0.2 | mA |
| | | | | All others | | −0.1 | | | −0.1 | |
| $I_O$ [§] | | $V_{CC}$ = MAX, | $V_O$ = 2.25 V | −30 | | −125 | −30 | | −125 | mA |
| $I_{CC}$ | | $V_{CC}$ = MAX, $V_I$ = 0 V | Outputs Open | | 75 | 95 | | 70 | 90 | mA |

[†]For conditions shown as MIN or MAX, use the appropriate value specified under recommended operating conditions.
[‡]All typical values are at $V_{CC}$ = 5 V, $T_A$ = 25°C.
[§]The output conditions have been chosen to produce a current that closely aproximates one half of the true short-circuit output current, $I_{OS}$.

### switching characteristics over recommended supply voltage and operating free-air temperature ranges (unless otherwise noted)

| PARAMETER | FROM | TO | TEST CONDITIONS | M SUFFIX | | | C SUFFIX | | | UNIT |
|---|---|---|---|---|---|---|---|---|---|---|
| | | | | MIN | TYP[‡] | MAX | MIN | TYP[‡] | MAX | |
| $f_{max}$ | | | | 16 | 25 | | 18 | 25 | | MHz |
| $t_{pd}$ | I, I/O | O, I/O | | | 25 | 40 | | 25 | 35 | ns |
| $t_{pd}$ | CLK↑ | Q | $R_L$ = 500 Ω, | | 11 | 35 | | 11 | 25 | ns |
| $t_{en}$ | $\overline{OE}$↓ | Q | $C_L$ = 50 pF, | | 20 | 35 | | 20 | 25 | ns |
| $t_{dis}$ | $\overline{OE}$↑ | Q | See Note 3 | | 11 | 30 | | 11 | 20 | ns |
| $t_{en}$ | I, I/O | O, I/O | | | 25 | 40 | | 25 | 35 | ns |
| $t_{dis}$ | I, I/O | O, I/O | | | 25 | 35 | | 25 | 30 | ns |

[‡]All typical values are at $V_{CC}$ = 5 V, $T_A$ = 25°C.
NOTE 3: Load circuits and voltage waveforms are shown in Section 1.

3

Field-Programmable Logic

## PAL16L8A, PAL16R4A, PAL16R6A, PAL16R8A
## STANDARD HIGH-SPEED PAL CIRCUITS

**PRODUCT TERMS 0 THRU 31**
**(TOP VIEW)**

| | | | |
|---|---|---|---|
| PGM ENABLE | 1 | 20 | V_CC |
| PIO | 2 | 19 | PO3 |
| PI1 | 3 | 18 | PO2 |
| PI2 | 4 | 17 | PO1 |
| PI3 | 5 | 16 | POO |
| PI4 | 6 | 15 | PAO |
| PI5 | 7 | 14 | PA1 |
| PI6 | 8 | 13 | PA2 |
| PI7 | 9 | 12 | L/R |
| GND | 10 | 11 | PGM VERIFY |

**PRODUCT TERMS 32 THRU 63**
**(TOP VIEW)**

| | | | |
|---|---|---|---|
| PGM VERIFY | 1 | 20 | V_CC |
| PIO | 2 | 19 | L/R |
| PI1 | 3 | 18 | PAO |
| PI2 | 4 | 17 | PA1 |
| PI3 | 5 | 16 | PA2 |
| PI4 | 6 | 15 | PO3 |
| PI5 | 7 | 14 | PO2 |
| PI6 | 8 | 13 | PO1 |
| PI7 | 9 | 12 | POO |
| GND | 10 | 11 | PGM ENABLE |

Pin assignments in programming mode (PGM ENABLE, pin 1 or 11, at $V_{IHH}$)

### TABLE 1 — INPUT LINE SELECT

| INPUT LINE NUMBER | PIN NAME | | | | | | | | |
|---|---|---|---|---|---|---|---|---|---|
| | PI7 | PI6 | PI5 | PI4 | PI3 | PI2 | PI1 | PI0 | L/R |
| 0 | HH | HH | HH | HH | HH | HH | HH | L | Z |
| 1 | HH | HH | HH | HH | HH | HH | HH | H | Z |
| 2 | HH | HH | HH | HH | HH | HH | HH | L | HH |
| 3 | HH | HH | HH | HH | HH | HH | HH | H | HH |
| 4 | HH | HH | HH | HH | HH | HH | L | HH | Z |
| 5 | HH | HH | HH | HH | HH | HH | H | HH | Z |
| 6 | HH | HH | HH | HH | HH | HH | L | HH | HH |
| 7 | HH | HH | HH | HH | HH | HH | H | HH | HH |
| 8 | HH | HH | HH | HH | HH | L | HH | HH | Z |
| 9 | HH | HH | HH | HH | HH | H | HH | HH | Z |
| 10 | HH | HH | HH | HH | HH | L | HH | HH | HH |
| 11 | HH | HH | HH | HH | HH | H | HH | HH | HH |
| 12 | HH | HH | HH | HH | L | HH | HH | HH | Z |
| 13 | HH | HH | HH | HH | H | HH | HH | HH | Z |
| 14 | HH | HH | HH | HH | L | HH | HH | HH | HH |
| 15 | HH | HH | HH | HH | H | HH | HH | HH | HH |
| 16 | HH | HH | HH | L | HH | HH | HH | HH | Z |
| 17 | HH | HH | HH | H | HH | HH | HH | HH | Z |
| 18 | HH | HH | HH | L | HH | HH | HH | HH | HH |
| 19 | HH | HH | HH | H | HH | HH | HH | HH | HH |
| 20 | HH | HH | L | HH | HH | HH | HH | HH | Z |
| 21 | HH | HH | H | HH | HH | HH | HH | HH | Z |
| 22 | HH | HH | L | HH | HH | HH | HH | HH | HH |
| 23 | HH | HH | H | HH | HH | HH | HH | HH | HH |
| 24 | HH | L | HH | HH | HH | HH | HH | HH | Z |
| 25 | HH | H | HH | HH | HH | HH | HH | HH | Z |
| 26 | HH | L | HH | HH | HH | HH | HH | HH | HH |
| 27 | HH | H | HH | HH | HH | HH | HH | HH | HH |
| 28 | L | HH | HH | HH | HH | HH | HH | HH | Z |
| 29 | H | HH | HH | HH | HH | HH | HH | HH | Z |
| 30 | L | HH | HH | HH | HH | HH | HH | HH | HH |
| 31 | H | HH | HH | HH | HH | HH | HH | HH | HH |

### TABLE 2 — PRODUCT LINE SELECT

| PRODUCT LINE NUMBER | PIN NAME | | | | | | |
|---|---|---|---|---|---|---|---|
| | PO0 | PO1 | PO2 | PO3 | PA2 | PA1 | PA0 |
| 0, 32 | Z | Z | Z | HH | Z | Z | Z |
| 1, 33 | Z | Z | Z | HH | Z | Z | HH |
| 2, 34 | Z | Z | Z | HH | Z | HH | Z |
| 3, 35 | Z | Z | Z | HH | Z | HH | HH |
| 4, 36 | Z | Z | Z | HH | HH | Z | Z |
| 5, 37 | Z | Z | Z | HH | HH | Z | HH |
| 6, 38 | Z | Z | Z | HH | HH | HH | Z |
| 7, 39 | Z | Z | Z | HH | HH | HH | HH |
| 8, 40 | Z | Z | HH | Z | Z | Z | Z |
| 9, 41 | Z | Z | HH | Z | Z | Z | HH |
| 10, 42 | Z | Z | HH | Z | Z | HH | Z |
| 11, 43 | Z | Z | HH | Z | Z | HH | HH |
| 12, 44 | Z | Z | HH | Z | HH | Z | Z |
| 13, 45 | Z | Z | HH | Z | HH | Z | HH |
| 14, 46 | Z | Z | HH | Z | HH | HH | Z |
| 15, 47 | Z | Z | HH | Z | HH | HH | HH |
| 16, 48 | Z | HH | Z | Z | Z | Z | Z |
| 17, 49 | Z | HH | Z | Z | Z | Z | HH |
| 18, 50 | Z | HH | Z | Z | Z | HH | Z |
| 19, 51 | Z | HH | Z | Z | Z | HH | HH |
| 20, 52 | Z | HH | Z | Z | HH | Z | Z |
| 21, 53 | Z | HH | Z | Z | HH | Z | HH |
| 22, 54 | Z | HH | Z | Z | HH | HH | Z |
| 23, 55 | Z | HH | Z | Z | HH | HH | HH |
| 24, 56 | HH | Z | Z | Z | Z | Z | Z |
| 25, 57 | HH | Z | Z | Z | Z | Z | HH |
| 26, 58 | HH | Z | Z | Z | Z | HH | Z |
| 27, 59 | HH | Z | Z | Z | Z | HH | HH |
| 28, 60 | HH | Z | Z | Z | HH | Z | Z |
| 29, 61 | HH | Z | Z | Z | HH | Z | HH |
| 30, 62 | HH | Z | Z | Z | HH | HH | Z |
| 31, 63 | HH | Z | Z | Z | HH | HH | HH |

L = $V_{IL}$, H = $V_{IH}$, HH = $V_{IHH}$, Z = high impedance (e.g. 10 kΩ to 5 V)

3

TEXAS
INSTRUMENTS

### programming procedure for array fuses

Array fuses are programmed using a linear select method. Each fuse can be opened by selecting the appropriate (one of 32) input line and then pulsing the correct (one of 64) product line. The levels for selecting input lines and product lines are shown in Tables 1 and 2.

Step 1    Raise PGM ENABLE to $V_{IHH}$.
Step 2    Select an input line by applying appropriate levels to L/R and PI pins.
Step 3    Begin selection of the output line with appropriate conditions on PA pins.
Step 4    Raise $V_{CC}$ to $V_{IHH}$.
Step 5    Blow the fuse by pulsing the appropriate PO pin to $V_{IHH}$ as shown in Table 2 for the product line.
Step 6    Return $V_{CC}$ to 5 volts and pulse PGM Verify. The PO pin selected in Step 5 will be less than $V_{OL}$ if the fuse is open.

Steps 1 through 6 may be repeated if the verification does not indicate that the fuse was successfully programmed (blown), but no more than four times. Verification is possible only with the verify-protect fuse intact.

### programming waveforms

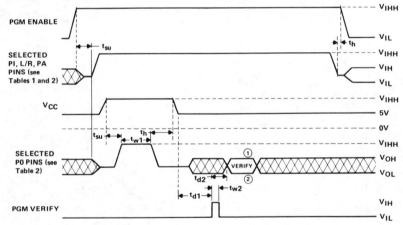

① A high level during the verify interval indicates that programming has not been successful.
② A low level during the verify interval indicates that programming has been successful.

### security fuse programming

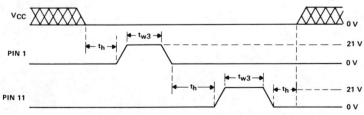

- Standard High Speed (25 ns) PAL Family

- Choice of Operating Speeds
  HIGH SPEED, A devices . . . 30 MHz
  HALF POWER, A-2 devices . . . 18 MHz

- Choice of Input/Output Configuration

- Preload Capability on Output Registers

- DIP Options Include Both 300-mil Plastic
  and 600-mil Ceramic

| DEVICE | I INPUTS | 3-STATE 0 OUTPUTS | REGISTERED Q OUTPUTS | I/O PORTS |
|--------|----------|-------------------|----------------------|-----------|
| 'PAL20L8A | 14 | 2 | 0 | 6 |
| 'PAL20R4A | 12 | 0 | 4 (3-state buffers) | 4 |
| 'PAL20R6A | 12 | 0 | 6 (3-state buffers) | 2 |
| 'PAL20R8A | 12 | 0 | 8 (3-state buffers) | 0 |

## description

These programmable array logic devices feature
high speed and a choice of either standard or
half-power speeds. They combine Advanced
Low-Power Schottky† technology with proven
titanium-tungsten fuses. These devices will
provide reliable, high performance substitutes
over conventional TTL logic. Their easy
programmability allows for quick design of
"custom" functions and typically result in a
more compact circuit board. In addition, chip
carriers are also available for further reduction
in board space.

The Half-Power versions offer a choice of
operating frequency, switching speeds, and
power dissipation. In many cases, these Half-
Power devices can result in significant power
reduction from an overall system level.

In addition, extra circuitry has been provided to
allow loading of each register asynchronously to
either a high or low state. This feature simplifies
testing because the registers can be set to an
initial state prior to executing the test sequence.

The PAL20' series is characterized for operation
over the full military temperature range of
−55°C to 125°C. The commercial range is
characterized from 0°C to 70°C.

PAL20L8'
M SUFFIX . . . JW PACKAGE
C SUFFIX . . . JW OR NT PACKAGE
(TOP VIEW)

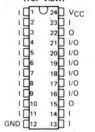

PAL20L8'
M SUFFIX . . . FH OR FK PACKAGE
C SUFFIX . . . FN PACKAGE
(TOP VIEW)

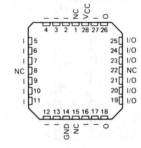

DIP pin assignments in operating mode (voltages at pins 1 and 13
less then $V_{IHH}$). PLCC pin assignments in operating mode (voltages
at pins 2 and 16 less then $V_{IHH}$).

PAL is a registered trademark of Monolithic Memories Inc.
†Integrated Schottky-Barrier diode-clamped transistor is patented
by Texas Instruments, U.S. Patent Number 3,463,975.

TEXAS
INSTRUMENTS

Copyright © 1985, Texas Instruments Incorporated

3-17

## PAL20R4A, PAL20R6A, PAL20R8A
## STANDARD HIGH SPEED PAL CIRCUITS

**PAL20R4'**
**M SUFFIX . . . JW PACKAGE**
**C SUFFIX . . . JW OR NT PACKAGE**
**(TOP VIEW)**

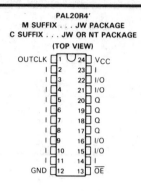

**PAL20R4'**
**M SUFFIX . . . FH OR FK PACKAGE**
**C SUFFIX . . . FN PACKAGE**
**(TOP VIEW)**

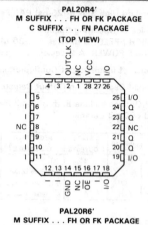

**PAL20R6'**
**M SUFFIX . . . JW PACKAGE**
**C SUFFIX . . . JW OR NT PACKAGE**
**(TOP VIEW)**

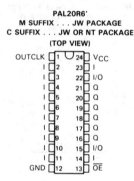

**PAL20R6'**
**M SUFFIX . . . FH OR FK PACKAGE**
**C SUFFIX . . . FN PACKAGE**
**(TOP VIEW)**

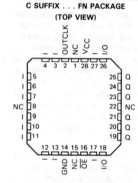

**PAL20R8'**
**M SUFFIX . . . JW PACKAGE**
**C SUFFIX . . . JW OR NT PACKAGE**
**(TOP VIEW)**

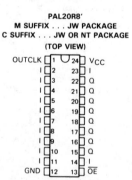

**PAL20R8'**
**M SUFFIX . . . FH OR FK PACKAGE**
**C SUFFIX . . . FN PACKAGE**
**(TOP VIEW)**

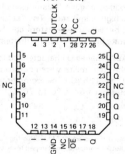

DIP pin assignments in operating mode (voltages at pins 1 and 13 less than $V_{IHH}$)
PLCC pin assignments in operating mode (voltages at pins 2 and 16 less than $V_{IHH}$)

**TEXAS**
**INSTRUMENTS**

**functional block diagrams (positive logic)**

**PAL20L8A**
**PAL20L8A-2**

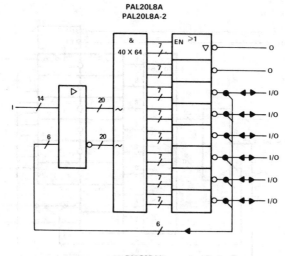

**PAL20R4A**
**PAL20R4A-2**

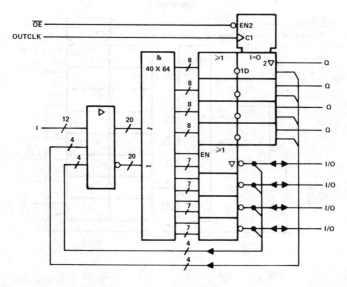

Field-Programmable Logic

3

## PAL20R6A, PAL20R8A
## STANDARD HIGH SPEED PAL CIRCUITS

**functional block diagrams (positive logic)**

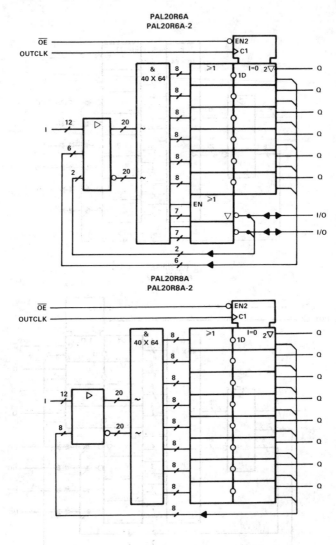

PAL20R6A
PAL20R6A-2

PAL20R8A
PAL20R8A-2

**TEXAS
INSTRUMENTS**

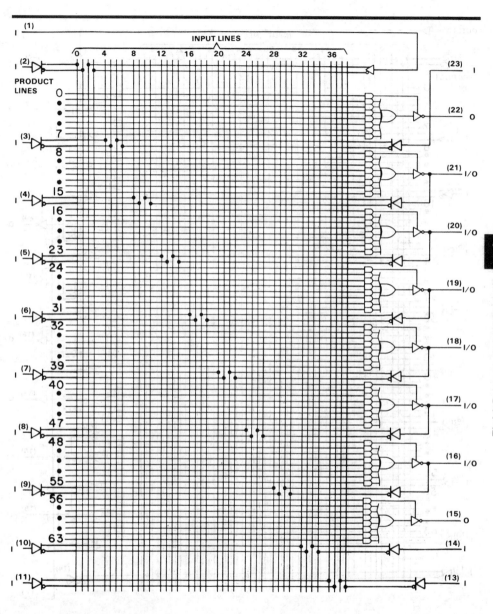

Field-Programmable Logic

TEXAS
INSTRUMENTS

## PAL20R4A
## STANDARD HIGH SPEED PAL CIRCUITS

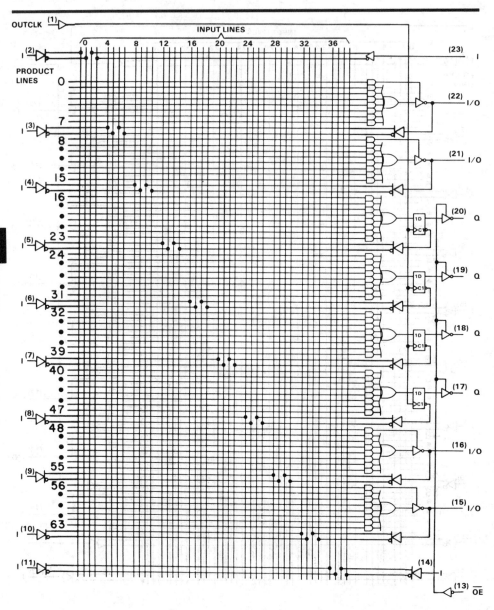

TEXAS
INSTRUMENTS

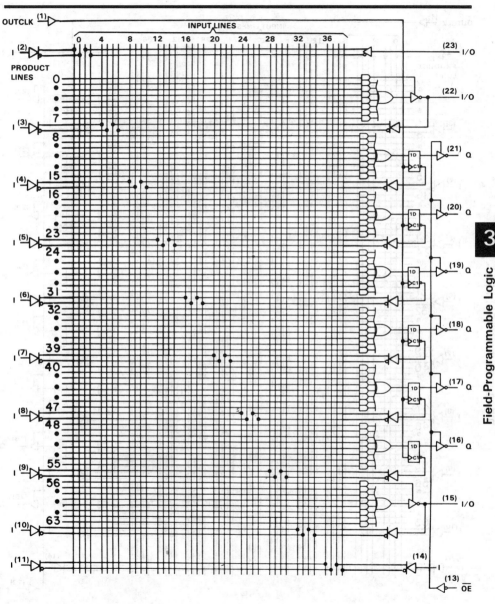

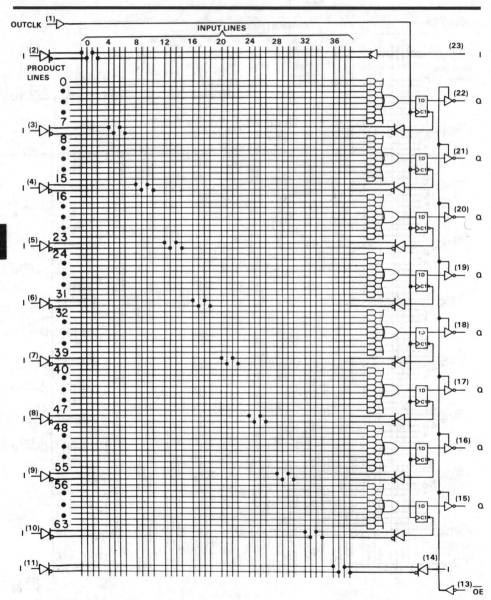

**3**

Field-Programmable Logic

TEXAS
INSTRUMENTS

### absolute maximum ratings over operating free-air temperature range (unless otherwise noted)

Supply voltage, $V_{CC}$ (see Note 1) . . . . . . . . . . . . . . . . . . . . . . . . . . . . . . . . . . . . . . . . . . . . . 7 V
Input voltage (see Note 1) . . . . . . . . . . . . . . . . . . . . . . . . . . . . . . . . . . . . . . . . . . . . . . . . . 5.5 V
Voltage applied to a disabled output (see Note 1) . . . . . . . . . . . . . . . . . . . . . . . . . . . . . . . 5.5 V
Operating free-air temperature range: M suffix . . . . . . . . . . . . . . . . . . . . . . . . . . . −55°C to 125°C
             C suffix . . . . . . . . . . . . . . . . . . . . . . . . . . . 0°C to 70°C
Storage temperature range . . . . . . . . . . . . . . . . . . . . . . . . . . . . . . . . . . . . . . . . −65°C to 150°C

NOTE 1: These ratings apply except for programming pins during a programming cycle.

### recommended operating conditions

| PARAMETER | | M SUFFIX MIN | NOM | MAX | C SUFFIX MIN | NOM | MAX | UNIT |
|---|---|---|---|---|---|---|---|---|
| $V_{CC}$ | Supply voltage | 4.5 | 5 | 5.5 | 4.75 | 5 | 5.25 | V |
| $V_{IH}$ | High-level input voltage | 2 | | 5.5 | 2 | | 5.5 | V |
| $V_{IL}$ | Low-level input voltage | | | 0.8 | | | 0.8 | V |
| $I_{OH}$ | High-level output current | | | −2 | | | −3.2 | mA |
| $I_{OL}$ | Low-level output current | | | 12 | | | 24 | mA |
| $T_A$ | Operating free-air temperature | −55 | | 125 | 0 | | 70 | °C |

### programming parameters, $T_A$ = 25°C

| | | MIN | NOM | MAX | UNIT |
|---|---|---|---|---|---|
| $V_{CC}$ | Verify-level supply voltage | ⁻4.5 | 5.0 | 5.5 | V |
| $V_{IH}$ | High-level input voltage | 2 | | 5.5 | V |
| $V_{IL}$ | Low-level input voltage | | | 0.8 | V |
| $V_{IHH}$ | Program-pulse input voltage | 10.25 | 10.5 | 10.75 | V |
| $I_{IHH}$ | Program-pulse input current | PO | | 20 | 50 | mA |
| | | PGM ENABLE, L/R | | 10 | 25 | |
| | | PI, PA | | 1.5 | 5 | |
| | | $V_{CC}$ | | 250 | 400 | |
| $t_{w1}$ | Program-pulse duration at PO pins | 10 | | 50 | µs |
| $t_{w2}$ | Pulse duration at PGM VERIFY | 100 | | | ns |
| | Program-pulse duty cycle at PO pins | | | 25 | % |
| $t_{su}$ | Setup time | 100 | | | ns |
| $t_h$ | Hold time | 100 | | | ns |
| $t_{d1}$ | Delay time from $V_{CC}$ to 5 V to PGM VERIFY† | 100 | | | µs |
| $t_{d2}$ | Delay time from PGM VERIFY† to valid output | 200 | | | ns |
| | Input voltage at pins 1 and 11 to open verify-protect (security) fuse | 20 | 21 | 22 | V |
| | Input current to open verify-protect (security) fuse | | | 400 | mA |
| $t_{w3}$ | Pulse duration to open verify-protect (security) fuse | 20 | | 50 | µs |
| | $V_{CC}$ value during security fuse programming | | 0 | 0.4 | V |

Field-Programmable Logic

3

## PAL20L8A, PAL20R4A, PAL20R6A, PAL20R8A
## STANDARD HIGH SPEED PAL CIRCUITS

### recommended operating conditions

| | | | M SUFFIX MIN | TYP | MAX | C SUFFIX MIN | TYP | MAX | UNIT |
|---|---|---|---|---|---|---|---|---|---|
| $f_{clock}$ | Clock frequency | | 0 | | 20 | 0 | | 30 | MHz |
| $t_w$ | Pulse duration, clock | High | 20 | | | 15 | | | ns |
| | | Low | 20 | | | 15 | | | ns |
| $t_{su}$ | Setup time, input or feedback before OUTCLK↑ | | 30 | | | 25 | | | ns |
| $t_h$ | Hold time, input or feedback after OUTCLK↑ | | 0 | | | 0 | | | ns |

### electrical characteristics over recommended free-air operating temperature range

| PARAMETER | | TEST CONDITIONS[†] | M SUFFIX MIN | TYP[‡] | MAX | C SUFFIX MIN | TYP[‡] | MAX | UNIT |
|---|---|---|---|---|---|---|---|---|---|
| $V_{IK}$ | | $V_{CC}$ = MIN, $I_I$ = −18 mA | | | −1.5 | | | −1.5 | V |
| $V_{OH}$ | | $V_{CC}$ = MIN, $I_{OH}$ = MAX | 2.4 | 3.2 | | 2.4 | 3.3 | | V |
| $V_{OL}$ | | $V_{CC}$ = MIN, $I_{OL}$ = MAX | | 0.25 | 0.4 | | 0.35 | 0.5 | V |
| $I_{OZH}$ | O, Q outputs | $V_{CC}$ = MAX, $V_{IH}$ = 2.7 V | | | 20 | | | 20 | μA |
| | I/O ports | | | | 100 | | | 100 | |
| $I_{OZL}$ | O, Q outputs | $V_{CC}$ = MAX, $V_{IH}$ = 0.4 V | | | −20 | | | −20 | μA |
| | I/O ports | | | | −250 | | | −250 | |
| $I_I$ | OE Input | $V_{CC}$ = MAX, $V_I$ = 5.5 V | | | 0.2 | | | 0.2 | mA |
| | All others | | | | 0.1 | | | 0.1 | |
| $I_{IH}$ | OE Input | $V_{CC}$ = MAX, $V_I$ = 2.7 V | | | 40 | | | 40 | μA |
| | All others | | | | 20 | | | 20 | |
| $I_{IL}$ | OE Input | $V_{CC}$ = MAX, $V_I$ = 0.4 V | | | −0.4 | | | −0.4 | mA |
| | All others | | | | −0.2 | | | −0.2 | |
| $I_O$[§] | | $V_{CC}$ = MAX, $V_O$ = 2.25 V | −30 | | −125 | −30 | | −125 | mA |
| $I_{CC}$ | | $V_{CC}$ = MAX, $V_I$ = 0 V, Outputs open, OE at $V_{IH}$ | | 150 | 210 | | 150 | 210 | mA |

[†]For conditions shown as MIN or MAX, use the appropriate value specified under recommended operating conditions.
[‡]All typical values are $V_{CC}$ = 5 V, $T_A$ = 25°C.
[§]The output conditions have been chosen to produce a current that closely approximates one half the true short-circuit current, $I_{OS}$.

### switching characteristics over recommended operating free-air temperature range (unless otherwise noted)

| PARAMETER | FROM | TO | TEST CONDITIONS | M SUFFIX MIN | TYP[‡] | MAX | C SUFFIX MIN | TYP[‡] | MAX | UNIT |
|---|---|---|---|---|---|---|---|---|---|---|
| $f_{max}$ | | | | 20 | | | 30 | | | MHz |
| $t_{pd}$ | I, I/O | O, I/O | $R_L$ = 500 Ω, $C_L$ = 50 pF See Note 2 | | 15 | 30 | | 15 | 25 | ns |
| $t_{pd}$ | OUTCLK↑ | Q | | | 10 | 20 | | 10 | 15 | ns |
| $t_{en}$ | OE | Q | | | 10 | 25 | | 10 | 20 | ns |
| $t_{dis}$ | OE↑ | Q | | | 11 | 25 | | 11 | 20 | ns |
| $t_{en}$ | I, I/O | O, I/O | | | 14 | 30 | | 14 | 25 | ns |
| $t_{dis}$ | I, I/O | O, I/O | | | 12 | 30 | | 12 | 25 | ns |

[‡]All typical values are at $V_{CC}$ = 5 V, $T_A$ = 25°C.
NOTE 2: Load circuits and voltage waveforms are shown in Section 1.

TEXAS INSTRUMENTS

3-26

### recommended operating conditions

| | | | M SUFFIX | | | C SUFFIX | | | UNIT |
|---|---|---|---|---|---|---|---|---|---|
| | | | MIN | TYP | MAX | MIN | TYP | MAX | |
| $f_{clock}$ | Clock frequency | | 0 | | 18 | 0 | | 18 | MHz |
| $t_w$ | Pulse duration, clock | High | | | | | | | ns |
| | | Low | | | | | | | ns |
| $t_{su}$ | Setup time, input or feedback before OUTCLK↑ | | | | | | | | ns |
| $t_h$ | Hold time, input or feedback after OUTCLK↑ | | | | | | | | ns |

### electrical characteristics over recommended free-air operating temperature range

| PARAMETER | | TEST CONDITIONS[†] | M SUFFIX | | | C SUFFIX | | | UNIT |
|---|---|---|---|---|---|---|---|---|---|
| | | | MIN | TYP[‡] | MAX | MIN | TYP[‡] | MAX | |
| $V_{IK}$ | | $V_{CC}$ = MIN, $I_I$ = −18 mA | | | −1.5 | | | −1.5 | V |
| $V_{OH}$ | | $V_{CC}$ = MIN, $I_{OH}$ = MAX | 2.4 | 3.2 | | 2.4 | 3.3 | | V |
| $V_{OL}$ | | $V_{CC}$ = MIN, $I_{OL}$ = MAX | | 0.25 | 0.4 | | 0.35 | 0.5 | V |
| $I_{OZH}$ | O, Q outputs | $V_{CC}$ = MAX, $V_{IH}$ = 2.7 V | | | 20 | | | 20 | µA |
| | I/O ports | | | | 100 | | | 100 | |
| $I_{OZL}$ | O, Q outputs | $V_{CC}$ = MAX, $V_{IH}$ = 0.4 V | | | −20 | | | −20 | µA |
| | I/O ports | | | | −250 | | | −250 | |
| $I_I$ | OE Input | $V_{CC}$ = MAX, $V_I$ = 5.5 V | | | 0.2 | | | 0.2 | mA |
| | All others | | | | 0.1 | | | 0.1 | |
| $I_{IH}$ | OE Input | $V_{CC}$ = MAX, $V_I$ = 2.7 V | | | 40 | | | 40 | µA |
| | All others | | | | 20 | | | 20 | |
| $I_{IL}$ | OE Input | $V_{CC}$ = MAX, $V_I$ = 0.4 V | | | −0.4 | | | −0.4 | mA |
| | All others | | | | −0.2 | | | −0.2 | |
| $I_O$ [§] | | $V_{CC}$ = MAX, $V_O$ = 2.25 V | −30 | | −125 | −30 | | −125 | mA |
| $I_{CC}$ | | $V_{CC}$ = MAX, $V_I$ = 0 V, Outputs open, OE at $V_{IH}$ | | 75 | 100 | | 75 | 100 | mA |

[†]For conditions shown as MIN or MAX, use the appropriate value specified under recommended operating conditions.
[‡]All typical values are $V_{CC}$ = 5 V, $T_A$ = 25°C.
[§]The output conditions have been chosen to produce a current that closely approximates one half the true short-circuit current, $I_{OS}$.

### switching characteristics over recommended operating free-air temperature range (unless otherwise noted)

| PARAMETER | FROM | TO | TEST CONDITIONS | M SUFFIX | | | C SUFFIX | | | UNIT |
|---|---|---|---|---|---|---|---|---|---|---|
| | | | | MIN | TYP[‡] | MAX | MIN | TYP[‡] | MAX | |
| $f_{max}$ | | | | 18 | | | 18 | | | MHz |
| $t_{pd}$ | I, I/O | O, I/O | | | 25 | | | 25 | | ns |
| $t_{pd}$ | OUTCLK↑ | Q | $R_L$ = 500 Ω, | | 20 | | | 20 | | ns |
| $t_{en}$ | OE | Q | $C_L$ = 50 pF, | | 15 | | | 15 | | ns |
| $t_{dis}$ | OE↑ | Q | See Note 2 | | 12 | | | 12 | | ns |
| $t_{en}$ | I, I/O | O, I/O | | | 25 | | | 25 | | ns |
| $t_{dis}$ | I, I/O | O, I/O | | | 20 | | | 20 | | ns |

[‡]All typical values are at $V_{CC}$ = 5 V, $T_A$ = 25°C.
NOTE 2: Load circuits and voltage waveforms are shown in Section 1.

**3**

**Field-Programmable Logic**

TEXAS
INSTRUMENTS

## PAL20L8A, PAL20R4A, PAL20R6A, PAL20R8A
## STANDARD HIGH SPEED PAL CIRCUITS

**Field-Programmable Logic**

### PRODUCT TERMS 0 THRU 31
#### (TOP VIEW)

```
PGM ENABLE [ 1   U  24 ] VCC
       PIO [ 2      23 ] †
       PI1 [ 3      22 ] PO3
       PI2 [ 4      21 ] PO2
       PI3 [ 5      20 ] POO1
       PI4 [ 6      19 ] POO
       PI5 [ 7      18 ] PAO
       PI6 [ 8      17 ] PA1
       PI7 [ 9      16 ] PA2
       PI8 [ 10     15 ] L/R
       PI9 [ 11     14 ] †
       GND [ 12     13 ] PGM VERIFY
```

### PRODUCT TERMS 32 THRU 63
#### (TOP VIEW)

```
PGM VERIFY [ 1   U  24 ] VCC
       PIO [ 2      23 ] †
       PI1 [ 3      22 ] L/R
       PI2 [ 4      21 ] PAO
       PI3 [ 5      20 ] PA1
       PI4 [ 6      19 ] PA2
       PI5 [ 7      18 ] PO3
       PI6 [ 8      17 ] PO2
       PI7 [ 9      16 ] PO1
       PI8 [ 10     15 ] POO
       PI9 [ 11     14 ] †
       GND [ 12     13 ] PGM ENABLE
```

†Pins 14 and 23 have no programming function. Make no connection.
Pin assignments in programming mode (PGM ENABLE at $V_{IHH}$)

### TABLE 1. INPUT LINE SELECT

| INPUT LINE NUMBER | PIN NAME | | | | | | | | | | |
|---|---|---|---|---|---|---|---|---|---|---|---|
| | PI9 | PI8 | PI7 | PI6 | PI5 | PI4 | PI3 | PI2 | PI1 | PI0 | L/R |
| 0 | HH | HH | HH | HH | HH | HH | HH | HH | HH | L | Z |
| 1 | HH | HH | HH | HH | HH | HH | HH | HH | HH | H | Z |
| 2 | HH | HH | HH | HH | HH | HH | HH | HH | HH | L | HH |
| 3 | HH | HH | HH | HH | HH | HH | HH | HH | HH | H | HH |
| 4 | HH | HH | HH | HH | HH | HH | HH | HH | L | HH | Z |
| 5 | HH | HH | HH | HH | HH | HH | HH | HH | H | HH | Z |
| 6 | HH | HH | HH | HH | HH | HH | HH | HH | L | HH | HH |
| 7 | HH | HH | HH | HH | HH | HH | HH | HH | H | HH | HH |
| 8 | HH | HH | HH | HH | HH | HH | HH | L | HH | HH | Z |
| 9 | HH | HH | HH | HH | HH | HH | HH | H | HH | HH | Z |
| 10 | HH | HH | HH | HH | HH | HH | HH | L | HH | HH | HH |
| 11 | HH | HH | HH | HH | HH | HH | HH | H | HH | HH | HH |
| 12 | HH | HH | HH | HH | HH | HH | L | HH | HH | HH | Z |
| 13 | HH | HH | HH | HH | HH | HH | H | HH | HH | HH | Z |
| 14 | HH | HH | HH | HH | HH | HH | L | HH | HH | HH | HH |
| 15 | HH | HH | HH | HH | HH | HH | H | HH | HH | HH | HH |
| 16 | HH | HH | HH | HH | HH | L | HH | HH | HH | HH | Z |
| 17 | HH | HH | HH | HH | HH | H | HH | HH | HH | HH | Z |
| 18 | HH | HH | HH | HH | HH | L | HH | HH | HH | HH | HH |
| 19 | HH | HH | HH | HH | HH | H | HH | HH | HH | HH | HH |
| 20 | HH | HH | HH | HH | L | HH | HH | HH | HH | HH | Z |
| 21 | HH | HH | HH | HH | H | HH | HH | HH | HH | HH | Z |
| 22 | HH | HH | HH | HH | L | HH | HH | HH | HH | HH | HH |
| 23 | HH | HH | HH | HH | H | HH | HH | HH | HH | HH | HH |
| 24 | HH | HH | HH | L | HH | HH | HH | HH | HH | HH | Z |
| 25 | HH | HH | HH | H | HH | HH | HH | HH | HH | HH | Z |
| 26 | HH | HH | HH | L | HH | HH | HH | HH | HH | HH | HH |
| 27 | HH | HH | HH | H | HH | HH | HH | HH | HH | HH | HH |
| 28 | HH | HH | L | HH | HH | HH | HH | HH | HH | HH | Z |
| 29 | HH | HH | H | HH | HH | HH | HH | HH | HH | HH | Z |
| 30 | HH | HH | L | HH | HH | HH | HH | HH | HH | HH | HH |
| 31 | HH | HH | H | HH | HH | HH | HH | HH | HH | HH | HH |
| 32 | HH | L | HH | HH | HH | HH | HH | HH | HH | HH | Z |
| 33 | HH | H | HH | HH | HH | HH | HH | HH | HH | HH | Z |
| 34 | HH | L | HH | HH | HH | HH | HH | HH | HH | HH | HH |
| 35 | HH | H | HH | HH | HH | HH | HH | HH | HH | HH | HH |
| 36 | L | HH | HH | HH | HH | HH | HH | HH | HH | HH | Z |
| 37 | H | HH | HH | HH | HH | HH | HH | HH | HH | HH | Z |
| 38 | L | HH | HH | HH | HH | HH | HH | HH | HH | HH | HH |
| 39 | H | HH | HH | HH | HH | HH | HH | HH | HH | HH | HH |

### TABLE 2. PRODUCT LINE SELECT

| PRODUCT LINE NUMBER | PIN NAME | | | | | | |
|---|---|---|---|---|---|---|---|
| | PO0 | PO1 | PO2 | PO3 | PA2 | PA1 | PA0 |
| 0, 32 | Z | Z | Z | HH | Z | Z | Z |
| 1, 33 | Z | Z | Z | HH | Z | Z | HH |
| 2, 34 | Z | Z | Z | HH | Z | HH | Z |
| 3, 35 | Z | Z | Z | HH | Z | HH | HH |
| 4, 36 | Z | Z | Z | HH | HH | Z | Z |
| 5, 37 | Z | Z | Z | HH | HH | Z | HH |
| 6, 38 | Z | Z | Z | HH | HH | HH | Z |
| 7, 39 | Z | Z | Z | HH | HH | HH | HH |
| 8, 40 | Z | Z | HH | Z | Z | Z | Z |
| 9, 41 | Z | Z | HH | Z | Z | Z | HH |
| 10, 42 | Z | Z | HH | Z | Z | HH | Z |
| 11, 43 | Z | Z | HH | Z | Z | HH | HH |
| 12, 44 | Z | Z | HH | Z | HH | Z | Z |
| 13, 45 | Z | Z | HH | Z | HH | Z | HH |
| 14, 46 | Z | Z | HH | Z | HH | HH | Z |
| 15, 47 | Z | Z | HH | Z | HH | HH | HH |
| 16, 48 | Z | HH | Z | Z | Z | Z | Z |
| 17, 49 | Z | HH | Z | Z | Z | Z | HH |
| 18, 50 | Z | HH | Z | Z | Z | HH | Z |
| 19, 51 | Z | HH | Z | Z | Z | HH | HH |
| 20, 52 | Z | HH | Z | Z | HH | Z | Z |
| 21, 53 | Z | HH | Z | Z | HH | Z | HH |
| 22, 54 | Z | HH | Z | Z | HH | HH | Z |
| 23, 55 | Z | HH | Z | Z | HH | HH | HH |
| 24, 56 | HH | Z | Z | Z | Z | Z | Z |
| 25, 57 | HH | Z | Z | Z | Z | Z | HH |
| 26, 58 | HH | Z | Z | Z | Z | HH | Z |
| 27, 59 | HH | Z | Z | Z | Z | HH | HH |
| 28, 60 | HH | Z | Z | Z | HH | Z | Z |
| 29, 61 | HH | Z | Z | Z | HH | Z | HH |
| 30, 62 | HH | Z | Z | Z | HH | HH | Z |
| 31, 63 | HH | Z | Z | Z | HH | HH | HH |

$L = V_{IL}$, $H = V_{IH}$, $HH = V_{IHH}$, Z = high impedance (e.g., 10 kΩ to 5 V)

**TEXAS INSTRUMENTS**

## programming procedure for array fuses

Array fuses are programmed using a linear select method. Each fuse can be opened by selecting the appropriate (one of 40) input line and then pulsing the correct (one of 64) product line. The levels for selecting input lines and product lines are shown in Tables 1 and 2.

Step 1    Raise PGM ENABLE to $V_{IHH}$.
Step 2    Select an input line by applying appropriate levels to L/R and PI pins.
Step 3    Begin selection of the output line with appropriate conditions on PA pins.
Step 4    Raise $V_{CC}$ to $V_{IHH}$.
Step 5    Blow the fuse by pulsing the appropriate PO pin to $V_{IHH}$ as shown in Table 2 for the product line.
Step 6    Return $V_{CC}$ to 5 volts and pulse PGM Verify. The PO pin selected in Step 5 will be less than $V_{OL}$ if the fuse is open.

Steps 1 through 6 may be repeated if the verification does not indicate that the fuse was successfully programmed (blown), but no more than four times. Verification is possible only with the verify-protect fuse intact.

## programming waveforms

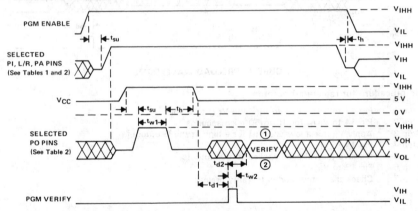

(1) A high level during the verify interval indicates that programming has not been successful.
(2) A low level during the verify interval indicates that programming has been successful.

## security fuse programming

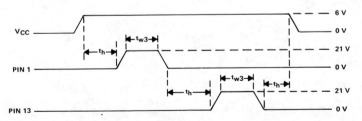

Field-Programmable Logic

3

## PAL20L8A, PAL20R4A, PAL20R6A, PAL20R8A
## STANDARD HIGH SPEED PAL CIRCUITS

### PRELOAD PROCEDURES

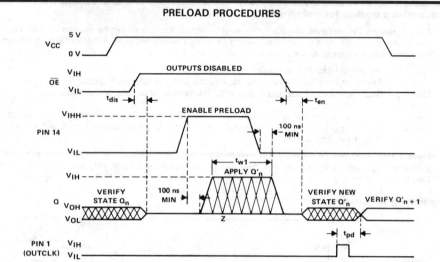

**FIGURE 1. PRELOAD WAVEFORMS**

### preload procedure for registered outputs

Step 1    Pin 13 to $V_{IH}$, Pin 1 to $V_{IL}$, and $V_{CC}$ to 5 volts.
Step 2    Pin 14 to $V_{IHH}$ for 10 to 50 microseconds.
Step 3    Apply $V_{IL}$ for a low and $V_{IH}$ for a high at the Q outputs.
Step 4    Pin 14 to $V_{IL}$.
Step 5    Remove the voltages applied to the outputs.
Step 6    Pin 13 to $V_{IL}$.
Step 7    Check the output states to verify preload.

**TEXAS INSTRUMENTS**
POST OFFICE BOX 225012 • DALLAS, TEXAS 75265

FEBRUARY 1984 – REVISED JANUARY 1985

- High-Performance Operation
  Propagation Delay . . . 15 ns
  $f_{MAX}$ . . . 50 MHz

- Functionally Equivalent, but Faster than
  PAL16L8A, PAL16R4A, PAL16R6A, and
  PAL16R8A

- Power-Up Clear on Registered Devices
  (All Registered Outputs are Set Low)

- Package Options Include Both Plastic and
  Ceramic Chip Carriers in Addition to Plastic
  and Ceramic DIPs

| DEVICE | INPUTS | 3-STATE O OUTPUTS | REGISTERED Q OUTPUTS | I/O PORTS |
|--------|--------|-------------------|----------------------|-----------|
| PAL16L8 | 10 | 2 | 0 | 6 |
| PAL16R4 | 8 | 0 | 4 (3-state) | 4 |
| PAL16R6 | 8 | 0 | 6 (3-state) | 2 |
| PAL16R8 | 8 | 0 | 8 (3-state) | 0 |

### description

These programmable array logic devices feature high speed and functional equivalency when compared with currently available devices. They combine the latest Advanced Low-Power Schottky† technology "IMPACT" with proven titanium-tungsten fuses. These devices will provide reliable, high-performance substitutes for conventional TTL logic. Their easy programmability allows for quick design of "custom" functions and typically results in a more compact circuit board. In addition, chip carriers are available for further reduction in board space.

The half-power devices offer a choice of operating frequency, switching speeds, and power dissipation. In many cases, these half-power devices are fast enough to be used where the high-speed, or "A", devices are used. From an overall system level, this can amount to a significant reduction in power consumption, with no sacrifice in speed.

The PAL16' M series is characterized for operation over the full military temperature range of −55°C to 125°C. The PAL16' C series is characterized for operation from 0°C to 70°C.

†Integrated Schottky-Barrier diode-clamped transistor is patented by Texas Instruments, U.S. Patent Number 3,463,975.

PAL is a registered trademark of Monolithic Memories Inc.

TIBPAL16L8'
M SUFFIX . . . J PACKAGE
C SUFFIX . . . J OR N PACKAGE
(TOP VIEW)

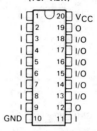

| | | |
|---|---|---|
| I | 1 | VCC |
| I | 2 | O |
| I | 3 | I/O |
| I | 4 | I/O |
| I | 5 | I/O |
| I | 6 | I/O |
| I | 7 | I/O |
| I | 8 | I/O |
| I | 9 | O |
| GND | 10 | I |

TIBPAL16L8'
M SUFFIX . . . FH OR FK PACKAGE
C SUFFIX . . . FN PACKAGE
(TOP VIEW)

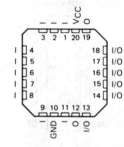

Pin assignments in operating mode (pins 1 and 11 less positive than $V_{IHH}$)

3

Field-Programmable Logic

**TEXAS INSTRUMENTS**

## TIBPAL16R4, TIBPAL16R6, TIBPAL16R8
## HIGH-PERFORMANCE IMPACT PAL CIRCUITS

**TIBPAL16R4'**
**M SUFFIX . . . J PACKAGE**
**C SUFFIX. . . J OR N PACKAGE**
**(TOP VIEW)**

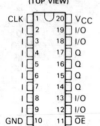

| | | | |
|---|---|---|---|
| CLK | 1 | 20 | VCC |
| I | 2 | 19 | I/O |
| I | 3 | 18 | I/O |
| I | 4 | 17 | Q |
| I | 5 | 16 | Q |
| I | 6 | 15 | Q |
| I | 7 | 14 | Q |
| I | 8 | 13 | I/O |
| I | 9 | 12 | I/O |
| GND | 10 | 11 | OE |

**TIBPAL16R4'**
**M SUFFIX . . . FH OR FK PACKAGE**
**C SUFFIX . . . FN PACKAGE**
**(TOP VIEW)**

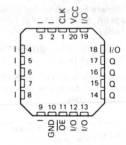

**TIBPAL16R6'**
**M SUFFIX . . . J PACKAGE**
**C SUFFIX . . . J OR N PACKAGE**
**(TOP VIEW)**

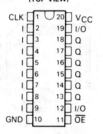

| | | | |
|---|---|---|---|
| CLK | 1 | 20 | VCC |
| I | 2 | 19 | I/O |
| I | 3 | 18 | Q |
| I | 4 | 17 | Q |
| I | 5 | 16 | Q |
| I | 6 | 15 | Q |
| I | 7 | 14 | Q |
| I | 8 | 13 | Q |
| I | 9 | 12 | I/O |
| GND | 10 | 11 | OE |

**TIBPAL16R6'**
**M SUFFIX . . . FH OR FK PACKAGE**
**C SUFFIX . . . FN PACKAGE**
**(TOP VIEW)**

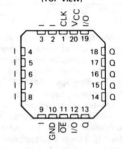

**TIBPAL16R8'**
**M SUFFIX . . . J PACKAGE**
**C SUFFIX . . . J OR N PACKAGE**
**(TOP VIEW)**

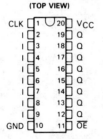

| | | | |
|---|---|---|---|
| CLK | 1 | 20 | VCC |
| I | 2 | 19 | Q |
| I | 3 | 18 | Q |
| I | 4 | 17 | Q |
| I | 5 | 16 | Q |
| I | 6 | 15 | Q |
| I | 7 | 14 | Q |
| I | 8 | 13 | Q |
| I | 9 | 12 | Q |
| GND | 10 | 11 | OE |

**TIBPAL16R8'**
**M SUFFIX. . . FH OR FK PACKAGE**
**C SUFFIX. . . FN PACKAGE**
**(TOP VIEW)**

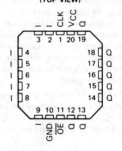

Pin assignments in operating mode (pins 1 and 11 less positive than
$V_{IHH}$)

3

**Field-Programmable Logic**

**functional block diagrams (positive logic)**

'PAL16L8

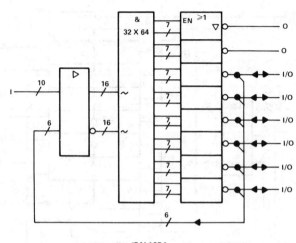

'PAL16R4

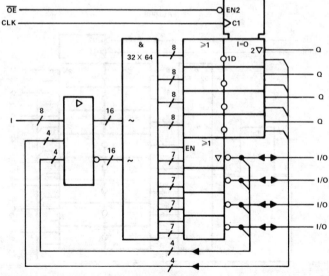

~ denotes fused inputs

Field-Programmable Logic

3

# TIBPAL16R6, TIBPAL16R8
## HIGH-PERFORMANCE IMPACT PAL CIRCUITS

functional block diagrams (positive logic)

'PAL16R6

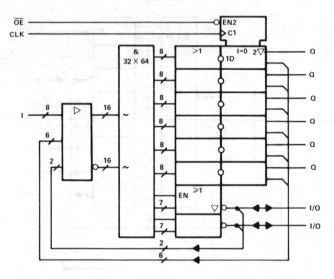

'PAL16R8

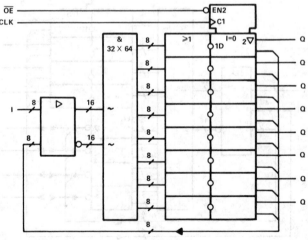

~ denotes fused inputs

**TEXAS INSTRUMENTS**

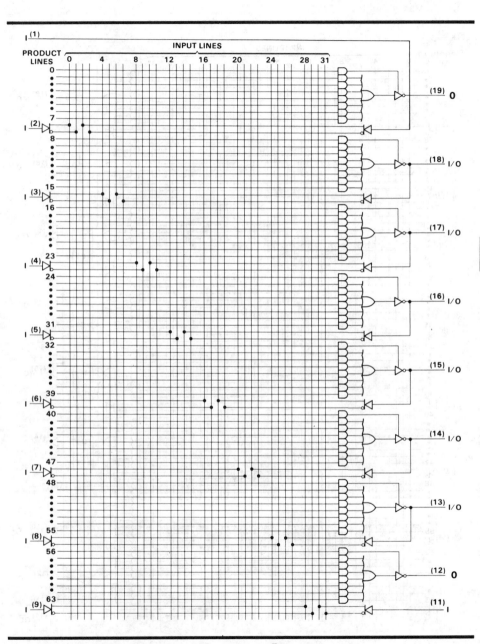

Field-Programmable Logic

**TEXAS INSTRUMENTS**

# TIBPAL16R4
## HIGH-PERFORMANCE IMPACT PAL CIRCUITS

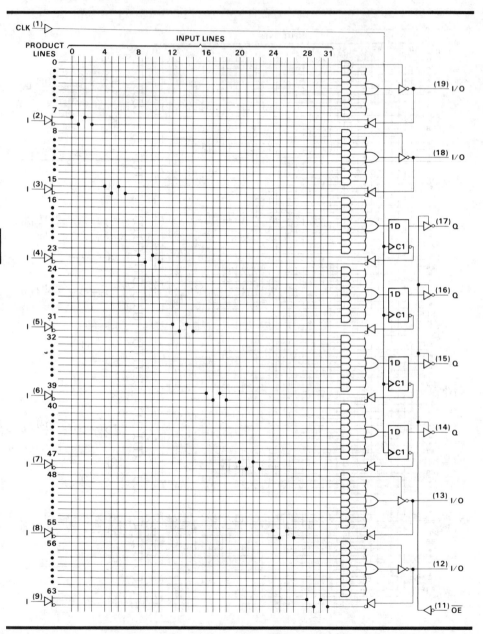

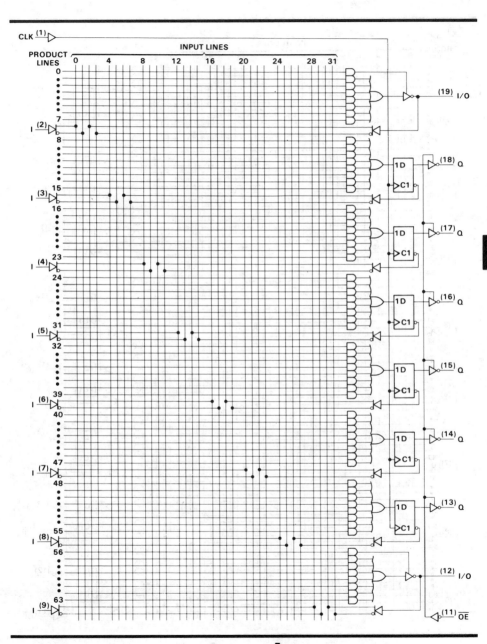

Field-Programmable Logic

3

## TIBPAL16R8
## HIGH-PERFORMANCE IMPACT PAL CIRCUITS

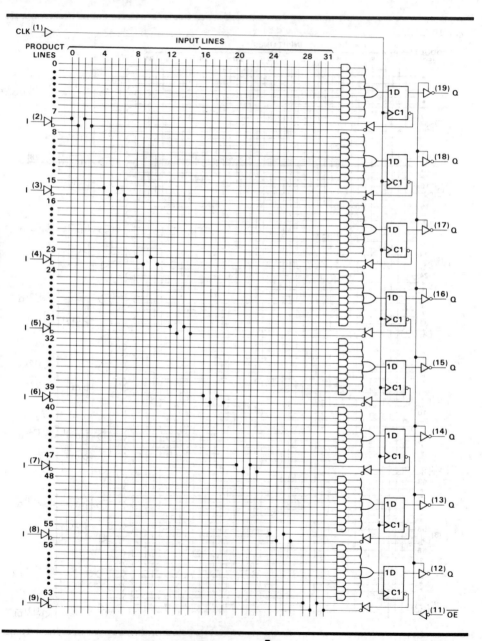

TEXAS
INSTRUMENTS

## absolute maximum ratings over operating free-air temperature range (unless otherwise noted)

```
Supply voltage, VCC (see Note 1) ........................................................... 7 V
Input voltage (see Note 1) ................................................................. 5.5 V
Voltage applied to a disabled output (see Note 1) ........................................... 5.5 V
Operating free-air temperature range: M suffix ......................................... −55°C to 125°C
                                       C suffix ........................................... 0°C to 70°C
Storage temperature range ......................................................... −65°C to 150°C
```

NOTE 1. These ratings apply except for programming pins during a programming cycle.

## recommended operating conditions (see Note 2)

| | PARAMETER | M SUFFIX | | | C SUFFIX | | | UNIT |
|---|---|---|---|---|---|---|---|---|
| | | MIN | NOM | MAX | MIN | NOM | MAX | |
| $V_{CC}$ | Supply voltage | 4.5 | 5 | 5.5 | 4.75 | 5 | 5.25 | V |
| $V_{IH}$ | High-level input voltage | 2 | | 5.5 | 2 | | 5.5 | V |
| $V_{IL}$ | Low-level input voltage | | | 0.8 | | | 0.8 | V |
| $I_{OH}$ | High-level output current | | | −2 | | | −3.2 | mA |
| $I_{OL}$ | Low-level output current | | | 12 | | | 24 | mA |
| $T_A$ | Operating free-air temperature | −55 | | 125 | 0 | | 70 | °C |

NOTE 2. These recommended operating conditions apply for all device dash numbers. Also refer to additional recommended operating
conditions information pertaining to appropriate device dash number, i.e., −20, −15, etc.

## programming parameters, $T_A = 25°C$

| | | | MIN | NOM | MAX | UNIT |
|---|---|---|---|---|---|---|
| $V_{CC}$ | Verify-level supply voltage | | 4.5 | 5.0 | 5.5 | V |
| $V_{IH}$ | High-level input voltage | | 2 | | 5.5 | V |
| $V_{IL}$ | Low-level input voltage | | | | 0.8 | V |
| $V_{IHH}$ | Program-pulse input voltage | | 10.25 | 10.5 | 10.75 | V |
| $I_{IHH}$ | Program-pulse input current | PO | | 20 | 50 | mA |
| | | PGM ENABLE, L/R | | 10 | 25 | |
| | | PI, PA | | 1.5 | 5 | |
| | | $V_{CC}$ | | 250 | 500 | |
| $t_{w1}$ | Program-pulse duration at PO pins | | 10 | | 50 | µs |
| $t_{w2}$ | Pulse duration at PGM VERIFY | | 100 | | | ns |
| | Program-pulse duty cycle at PO pins | | | | 25 | % |
| $t_{su}$ | Setup time | | 100 | | | ns |
| $t_h$ | Hold time | | 100 | | | ns |
| $t_{d1}$ | Delay time from $V_{CC}$ to 5 V to PGM VERIFY† | | 100 | | | µs |
| $t_{d2}$ | Delay time from PGM VERIFY ↑ to valid output | | 200 | | | ns |
| | Input voltage at pins 1 and 11 to open verify-protect (security) fuse | | 20 | 21 | 22 | V |
| | Input current to open verify-protect (security) fuse | | | | 400 | mA |
| $t_{w3}$ | Pulse duration to open verify-protect (security) fuse | | 20 | | 50 | µs |
| | $V_{CC}$ value during security fuse programming | | | 0 | 0.4 | V |

**3**

**Field-Programmable Logic**

**TEXAS**
**INSTRUMENTS**

## TIBPAL16L8, TIBPAL16R4, TIBPAL16R6, TIBPAL16R8
## HIGH-PERFORMANCE IMPACT PAL CIRCUITS

### recommended operating conditions

| | | | M SUFFIX −20 | | | C SUFFIX −15 | | | UNIT |
|---|---|---|---|---|---|---|---|---|---|
| | | | MIN | TYP | MAX | MIN | TYP | MAX | |
| $f_{clock}$ | Clock frequency | | 0 | | 40 | 0 | | 50 | MHz |
| $t_W$ | Pulse duration, clock, (see Note 3) | High | 10 | | | 8 | | | ns |
| | | Low | 11 | | | 9 | | | |
| $t_{su}$ | Setup time, input or feedback before CLK↑ | | 20 | | | 15 | | | ns |
| $t_h$ | Hold time, input or feedback after CLK↑ | | 0 | | | 0 | | | ns |

NOTE 3: The total clock period of CLK high and CLK low must not exceed clock frequency, $f_{clock}$. Minimum pulse durations specified are only for CLK high or CLK low, but not for both simultaneously.

### electrical characteristics, over recommended operating free-air temperature range

| PARAMETER | | TEST CONDITIONS[†] | | M SUFFIX −20 | | | C SUFFIX −15 | | | UNIT |
|---|---|---|---|---|---|---|---|---|---|---|
| | | | | MIN | TYP[‡] | MAX | MIN | TYP[‡] | MAX | |
| $V_{IK}$ | | $V_{CC}$ = MIN, | $I_I$ = −18 mA | | | −1.5 | | | −1.5 | V |
| $V_{OH}$ | | $V_{CC}$ = MIN, | $I_{OH}$ = MAX | 2.4 | 3.2 | | 2.4 | 3.3 | | V |
| $V_{OL}$ | | $V_{CC}$ = MIN, | $I_{OL}$ = MAX | | 0.25 | 0.4 | | 0.35 | 0.5 | V |
| $I_{OZH}$ | Outputs | $V_{CC}$ = MAX, | $V_O$ = 2.7 V | | | 20 | | | 20 | μA |
| | I/O ports | | | | | 100 | | | 100 | |
| $I_{OZL}$ | Outputs | $V_{CC}$ = MAX, | $V_O$ = 0.4 V | | | −20 | | | −20 | μA |
| | I/O ports | | | | | −250 | | | −250 | |
| $I_I$ | | $V_{CC}$ = MAX, | $V_I$ = 5.5 V | Pin 1, 11 | | 0.2 | | | 0.1 | mA |
| | | | | All others | | 0.1 | | | 0.1 | |
| $I_{IH}$ | | $V_{CC}$ = MAX, | $V_I$ = 2.7 V | Pin 1, 11 | | 50 | | | 20 | μA |
| | | | | All others | | 20 | | | 20 | |
| $I_{IL}$ | | $V_{CC}$ = MAX, | $V_I$ = 0.4 V | | | −0.2 | | | −0.2 | mA |
| $I_O$ [§] | | $V_{CC}$ = MAX, | $V_O$ = 2.25 V | −30 | | −125 | −30 | | −125 | mA |
| $I_{CC}$ | | $V_{CC}$ = MAX, $V_I$ = 0 V, | Outputs Open | | 140 | 190 | | 140 | 180 | mA |

[†]For conditions shown as MIN or MAX, use the appropriate value specified under recommended operating conditions.
[‡]All typical values are at $V_{CC}$ = 5 V, $T_A$ = 25°C.
[§]The output conditions have been chosen to produce a current that closely approximates one half of the true short-circuit output current, $I_{OS}$.

### switching characteristics over recommended supply voltage and operating free-air temperature ranges (unless otherwise noted)

| PARAMETER | FROM | TO | TEST CONDITIONS | M SUFFIX −20 | | | C SUFFIX −15 | | | UNIT |
|---|---|---|---|---|---|---|---|---|---|---|
| | | | | MIN | TYP[‡] | MAX | MIN | TYP[‡] | MAX | |
| $f_{max}$ | | | | 40 | | | 50 | | | MHz |
| $t_{pd}$ | I, I/O | O, I/O | $R_L$ = 500 Ω, $C_L$ = 50 pF See Note 4 | | 10 | 20 | | 10 | 15 | ns |
| $t_{pd}$ | CLK↑ | Q | | | 8 | 15 | | 8 | 12 | ns |
| $t_{en}$ | OE↓ | Q | | | 8 | 15 | | 8 | 12 | ns |
| $t_{dis}$ | OE↑ | Q | | | 7 | 15 | | 7 | 10 | ns |
| $t_{en}$ | I, I/O | O, I/O | | | 10 | 20 | | 10 | 15 | ns |
| $t_{dis}$ | I, I/O | O, I/O | | | 10 | 20 | | 10 | 15 | ns |

[‡]All typical values are at $V_{CC}$ = 5 V, $T_A$ = 25°C.
NOTE 4: Load circuits and voltage waveforms are shown in Section 1.

**TEXAS INSTRUMENTS**

**3**

**Field-Programmable Logic**

### recommended operating conditions

| | | | M SUFFIX −30 | | | C SUFFIX −25 | | | UNIT |
|---|---|---|---|---|---|---|---|---|---|
| | | | MIN | TYP | MAX | MIN | TYP | MAX | |
| $f_{clock}$ | Clock frequency | | 0 | | 25 | 0 | | 30 | MHz |
| $t_w$ | Pulse duration, clock, (see Note 3) | High | 15 | | | 10 | | | ns |
| | | Low | 20 | | | 15 | | | |
| $t_{su}$ | Setup time, input or feedback before CLK↑ | | 25 | | | 20 | | | ns |
| $t_h$ | Hold time, input or feedback after CLK↑ | | 0 | | | 0 | | | ns |

NOTE 3: The total clock period of CLK high and CLK low must not exceed clock frequency, $f_{clock}$. Minimum pulse durations specified are only for CLK high or CLK low, but not for both simultaneously.

### electrical characteristics over recommended operating free-air temperature range

| PARAMETER | | TEST CONDITIONS† | | M SUFFIX −30 | | | C SUFFIX −25 | | | UNIT |
|---|---|---|---|---|---|---|---|---|---|---|
| | | | | MIN | TYP‡ | MAX | MIN | TYP‡ | MAX | |
| $V_{IK}$ | | $V_{CC}$ = MIN, | $I_I$ = −18 mA | | | −1.5 | | | −1.5 | V |
| $V_{OH}$ | | $V_{CC}$ = MIN, | $I_{OH}$ = MAX | 2.4 | 3.2 | | 2.4 | 3.3 | | V |
| $V_{OL}$ | | $V_{CC}$ = MIN, | $I_{OL}$ = MAX | | 0.25 | 0.4 | | 0.35 | 0.5 | V |
| $I_{OZH}$ | Outputs | $V_{CC}$ = MAX, | $V_O$ = 2.7 V | | | 20 | | | 20 | μA |
| | I/O ports | | | | | 100 | | | 100 | |
| $I_{OZL}$ | Outputs | $V_{CC}$ = MAX, | $V_O$ = 0.4 V | | | −20 | | | −20 | μA |
| | I/O ports | | | | | −250 | | | −250 | |
| $I_I$ | | $V_{CC}$ = MAX, | $V_I$ = 5.5 V | Pin 1, 11 | | 0.2 | | | 0.1 | | mA |
| | | | | All others | 0.1 | | | 0.1 | | |
| $I_{IH}$ | | $V_{CC}$ = MAX, | $V_I$ = 2.7 V | Pin 1, 11 | | 50 | | | 20 | | μA |
| | | | | All others | 20 | | | 20 | | |
| $I_{IL}$ | | $V_{CC}$ = MAX, | $V_I$ = 0.4 V | | | −0.2 | | | −0.2 | mA |
| $I_O$ § | | $V_{CC}$ = MAX, | $V_O$ = 2.25 V | −30 | | −125 | −30 | | −125 | mA |
| $I_{CC}$ | | $V_{CC}$ = MAX, $V_I$ = 0 V, | Outputs Open | | 75 | 105 | | 75 | 100 | mA |

†For conditions shown as MIN or MAX, use the appropriate value specified under recommended operating conditions.
‡All typical values are at $V_{CC}$ = 5 V, $T_A$ = 25°C.
§The output conditions have been chosen to produce a current that closely approximates one half of the true short-circuit output current, $I_{OS}$.

### switching characteristics over recommended supply voltage and operating free-air temperature ranges (unless otherwise noted)

| PARAMETER | FROM | TO | TEST CONDITIONS | M SUFFIX −30 | | | C SUFFIX −25 | | | UNIT |
|---|---|---|---|---|---|---|---|---|---|---|
| | | | | MIN | TYP‡ | MAX | MIN | TYP‡ | MAX | |
| $f_{max}$ | | | | 25 | | | 30 | | | MHz |
| $t_{pd}$ | I, I/O | O, I/O | | | 15 | 30 | | 15 | 25 | ns |
| $t_{pd}$ | CLK↑ | Q | $R_L$ = 500 Ω, | | 10 | 20 | | 10 | 15 | ns |
| $t_{en}$ | OE↓ | Q | $C_L$ = 50 pF, | | 15 | 25 | | 15 | 20 | ns |
| $t_{dis}$ | OE↑ | Q | See Note 4 | | 10 | 25 | | 10 | 20 | ns |
| $t_{en}$ | I, I/O | O, I/O | | | 14 | 30 | | 14 | 25 | ns |
| $t_{dis}$ | I, I/O | O, I/O | | | 13 | 30 | | 13 | 25 | ns |

‡All typical values are at $V_{CC}$ = 5 V, $T_A$ = 25°C.
NOTE 4: Load circuits and voltage waveforms are shown in Section 1.

TEXAS
INSTRUMENTS

**3**

Field-Programmable Logic

## TIBPAL16L8, TIBPAL16R4, TIBPAL16R6, TIBPAL16R8
## HIGH-PERFORMANCE IMPACT PAL CIRCUITS

**PRODUCT TERMS 0 THRU 31**
**(TOP VIEW)**

```
PGM ENABLE [ 1    20 ] VCC
       PIO [ 2    19 ] PO3
       PI1 [ 3    18 ] PO2
       PI2 [ 4    17 ] PO1
       PI3 [ 5    16 ] PO0
       PI4 [ 6    15 ] PA0
       PI5 [ 7    14 ] PA1
       PI6 [ 8    13 ] PA2
       PI7 [ 9    12 ] L/R
       GND [ 10   11 ] PGM VERIFY
```

**PRODUCT TERMS 32 THRU 63**
**(TOP VIEW)**

```
PGM VERIFY [ 1    20 ] VCC
       PIO [ 2    19 ] L/R
       PI1 [ 3    18 ] PA0
       PI2 [ 4    17 ] PA1
       PI3 [ 5    16 ] PA2
       PI4 [ 6    15 ] PO3
       PI5 [ 7    14 ] PO2
       PI6 [ 8    13 ] PO1
       PI7 [ 9    12 ] PO0
       GND [ 10   11 ] PGM ENABLE
```

Pin assignments in programming mode (PGM ENABLE, pin 1 or 11, at $V_{IHH}$)

### TABLE 1 — INPUT LINE SELECT

| INPUT LINE NUMBER | PI7 | PI6 | PI5 | PI4 | PI3 | PI2 | PI1 | PI0 | L/R |
|---|---|---|---|---|---|---|---|---|---|
| 0 | HH | HH | HH | HH | HH | HH | HH | L | Z |
| 1 | HH | HH | HH | HH | HH | HH | HH | H | Z |
| 2 | HH | HH | HH | HH | HH | HH | HH | L | HH |
| 3 | HH | HH | HH | HH | HH | HH | HH | H | HH |
| 4 | HH | HH | HH | HH | HH | HH | L | HH | Z |
| 5 | HH | HH | HH | HH | HH | HH | H | HH | Z |
| 6 | HH | HH | HH | HH | HH | HH | L | HH | HH |
| 7 | HH | HH | HH | HH | HH | HH | H | HH | HH |
| 8 | HH | HH | HH | HH | HH | L | HH | HH | Z |
| 9 | HH | HH | HH | HH | HH | H | HH | HH | Z |
| 10 | HH | HH | HH | HH | HH | L | HH | HH | HH |
| 11 | HH | HH | HH | HH | HH | H | HH | HH | HH |
| 12 | HH | HH | HH | HH | L | HH | HH | HH | Z |
| 13 | HH | HH | HH | HH | H | HH | HH | HH | Z |
| 14 | HH | HH | HH | HH | L | HH | HH | HH | HH |
| 15 | HH | HH | HH | HH | H | HH | HH | HH | HH |
| 16 | HH | HH | HH | L | HH | HH | HH | HH | Z |
| 17 | HH | HH | HH | H | HH | HH | HH | HH | Z |
| 18 | HH | HH | HH | L | HH | HH | HH | HH | HH |
| 19 | HH | HH | HH | H | HH | HH | HH | HH | HH |
| 20 | HH | HH | L | HH | HH | HH | HH | HH | Z |
| 21 | HH | HH | H | HH | HH | HH | HH | HH | Z |
| 22 | HH | HH | L | HH | HH | HH | HH | HH | HH |
| 23 | HH | HH | H | HH | HH | HH | HH | HH | HH |
| 24 | HH | L | HH | HH | HH | HH | HH | HH | Z |
| 25 | HH | H | HH | HH | HH | HH | HH | HH | Z |
| 26 | HH | L | HH | HH | HH | HH | HH | HH | HH |
| 27 | HH | H | HH | HH | HH | HH | HH | HH | HH |
| 28 | L | HH | HH | HH | HH | HH | HH | HH | Z |
| 29 | H | HH | HH | HH | HH | HH | HH | HH | Z |
| 30 | L | HH | HH | HH | HH | HH | HH | HH | HH |
| 31 | H | HH | HH | HH | HH | HH | HH | HH | HH |

### TABLE 2 — PRODUCT LINE SELECT

| PRODUCT LINE NUMBER | PO0 | PO1 | PO2 | PO3 | PA2 | PA1 | PA0 |
|---|---|---|---|---|---|---|---|
| 0, 32 | Z | Z | Z | HH | Z | Z | Z |
| 1, 33 | Z | Z | Z | HH | Z | Z | HH |
| 2, 34 | Z | Z | Z | HH | Z | HH | Z |
| 3, 35 | Z | Z | Z | HH | Z | HH | HH |
| 4, 36 | Z | Z | Z | HH | HH | Z | Z |
| 5, 37 | Z | Z | Z | HH | HH | Z | HH |
| 6, 38 | Z | Z | Z | HH | HH | HH | Z |
| 7, 39 | Z | Z | Z | HH | HH | HH | HH |
| 8, 40 | Z | Z | HH | Z | Z | Z | Z |
| 9, 41 | Z | Z | HH | Z | Z | Z | HH |
| 10, 42 | Z | Z | HH | Z | Z | HH | Z |
| 11, 43 | Z | Z | HH | Z | Z | HH | HH |
| 12, 44 | Z | Z | HH | Z | HH | Z | Z |
| 13, 45 | Z | Z | HH | Z | HH | Z | HH |
| 14, 46 | Z | Z | HH | Z | HH | HH | Z |
| 15, 47 | Z | Z | HH | Z | HH | HH | HH |
| 16, 48 | Z | HH | Z | Z | Z | Z | Z |
| 17, 49 | Z | HH | Z | Z | Z | Z | HH |
| 18, 50 | Z | HH | Z | Z | Z | HH | Z |
| 19, 51 | Z | HH | Z | Z | Z | HH | HH |
| 20, 52 | Z | HH | Z | Z | HH | Z | Z |
| 21, 53 | Z | HH | Z | Z | HH | Z | HH |
| 22, 54 | Z | HH | Z | Z | HH | HH | Z |
| 23, 55 | Z | HH | Z | Z | HH | HH | HH |
| 24, 56 | HH | Z | Z | Z | Z | Z | Z |
| 25, 57 | HH | Z | Z | Z | Z | Z | HH |
| 26, 58 | HH | Z | Z | Z | Z | HH | Z |
| 27, 59 | HH | Z | Z | Z | Z | HH | HH |
| 28, 60 | HH | Z | Z | Z | HH | Z | Z |
| 29, 61 | HH | Z | Z | Z | HH | Z | HH |
| 30, 62 | HH | Z | Z | Z | HH | HH | Z |
| 31, 63 | HH | Z | Z | Z | HH | HH | HH |

$L = V_{IL}$, $H = V_{IH}$, $HH = V_{IHH}$, $Z$ = high impedance (e.g., 10 kΩ to 5 V)

TEXAS INSTRUMENTS

### programming procedure for array fuses

Array fuses are programmed using a linear select method. Each fuse can be opened by selecting the appropriate (one of 32) input line and then pulsing the correct (one of 64) product line. The levels for selecting input lines and product lines are shown in Tables 1 and 2.

Step 1      Raise PGM ENABLE to $V_{IHH}$.

Step 2      Select an input line by applying appropriate levels to L/R and PI pins.

Step 3      Begin selection of the output line with appropriate conditions on PA pins.

Step 4      Raise $V_{CC}$ to $V_{IHH}$.

Step 5      Blow the fuse by pulsing the appropriate PO pin to $V_{IHH}$ as shown in Table 2 for the product line.

Step 6      Return $V_{CC}$ to 5 volts and pulse PGM Verify. The PO pin selected in Step 5 will be less than $V_{OL}$ if the fuse is open.

Steps 1 through 6 may be repeated if the verification does not indicate that the fuse was successfully programmed (blown), but no more than four times. Verification is possible only with the verify-protect fuse intact.

### programming waveforms

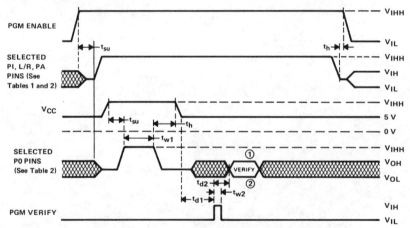

① A high level during verify interval indicates that programming has not been successful.

② A low level during verify interval indicates that programming has been successful.

### security fuse programming

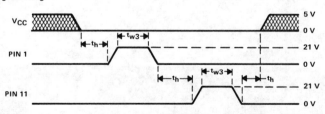

**Field-Programmable Logic**

**3**

# TIBPAL16L8-12, TIBPAL16R4-12, TIBPAL16R6-12, TIBPAL16R8-12
# TIBPAL16L8-15, TIBPAL16R4-15, TIBPAL16R6-15, TIBPAL16R8-15
## HIGH-PERFORMANCE *IMPACT*™ PAL® CIRCUITS

JANUARY 1986 – REVISED JUNE 1986

- **High-Performance Operation**
  **Propagation Delay**
    C Suffix . . . 12 ns Max
    M Suffix . . . 15 ns Max

- **Functionally Equivalent, but Faster than PAL16L8B, PAL16R4B, PAL16R6B, and PAL16R8B**

- **Power-Up Clear on Registered Devices (All Registered Outputs are Set Low)**

- **Package Options Include Both Plastic and Ceramic Chip Carriers in Addition to Plastic and Ceramic DIPs**

- **Dependable Texas Instruments Quality and Reliability**

| DEVICE | INPUTS | 3-STATE Q OUTPUTS | REGISTERED Q OUTPUTS | I/O PORTS |
|--------|--------|-------------------|----------------------|-----------|
| PAL16L8 | 10 | 2 | 0 | 6 |
| PAL16R4 | 8 | 0 | 4 (3-state) | 4 |
| PAL16R6 | 8 | 0 | 6 (3-state) | 2 |
| PAL16R8 | 8 | 0 | 8 (3-state) | 0 |

### description

These programmable array logic devices feature high speed and functional equivalency when compared with currently available devices. These IMPACT™ circuits combine the latest Advanced Low-Power Schottky† technology with proven titanium-tungsten fuses to provide reliable, high-performance substitutes for conventional TTL logic. Their easy programmability allows for quick design of "custom" functions and typically results in a more compact circuit board. In addition, chip carriers are available for further reduction in board space.

The TIBPAL16' M series is characterized for operation over the full military temperature range of −55 °C to 125 °C. The TIBPAL16' C series is characterized for operation from 0 °C to 75 °C.

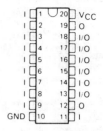

TIBPAL16L8'
M SUFFIX . . . J PACKAGE
C SUFFIX . . . J OR N PACKAGE
(TOP VIEW)

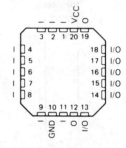

TIBPAL16L8'
M SUFFIX . . . FK PACKAGE
C SUFFIX . . . FN PACKAGE
(TOP VIEW)

Pin assignments in operating mode

**Field-Programmable Logic** · 3

IMPACT™ is a trademark of Texas Instruments.
PAL® is a registered trademark of Monolithic Memories, Inc.
†Integrated Schottky-Barrier diode-clamped transistor is patented by Texas Instruments, U.S. Patent Number 3,463,975.

INSTRUMENTS

# TIBPAL16R4-12, TIBPAL16R6-12, TIBPAL16R8-12
# TIBPAL16R4-15, TIBPAL16R6-15, TIBPAL16R8-15
## HIGH-PERFORMANCE *IMPACT*™ *PAL*® CIRCUITS

**TIBPAL16R4'**
M SUFFIX . . . J PACKAGE
C SUFFIX. . . J OR N PACKAGE
(TOP VIEW)

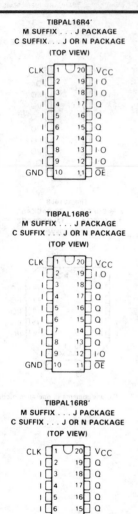

| | | | |
|---|---|---|---|
| CLK | 1 | 20 | V_CC |
| I | 2 | 19 | I O |
| I | 3 | 18 | I O |
| I | 4 | 17 | Q |
| I | 5 | 16 | Q |
| I | 6 | 15 | Q |
| I | 7 | 14 | Q |
| I | 8 | 13 | I O |
| I | 9 | 12 | I O |
| GND | 10 | 11 | OE |

**TIBPAL16R4'**
M SUFFIX . . . FK PACKAGE
C SUFFIX . . . FN PACKAGE
(TOP VIEW)

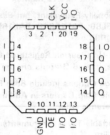

**TIBPAL16R6'**
M SUFFIX . . . J PACKAGE
C SUFFIX . . . J OR N PACKAGE
(TOP VIEW)

| | | | |
|---|---|---|---|
| CLK | 1 | 20 | V_CC |
| I | 2 | 19 | I O |
| I | 3 | 18 | Q |
| I | 4 | 17 | Q |
| I | 5 | 16 | Q |
| I | 6 | 15 | Q |
| I | 7 | 14 | Q |
| I | 8 | 13 | Q |
| I | 9 | 12 | I O |
| GND | 10 | 11 | OE |

**TIBPAL16R6'**
M SUFFIX . . . FK PACKAGE
C SUFFIX . . . FN PACKAGE
(TOP VIEW)

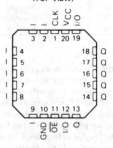

**TIBPAL16R8'**
M SUFFIX . . . J PACKAGE
C SUFFIX . . . J OR N PACKAGE
(TOP VIEW)

| | | | |
|---|---|---|---|
| CLK | 1 | 20 | V_CC |
| I | 2 | 19 | Q |
| I | 3 | 18 | Q |
| I | 4 | 17 | Q |
| I | 5 | 16 | Q |
| I | 6 | 15 | Q |
| I | 7 | 14 | Q |
| I | 8 | 13 | Q |
| I | 9 | 12 | Q |
| GND | 10 | 11 | OE |

**TIBPAL16R8'**
M SUFFIX . . . FK PACKAGE
C SUFFIX . . . FN PACKAGE
(TOP VIEW)

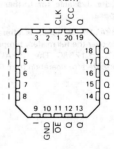

Pin assignments in operating mode

3

Field-Programmable Logic

3-46

**TEXAS**
**INSTRUMENTS**

**functional block diagrams (positive logic)**

'PAL16L8

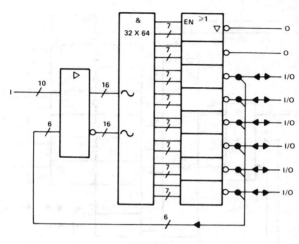

'PAL16R4

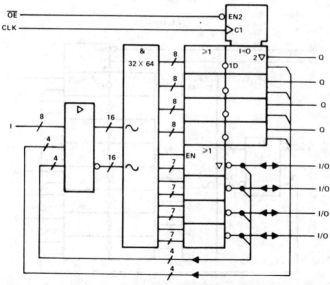

∿ denotes fused inputs

Field-Programmable Logic

3

### functional block diagrams (positive logic)

'PAL16R6

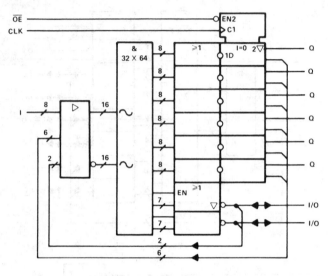

'PAL16R8

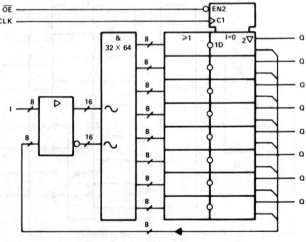

∿denotes fused inputs

TEXAS
INSTRUMENTS

**3**

**Field-Programmable Logic**

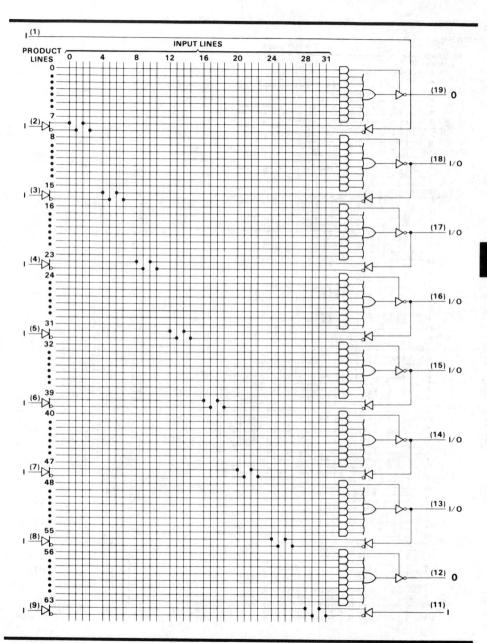

**Field-Programmable Logic**

3

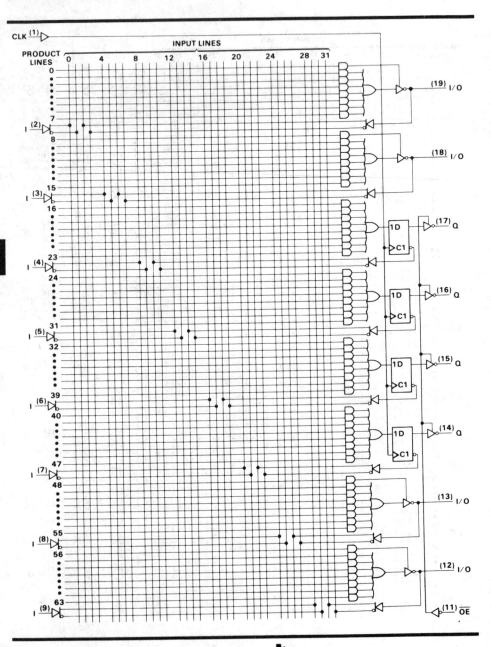

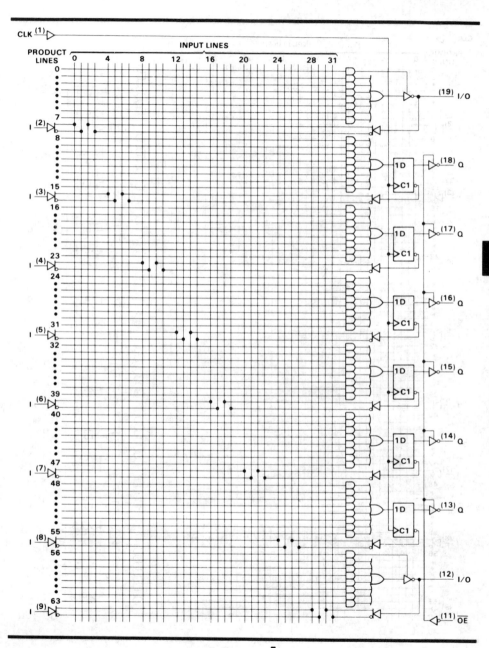

**Field-Programmable Logic**

3

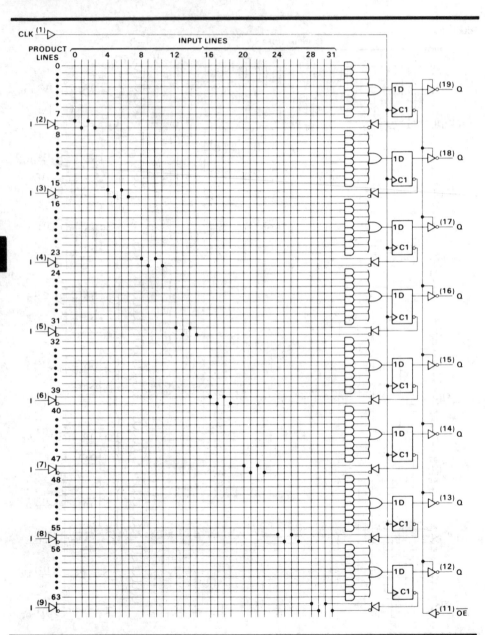

**3**

Field-Programmable Logic

TEXAS
INSTRUMENTS

### absolute maximum ratings over operating free-air temperature range (unless otherwise noted)

Supply voltage, $V_{CC}$ (see Note 1) . . . . . . . . . . . . . . . . . . . . . . . . . . . . . . . . . . . . . . . . . . 7 V
Input voltage (see Note 1) . . . . . . . . . . . . . . . . . . . . . . . . . . . . . . . . . . . . . . . . . . . . . . . 5.5 V
Voltage applied to a disabled output (see Note 1) . . . . . . . . . . . . . . . . . . . . . . . . . . . . . . 5.5 V
Operating free-air temperature range: M suffix . . . . . . . . . . . . . . . . . . . . . . . . . . −55 °C to 125 °C
            C suffix . . . . . . . . . . . . . . . . . . . . . . . . . . . 0 °C to 75 °C
Storage temperature range . . . . . . . . . . . . . . . . . . . . . . . . . . . . . . . . . . . . . . . −65 °C to 150 °C

NOTE 1: These ratings apply except for programming pins during a programming cycle.

### recommended operating conditions (see Note 2)

| PARAMETER | | | M SUFFIX−15 | | | C SUFFIX−12 | | | UNIT |
|---|---|---|---|---|---|---|---|---|---|
| | | | MIN | NOM | MAX | MIN | NOM | MAX | |
| $V_{CC}$ | Supply voltage | | 4.5 | 5 | 5.5 | 4.5 | 5 | 5.25 | V |
| $V_{IH}$ | High-level input voltage | | 2 | | 5.5 | 2 | | 5.5 | V |
| $V_{IL}$ | Low-level input voltage | | | | 0.8 | | | 0.8 | V |
| $I_{OH}$ | High-level output current | | | | −2 | | | −3.2 | mA |
| $I_{OL}$ | Low-level output current | | | | 12 | | | 24 | mA |
| $f_{clock}$ | Clock frequency | | 0 | | 50 | 0 | | 62 | MHz |
| $t_w$ | Pulse duration, clock (see Note2) | High | 9 | | | 7 | | | ns |
| | | Low | 10 | | | 8 | | | |
| $t_{su}$ | Setup time, input or feedback before CLK↑ | | 15 | | | 10 | | | ns |
| $t_h$ | Hold time, input or feedback after CLK↑ | | 0 | | | 0 | | | ns |
| $T_A$ | Operating free-air temperature | | −55 | | 125 | 0 | | 75 | °C |

NOTE 2: The total clock period of CLK high and CLK low must not exceed clock frequency, $f_{clock}$. Minimum pulse durations specified are only for CLK high or CLK low, but not for both simultaneously.

### electrical characteristics, over recommended operating free-air temperature range

| PARAMETER | | TEST CONDITIONS[†] | | M SUFFIX−15 | | | C SUFFIX−12 | | | UNIT |
|---|---|---|---|---|---|---|---|---|---|---|
| | | | | MIN | TYP[‡] | MAX | MIN | TYP[‡] | MAX | |
| $V_{IK}$ | | $V_{CC}$ = MIN, | $I_I$ = −18 mA | | | −1.5 | | | −1.5 | V |
| $V_{OH}$ | | $V_{CC}$ = MIN, | $I_{OH}$ = MAX | 2.4 | 3.3 | | 2.4 | 3.3 | | V |
| $V_{OL}$ | | $V_{CC}$ = MIN, | $I_{OL}$ = MAX | | 0.35 | 0.5 | | 0.35 | 0.5 | V |
| $I_{OZH}$ | Outputs | $V_{CC}$ = MAX, | $V_O$ = 2.7 V | | | 20 | | | 20 | μA |
| | I/O ports | | | | | 100 | | | 100 | |
| $I_{OZL}$ | Outputs | $V_{CC}$ = MAX, | $V_O$ = 0.4 V | | | −20 | | | −20 | μA |
| | I/O ports | | | | | −250 | | | −250 | |
| $I_I$ | | $V_{CC}$ = MAX, | $V_I$ = 5.5 V | Pin 1, 11 | | 0.2 | | | 0.1 | mA |
| | | | | All others | | 0.1 | | | 0.1 | |
| $I_{IH}$ | | $V_{CC}$ = MAX, | $V_I$ = 2.7 V | Pin 1, 11 | | 50 | | | 20 | μA |
| | | | | All others | | 20 | | | 20 | |
| $I_{IL}$ | | $V_{CC}$ = MAX, | $V_I$ = 0.4 V | | | −0.2 | | | −0.2 | mA |
| $I_O$[§] | | $V_{CC}$ = MAX, | $V_O$ = 2.25 V | −30 | | −125 | −30 | | −125 | mA |
| $I_{CC}$ | | $V_{CC}$ = MAX, $V_I$ = 0 V, | Outputs Open | | 170 | 220 | | 170 | 220 | mA |

[†]For conditions shown as MIN or MAX use the appropriate value specified under recommended operating conditions.
[‡]All typical values are at $V_{CC}$ = 5 V, $T_A$ = 25 °C.
[§]The output conditions have been chosen to produce a current that closely approximates one half of the true short-circuit output current, $I_{OS}$.

Field-Programmable Logic

3

## TIBPAL16L8-12, TIBPAL16R4-12, TIBPAL16R6-12, TIBPAL16R8-12
## TIBPAL16L8-15, TIBPAL16R4-15, TIBPAL16R6-15, TIBPAL16R8-15
## HIGH-PERFORMANCE *IMPACT™ PAL®* CIRCUITS

**switching characteristics over recommended supply voltage and operating free-air temperature ranges (unless otherwise noted)**

| PARAMETER | FROM | TO | TEST CONDITIONS | M SUFFIX – 15 | | | C SUFFIX – 12 | | | UNIT |
|---|---|---|---|---|---|---|---|---|---|---|
| | | | | MIN | TYP† | MAX | MIN | TYP† | MAX | |
| $f_{max}$‡ | | | | 50 | | | 62 | | | MHz |
| $t_{pd}$‡ | I, I/O | O, I/O | | | 8 | 15 | | 8 | 12 | ns |
| $t_{pd}$ | CLK↑ | Q | $R_L = 500\ \Omega$, $C_L = 50$ pF See Note 3 | | 7 | 12 | | 7 | 10 | ns |
| $t_{en}$ | OE↓ | Q | | | 8 | 12 | | 8 | 10 | ns |
| $t_{dis}$ | OE↑ | Q | | | 7 | 12 | | 7 | 10 | ns |
| $t_{en}$ | I, I/O | O, I/O | | | 8 | 15 | | 8 | 12 | ns |
| $t_{dis}$ | I, I/O | O, I/O | | | 8 | 15 | | 8 | 12 | ns |

† All typical values are at $V_{CC} = 5$ V, $T_A = 25\,°C$.
‡ Maximum operating frequency and propagation delay are specified for the basic building block. When using feedback, limits must be calculated accordingly.
NOTE 3: Load circuits and voltage waveforms are shown in Section 1 .

### programming information

Texas Instruments Programmable Logic Devices can be programmed using widely available software and inexpensive device programmers.

Complete programming specifications, algorithms, and the latest information on hardware, software, and firmware are available upon request. Information on programmers capable of programming Texas Instruments Programmable Logic is also available, upon request, from the nearest TI field sales office, local authorized TI distributor, or by calling Texas Instruments at (214) 995-2980.

TEXAS
INSTRUMENTS

**TICPAL16L8, TICPAL16R4, TICPAL16R6, TICPAL16R8**
**HIGH-SPEED CMOS PAL CIRCUITS**
**PRELIMINARY DATA**

..., OCTOBER 1985

- Standard 20-Pin PAL Family
- Low Standby Power CMOS Logic
- User-Programmable Custom Designs Combine Many SSI and MSI Functions on One Chip
- TTL- and HC-Compatible Inputs and Outputs
- Security Cell for Proprietary Design Protection
- Preload Feature to Aid Testing
- Choice of DIP or SO (Small Outline) Package
- Fully Tested for High Programming Yield Before Packaging
- Dependable Texas Instruments Quality and Reliability

### description

The PAL16L8, PAL16R4, PAL16R6, and PAL16R8 are compatible with TTL and HCT logic. They are also compatible with HC logic over the $V_{CC}$ range of 4.5 to 5.5 volts and have electrical characteristics that are similar to the SN74HC family. The devices have negligible static power dissipation.

These PAL devices implement the sum-of-product (AND-OR) structure. The user can select the product terms and customize the device function to fit a wide variety of applications. The user can select any combination of the true or complement terms from the eight inputs and a variety of feedback terms of the device.

The programming cell consists of a FAMOS (floating-gate) device like those used in EPROMs. All 32 terms of each AND gate are initially connected. The unwanted terms are programmed out by applying a high voltage to the programming cell of the selected term. When both the true and complement cells of a term are left unprogrammed, the output of the AND gate is a low logic level. When only the true term is programmed, its complement becomes an input to the AND gate. When the complement term is programmed, its true term becomes an input to the AND gate. When both the true and complement of a term are programmed, the term level is irrelevant. Up to eight products are summed by an OR gate.

TICPAL16L8-M . . . J PACKAGE
TICPAL16L8-C . . . J OR N PACKAGE
**(TOP VIEW)**

```
        ┌───┴───┐
   I  [ 1     20 ]  VCC
   I  [ 2     19 ]  O
   I  [ 3     18 ]  I/O
   I  [ 4     17 ]  I/O
   I  [ 5     16 ]  I/O
   I  [ 6     15 ]  I/O
   I  [ 7     14 ]  I/O
   I  [ 8     13 ]  I/O
   I  [ 9     12 ]  O
  GND [ 10    11 ]  I
        └───────┘
```

TICPAL16R4-M . . . J PACKAGE
TICPAL16R4-C . . . J OR N PACKAGE
**(TOP VIEW)**

```
        ┌───┴───┐
  CLK [ 1     20 ]  VCC
   I  [ 2     19 ]  I/O
   I  [ 3     18 ]  I/O
   I  [ 4     17 ]  Q
   I  [ 5     16 ]  Q
   I  [ 6     15 ]  Q
   I  [ 7     14 ]  Q
   I  [ 8     13 ]  I/O
   I  [ 9     12 ]  I/O
  GND [ 10    11 ]  OE
        └───────┘
```

TICPAL16R6-M . . . J PACKAGE
TICPAL16R6-C . . . J OR N PACKAGE
**(TOP VIEW)**

```
        ┌───┴───┐
  CLK [ 1     20 ]  VCC
   I  [ 2     19 ]  I/O
   I  [ 3     18 ]  Q
   I  [ 4     17 ]  Q
   I  [ 5     16 ]  Q
   I  [ 6     15 ]  Q
   I  [ 7     14 ]  Q
   I  [ 8     13 ]  Q
   I  [ 9     12 ]  I/O
  GND [ 10    11 ]  OE
        └───────┘
```

TICPAL16R8-M . . . J PACKAGE
TICPAL16R8-C . . . J OR N PACKAGE
**(TOP VIEW)**

```
        ┌───┴───┐
  CLK [ 1     20 ]  VCC
   I  [ 2     19 ]  Q
   I  [ 3     18 ]  Q
   I  [ 4     17 ]  Q
   I  [ 5     16 ]  Q
   I  [ 6     15 ]  Q
   I  [ 7     14 ]  Q
   I  [ 8     13 ]  Q
   I  [ 9     12 ]  Q
  GND [ 10    11 ]  OE
        └───────┘
```

**3**

Field-Programmable Logic

**TEXAS INSTRUMENTS**

The floating-gate programming cells allow the PALs to be fully programmed and tested before assembly to ensure high field-programming yield. The test program is then erased by ultraviolet light before packaging. When programmed with the required pattern, a security cell can be programmed to prevent the pattern from being read. Because the device uses floating-gate technology, the design cannot be determined by observing the blown fuses used in other PALs.

During testing, the registers can be preloaded by entering the preload mode.

The M suffix devices will be characterized for operation over the full military temperature range of $-55\,^{\circ}\text{C}$ to $125\,^{\circ}\text{C}$. The C suffix devices will be characterized for operation from $0\,^{\circ}\text{C}$ to $70\,^{\circ}\text{C}$.

### TABLE 1. INPUT/OUTPUT CONFIGURATION

| DEVICE | INPUTS | 3-STATE 0 OUTPUTS | REGISTERED 0 OUTPUTS | I/O PORTS |
|--------|--------|-------------------|----------------------|-----------|
| PAL16L8 | 10 | 2 | 0 | 6 |
| PAL16R4 | 8 | 0 | 4 | 4 |
| PAL16R6 | 8 | 0 | 6 | 2 |
| PAL16R8 | 8 | 0 | 8 | 0 |

TEXAS
INSTRUMENTS

- High Performance: $f_{max}$ (w/o feedback)
  TIBPAL20R' C series . . . 45 MHz
  TIBPAL20R' M series . . . 41.5 MHz

- High Performance . . . 45 MHz Min

- Functionally Equivalent to, but Faster than,
  PAL20L8, PAL20R4, PAL20R6, PAL20R8

- Preload Capability on Output Registers
  Simplifies Testing

- Package Options Include Plastic and
  Ceramic Chip Carriers in Addition to Plastic
  and Ceramic DIPs

- Reduced $I_{CC}$ of 180 mA Max

| DEVICE | I INPUTS | 3-STATE O OUTPUTS | REGISTERED Q OUTPUTS | I/O PORTS |
|--------|----------|-------------------|----------------------|-----------|
| 'PAL20L8 | 14 | 2 | 0 | 6 |
| 'PAL20R4 | 12 | 0 | 4 (3-state buffers) | 4 |
| 'PAL20R6 | 12 | 0 | 6 (3-state buffers) | 2 |
| 'PAL20R8 | 12 | 0 | 8 (3-state buffers) | 0 |

### description

These programmable array logic devices feature high speed and functional equivalency when compared with currently available devices. These IMPACT™ circuits combine the latest Advanced Low-Power Schottky† technology with proven titanium-tungsten fuses to provide reliable, high performance substitutes for conventional TTL logic. Their easy programmability allows for quick design of custom functions and typically results in a more compact circuit board. In addition, chip carriers are also available for further reduction in board space.

**TIBPAL20L8'**
**M SUFFIX . . . JT PACKAGE**
**C SUFFIX . . . JT OR NT PACKAGE**
**(TOP VIEW)**

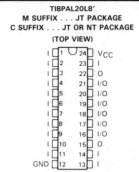

```
        1  ⌣ 24   VCC
I   ⌷ 1      24 ⌷  VCC
I   ⌷ 2      23 ⌷  I
I   ⌷ 3      22 ⌷  O
I   ⌷ 4      21 ⌷  I/O
I   ⌷ 5      20 ⌷  I/O
I   ⌷ 6      19 ⌷  I/O
I   ⌷ 7      18 ⌷  I/O
I   ⌷ 8      17 ⌷  I/O
I   ⌷ 9      16 ⌷  I/O
I   ⌷ 10     15 ⌷  O
I   ⌷ 11     14 ⌷  I
GND ⌷ 12     13 ⌷  I
```

**TIBPAL20L8'**
**M SUFFIX . . . FK PACKAGE**
**C SUFFIX . . . FN PACKAGE**
**(TOP VIEW)**

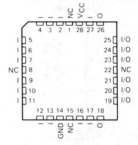

```
           N  V  N
           C  CC C  O
         4  3  2  1  28 27 26
I    ⌷ 5                    25 ⌷ I/O
I    ⌷ 6                    24 ⌷ I/O
I    ⌷ 7                    23 ⌷ I/O
NC   ⌷ 8                    22 ⌷ NC
I    ⌷ 9                    21 ⌷ I/O
I    ⌷ 10                   20 ⌷ I/O
I    ⌷ 11                   19 ⌷ I/O
         12 13 14 15 16 17 18
           G  N        O
           N  C
           D
```

NC – No internal connection

Pin assignments in operating mode

Extra circuitry has been provided to allow loading of each register asynchronously to either a high or low state. This feature simplifies testing because the registers can be set to an initial state prior to executing the test sequence.

The TIBPAL20'M series is characterized for operation over the full military temperature range of −55 °C to 125 °C. The TIBPAL20'C is characterized from 0 °C to 75 °C.

IMPACT is a trademark of Texas Instruments Incorporated
PAL is a registered trademark of Monolithic Memories Inc.
†Integrated Schottky-Barrier diode-clamped transistor is patented
by Texas Instruments, U.S. Patent Number 3,463,975.

TEXAS
INSTRUMENTS

**Field-Programmable Logic**

**3**

## TIBPAL20R4-15, TIBPAL20R6-15, TIBPAL20R8-15
## TIBPAL20R4-20, TIBPAL20R6-20, TIBPAL20R8-20
## HIGH-PERFORMANCE IMPACT™ PAL® CIRCUITS

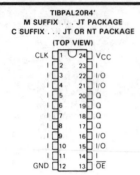

**TIBPAL20R4'**
M SUFFIX . . . FK PACKAGE
C SUFFIX . . . FN PACKAGE
(TOP VIEW)

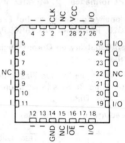

**TIBPAL20R6'**
M SUFFIX . . . JT PACKAGE
C SUFFIX . . . JT OR NT PACKAGE
(TOP VIEW)

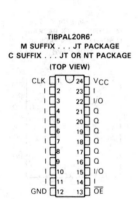

**TIBPAL20R6'**
M SUFFIX . . . FK PACKAGE
C SUFFIX . . . FN PACKAGE
(TOP VIEW)

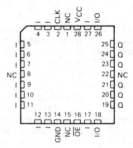

**TIBPAL20R8'**
M SUFFIX . . . JT PACKAGE
C SUFFIX . . . JT OR NT PACKAGE
(TOP VIEW)

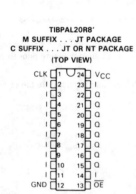

**TIBPAL20R8'**
M SUFFIX . . . FK PACKAGE
C SUFFIX . . . FN PACKAGE
(TOP VIEW)

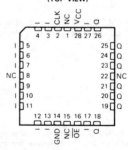

Pin assignments in operating mode

NC—No internal connection

TEXAS
INSTRUMENTS

## functional block diagrams (positive logic)

**TIBPAL20L8'**

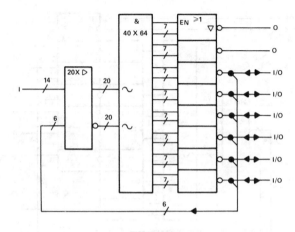

**TIBPAL20R4'**

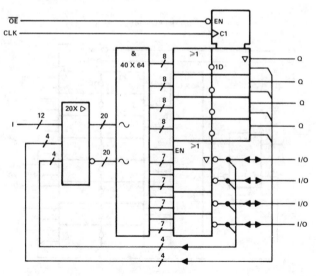

∿ denotes fused inputs

**Field-Programmable Logic**

**3**

## TIBPAL20R6-15, TIBPAL20R8-15
## TIBPAL20R6-20, TIBPAL20R8-20
## HIGH-PERFORMANCE IMPACT™ PAL® CIRCUITS

### functional block diagrams (positive logic)

TIBPAL20R6'

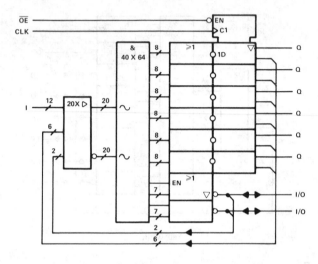

TIBPAL20R8'

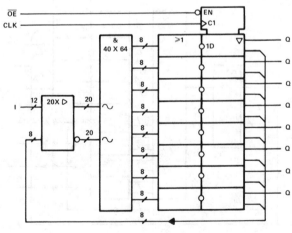

∿ denotes fused inputs

TEXAS
INSTRUMENTS

**logic diagram (positive logic)**

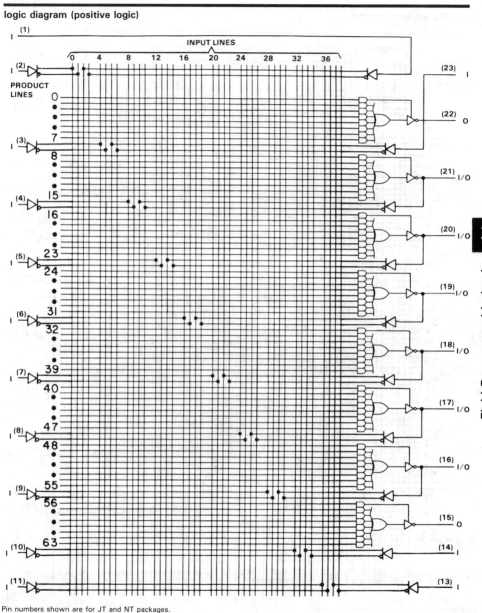

Pin numbers shown are for JT and NT packages.

Field-Programmable Logic

3

TEXAS
INSTRUMENTS

# TIBPAL20R4-15
# TIBPAL20R4-20
# HIGH-PERFORMANCE IMPACT™ PAL® CIRCUITS

**logic diagram (positive logic)**

Pin numbers shown are for JT and NT packages.

TEXAS
INSTRUMENTS

**logic diagram (positive logic)**

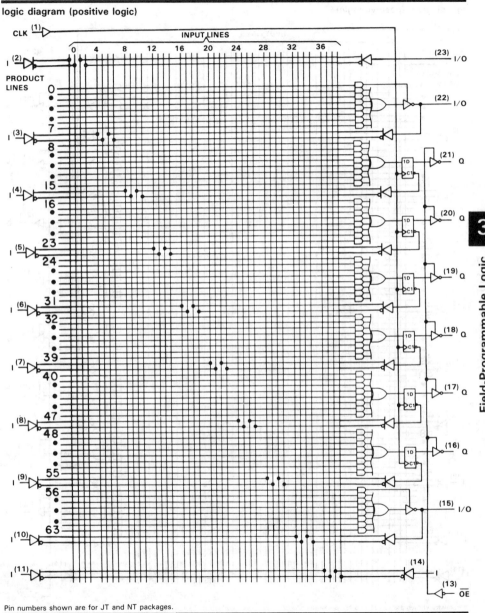

Pin numbers shown are for JT and NT packages.

Field-Programmable Logic

3

# TIBPAL20R8-15
# TIBPAL20R8-20
## HIGH-PERFORMANCE IMPACT™ PAL® CIRCUITS

logic diagram (positive logic)

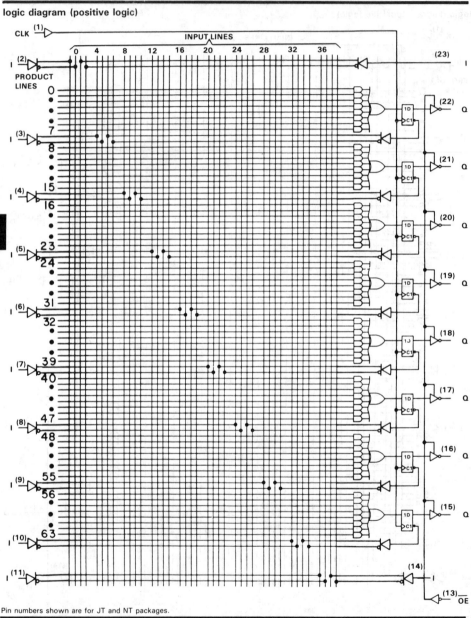

Pin numbers shown are for JT and NT packages.

TEXAS
INSTRUMENTS

## absolute maximum ratings over operating free-air temperature range (unless otherwise noted)

Supply voltage, $V_{CC}$ (see Note 1) . . . . . . . . . . . . . . . . . . . . . . . . . . . . . . . . . . . . . . . . . . . . . . . 7 V
Input voltage (see Note 1) . . . . . . . . . . . . . . . . . . . . . . . . . . . . . . . . . . . . . . . . . . . . . . . . . . . . 5.5 V
Voltage applied to a disabled output (see Note 1) . . . . . . . . . . . . . . . . . . . . . . . . . . . . . . . . 5.5 V
Operating free-air temperature range: M SUFFIX . . . . . . . . . . . . . . . . . . . . . . . . −55°C to 125°C
C SUFFIX . . . . . . . . . . . . . . . . . . . . . . . . . . 0°C to 75°C
Storage temperature range . . . . . . . . . . . . . . . . . . . . . . . . . . . . . . . . . . . . . . . . −65°C to 150°C

NOTE 1: These ratings apply except for programming pins during a programming cycle.

## recommended operating conditions

| | PARAMETER | | M SUFFIX | | | C SUFFIX | | | UNIT |
|---|---|---|---|---|---|---|---|---|---|
| | | | MIN | NOM | MAX | MIN | NOM | MAX | |
| $V_{CC}$ | Supply voltage | | 4.5 | 5 | 5.5 | 4.75 | 5 | 5.25 | V |
| $V_{IH}$ | High-level input voltage | | 2 | | 5.5 | 2 | | 5.5 | V |
| $V_{IL}$ | Low-level input voltage | | | | 0.8 | | | 0.8 | V |
| $I_{OH}$ | High-level output current | | | | −2 | | | −3.2 | mA |
| $I_{OL}$ | Low-level output current | | | | 12 | | | 24 | mA |
| $f_{clock}$ | Clock frequency | | 0 | | 41.5 | 0 | | 45 | MHz |
| $t_w$ | Pulse duration, clock | High | 12 | | | 10 | | | ns |
| | | Low | 12 | | | 12 | | | ns |
| $t_{su}$ | Setup time, input or feedback before CLK↑ | | 20 | 10 | | 15 | 10 | | ns |
| $t_h$ | Hold time, input or feedback after CLK↑ | | 0 | | | 0 | | | ns |
| $T_A$ | Operating free-air temperature | | −55 | | 125 | 0 | | 75 | °C |

$f_{clock}$, $t_w$, $t_{su}$, and $t_h$ do not apply for TIBPAL20L8'.

## TIBPAL20L8-15, TIBPAL20R4-15, TIBPAL20R6-15, TIBPAL20R8-15
## HIGH-PERFORMANCE IMPACT™ PAL® CIRCUITS

### electrical characteristics over recommended free-air operating temperature range

| PARAMETER | | TEST CONDITIONS | C SUFFIX | | | UNIT |
|---|---|---|---|---|---|---|
| | | | MIN | TYP† | MAX | |
| $V_{IK}$ | | $V_{CC} = 4.75$ V, $I_I = -18$ mA | | $-0.8$ | $-1.5$ | V |
| $V_{OH}$ | | $V_{CC} = 4.75$ V, $I_{OH} = -3.2$ mA | 2.4 | | | V |
| $V_{OL}$ | | $V_{CC} = 4.75$ V, $I_{OL} = 24$ mA | | 0.3 | 0.5 | V |
| $I_{OZH}$ | O, Q outputs | $V_{CC} = 5.25$ V, $V_O = 2.7$ V | | | 20 | μA |
| | I/O ports | | | | 100 | |
| $I_{OZL}$ | O, Q outputs | $V_{CC} = 5.25$ V, $V_O = 0.4$ V | | | $-20$ | μA |
| | I/O ports | | | | $-100$ | |
| $I_I$ | | $V_{CC} = 5.25$ V, $V_I = 5.5$ V | | | 1 | mA |
| $I_{IH}$‡ | | $V_{CC} = 5.25$ V, $V_I = 2.4$ V | | | 25 | μA |
| $I_{IL}$‡ | | $V_{CC} = 5.25$ V, $V_I = 0.4$ V | | | $-0.25$ | mA |
| $I_{OS}$§ | | $V_{CC} = 5.25$ V, $V_O = 0$ | $-30$ | $-70$ | $-130$ | mA |
| $I_{CC}$ | | $V_{CC} = 5.25$ V, $V_I = 0$, Outputs open, $\overline{OE}$ at $V_{IH}$ | | 120 | 180 | mA |

† All typical values are $V_{CC} = 5$ V, $T_A = 25°C$.
‡ For I/O ports, the parameters $I_{IH}$ and $I_{IL}$ include the off-state output current.
§ Not more than one output should be shorted at a time, and duration of the short-circuit should not exceed one second.

### switching characteristics over recommended operating free-air temperature range (unless otherwise noted)

| PARAMETER | FROM | TO | TEST CONDITIONS | C SUFFIX | | | UNIT |
|---|---|---|---|---|---|---|---|
| | | | | MIN | TYP† | MAX | |
| $f_{max}$¶ | with feedback | | | 37 | 40 | | MHz |
| | without feedback | | | 45 | 50 | | |
| $t_{pd}$ | I, I/O | O, I/O | | | 12 | 15 | ns |
| $t_{pd}$ | CLK↑ | Q | $R_1 = 200$ Ω, $R2 = 390$ Ω, | | 8 | 12 | ns |
| $t_{en}$ | $\overline{OE}$ | Q | $C_L = 50$ pF, See Figure 1 | | 10 | 15 | ns |
| $t_{dis}$ | $\overline{OE}$↑ | Q | | | 8 | 12 | ns |
| $t_{en}$ | I, I/O | O, I/O | | | 12 | 18 | ns |
| $t_{dis}$ | I, I/O | O, I/O | | | 12 | 15 | ns |

† All typical values are at $V_{CC} = 5$ V, $T_A = 25°C$.

¶ $f_{max}$ (with feedback) $= \dfrac{1}{t_{su} + t_{pd} \text{ (CLK to Q)}}$, $f_{max}$ (without feedback) $= \dfrac{1}{t_w \text{ high} + t_w \text{ low}}$

$f_{max}$ does not apply for TIBPAL20L8'

TEXAS
INSTRUMENTS

**3**

Field-Programmable Logic

**electrical characteristics over recommended free-air operating temperature range**

| PARAMETER | | TEST CONDITIONS | M SUFFIX | | | UNIT |
|---|---|---|---|---|---|---|
| | | | MIN | TYP† | MAX | |
| $V_{IK}$ | | $V_{CC} = 4.5$ V, $\quad I_I = -18$ mA | | $-0.8$ | $-1.5$ | V |
| $V_{OH}$ | | $V_{CC} = 4.5$ V, $\quad I_{OH} = -2$ mA | 2.4 | 3.2 | | V |
| $V_{OL}$ | | $V_{CC} = 4.5$ V, $\quad I_{OL} = 12$ mA | | 0.25 | 0.5 | V |
| $I_{OZH}$ | O, Q outputs | $V_{CC} = 5.5$ V, $\quad V_O = 2.7$ V | | | 20 | $\mu$A |
| | I/O ports | | | | 100 | |
| $I_{OZL}$ | O, Q outputs | $V_{CC} = 5.5$ V, $\quad V_O = 0.4$ V | | | $-20$ | $\mu$A |
| | I/O ports | | | | $-100$ | |
| $I_I$ | | $V_{CC} = 5.5$ V, $\quad V_I = 5.5$ V | | | 1 | mA |
| $I_{IH}$‡ | | $V_{CC} = 5.5$ V, $\quad V_I = 2.4$ V | | | 25 | $\mu$A |
| $I_{IL}$‡ | | $V_{CC} = 5.5$ V, $\quad V_I = 0.4$ V | | | $-0.25$ | mA |
| $I_{OS}$§ | | $V_{CC} = 5.5$ V, $\quad V_O = 0$ | $-30$ | $-70$ | $-130$ | mA |
| $I_{CC}$ | | $V_{CC} = 5.5$ V, $\quad V_I = 0$, Outputs open, $\quad \overline{OE}$ at $V_{IH}$ | | 120 | 180 | mA |

† All typical values are $V_{CC} = 5$ V, $T_A = 25\,°C$.
‡ For I/O ports, the parameters $I_{IH}$ and $I_{IL}$ include the off-state output current.
§ Not more than one output should be shorted at a time, and duration of the short-circuit should not exceed one second.

**switching characteristics over recommended operating free-air temperature range (unless otherwise noted)**

| PARAMETER | FROM | TO | TEST CONDITIONS | M SUFFIX | | | UNIT |
|---|---|---|---|---|---|---|---|
| | | | | MIN | TYP† | MAX | |
| $f_{max}$¶ | with feedback | | | 28.5 | 40 | | MHz |
| | without feedback | | | 41.5 | 50 | | |
| $t_{pd}$ | I, I/O | O, I/O | | | 12 | 20 | ns |
| $t_{pd}$ | CLK↑ | Q | $R_1 = 390\ \Omega$, $\quad R2 = 750\ \Omega$, | | 8 | 15 | ns |
| $t_{en}$ | $\overline{OE}$ | Q | $C_L = 50$ pF, $\quad$ See Figure 1 | | 10 | 20 | ns |
| $t_{dis}$ | $\overline{OE}$↑ | Q | | | 8 | 20 | ns |
| $t_{en}$ | I, I/O | O, I/O | | | 12 | 25 | ns |
| $t_{dis}$ | I, I/O | O, I/O | | | 12 | 20 | ns |

† All typical values are at $V_{CC} = 5$ V, $T_A = 25\,°C$.
¶ $f_{max}$ (with feedback) $= \dfrac{1}{t_{su} + t_{pd} \text{ (CLK to Q)}}$, $f_{max}$ (without feedback) $= \dfrac{1}{t_W \text{ high} + t_W \text{ low}}$

$f_{max}$ does not apply for TIBPAL20L8'

**TEXAS INSTRUMENTS**

**3**

**Field-Programmable Logic**

## TIBPAL20L8-15, TIBPAL20R4-15, TIBPAL20R6-15, TIBPAL20R8-15
## TIBPAL20L8-20, TIBPAL20R4-20, TIBPAL20R6-20, TIBPAL20R8-20
## HIGH-PERFORMANCE IMPACT™ PAL® CIRCUITS

### programming information

Texas Instruments Programmable Logic Devices can be programmed using widely available software and inexpensive device programmers.

Complete programming specifications, algorithms, and the latest information on hardware, software, and firmware are available upon request. Information on programmers capable of programming Texas Instruments Programmable Logic is also available, upon request, from the nearest TI field sales office, local authorized TI distributor, or by calling Texas Instruments at (214) 995-2980.

## PARAMETER MEASUREMENT INFORMATION

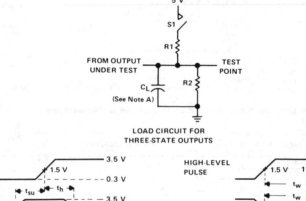

LOAD CIRCUIT FOR
THREE-STATE OUTPUTS

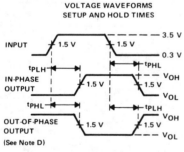

VOLTAGE WAVEFORMS
SETUP AND HOLD TIMES

VOLTAGE WAVEFORMS
PULSE DURATIONS

VOLTAGE WAVEFORMS
PROPAGATION DELAY TIMES

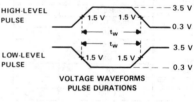

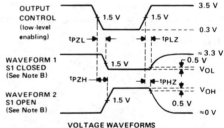

VOLTAGE WAVEFORMS
ENABLE AND DISABLE TIMES, THREE-STATE OUTPUTS

NOTES: A. $C_L$ includes probe and jig capacitance.
 B. Waveform 1 is for an output with internal conditions such that the output is low except when disabled by the output control.
 Waveform 2 is for an output with internal conditions such that the output is high except when disabled by the output control.
 C. All input pulses have the following characteristics: PRR ≤ 1 MHz, $t_r = t_f = 2$ ns, duty cycle = 50%.
 D. When measuring propagation delay times of 3-state outputs, switch S1 is closed.

### FIGURE 1

- **Choice of Operating Speeds**
  **HIGH PERFORMANCE . . . 40 MHz**
  **Typical**
  **HALF-POWER . . . 25 MHz Typical**

- **Preload Capability on Output Registers**

- **Power-Up Clear on Registered Devices**

- **Package Options Include Both Plastic and Ceramic Chip Carriers in Addition to Plastic and Ceramic DIPs**

| DEVICE | I INPUTS | 3-STATE O OUTPUTS | REGISTERED Q OUTPUTS | I/O PORTS |
|--------|----------|---------|----------|-------|
| 'PAL20L10 | 12 | 2 | 0 | 8 |
| 'PAL20X4 | 10 | 0 | 4 (3-state buffers) | 6 |
| 'PAL20X8 | 10 | 0 | 8 (3-state buffers) | 2 |
| 'PAL20X10 | 10 | 0 | 10 (3-state buffers) | 0 |

## description

These programmable array logic devices feature high speed and functional equivalency when compared with currently available devices. They combine the latest Advanced Low-Power Schottky† technology "IMPACT" with proven titanium-tungsten fuses. These devices will provide reliable, high performance substitutes over conventional TTL logic. Their easy programmability allows for quick design of custom functions and typically result in a more compact circuit board. In addition, chip carriers are available for further reduction in board space.

The Half-Power versions offer a choice of operating frequency, switching speeds, and power dissipation. In many cases, these Half-Power devices are as fast as the currently available "standard" devices.

All of the registered outputs are set to a low level during power-up. In addition, extra circuitry has been provided to allow loading of each register asynchronously to either a high or low state. This feature simplifies testing because the registers can be set to an initial state prior to executing the test sequence.

**TIBPAL20L10'**
**M SUFFIX . . . JT PACKAGE**
**C SUFFIX . . . JT OR NT PACKAGE**
**(TOP VIEW)**

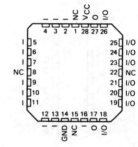

```
          ___
I  [ 1    24 ]  VCC
I  [ 2    23 ]  O
I  [ 3    22 ]  I/O
I  [ 4    21 ]  I/O
I  [ 5    20 ]  I/O
I  [ 6    19 ]  I/O
I  [ 7    18 ]  I/O
I  [ 8    17 ]  I/O
I  [ 9    16 ]  I/O
I  [ 10   15 ]  I/O
I  [ 11   14 ]  O
GND[ 12   13 ]  I
```

**TIBPAL20L10'**
**M SUFFIX . . . FH OR FK PACKAGE**
**C SUFFIX . . . FN PACKAGE**
**(TOP VIEW)**

```
           N  V  O  I
           C  CC    /O
          4  3  2  1 28 27 26
I  [ 5                25 ]  I/O
I  [ 6                24 ]  I/O
I  [ 7                23 ]  I/O
NC [ 8                22 ]  NC
I  [ 9                21 ]  I/O
I  [ 10               20 ]  I/O
I  [ 11               19 ]  I/O
          12 13 14 15 16 17 18
           G  N     O  I
           N  C     /O
           D
```

Pin assignments in operating mode (pins 1 and 11 less positive than V_IHH)

---

†Integrated Schottky-Barrier diode-clamped transistor is patented by Texas Instruments, U.S. Patent Number 3,463,975.
PAL is a registered trademark of Monolithic Memories Inc.

**TEXAS INSTRUMENTS**

**3** Field-Programmable Logic

**TIBPAL20X4'**
**M SUFFIX . . . JT PACKAGE**
**C SUFFIX . . . JT OR NT PACKAGE**
**(TOP VIEW)**

```
OUTCLK  [ 1    24 ]  VCC
     I  [ 2    23 ]  I/O
     I  [ 3    22 ]  I/O
     I  [ 4    21 ]  I/O
     I  [ 5    20 ]  Q
     I  [ 6    19 ]  Q
     I  [ 7    18 ]  Q
     I  [ 8    17 ]  Q
     I  [ 9    16 ]  I/O
     I  [ 10   15 ]  I/O
     I  [ 11   14 ]  I/O
   GND  [ 12   13 ]  OE
```

**TIBPAL20X4'**
**M SUFFIX . . . FH OR FK PACKAGE**
**C SUFFIX . . . FN PACKAGE**
**(TOP VIEW)**

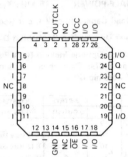

**TIBPAL20X8'**
**M SUFFIX . . . JT PACKAGE**
**C SUFFIX . . . JT OR NT PACKAGE**
**(TOP VIEW)**

```
OUTCLK  [ 1    24 ]  VCC
     I  [ 2    23 ]  I/O
     I  [ 3    22 ]  Q
     I  [ 4    21 ]  Q
     I  [ 5    20 ]  Q
     I  [ 6    19 ]  Q
     I  [ 7    18 ]  Q
     I  [ 8    17 ]  Q
     I  [ 9    16 ]  Q
     I  [ 10   15 ]  Q
     I  [ 11   14 ]  I/O
   GND  [ 12   13 ]  OE
```

**TIBPAL20X8'**
**M SUFFIX . . . FH OR FK PACKAGE**
**C SUFFIX . . . FN PACKAGE**
**(TOP VIEW)**

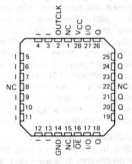

**TIBPAL20X10'**
**M SUFFIX . . . JT PACKAGE**
**C SUFFIX . . . JT OR NT PACKAGE**
**(TOP VIEW)**

```
OUTCLK  [ 1    24 ]  VCC
     I  [ 2    23 ]  Q
     I  [ 3    22 ]  Q
     I  [ 4    21 ]  Q
     I  [ 5    20 ]  Q
     I  [ 6    19 ]  Q
     I  [ 7    18 ]  Q
     I  [ 8    17 ]  Q
     I  [ 9    16 ]  Q
     I  [ 10   15 ]  Q
     I  [ 11   14 ]  Q
   GND  [ 12   13 ]  OE
```

**TIBPAL20X10'**
**M SUFFIX . . . FH OR FK PACKAGE**
**C SUFFIX . . . FN PACKAGE**
**(TOP VIEW)**

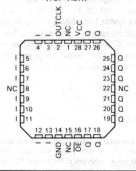

Pin assignments in operating mode (pins 1 and 11 less positive than V_IHH)

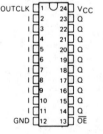

**TEXAS**
**INSTRUMENTS**

**functional block diagrams (positive logic)**

'PAL20L10

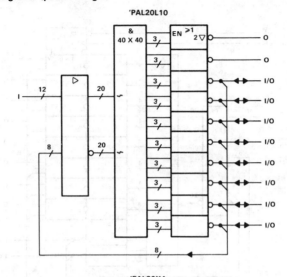

'PAL20X4

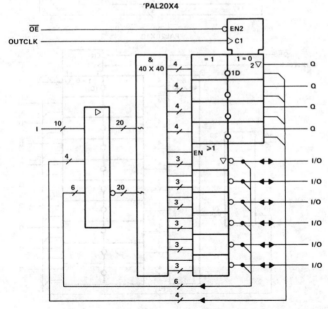

~ denotes fused inputs

**Field-Programmable Logic**

3

# TIBPAL20X8, TIBPAL20X10
## HIGH PERFORMANCE EXCLUSIVE-OR IMPACT PAL CIRCUITS

functional block diagrams (positive logic)

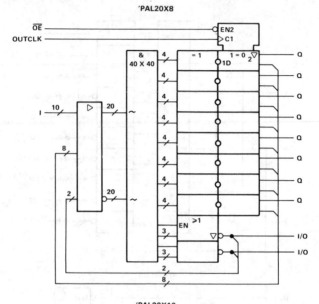

'PAL20X8

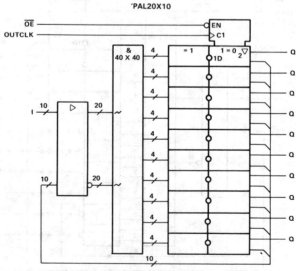

'PAL20X10

~denotes fused inputs

TEXAS
INSTRUMENTS

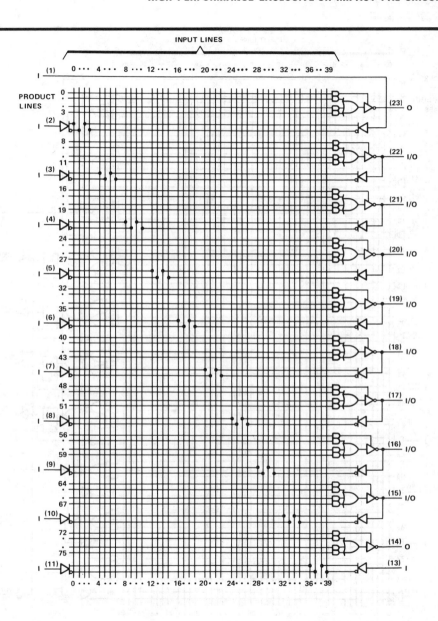

Field-Programmable Logic

TEXAS
INSTRUMENTS

# TIBPAL20X4
## HIGH PERFORMANCE EXCLUSIVE-OR IMPACT PAL CIRCUITS

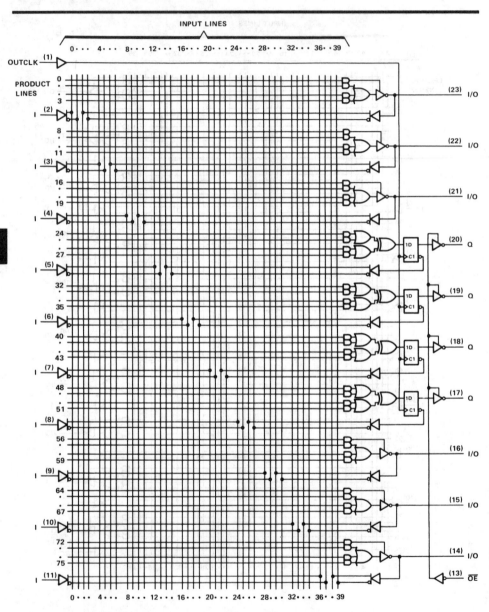

TEXAS
INSTRUMENTS

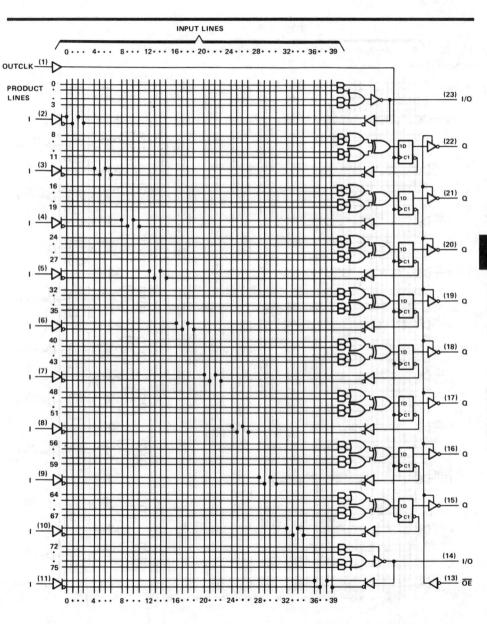

Field-Programmable Logic

3

## TIBPAL20X10
### HIGH PERFORMANCE EXCLUSIVE-OR IMPACT PAL CIRCUITS

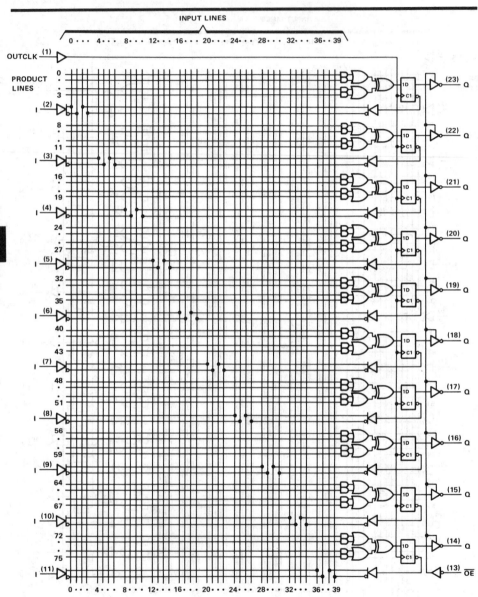

TEXAS
INSTRUMENTS

### absolute maximum ratings over operating free-air temperature range (unless otherwise noted)

Supply voltage, $V_{CC}$ (see Note 1) . . . . . . . . . . . . . . . . . . . . . . . . . . . . . . . . . . . . . . . . . . . . . . . . . . . 7 V
Input voltage (see Note 1) . . . . . . . . . . . . . . . . . . . . . . . . . . . . . . . . . . . . . . . . . . . . . . . . . . . . . . . 5.5 V
Voltage applied to a disabled output (see Note 1) . . . . . . . . . . . . . . . . . . . . . . . . . . . . . . . . . . . . 5.5 V
Operating free-air temperature range: M suffix . . . . . . . . . . . . . . . . . . . . . . . . . . . . −55 °C to 125 °C
C suffix . . . . . . . . . . . . . . . . . . . . . . . . . . . . 0 °C to 70 °C
Storage temperature range . . . . . . . . . . . . . . . . . . . . . . . . . . . . . . . . . . . . . . . . . −65 °C to 150 °C

NOTE 1: These ratings apply except for programming pins during a programming cycle.

### recommended operating conditions

| PARAMETER | | M SUFFIX | | | C SUFFIX | | | UNIT |
|---|---|---|---|---|---|---|---|---|
| | | MIN | NOM | MAX | MIN | NOM | MAX | |
| $V_{CC}$ | Supply voltage | | | | 4.75 | 5 | 5.25 | V |
| $V_{IH}$ | High-level input voltage | | | | 2 | | 5.5 | V |
| $V_{IL}$ | Low-level input voltage | | | | | | 0.8 | V |
| $I_{OH}$ | High-level output current | | | | | | −3.2 | mA |
| $I_{OL}$ | Low-level output current | | | | | | 24 | mA |
| $T_A$ | Operating free-air temperature | | | | 0 | | 70 | °C |

### programming parameters, $T_A$ = 25 °C

| | | | MIN | NOM | MAX | UNIT |
|---|---|---|---|---|---|---|
| $V_{CC}$ | Verify-level supply voltage | | 4.5 | 5.0 | 5.5 | V |
| $V_{IH}$ | High-level input voltage | | 2 | | 5.5 | V |
| $V_{IL}$ | Low-level input voltage | | | | 0.8 | V |
| $V_{IHH}$ | Program-pulse input voltage | | 10.25 | 10.5 | 10.75 | V |
| $I_{IHH}$ | Program-pulse input current | PGM ENABLE | | | 25 | mA |
| | | PO | | | 50 | |
| | | $V_{CC}$ | | | 400 | |
| $t_{w1}$ | Pulse duration at $V_{CC}$ | | 10 | | 50 | μs |
| $t_{w2}$ | Pulse duration at PGM VERIFY | | 100 | | | ns |
| $t_{su}$ | Setup time $\overline{OE}$↑ before PO↑ ($V_{IHH}$) | | 100 | | | ns |
| | Setup time PO↑ ($V_{IHH}$) before $V_{CC}$↑ ($V_{IHH}$) | | 100 | | | |
| $t_h$ | Hold time PO ($V_{IHH}$) after $V_{CC}$↓ | | 100 | | | ns |
| | Hold time $\overline{OE}$ high after PO↓ | | 100 | | | |
| $t_{d1}$ | Delay time from $\overline{OE}$ low to PGM VERIFY↑ | | 100 | | | μs |
| $t_{d2}$ | Delay time from PGM VERIFY↑ to valid output | | 200 | | | ns |
| | Input voltage at pins 1 and 13 to open verify-protect (security) fuse | | 20 | 21 | 22 | V |
| | Input current to open verify-protect (security) fuse | | | | 400 | mA |
| | Pulse duration to open verify-protect (security) fuse | | 20 | | 50 | μs |

## TIBPAL20L10, TIBPAL20X4, TIBPAL20X8, TIBPAL20X10
## HIGH PERFORMANCE EXCLUSIVE-OR IMPACT PAL CIRCUITS

### recommended operating conditions

| | | | M SUFFIX-XX | | | C SUFFIX-XX | | | UNIT |
|---|---|---|---|---|---|---|---|---|---|
| | | | MIN | TYP | MAX | MIN | TYP | MAX | |
| $f_{clock}$ | Clock frequency | | | | | 0 | | 35 | MHz |
| $t_w$ | Pulse duration, clock | High | | | | 10 | | | ns |
| | | Low | | | | 14 | | | ns |
| $t_{su}$ | Setup time, input or feedback before OUTCLK↑ | | | | | 20 | | | ns |
| $t_h$ | Hold time, input or feedback after OUTCLK↑ | | | | | 0 | | | ns |

### electrical characteristics over recommended free-air operating temperature range

| PARAMETER | | TEST CONDITIONS† | | M SUFFIX-XX | | | C SUFFIX-XX | | | UNIT |
|---|---|---|---|---|---|---|---|---|---|---|
| | | | | MIN | TYP* | MAX | MIN | TYP* | MAX | |
| $V_{IK}$ | | $V_{CC} = 4.75$ V | $I_I = -18$ mA | | | | | | -1.2 | V |
| $V_{OH}$ | | $V_{CC} = 4.75$ V | $I_{OH} = -3.2$ mA | | | | 2.4 | 3.3 | | V |
| $V_{OL}$ | | $V_{CC} = 4.75$ V | $I_{OL} = 24$ mA | | | | | 0.35 | 0.5 | V |
| $I_{OZH}$ | Outputs | $V_{CC} = 5.25$ V | $V_O = 2.7$ V | | | | | | 20 | μA |
| | I/O ports | $V_{CC} = 5.25$ V | $V_O = 2.7$ V | | | | | | 100 | |
| $I_{OZL}$ | Outputs | $V_{CC} = 5.25$ V | $V_O = 0.4$ V | | | | | | -20 | μA |
| | I/O ports | $V_{CC} = 5.25$ V | $V_O = 0.4$ V | | | | | | -250 | |
| $I_I$ | | $V_{CC} = 5.25$ V | $V_O = 5.5$ V | | | | | | 0.1 | mA |
| $I_{IH}$ | | $V_{CC} = 5.25$ V | $V_I = 2.7$ V | | | | | | 20 | μA |
| $I_{IL}$ | | $V_{CC} = 5.25$ V | $V_I = 0.4$ V | | | | | | -0.25 | mA |
| $I_O$§ | | $V_{CC} = 5.25$ V | $V_O = 0$ V | | | | -30 | | -170 | mA |
| $I_{CC}$ | 20X4, X8, X10 | $V_{CC} = 5.25$ V | $V_I = 0$ V | | | | | 120 | 130 | mA |
| $I_{CC}$ | 20L10 | $V_{CC} = 5.25$ V | $V_O = 0$ V | | | | | 120 | 165 | mA |

† For conditions shown as MIN or MAX, use the appropriate value specified under recommended operating conditions.
* All typical values are $V_{CC} = 5$ V, $T_A = 25°C$.
§ The output conditions have been chosen to produce a current that closely approximates one half the true short-circuit current, $I_{OS}$.

### switching characteristics over recommended operating free-air temerature range (unless otherwise noted)

| PARAMETER | FROM | TO | TEST CONDITIONS | M SUFFIX-XX | | | C SUFFIX-XX | | | UNIT |
|---|---|---|---|---|---|---|---|---|---|---|
| | | | | MIN | TYP* | MAX | MIN | TYP* | MAX | |
| $f_{max}$ | | | | | | | 35 | | | MHz |
| $t_{pd}$ | I, I/O | O, I/O | $C_L = 50$ pF | | | | | 12 | 20 | ns |
| $t_{pd}$ | OUTCLK† | Q | $R_1 = 200$ Ω | | | | | 10 | 15 | ns |
| $t_{en}$ | OE | Q | $R_2 = 390$ Ω | | | | | 7 | 15 | ns |
| $t_{dis}$ | OE† | Q | | | | | | 15 | 20 | ns |
| $t_{en}$ | I, I/O | O, I/O | | | | | | 7 | 15 | ns |
| $t_{dis}$ | I, I/O | O, I/O | SEE FIGURE BELOW | | | | | 15 | 20 | ns |

* All typical values are at $V_{CC} = 5$ V, $T_A = 25°C$

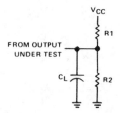

**PRODUCT TERMS**
(TOP VIEW)

```
    PGM VERIFY  [ 1   U  24 ]  VCC
          PI0  [ 2      23 ]  PO0
          PI1  [ 3      22 ]  PO1
          PI2  [ 4      21 ]  PO2
          PI3  [ 5      20 ]  PO3
          PI4  [ 6      19 ]  PO4
          PI5  [ 7      18 ]  PO5
          PA8  [ 8      17 ]  PO6
          PA9  [ 9      16 ]  PO7
         PA10  [ 10     15 ]  PO8
   PGM ENABLE  [ 11     14 ]  PO9
          GND  [ 12     13 ]  OE
```

Pin assignments in programmming mode (PGM ENABLE, pin 11 at $V_{IHH}$)

## TABLE 2. PRODUCT LINE SELECT

| PRODUCT LINE ADDRESS | | | PRODUCT LINE NUMBER | | | | | | | | | |
|---|---|---|---|---|---|---|---|---|---|---|---|---|
| PA8 | PA9 | PA10 | | | | | | | | | | |
| L | L | L | 0 | 8 | 16 | 24 | 32 | 40 | 48 | 56 | 64 | 72 |
| L | L | H | 1 | 9 | 17 | 25 | 33 | 41 | 49 | 57 | 65 | 73 |
| L | H | L | 2 | 10 | 18 | 26 | 34 | 42 | 50 | 58 | 66 | 74 |
| L | H | H | 3 | 11 | 19 | 27 | 35 | 43 | 51 | 59 | 67 | 75 |
| | | | PO0 | PO1 | PO2 | PO3 | PO4 | PO5 | PO6 | PO7 | PO8 | PO9 |
| | | | OUTPUT PIN NAME | | | | | | | | | |

$L = V_{IL}, H = V_{IH}$

3

Field-Programmable Logic

**TEXAS**
**INSTRUMENTS**

## TABLE 1. INPUT LINE SELECT

| INPUT LINE NUMBER | PIN NAME | | | | | |
|---|---|---|---|---|---|---|
| | PI0 | PI1 | PI2 | PI3 | PI4 | PI5 |
| 0 | L | L | L | L | L | L |
| 1 | L | L | L | L | L | H |
| 2 | L | L | L | L | H | L |
| 3 | L | L | L | L | H | H |
| 4 | L | L | L | H | L | L |
| 5 | L | L | L | H | L | H |
| 6 | L | L | L | H | H | L |
| 7 | L | L | L | H | H | H |
| 8 | L | L | H | L | L | L |
| 9 | L | L | H | L | L | H |
| 10 | L | L | H | L | H | L |
| 11 | L | L | H | L | H | H |
| 12 | L | L | H | H | L | L |
| 13 | L | L | H | H | L | H |
| 14 | L | L | H | H | H | L |
| 15 | L | L | H | H | H | H |
| 16 | L | H | L | L | L | L |
| 17 | L | H | L | L | L | H |
| 18 | L | H | L | L | H | L |
| 19 | L | H | L | L | H | H |
| 20 | L | H | L | H | L | L |
| 21 | L | H | L | H | L | H |
| 22 | L | H | L | H | H | L |
| 23 | L | H | L | H | H | H |
| 24 | L | H | H | L | L | L |
| 25 | L | H | H | L | L | H |
| 26 | L | H | H | L | H | L |
| 27 | L | H | H | L | H | H |
| 28 | L | H | H | H | L | L |
| 29 | L | H | H | H | L | H |
| 30 | L | H | H | H | H | L |
| 31 | L | H | H | H | H | H |
| 32 | H | L | L | L | L | L |
| 33 | H | L | L | L | L | H |
| 34 | H | L | L | L | H | L |
| 35 | H | L | L | L | H | H |
| 36 | H | L | L | H | L | L |
| 37 | H | L | L | H | L | H |
| 38 | H | L | L | H | H | L |
| 39 | H | L | L | H | H | H |

$L = V_{IL}, H = V_{IH}$

TEXAS
INSTRUMENTS

## programming procedure for array fuses

Array fuses are programmed by excuting the following programming sequence. Each fuse can be opened by selecting the appropriate (one of 40) input line and (one of 80) product line. The levels for selecting input lines and product lines are shown in Tables 1 and 2.

Step 1    Raise PGM ENABLE to $V_{IHH}$.
Step 2    Select an input line by applying appropriate logic levels to PI pins.
Step 3    Select a product line group by applying appropriate logic levels to PA pins. The actual product line selected will be determined by the PO pin (described in Step 5).
Step 4    Raise $\overline{OE}$ to $V_{IH}$.
Step 5    Raise the selected PO pin to $V_{IHH}$.
Step 6    Program the fuse by pulsing $V_{CC}$ to $V_{IHH}$.
Step 7    Remove the output voltage
Step 8    Lower $\overline{OE}$ to $V_{IL}$ to enable device
Step 9    Verify the blowing of the fuse by checking for a $V_{OL}$, at the selected PO pin. Register devices require a position pulse on the PGM verify pin.

Steps 1 through 9 may be repeated if the verification does not indicate that the fuse was successfully programmed (blown), but no more than four times. Verification is possible only with the verify-protect fuse intact.

## programming waveforms

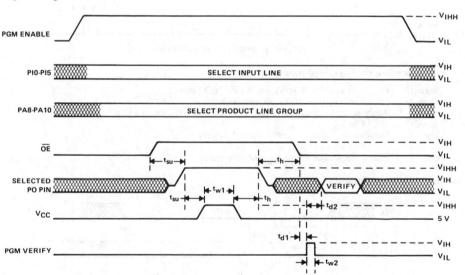

Field-Programmable Logic

3

## PRELOAD PROCEDURES

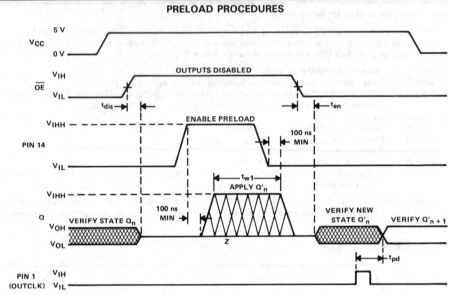

**FIGURE 1. PRELOAD WAVEFORMS**

### preload procedure for registered outputs

Step 1    Pin 13 to $V_{IH}$, Pin 1 to $V_{IL}$, and $V_{CC}$ to 5 volts.
Step 2    Pin 14 to $V_{IHH}$ for 10 to 50 microseconds.
Step 3    Apply an open circuit for a low and $V_{IHH}$ for a high at the Q outputs.
Step 4    Pin 14 to $V_{IL}$.
Step 5    Remove the voltages applied to the outputs.
Step 6    Pin 13 to $V_{IL}$.
Step 7    Check the output states to verify preload.

### security fuse programming

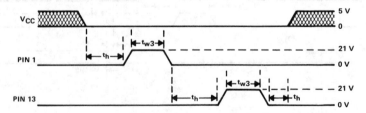

TEXAS
INSTRUMENTS

Field-Programmable Logic

3

# TIBPALR19L8, TIBPALR19R4, TIBPALR19R6, TIBPALR19R8
## HIGH PERFORMANCE REGISTERED-INPUT PAL® CIRCUITS

D2709, REVISED FEB. 86

- **Choice of Operating Speeds**
  **HIGH PERFORMANCE . . . 30 MHz Max**
  **HALF-POWER . . . 20 MHz Max**

- **Preload Capability on Output Registers**

- **Power-up Clear on Registered Devices**

- **DIP Options Include Both 300-mil Plastic and 600-mil Ceramic**

| DEVICE | I/D INPUTS | I INPUTS | 3-STATE O OUTPUTS | REGISTERED Q OUTPUTS | I/O PORTS |
|--------|-----------|----------|-------------------|----------------------|-----------|
| 'PALR19L8 | 11 | 2 | 2 | 0 | 6 |
| 'PALR19R4 | 11 | 0 | 0 | 4 (3-state buffers) | 4 |
| 'PALR19R6 | 11 | 0 | 0 | 6 (3-state buffers) | 2 |
| 'PALR19R8 | 11 | 0 | 0 | 8 (3-state buffers) | 0 |

## description

These programmable array logic devices feature high speed and functionality similar to the TIBPAL16L8, 16R4, 16R6, 16R8 series, but with the added advantage of D-type input registers. If any input register is not desired, it can be converted to an input buffer by simply programming the architectural fuse.

Combining Advanced Low-Power Schottky† technology, with proven titanium-tungsten fuses, these devices will provide reliable high performance substitutes over conventional TTL logic. Their easy programmability allows for quick design of custom functions and typically result in a more compact circuit board. In addition, chip carriers are available for further reduction in board space. The Half-power devices offer a choice of operating frequency, switching speed, and power dissipation.

All of the registered outputs are set to a low level during power-up. In addition, extra circuitry has been provided to allow loading of each register asynchronously to either a high or low state. this feature simplifies testing because the registers can be set to an initial state prior to executing the test sequence.

### INPUT REGISTER FUNCTION TABLE

| INPUT | | OUTPUT OF |
|-------|---|-----------|
| INCLK | D | INPUT REGISTER |
| ↑ | H | H |
| ↑ | L | L |
| L | X | Q_0 |

**TIBPALR19L8'**
**M SUFFIX . . . JW PACKAGE**
**C SUFFIX . . . JW OR NT PACKAGE**
**(TOP VIEW)**

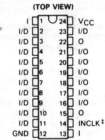

```
        ___ ___
   I  [ 1    24 ] VCC
  I/D [ 2    23 ] I/D
  I/D [ 3    22 ] O
  I/D [ 4    21 ] I/O
  I/D [ 5    20 ] I/O
  I/D [ 6    19 ] I/O
  I/D [ 7    18 ] I/O
  I/D [ 8    17 ] I/O
  I/D [ 9    16 ] I/O
  I/D [ 10   15 ] O
  I/D [ 11   14 ] INCLK ‡
  GND [ 12   13 ] I
```

**TIBPALR19L8'**
**M SUFFIX . . . FH OR FK PACKAGE**
**C SUFFIX . . . FN PACKAGE**
**(TOP VIEW)**

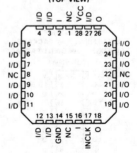

```
        I/D  I/D  NC  VCC  I/D  O
         4    3   2   1   28  27  26
  I/D [ 5                        25 ] I/O
  I/D [ 6                        24 ] I/O
  I/D [ 7                        23 ] I/O
  NC  [ 8                        22 ] NC
  I/D [ 9                        21 ] I/O
  I/D [ 10                       20 ] I/O
  I/D [ 11                       19 ] I/O
         12  13  14  15  16  17  18
        I/D  GND  NC   I   INCLK  O
```

‡Pin 14 is also used for the preload
Pin assignments in operating mode (voltage at pins 1 and 13 less than V_IHH)

†Integrated Schottky-Barrier diode-clamped transistor is patented by Texas Instruments, U.S. Patent Number 3,463,975.
PAL is a registered trademark of Monolithic Memories Inc.

## TEXAS INSTRUMENTS

**3**

**Field-Programmable Logic**

# TIBPALR19R4, TIBPALR19R6, TIBPALR19R8
## HIGH PERFORMANCE REGISTERED-INPUT PAL CIRCUITS

**TIBPALR19R4'**
**M SUFFIX . . . JW PACKAGE**
**C SUFFIX . . . JW OR NT PACKAGE**
(TOP VIEW)

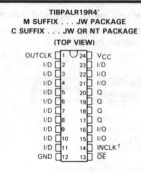

```
OUTCLK [ 1    24 ] Vcc
   I/D [ 2    23 ] I/D
   I/D [ 3    22 ] I/O
   I/D [ 4    21 ] I/O
   I/D [ 5    20 ] Q
   I/D [ 6    19 ] Q
   I/D [ 7    18 ] Q
   I/D [ 8    17 ] Q
   I/D [ 9    16 ] I/O
   I/D [ 10   15 ] I/O
   I/D [ 11   14 ] INCLK †
   GND [ 12   13 ] OE
```

**TIBPALR19R4'**
**M SUFFIX . . . FH OR FK PACKAGE**
**C SUFFIX . . . FN PACKAGE**
(TOP VIEW)

```
              I/D  I/D OUTCLK NC Vcc I/D I/O
               4    3    2    1  28  27  26
        I/D [ 5                         25 ] I/O
        I/D [ 6                         24 ] Q
        I/D [ 7                         23 ] Q
         NC [ 8                         22 ] NC
        I/D [ 9                         21 ] Q
        I/D [ 10                        20 ] Q
        I/D [ 11                        19 ] I/O
               12 13 14 15 16 17 18
              I/D  I/D GND NC OE INCLK† I/O
```

**TIBPALR19R6'**
**M SUFFIX . . . JW PACKAGE**
**C SUFFIX . . . JW OR NT PACKAGE**
(TOP VIEW)

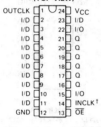

```
OUTCLK [ 1    24 ] Vcc
   I/D [ 2    23 ] I/D
   I/D [ 3    22 ] I/O
   I/D [ 4    21 ] Q
   I/D [ 5    20 ] Q
   I/D [ 6    19 ] Q
   I/D [ 7    18 ] Q
   I/D [ 8    17 ] Q
   I/D [ 9    16 ] Q
   I/D [ 10   15 ] I/O
   I/D [ 11   14 ] INCLK †
   GND [ 12   13 ] OE
```

**TIBPALR19R6'**
**M SUFFIX . . . FH OR FK PACKAGE**
**C SUFFIX . . . FN PACKAGE**
(TOP VIEW)

```
              I/D  I/D OUTCLK NC Vcc I/D I/O
               4    3    2    1  28  27  26
        I/D [ 5                         25 ] Q
        I/D [ 6                         24 ] Q
        I/D [ 7                         23 ] Q
         NC [ 8                         22 ] NC
        I/D [ 9                         21 ] Q
        I/D [ 10                        20 ] Q
        I/D [ 11                        19 ] Q
               12 13 14 15 16 17 18
              I/D  I/D GND NC OE INCLK† I/O
```

**TIBPALR19R8'**
**M SUFFIX . . . JW PACKAGE**
**C SUFFIX . . . JW OR NT PACKAGE**
(TOP VIEW)

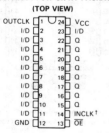

```
OUTCLK [ 1    24 ] Vcc
   I/D [ 2    23 ] I/D
   I/D [ 3    22 ] Q
   I/D [ 4    21 ] Q
   I/D [ 5    20 ] Q
   I/D [ 6    19 ] Q
   I/D [ 7    18 ] Q
   I/D [ 8    17 ] Q
   I/D [ 9    16 ] Q
   I/D [ 10   15 ] Q
   I/D [ 11   14 ] INCLK †
   GND [ 12   13 ] OE
```

**TIBPALR19R8'**
**M SUFFIX . . . FH OR FK PACKAGE**
**C SUFFIX . . . FN PACKAGE**
(TOP VIEW)

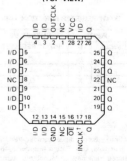

```
              I/D  I/D OUTCLK NC Vcc I/D Q
               4    3    2    1  28  27  26
        I/D [ 5                         25 ] Q
        I/D [ 6                         24 ] Q
        I/D [ 7                         23 ] Q
         NC [ 8                         22 ] NC
        I/D [ 9                         21 ] Q
        I/D [ 10                        20 ] Q
        I/D [ 11                        19 ] Q
               12 13 14 15 16 17 18
              I/D  I/D GND NC OE INCLK† Q
```

NC — No internal connection
† PIN 14 is also used for preload

**TEXAS INSTRUMENTS**

**functional block diagrams (positive logic)**

'PALR19L8

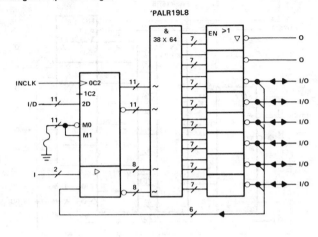

'PALR19R4

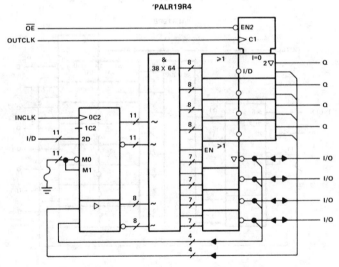

**3**

Field-Programmable Logic

**functional block diagrams (positive logic)**

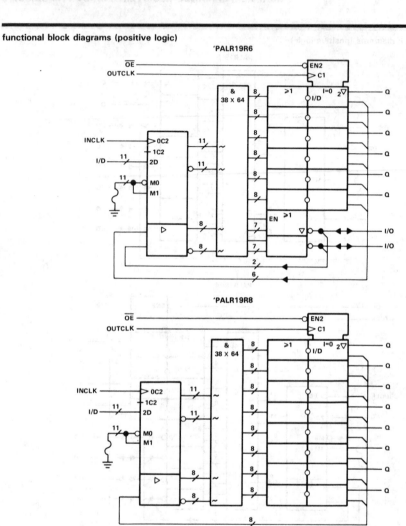

'PALR19R6

'PALR19R8

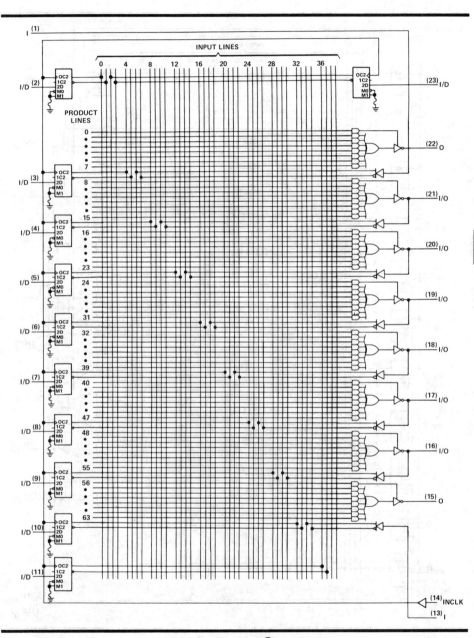

Field-Programmable Logic

3

## TIBPALR19R4
## HIGH PERFORMANCE REGISTERED-INPUT PAL CIRCUITS

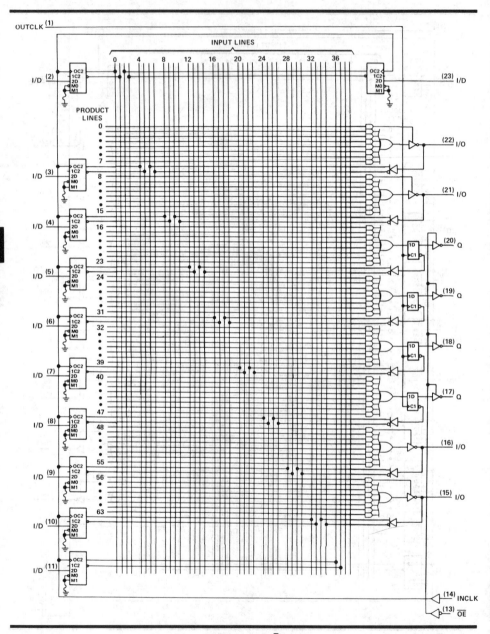

**TEXAS INSTRUMENTS**

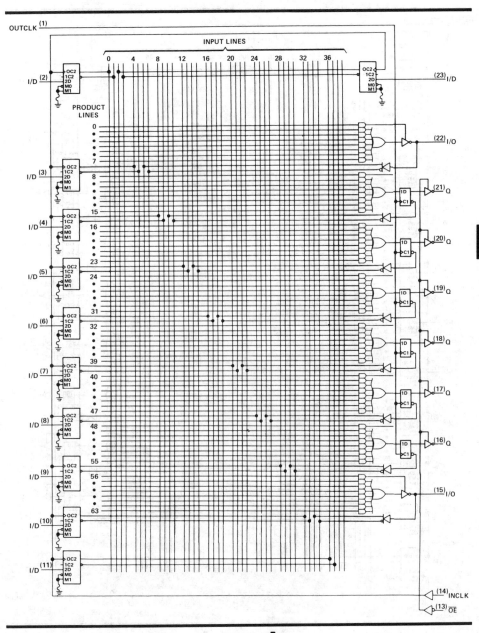

Field-Programmable Logic

3

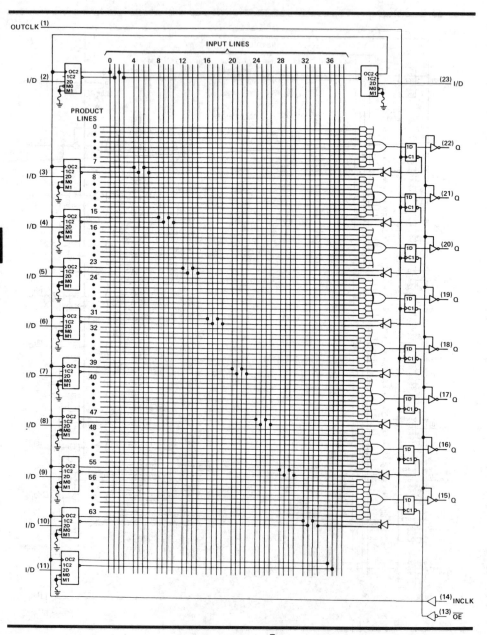

**3**

**Field-Programmable Logic**

**absolute maximum ratings over operating free-air temperature range (unless otherwise noted)**

Supply voltage, $V_{CC}$ (see Note 1) . . . . . . . . . . . . . . . . . . . . . . . . . . . . . . . . . . . . . . . . . . . . . . 7 V
Input voltage (see Note 1) . . . . . . . . . . . . . . . . . . . . . . . . . . . . . . . . . . . . . . . . . . . . . . . . . . . . . 5.5 V
Voltage applied to a disabled output (see Note 1) . . . . . . . . . . . . . . . . . . . . . . . . . . . . . . . . 5.5 V
Operating free-air temperature range: M suffix . . . . . . . . . . . . . . . . . . . . . . . . . $-55\,°C$ to $125\,°C$
C suffix . . . . . . . . . . . . . . . . . . . . . . . . . . . $0\,°C$ to $70\,°C$
Storage temperature range . . . . . . . . . . . . . . . . . . . . . . . . . . . . . . . . . . . . . $-65\,°C$ to $150\,°C$

NOTE 1:   These ratings apply except for programming pins during a programming cycle or during preload cycle.

**recommended operating conditions (see Note 2)**

| | | M SUFFIX | | | C SUFFIX | | | UNIT |
|---|---|---|---|---|---|---|---|---|
| | | MIN | NOM | MAX | MIN | NOM | MAX | |
| $V_{CC}$ | Supply voltage | | | | 4.75 | 5 | 5.25 | V |
| $V_{IH}$ | High-level input voltage | | | | 2 | | 5.5 | V |
| $V_{IL}$ | Low-level input voltage | | | | | | 0.8 | V |
| $I_{OH}$ | High-level output current | | | | | | $-3.2$ | mA |
| $I_{OL}$ | Low-level output current | | | | | | 24 | mA |
| $T_A$ | Operating free-air temperature | | | | 0 | | 70 | °C |

NOTE 2:   These recommended operating conditions apply for all device dash numbers. Also refer to additional recommended operating conditions information
pertaining to appropriate device dash numbers.

**programming parameters, $T_A = 25\,°C$**

| | | | MIN | NOM | MAX | UNIT |
|---|---|---|---|---|---|---|
| $V_{CC}$ | Verify-level supply voltage | | 4.5 | 5.0 | 5.5 | V |
| $V_{IH}$ | High-level input voltage | | 2 | | 5.5 | V |
| $V_{IL}$ | Low-level input voltage | | | | 0.8 | V |
| $V_{OH}$ | High-level output voltage | | | | 5.5 | V |
| $V_{IHH}$ | Program-pulse input voltage | | 10.25 | 10.5 | 10.75 | V |
| $I_{IHH}$ | Program-pulse input current | PO | | | 50 | mA |
| | | PGM ENABLE, L/R | | | 25 | |
| | | PI, PA | | | 5 | |
| | | $V_{CC}$ | | | 400 | |
| $t_{w1}$ | Program-pulse duration at PO or I/D pins | | 10 | | 50 | $\mu s$ |
| $t_{w2}$ | Pulse duration at PGM VERIFY and INCLK | | 100 | | | ns |
| $t_{su}$ | Setup time | | 100 | | | ns |
| $t_h$ | Hold time | | 100 | | | ns |
| $t_{d1}$ | Delay time from $V_{CC}$ to 5 V to PGM VERIFY† | | 100 | | | $\mu s$ |
| $t_{d2}$ | Delay time from PGM VERIFY† to verification of output | | 200 | | | ns |
| $t_{d3}$ | Delay time | | 100 | | | ns |
| | Input voltage at pins 1 and 13 to open verify-protect (security) fuse | | 20 | 21 | 22 | V |
| $t_{w3}$ | Input current to open verify-protect (security) fuse | | | | 400 | mA |
| | Pulse duration to open verify-protect (security) fuse | | 20 | | 50 | $\mu s$ |
| | $V_{CC}$ value during security fuse programming | | | 0 | 0.4 | V |

Field-Programmable Logic

3

### recommended operating conditions

| | | | M SUFFIX-XX | | | C SUFFIX-XX | | | UNIT |
|---|---|---|---|---|---|---|---|---|---|
| | | | MIN | TYP | MAX | MIN | TYP | MAX | |
| $f_{clock}$ | Clock frequency | INCLK | | | | 0 | | 30 | MHz |
| | | OUTCLK | | | | 0 | | 30 | |
| $t_w$ | Pulse duration, clock | INCLK high | | | | 15 | | | ns |
| | | INCLK low | | | | 15 | | | |
| | | OUTCLK high | | | | 15 | | | ns |
| | | OUTCLK low | | | | 15 | | | |
| $t_{su}$ | Setup time, input or feedback before | INCLK↑ | | | | 10 | | | ns |
| | | OUTCLK↑ | | | | 25 | | | |
| $t_h$ | Hold time, DATA AFTER INCLK↑ | | | | | 5 | | | ns |
| $t_h$ | Hold time, DATA AFTER OUTCLK↑ | | | | | 0 | | | ns |

### electrical characteristics over recommended free-air operating temperature range

| PARAMETER | | TEST CONDITIONS[†] | | M SUFFIX-XX | | | C SUFFIX-XX | | | UNIT |
|---|---|---|---|---|---|---|---|---|---|---|
| | | | | MIN | TYP[‡] | MAX | MIN | TYP[‡] | MAX | |
| $V_{IK}$ | | $V_{CC} = 4.75$ V | $I_I = -18$ mA | | | | | | $-1.5$ | V |
| $V_{OH}$ | | $V_{CC} = 4.75$ V | $I_{OH} = $ MAX | | | | 2.4 | 3.3 | | V |
| $V_{OL}$ | | $V_{CC} = 4.75$ V | $I_{OL} = $ MAX | | | | | 0.25 | 0.4 | V |
| $I_{OZH}$ | Outputs | $V_{CC} = 5.25$ V | $V_{IH} = 2.7$ V | | | | | | 20 | $\mu$A |
| | I/O ports | | | | | | | | 100 | |
| $I_{OZL}$ | Outputs | $V_{CC} = 5.25$ V | $V_{IH} = 0.4$ V | | | | | | $-20$ | $\mu$A |
| | I/O ports | | | | | | | | $-250$ | |
| $I_I$ | $\overline{OE}$ Input | $V_{CC} = 5.25$ V | $V_I = 5.5$ V | | | | | | 0.2 | mA |
| | I/D Inputs | | | | | | | | 0.1 | |
| | All others | | | | | | | | 0.1 | |
| $I_{IH}$ | $\overline{OE}$ Input | $V_{CC} = 5.25$ V | $V_I = 2.7$ V | | | | | | 40 | $\mu$A |
| | I/D Inputs | | | | | | | | 20 | |
| | All others | | | | | | | | 20 | |
| $I_{IL}$ | $\overline{OE}$ Input | $V_{CC} = 5.25$ V | $V_I = 0.4$ V | | | | | | $-0.4$ | mA |
| | I/D Inputs | | | | | | | | $-0.6$ | |
| | All others | | | | | | | | $-0.2$ | |
| $I_O$[§] | | $V_{CC} = 5.25$ V | $V_O = 2.25$ V | | | | $-30$ | | $-125$ | mA |
| $I_{CC}$ | | $V_{CC} = 5.25$ V, Outputs open | $V_I = 0$ V, | | | | | 150 | 210 | mA |

[†]For conditions shown as MIN or MAX, use the appropriate value specified under recommended operating conditions.
[‡]All typical values are $V_{CC} = 5$ V, $T_A = 25$°C.
[§]The output conditions have been chosen to produce a current that closely approximates one half the true short-circuit current, $I_{OS}$.

TEXAS
INSTRUMENTS

**switching characteristics over recommended operating free-air temperature range (unless otherwise noted)**

| PARAMETER | FROM | TO | INPUT MODE | TEST CONDITIONS | M SUFFIX-XX | | | C SUFFIX-XX | | | UNIT |
|---|---|---|---|---|---|---|---|---|---|---|---|
| | | | | | MIN | TYP† | MAX | MIN | TYP† | MAX | |
| $f_{max}$ | | | Either | | | | 30 | | | | MHz |
| $t_{pd}$ | I, I/O | I/O, O | Either | | | | | | 15 | 25 | ns |
| $t_{pd}$ | OUTCLK↑ | Q | Either | | | | | | 10 | 20 | ns |
| $t_{en}$ | $\overline{OE}$↑ | Q | Either | | | | | | 10 | 20 | ns |
| $t_{dis}$ | $\overline{OE}$↑ | Q | Either | $R_L$ = 500 Ω, | | | | | 11 | 20 | ns |
| $t_{pd}$ | INCLK↑ | I/O, O | Registered | $C_L$ = 50 pF, | | | | | 20 | 35 | ns |
| $t_{en}$ | I/D, INCLK↑ | I/O, O, Q | Registered | See Note 3 | | | | | 27 | 40 | ns |
| $t_{dis}$ | INCLK↑ | I/O, O, Q | Registered | | | | | | 13 | 25 | ns |
| $t_{pd}$ | I/D | I/O, O | Buffered | | | | | | 20 | 35 | ns |
| $t_{en}$ | I/O | I/O | Buffered | | | | | | 14 | 25 | ns |
| $t_{dis}$ | I/D, I/O | I/O | Buffered | | | | | | 13 | 30 | ns |

†All typical values are $V_{CC}$ = 5 V, $T_A$ = 25°C.
NOTE 3: Load circuits and voltage waveforms are shown in Section 1.

**3**

**Field-Programmable Logic**

TEXAS
INSTRUMENTS

## TIBPALR19L8, TIBPALR19R4, TIBPALR19R6, TIBPALR19R8
## HIGH PERFORMANCE REGISTERED-INPUT PAL CIRCUITS

**PRODUCT TERMS 0 THRU 31**
**(TOP VIEW)**

| | | | | |
|---|---|---|---|---|
| PGM ENABLE | 1 | ∪ | 24 | V_CC |
| PI0 | 2 | | 23 | † |
| PI1 | 3 | | 22 | PO3 |
| PI2 | 4 | | 21 | PO2 |
| PI3 | 5 | | 20 | PO1 |
| PI4 | 6 | | 19 | PO0 |
| PI5 | 7 | | 18 | PA0 |
| PI6 | 8 | | 17 | PA1 |
| PI7 | 9 | | 16 | PA2 |
| PI8 | 10 | | 15 | L/R |
| PI9 | 11 | | 14 | INCLK |
| GND | 12 | | 13 | PGM VERIFY |

**PRODUCT TERMS 32 THRU 63**
**(TOP VIEW)**

| | | | | |
|---|---|---|---|---|
| PGM VERIFY | 1 | ∪ | 24 | V_CC |
| PI0 | 2 | | 23 | † |
| PI1 | 3 | | 22 | L/R |
| PI2 | 4 | | 21 | PA0 |
| PI3 | 5 | | 20 | PA1 |
| PI4 | 6 | | 19 | PA2 |
| PI5 | 7 | | 18 | PO3 |
| PI6 | 8 | | 17 | PO2 |
| PI7 | 9 | | 16 | PO1 |
| PI8 | 10 | | 15 | PO0 |
| PI9 | 11 | | 14 | INCLK |
| GND | 12 | | 13 | PGM ENABLE |

†No programming function. Make no connections.
Pin assignments in programming mode (PGM ENABLE , pin 1 or 13, at V_IHH)

### TABLE 1. INPUT LINE SELECT

| INPUT LINE NUMBER | PI9 | PI8 | PI7 | PI6 | PI5 | PI4 | PI3 | PI2 | PI1 | PI0 | L/R |
|---|---|---|---|---|---|---|---|---|---|---|---|
| 0 | HH | HH | HH | HH | HH | HH | HH | HH | HH | L | Z |
| 1 | HH | HH | HH | HH | HH | HH | HH | HH | HH | H | Z |
| 2 | HH | HH | HH | HH | HH | HH | HH | HH | HH | L | HH |
| 3 | HH | HH | HH | HH | HH | HH | HH | HH | HH | H | HH |
| 4 | HH | HH | HH | HH | HH | HH | HH | HH | L | HH | Z |
| 5 | HH | HH | HH | HH | HH | HH | HH | HH | H | HH | Z |
| 6 | HH | HH | HH | HH | HH | HH | HH | HH | L | HH | HH |
| 7 | HH | HH | HH | HH | HH | HH | HH | HH | H | HH | HH |
| 8 | HH | HH | HH | HH | HH | HH | HH | L | HH | HH | Z |
| 9 | HH | HH | HH | HH | HH | HH | HH | H | HH | HH | Z |
| 10 | HH | HH | HH | HH | HH | HH | HH | L | HH | HH | HH |
| 11 | HH | HH | HH | HH | HH | HH | HH | H | HH | HH | HH |
| 12 | HH | HH | HH | HH | HH | HH | L | HH | HH | HH | Z |
| 13 | HH | HH | HH | HH | HH | HH | H | HH | HH | HH | Z |
| 14 | HH | HH | HH | HH | HH | HH | L | HH | HH | HH | HH |
| 15 | HH | HH | HH | HH | HH | HH | H | HH | HH | HH | HH |
| 16 | HH | HH | HH | HH | HH | L | HH | HH | HH | HH | Z |
| 17 | HH | HH | HH | HH | HH | H | HH | HH | HH | HH | Z |
| 18 | HH | HH | HH | HH | HH | L | HH | HH | HH | HH | HH |
| 19 | HH | HH | HH | HH | HH | H | HH | HH | HH | HH | HH |
| 20 | HH | HH | HH | HH | L | HH | HH | HH | HH | HH | Z |
| 21 | HH | HH | HH | HH | H | HH | HH | HH | HH | HH | Z |
| 22 | HH | HH | HH | HH | L | HH | HH | HH | HH | HH | HH |
| 23 | HH | HH | HH | HH | H | HH | HH | HH | HH | HH | HH |
| 24 | HH | HH | HH | L | HH | HH | HH | HH | HH | HH | Z |
| 25 | HH | HH | HH | H | HH | HH | HH | HH | HH | HH | Z |
| 26 | HH | HH | HH | L | HH | HH | HH | HH | HH | HH | HH |
| 27 | HH | HH | HH | H | HH | HH | HH | HH | HH | HH | HH |
| 28 | HH | HH | L | HH | HH | HH | HH | HH | HH | HH | Z |
| 29 | HH | HH | H | HH | HH | HH | HH | HH | HH | HH | Z |
| 30 | HH | HH | L | HH | HH | HH | HH | HH | HH | HH | HH |
| 31 | HH | HH | H | HH | HH | HH | HH | HH | HH | HH | HH |
| 32 | HH | L | HH | HH | HH | HH | HH | HH | HH | HH | Z |
| 33 | HH | H | HH | HH | HH | HH | HH | HH | HH | HH | Z |
| 34 | HH | L | HH | HH | HH | HH | HH | HH | HH | HH | HH |
| 35 | HH | H | HH | HH | HH | HH | HH | HH | HH | HH | HH |
| 36 | L | HH | HH | HH | HH | HH | HH | HH | HH | HH | Z |
| 37 | H | HH | HH | HH | HH | HH | HH | HH | HH | HH | Z |

L = V_IL, H = V_IH, HH = V_IHH, Z = high impedance (e.g., 10 kΩ to 5 V)

### TABLE 2. PRODUCT LINE SELECT

| PRODUCT LINE NUMBER | PO0 | PO1 | PO2 | PO3 | PA2 | PA1 | PA0 |
|---|---|---|---|---|---|---|---|
| 0, 32 | Z | Z | Z | HH | Z | Z | Z |
| 1, 33 | Z | Z | Z | HH | Z | Z | HH |
| 2, 34 | Z | Z | Z | HH | Z | HH | Z |
| 3, 35 | Z | Z | Z | HH | Z | HH | HH |
| 4, 36 | Z | Z | Z | HH | HH | Z | Z |
| 5, 37 | Z | Z | Z | HH | HH | Z | HH |
| 6, 38 | Z | Z | Z | HH | HH | HH | Z |
| 7, 39 | Z | Z | Z | HH | HH | HH | HH |
| 8, 40 | Z | Z | HH | Z | Z | Z | Z |
| 9, 41 | Z | Z | HH | Z | Z | Z | HH |
| 10, 42 | Z | Z | HH | Z | Z | HH | Z |
| 11, 43 | Z | Z | HH | Z | Z | HH | HH |
| 12, 44 | Z | Z | HH | Z | HH | Z | Z |
| 13, 45 | Z | Z | HH | Z | HH | Z | HH |
| 14, 46 | Z | Z | HH | Z | HH | HH | Z |
| 15, 47 | Z | Z | HH | Z | HH | HH | HH |
| 16, 48 | Z | HH | Z | Z | Z | Z | Z |
| 17, 49 | Z | HH | Z | Z | Z | Z | HH |
| 18, 50 | Z | HH | Z | Z | Z | HH | Z |
| 19, 51 | Z | HH | Z | Z | Z | HH | HH |
| 20, 52 | Z | HH | Z | Z | HH | Z | Z |
| 21, 53 | Z | HH | Z | Z | HH | Z | HH |
| 22, 54 | Z | HH | Z | Z | HH | HH | Z |
| 23, 55 | Z | HH | Z | Z | HH | HH | HH |
| 24, 56 | HH | Z | Z | Z | Z | Z | Z |
| 25, 57 | HH | Z | Z | Z | Z | Z | HH |
| 26, 58 | HH | Z | Z | Z | Z | HH | Z |
| 27, 59 | HH | Z | Z | Z | Z | HH | HH |
| 28, 60 | HH | Z | Z | Z | HH | Z | Z |
| 29, 61 | HH | Z | Z | Z | HH | Z | HH |
| 30, 62 | HH | Z | Z | Z | HH | HH | Z |
| 31, 63 | HH | Z | Z | Z | HH | HH | HH |

TEXAS
INSTRUMENTS

## PROGRAMMING WAVEFORMS FOR ARRAY FUSES

### programming procedure for array fuses

Array fuses are programmed using a linear select method. Each fuse can be opened by selecting the appropriate (one of 40) input line and then pulsing the correct (one of 64) product line. The levels for selecting input lines and product lines are shown in Tables 1 and 2.

Step 1   Raise PGM ENABLE to $V_{IHH}$.
Step 2   Select an input line by applying appropriate levels to L/R and PI pins.
Step 3   Begin selection of the output line with appropriate conditions on PA pins.
Step 4   Pulse INCLK to $V_{IH}$.
Step 5   Raise $V_{CC}$ to $V_{IHH}$.
Step 6   Blow the fuse by pulsing the appropriate PO pin to $V_{IHH}$ as shown in Table 2 for the product line.
Step 7   Return $V_{CC}$ to 5 volts and pulse PGM VERIFY. The PO pin selected in Step 6 will be less than $V_{OL}$ if the fuse is open.

Steps 1 thru 7 may be repeated if the verification does not indicate that the fuse was successfully programmed (blown), but no more than 4 times. Verificatin is possible only with the verify-protect fuse intact.

To prevent further verification, two last fuses may be blown by raising pin 1 and pin 13 to 21 volts $\pm 1$ volts. $V_{CC}$ is required to be at 0 during this operation.

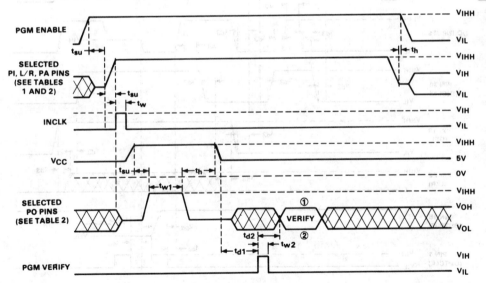

① A high level during the verify interval indicates that programming has not been successful.
② A low level during the verify interval indicates that programming has been successful.

**Field-Programmable Logic** — 3

## TIBPALR19L8, TIBPALR19R4, TIBPALR19R6, TIBPALR19R8
## HIGH PERFORMANCE REGISTERED-INPUT PAL CIRCUITS

### programming procedure for architectural fuses (see Note 2)

Step 1      Apply low levefls to all I/D pins and 5 volts to the $V_{CC}$ pin.

Step 2      Raise $V_{CC}$ pin to $V_{IHH}$.

Step 3      Raise INCLK pin to $V_{IHH}$.

Step 4      To program a D input pin into an I input pin pulse the selected pin to $V_{IHH}$.

Step 5      Lower INCLK to $V_{IL}$ and $V_{CC}$ to 5 volts.

Step 6      Raise pin 13 and all I/D input pins to $V_{IHH}$.

Step 7      Set pin 22 to Z to select pins 2 thru 11 or set pin 22 to $V_{IHH}$ to select pin 23.

Step 8      Raise INCLK to $V_{IHH}$.

Step 9      To verify that fuse has been blown, pulse selected I pin from $V_{IHH}$ to $V_{IL}$, then to $V_{IH}$ and back to $V_{IHH}$ while clocking pin 1. If output at pin 15 follows the I input the fuse has been blown. The fuse on pin 25 is verified from pin 2.

Step 10     Repeat above steps 1 thru 9 for each D input to be programmed into an I input.

NOTE 2: Refer to pin assignments in operating mode for programming selected I/D pins from D input to I inputs.

### programming waveforms

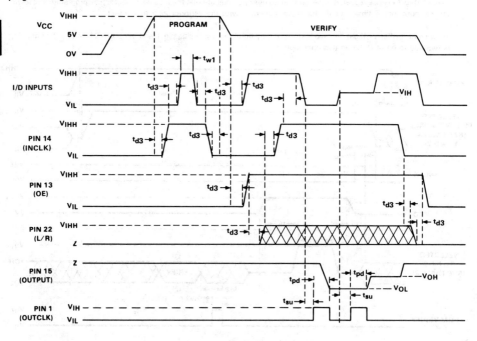

**preload procedure for registered outputs**

| | |
|---|---|
| Step 1 | Pin 13 to $V_{IH}$, Pin 1 to $V_{IL}$, and $V_{CC}$ to 5 volts. |
| Step 2 | Pin 14 to $V_{IHH}$. |
| Step 3 | Apply an open circuit or $V_{IL}$ for a low and $V_{IHH}$ for a high at the Q outputs |
| Step 4 | Pin 14 to $V_{IL}$. |
| Step 5 | Remove the voltages applied to the outputs. |
| Step 6 | Pin 13 to $V_{IL}$. |
| Step 7 | Check the output states to verify preload. |

**preload waveforms**

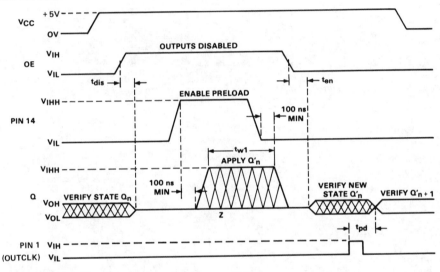

**security fuse programming**

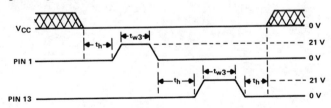

**Field-Programmable Logic**

3

3

**Field-Programmable Logic**

# TIBPALT19L8, TIBPALT19R4, TIBPALT19R6, TIBPALT19R8
## HIGH PERFORMANCE LATCHED-INPUT PAL® CIRCUITS

REVISED FEB. 86

- **Choice of Operating Speeds**
  **HIGH PERFORMANCE . . . 30 MHz Max**
  **HALF-POWER . . . 18 MHz Max**

- **Preload Capability on Output Registers**

- **Power-up Clear on Registered Devices**

- **DIP Options Include Both 300-mil Plastic and 600-mil Ceramic**

| DEVICE | I/D INPUTS | I INPUTS | 3-STATE O OUTPUTS | REGISTERED Q OUTPUTS | I/O PORTS |
|--------|-----------|----------|-------------------|----------------------|-----------|
| 'PALT19L8 | 11 | 2 | 2 | 0 | 6 |
| 'PALT19R8 | 11 | 0 | 0 | 8 (3-state buffers) | 4 |
| 'PALT19R6 | 11 | 0 | 0 | 6 (3-state buffers) | 2 |
| 'PALT19R4 | 11 | 0 | 0 | 4 (3-state buffers) | 0 |

## description

These programmable array logic devices feature high speed and functionality similar to the TIBPAL16L8, 16R4, 16R6, 16R8 series, but with the added feature of D-type transparent latches on the inputs. If an input latch is not desired, it can be converted to an input buffer by simply programming the architectural fuse.

Combining Advanced Low-Power Schottky[†] technology, with proven titanium-tungsten fuses, these devices will provide reliable high performance substitutes over conventional TTL logic. Their easy programmability allows for quick design of custom functions and typically result in a more compact circuit board. In addition, chip carriers are available for further reduction in board space. The Half-power devices offer a choice of operating frequency, switching speed, and power dissipation.

All of the registered outputs are set to a low level during power-up. In addition, extra circuitry has been provided to allow loading of each register asynchronously to either a high or low state. This feature simplifies testing because the registers can be set to an initial state prior to executing the test sequence.

### INPUT LATCH FUNCTION TABLE

| INLE | D | LATCH OUTPUT |
|------|---|--------------|
| L | L | L |
| L | H | H |
| H | X | $Q_0$ |

[†]Integrated Schottky-Barrier diode-clamped transistor is patented by Texas Instruments, U.S. Patent Number 3,463,975.
[‡]INLE is also used for the preload.
PAL is a registered trademark of Monolithic Memories Inc.

**TIBPALT19L8'**
**M SUFFIX . . . JW PACKAGE**
**C SUFFIX . . . JW OR NT PACKAGE**
**(TOP VIEW)**

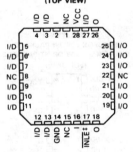

**TIBPALT19L8'**
**M SUFFIX . . . FH OR FK PACKAGE**
**C SUFFIX . . . FN PACKAGE**
**(TOP VIEW)**

Pin assignments in operating mode (voltage at pins 1 and 13 less than $V_{IHH}$)

**3** Field-Programmable Logic

Copyright © 1985, Texas Instruments Incorporated

## TIBPALT19R4, TIBPALT19R6, TIBPALT19R8
## HIGH PERFORMANCE LATCHED-INPUT PAL CIRCUITS

**TIBPALT19R4'**
**M SUFFIX . . . JW PACKAGE**
**C SUFFIX . . . JW OR NT PACKAGE**
**(TOP VIEW)**

```
OUTCLK [ 1    24 ] VCC
   I/D [ 2    23 ] I/D
   I/D [ 3    22 ] I/O
   I/D [ 4    21 ] I/O
   I/D [ 5    20 ] Q
   I/D [ 6    19 ] Q
   I/D [ 7    18 ] Q
   I/D [ 8    17 ] Q
   I/D [ 9    16 ] I/O
   I/D [ 10   15 ] I/O
   I/D [ 11   14 ] INLE†
   GND [ 12   13 ] OE
```

**TIBPALT19R4'**
**M SUFFIX . . . FH OR FK PACKAGE**
**C SUFFIX . . . FN PACKAGE**
**(TOP VIEW)**

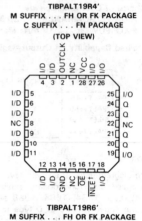

**TIBPALT19R6'**
**M SUFFIX . . . JW PACKAGE**
**C SUFFIX . . . JW OR NT PACKAGE**
**(TOP VIEW)**

```
OUTCLK [ 1    24 ] VCC
   I/D [ 2    23 ] I/D
   I/D [ 3    22 ] I/O
   I/D [ 4    21 ] Q
   I/D [ 5    20 ] Q
   I/D [ 6    19 ] Q
   I/D [ 7    18 ] Q
   I/D [ 8    17 ] Q
   I/D [ 9    16 ] Q
   I/D [ 10   15 ] I/O
   I/D [ 11   14 ] INLE†
   GND [ 12   13 ] OE
```

**TIBPALT19R6'**
**M SUFFIX . . . FH OR FK PACKAGE**
**C SUFFIX . . . FN PACKAGE**
**(TOP VIEW)**

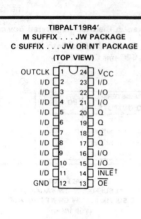

**TIBPALT19R8'**
**M SUFFIX . . . JW PACKAGE**
**C SUFFIX . . . JW OR NT PACKAGE**
**(TOP VIEW)**

```
OUTCLK [ 1    24 ] VCC
   I/D [ 2    23 ] I/D
   I/D [ 3    22 ] Q
   I/D [ 4    21 ] Q
   I/D [ 5    20 ] Q
   I/D [ 6    19 ] Q
   I/D [ 7    18 ] Q
   I/D [ 8    17 ] Q
   I/D [ 9    16 ] Q
   I/D [ 10   15 ] Q
   I/D [ 11   14 ] INLE†
   GND [ 12   13 ] OE
```

**TIBPALT19R8'**
**M SUFFIX . . . FH OR FK PACKAGE**
**C SUFFIX . . . FN PACKAGE**
**(TOP VIEW)**

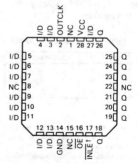

†INLE is also used for preload
Pin assignments in operating mode (voltage at pins 1 and 13 less than V_IHH)

TEXAS
INSTRUMENTS

**functional block diagrams (positive logic)**

'PALT19L8

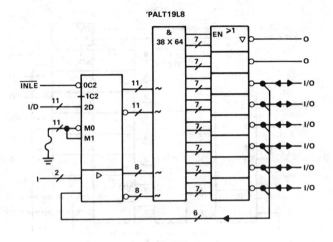

'PALT19R4

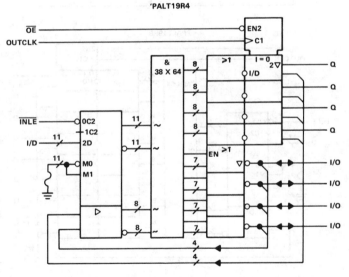

Field-Programmable Logic

3

TEXAS
INSTRUMENTS

# TIBPALT19R6, TIBPALT19R8
## HIGH PERFORMANCE LATCHED-INPUT PAL CIRCUITS

functional block diagrams (positive logic)

'PALT19R6

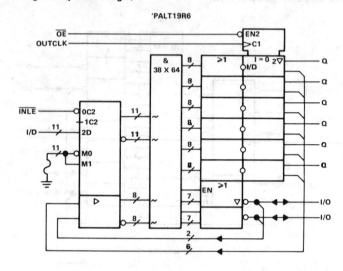

'PALT19R8

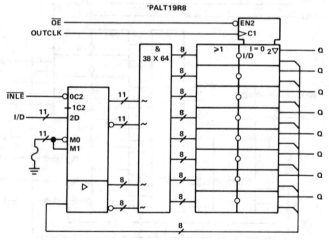

TEXAS
INSTRUMENTS

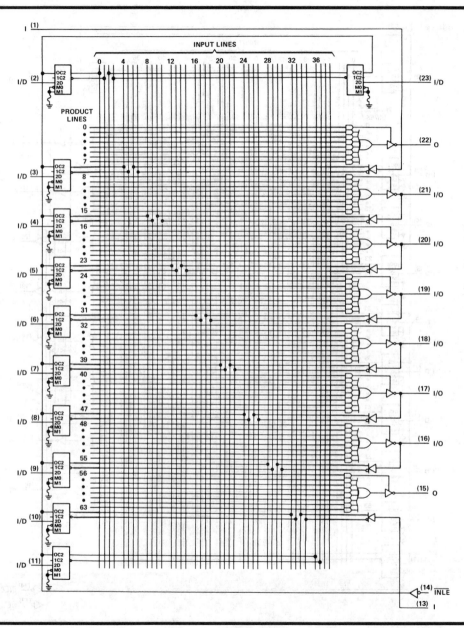

Field-Programmable Logic

3

# TIBPALT19R4
## HIGH PERFORMANCE LATCHED-INPUT PAL CIRCUITS

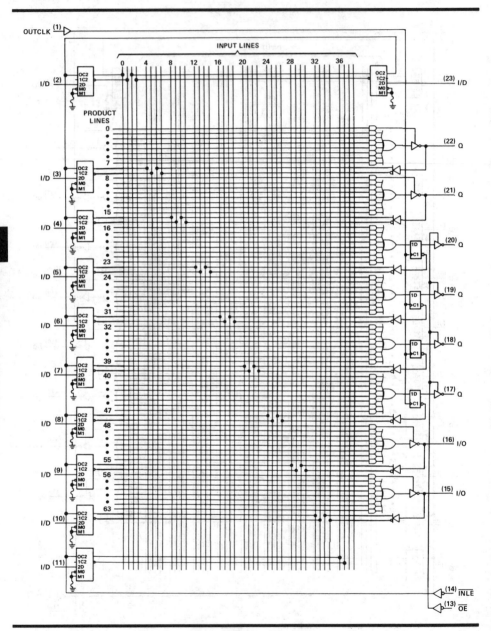

**TEXAS INSTRUMENTS**

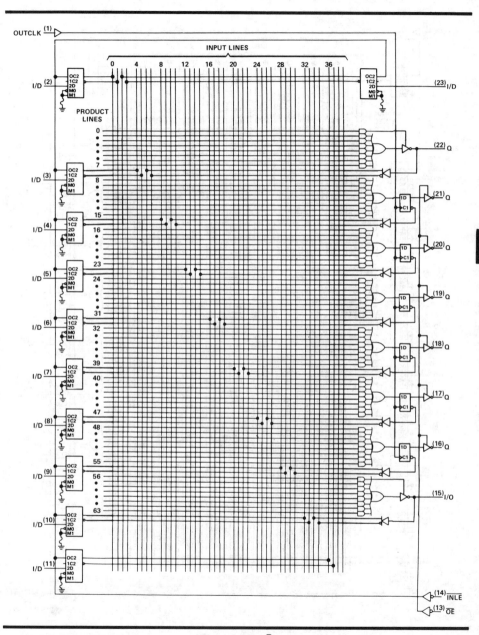

TEXAS
INSTRUMENTS

Field-Programmable Logic

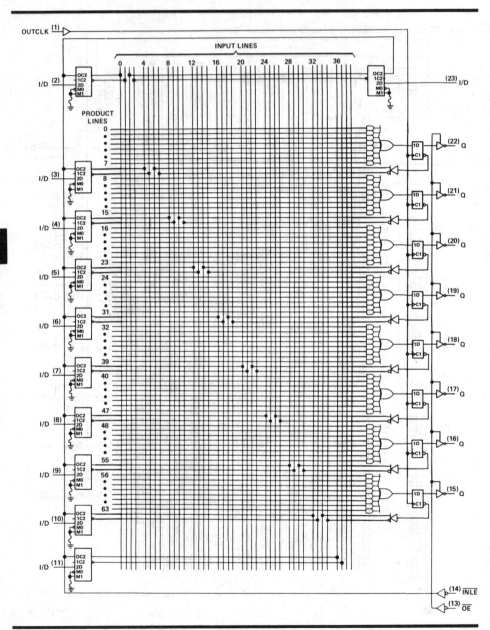

**TEXAS INSTRUMENTS**

## absolute maximum ratings over operating free-air temperature range (unless otherwise noted)

| | |
|---|---|
| Supply voltage, $V_{CC}$ (see Note 1) . . . . . . . . . . . . . . . . . . . . . . . . . . . . . . . . . . . . . . . . . . . . . . . . | 7 V |
| Input voltage (see Note 1) . . . . . . . . . . . . . . . . . . . . . . . . . . . . . . . . . . . . . . . . . . . . . . . . . . . . . . | 5.5 V |
| Voltage applied to a disabled output (see Note 1) . . . . . . . . . . . . . . . . . . . . . . . . . . . . . . . . . | 5.5 V |
| Operating free-air temperature range: M suffix . . . . . . . . . . . . . . . . . . . . . . . . . . | −55°C to 125°C |
| C suffix . . . . . . . . . . . . . . . . . . . . . . . . . . . . | 0°C to 70°C |
| Storage temperature range . . . . . . . . . . . . . . . . . . . . . . . . . . . . . . . . . . . . . . . . . . | −65°C to 150°C |

NOTE 1: These ratings apply except for programming pins during a programming cycle or during preload cycle.

## recommended operating conditions (see Note 2)

| | | M SUFFIX | | | C SUFFIX | | | UNIT |
|---|---|---|---|---|---|---|---|---|
| | | MIN | NOM | MAX | MIN | NOM | MAX | |
| $V_{CC}$ | Supply voltage | | | | 4.75 | 5 | 5.25 | V |
| $V_{IH}$ | High-level input voltage | | | | 2 | | 5.5 | V |
| $V_{IL}$ | Low-level input voltage | | | | | | 0.8 | V |
| $I_{OH}$ | High-level output current | | | | | | −3.2 | mA |
| $I_{OL}$ | Low-level output current | | | | | | 24 | mA |
| $T_A$ | Operating free-air temperature | | | | 0 | | 70 | °C |

NOTE 2: These recommended operating conditions apply for all device dash numbers. Also refer to additional recommended operating conditions information pertaining to appropriate device dash numbers.

## programming parameters, $T_A$ = 25°C

| | | | MIN | NOM | MAX | UNIT |
|---|---|---|---|---|---|---|
| $V_{CC}$ | Verify-level supply voltage | | 4.5 | 5.0 | 5.5 | V |
| $V_{IH}$ | High-level input voltage | | 2 | | 5.5 | V |
| $V_{IL}$ | Low-level input voltage | | | | 0.8 | V |
| $V_{OH}$ | High-level output voltage | | | | 5.5 | V |
| $V_{IHH}$ | Program-pulse input voltage | | 10.25 | 10.5 | 10.75 | V |
| $I_{IHH}$ | Program-pulse input current | PO | | | 50 | mA |
| | | PGM ENABLE, L/R | | | 25 | |
| | | PI, PA | | | 5 | |
| | | $V_{CC}$ | | | 400 | |
| $t_{w1}$ | Program-pulse duration at PO or I/D pins | | 10 | | 50 | µs |
| $t_{w2}$ | Pulse duration at PGM VERIFY and INCLK | | 100 | | | ns |
| $t_{su}$ | Setup time | | 100 | | | ns |
| $t_h$ | Hold time | | 100 | | | ns |
| $t_{d1}$ | Delay time from $V_{CC}$ to 5 V to PGM VERIFY↑ | | 100 | | | µs |
| $t_{d2}$ | Delay time from PGM VERIFY↑ to verification of output | | 200 | | | ns |
| $t_{d3}$ | Delay time | | 100 | | | ns |
| | Input voltage at pins 1 and 13 to open verify-protect (security) fuse | | 20 | 21 | 22 | V |
| $t_{w3}$ | Input current to open verify-protect (security) fuse | | | | 400 | mA |
| | Pulse duration to open verify-protect (security) fuse | | 20 | | 50 | µs |
| | $V_{CC}$ value during security fuse programming | | | 0 | 0.4 | V |

**Field-Programmable Logic** 3

### recommended operating conditions

| | | | M SUFFIX-XX | | | C SUFFIX-XX | | | UNIT |
|---|---|---|---|---|---|---|---|---|---|
| | | | MIN | TYP | MAX | MIN | TYP | MAX | |
| $f_{clock}$ | Clock frequency | INCLK | | | | 0 | | 30 | MHz |
| | | OUTCLK | | | | 0 | | 30 | |
| $t_w$ | Pulse duration, clock | INCLK high | | | | 15 | | | ns |
| | | INCLK low | | | | 15 | | | |
| | | OUTCLK high | | | | 15 | | | ns |
| | | OUTCLK low | | | | 15 | | | |
| $t_{su}$ | Setup time, input or feedback before | INCLK↑ | | | | 10 | | | ns |
| | | OUTCLK↑ | | | | 25 | | | |
| $t_h$ | Hold time, DATA AFTER INCLK↑ | | | | | 5 | | | ns |
| $t_h$ | Hold time, DATA AFTER OUTCLK↑ | | | | | 0 | | | ns |

### electrical characteristics over recommended free-air operating temperature range

| PARAMETER | | | TEST CONDITIONS† | | M SUFFIX-XX | | | C SUFFIX-XX | | | UNIT |
|---|---|---|---|---|---|---|---|---|---|---|---|
| | | | | | MIN | TYP‡ | MAX | MIN | TYP‡ | MAX | |
| $V_{IK}$ | | | $V_{CC}$ = 4.75 V | $I_I$ = -18 mA | | | | | | -1.5 | V |
| $V_{OH}$ | | | $V_{CC}$ = 4.75 V | $I_{OH}$ = MAX | | | | 2.4 | 3.3 | | V |
| $V_{OL}$ | | | $V_{CC}$ = 4.75 V | $I_{OL}$ = MAX | | | | | 0.25 | 0.4 | V |
| $I_{OZH}$ | Outputs | | $V_{CC}$ = 5.25 V | $V_{IH}$ = 2.7 V | | | | | | 20 | μA |
| | I/O ports | | | | | | | | | 100 | |
| $I_{OZL}$ | Outputs | | $V_{CC}$ = 5.25 V | $V_{IH}$ = 0.4 V | | | | | | -20 | μA |
| | I/O ports | | | | | | | | | -250 | |
| $I_I$ | $\overline{OE}$ input | | $V_{CC}$ = 5.25 V | $V_I$ = 5.5 V | | | | | | 0.2 | mA |
| | I/D Inputs | | | | | | | | | 0.1 | |
| | All others | | | | | | | | | 0.1 | |
| $I_{IH}$ | $\overline{OE}$ Input | | $V_{CC}$ = 5.25 V | $V_I$ = 2.7 V | | | | | | 40 | μA |
| | I/D Inputs | | | | | | | | | 20 | |
| | All others | | | | | | | | | 20 | |
| $I_{IL}$ | $\overline{OE}$ Input | | $V_{CC}$ = 5.25 V | $V_I$ = 0.4 V | | | | | | -0.4 | mA |
| | I/D Inputs | | | | | | | | | -0.6 | |
| | All others | | | | | | | | | -0.2 | |
| $I_O$§ | | | $V_{CC}$ = 5.25 V | $V_O$ = 2.25 V | | | | -30 | | -125 | mA |
| $I_{CC}$ | | | $V_{CC}$ = 5.25 V | $V_I$ = 0 V. Outputs open | | | | | 150 | 210 | mA |

†For conditions shown as MIN or MAX, use the appropriate value specified under recommended operating conditions.
‡All typical values are $V_{CC}$ = 5 V, $T_A$ = 25°C.
§The output conditions have been chosen to produce a current that closely approximates one half the true short-circuit current, $I_{OS}$.

TEXAS
INSTRUMENTS

**switching characteristics over recommended operating free-air temperature range (unless otherwise noted)**

| PARAMETER | FROM | TO | INPUT MODE | TEST CONDITIONS | M SUFFIX-XX | | | C SUFFIX-XX | | | UNIT |
|---|---|---|---|---|---|---|---|---|---|---|---|
| | | | | | MIN | TYP[†] | MAX | MIN | TYP[†] | MAX | |
| $f_{max}$ | | | Either | | | | | 30 | | | MHz |
| $t_{pd}$ | I, I/O | I/O, O | Either | | | | | | 15 | 25 | ns |
| $t_{pd}$ | OUTCLK↑ | Q | Either | | | | | | 10 | 20 | ns |
| $t_{en}$ | $\overline{OE}$↑ | Q | Either | | | | | | 10 | 20 | ns |
| $t_{dis}$ | $\overline{OE}$↑ | Q | Either | $R_L = 500\ \Omega$, | | | | | 11 | 20 | ns |
| $t_{pd}$ | INCLK↑ | I/O, O | Registered | $C_L = 50$ pF, | | | | | 20 | 35 | ns |
| $t_{en}$ | I/D, INCLK' | I/O, O, Q | Registered | See Note 3 | | | | | 27 | 40 | ns |
| $t_{dis}$ | INCLK↑ | I/O, O, Q | Registered | | | | | | 13 | 25 | ns |
| $t_{pd}$ | I/D | I/O, O | Buffered | | | | | | 20 | 35 | ns |
| $t_{en}$ | I/O | I/O | Buffered | | | | | | 14 | 25 | ns |
| $t_{dis}$ | I/D, I/O | I/O | Buffered | | | | | | 13 | 30 | ns |

[†]All typical values are $V_{CC} = 5$ V, $T_A = 25°C$.
NOTE 3: Load circuits and voltage waveforms are shown in Section 1.

**Field-Programmable Logic**

3

# TIBPALT19L8, TIBPALT19R4, TIBPALT19R6, TIBPALT19R8
# HIGH PERFORMANCE LATCHED-INPUT PAL CIRCUITS

**PRODUCT TERMS 0 THRU 31**
**(TOP VIEW)**

```
PGM ENABLE [ 1  U 24 ] Vcc
       PIO [ 2    23 ] †
       PI1 [ 3    22 ] PO3
       PI2 [ 4    21 ] PO2
       PI3 [ 5    20 ] PO1
       PI4 [ 6    19 ] PO0
       PI5 [ 7    18 ] PA0
       PI6 [ 8    17 ] PA1
       PI7 [ 9    16 ] PA2
       PI8 [ 10   15 ] L/R
       PI9 [ 11   14 ] INLE
       GND [ 12   13 ] PGM VERIFY
```

**PRODUCT TERMS 32 THRU 63**
**(TOP VIEW)**

```
PGM VERIFY [ 1  U 24 ] Vcc
       PIO [ 2    23 ] †
       PI1 [ 3    22 ] L/R
       PI2 [ 4    21 ] PA0
       PI3 [ 5    20 ] PA1
       PI4 [ 6    19 ] PA2
       PI5 [ 7    18 ] PO3
       PI6 [ 8    17 ] PO2
       PI7 [ 9    16 ] PO1
       PI8 [ 10   15 ] PO0
       PI9 [ 11   14 ] INLE
       GND [ 12   13 ] PGM ENABLE
```

†No programming function. Make no connection.
Pin assignments in programming mode (PGM ENABLE, pin 1 or 13, at $V_{IHH}$)

### TABLE 1. INPUT LINE SELECT

| INPUT LINE NUMBER | PI9 | PI8 | PI7 | PI6 | PI5 | PI4 | PI3 | PI2 | PI1 | PI0 | L/R |
|---|---|---|---|---|---|---|---|---|---|---|---|
| 0 | HH | HH | HH | HH | HH | HH | HH | HH | HH | L | Z |
| 1 | HH | HH | HH | HH | HH | HH | HH | HH | HH | H | Z |
| 2 | HH | HH | HH | HH | HH | HH | HH | HH | HH | L | HH |
| 3 | HH | HH | HH | HH | HH | HH | HH | HH | HH | H | HH |
| 4 | HH | HH | HH | HH | HH | HH | HH | HH | L | HH | Z |
| 5 | HH | HH | HH | HH | HH | HH | HH | HH | H | HH | Z |
| 6 | HH | HH | HH | HH | HH | HH | HH | HH | L | HH | HH |
| 7 | HH | HH | HH | HH | HH | HH | HH | HH | H | HH | HH |
| 8 | HH | HH | HH | HH | HH | HH | HH | L | HH | HH | Z |
| 9 | HH | HH | HH | HH | HH | HH | HH | H | HH | HH | Z |
| 10 | HH | HH | HH | HH | HH | HH | HH | L | HH | HH | HH |
| 11 | HH | HH | HH | HH | HH | HH | HH | H | HH | HH | HH |
| 12 | HH | HH | HH | HH | HH | HH | L | HH | HH | HH | Z |
| 13 | HH | HH | HH | HH | HH | HH | H | HH | HH | HH | Z |
| 14 | HH | HH | HH | HH | HH | HH | L | HH | HH | HH | HH |
| 15 | HH | HH | HH | HH | HH | HH | H | HH | HH | HH | HH |
| 16 | HH | HH | HH | HH | HH | L | HH | HH | HH | HH | Z |
| 17 | HH | HH | HH | HH | HH | H | HH | HH | HH | HH | Z |
| 18 | HH | HH | HH | HH | HH | L | HH | HH | HH | HH | HH |
| 19 | HH | HH | HH | HH | HH | H | HH | HH | HH | HH | HH |
| 20 | HH | HH | HH | HH | L | HH | HH | HH | HH | HH | Z |
| 21 | HH | HH | HH | HH | H | HH | HH | HH | HH | HH | Z |
| 22 | HH | HH | HH | HH | L | HH | HH | HH | HH | HH | HH |
| 23 | HH | HH | HH | HH | H | HH | HH | HH | HH | HH | HH |
| 24 | HH | HH | HH | L | HH | HH | HH | HH | HH | HH | Z |
| 25 | HH | HH | HH | H | HH | HH | HH | HH | HH | HH | Z |
| 26 | HH | HH | HH | L | HH | HH | HH | HH | HH | HH | HH |
| 27 | HH | HH | HH | H | HH | HH | HH | HH | HH | HH | HH |
| 28 | HH | HH | L | HH | HH | HH | HH | HH | HH | HH | Z |
| 29 | HH | HH | H | HH | HH | HH | HH | HH | HH | HH | Z |
| 30 | HH | HH | L | HH | HH | HH | HH | HH | HH | HH | HH |
| 31 | HH | HH | H | HH | HH | HH | HH | HH | HH | HH | HH |
| 32 | HH | L | HH | HH | HH | HH | HH | HH | HH | HH | Z |
| 33 | HH | H | HH | HH | HH | HH | HH | HH | HH | HH | Z |
| 34 | HH | L | HH | HH | HH | HH | HH | HH | HH | HH | HH |
| 35 | HH | H | HH | HH | HH | HH | HH | HH | HH | HH | HH |
| 36 | L | HH | HH | HH | HH | HH | HH | HH | HH | HH | Z |
| 37 | H | HH | HH | HH | HH | HH | HH | HH | HH | HH | Z |

### TABLE 2. PRODUCT LINE SELECT

| PRODUCT LINE NUMBER | PO0 | PO1 | PO2 | PO3 | PA2 | PA1 | PA0 |
|---|---|---|---|---|---|---|---|
| 0, 32 | Z | Z | Z | HH | Z | Z | Z |
| 1, 33 | Z | Z | Z | HH | Z | Z | HH |
| 2, 34 | Z | Z | Z | HH | Z | HH | Z |
| 3, 35 | Z | Z | Z | HH | Z | HH | HH |
| 4, 36 | Z | Z | Z | HH | HH | Z | Z |
| 5, 37 | Z | Z | Z | HH | HH | Z | HH |
| 6, 38 | Z | Z | Z | HH | HH | HH | Z |
| 7, 39 | Z | Z | Z | HH | HH | HH | HH |
| 8, 40 | Z | Z | HH | Z | Z | Z | Z |
| 9, 41 | Z | Z | HH | Z | Z | Z | HH |
| 10, 42 | Z | Z | HH | Z | Z | HH | Z |
| 11, 43 | Z | Z | HH | Z | Z | HH | HH |
| 12, 44 | Z | Z | HH | Z | HH | Z | Z |
| 13, 45 | Z | Z | HH | Z | HH | Z | HH |
| 14, 46 | Z | Z | HH | Z | HH | HH | Z |
| 15, 47 | Z | Z | HH | Z | HH | HH | HH |
| 16, 48 | Z | HH | Z | Z | Z | Z | Z |
| 17, 49 | Z | HH | Z | Z | Z | Z | HH |
| 18, 50 | Z | HH | Z | Z | Z | HH | Z |
| 19, 51 | Z | HH | Z | Z | Z | HH | HH |
| 20, 52 | Z | HH | Z | Z | HH | Z | Z |
| 21, 53 | Z | HH | Z | Z | HH | Z | HH |
| 22, 54 | Z | HH | Z | Z | HH | HH | Z |
| 23, 55 | Z | HH | Z | Z | HH | HH | HH |
| 24, 56 | HH | Z | Z | Z | Z | Z | Z |
| 25, 57 | HH | Z | Z | Z | Z | Z | HH |
| 26, 58 | HH | Z | Z | Z | Z | HH | Z |
| 27, 59 | HH | Z | Z | Z | Z | HH | HH |
| 28, 60 | HH | Z | Z | Z | HH | Z | Z |
| 29, 61 | HH | Z | Z | Z | HH | Z | HH |
| 30, 62 | HH | Z | Z | Z | HH | HH | Z |
| 31, 63 | HH | Z | Z | Z | HH | HH | HH |

$L = V_{IL}$, $H = V_{IH}$, $HH = V_{IHH}$, $Z$ = high impedance (e.g., 10 kΩ to 5 V)

TEXAS INSTRUMENTS

Field-Programmable Logic

3

### programming procedure for array fuses

Array fuses are programmed using a linear select method. Each fuse can be opened by selecting the appropriate (one of 40) input line and then pulsing the correct (one of 64) product line. The levels for selecting input lines and product lines are shown in Tables 1 and 2.

Step 1   Raise PGM ENABLE to $V_{IHH}$.
Step 2   Select an input line by applying appropriate levels to L/R and PI pins.
Step 3   Begin selection of the output line with appropriate conditions on PA pins.
Step 4   Pulse $\overline{INLE}$ to $V_{IH}$.
Step 5   Raise $V_{CC}$ to $V_{IHH}$.
Step 6   Blow the fuse by pulsing the appropriate PO pin to $V_{IHH}$ as shown in Table 2 for the product line.
Step 7   Return $V_{CC}$ to 5 volts and pulse PGM VERIFY. The PO pin selected in Step 6 will be less than $V_{OL}$ if the fuse is open.

Steps 1 thru 7 may be repeated if the verification does not indicate that the fuse was successfully programmed (blown), but no more than 4 times. Verification is possible only with the verify-protect fuse intact.

To prevent further verification, two last fuses may be blown by raising pin 1 and pin 13 to 21 volts $\pm 1$ volt. $V_{CC}$ is required to be at 0 during this operation.

### programming waveforms

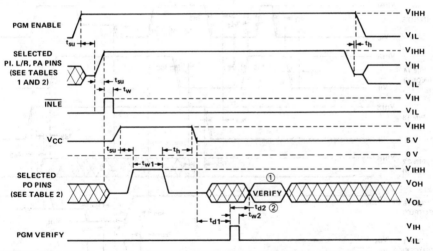

① A high level during the verify interval indicates that programming has not been successful.

② A low level during the verify interval indicates that programming has been successful.

Field-Programmable Logic

TEXAS
INSTRUMENTS

## TIBPALT19L8, TIBPALT19R4, TIBPALT19R6, TIBPALT19R8
## HIGH PERFORMANCE LATCHED-INPUT PAL CIRCUITS

### programming procedure for architectural fuses (see Note 2)

Step 1     Apply low levels to all I/D pins and 5 volts to the $V_{CC}$ pin.

Step 2     Raise $V_{CC}$ pin to $V_{IHH}$.

Step 3     Raise INCLK pin to $V_{IHH}$.

Step 4     To program a D input pin into an I input pin pulse the selected pin to $V_{IHH}$.

Step 5     Lower INCLK to $V_{IL}$ and $V_{CC}$ to 5 volts.

Step 6     Raise pin 13 and all I/D input pins to $V_{IHH}$.

Step 7     Set pin 22 to Z to select pins 2 thru 11 or set pin 22 to $V_{IHH}$ to select pin 23.

Step 8     Raise INCLK to $V_{IHH}$.

Step 9     To verify that fuse has been blown, pulse selected I pin from $V_{IHH}$ to $V_{IL}$, then to $V_{IH}$ and back to $V_{IHH}$ while clocking pin 1. If output at pin 15 follows the I input the fuse has been blown. The fuse on pin 23 is verified from pin 2.

Step 10    Repeat above steps 1 thru 9 for each D input to be programmed into an I input.

NOTE 2: Refer to pin assignments in operating mode for programming selected I/D pins from D input to I inputs.

### programming waveforms

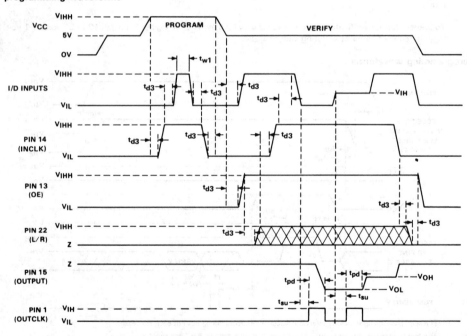

TEXAS
INSTRUMENTS

## TIBPALT19L8, TIBPALT19R4, TIBPALT19R6, TIBPALT19R8
## HIGH PERFORMANCE LATCHED-INPUT PAL CIRCUITS

### preload procedure for registered outputs

Step 1    Pin 13 to $V_{IH}$, Pin 1 to $V_{IL}$, and $V_{CC}$ to 5 volts.
Step 2    Pin 14 to $V_{IHH}$.
Step 3    Apply an open circuit or $V_{IL}$ for a low and $V_{IHH}$ for a high at the Q outputs.
Step 4    Pin 14 to $V_{IL}$.
Step 5    Remove the voltages applied to the outputs.
Step 6    Pin 13 to $V_{IL}$.
Step 7    Check the output states to verify preload.

### preload waveforms

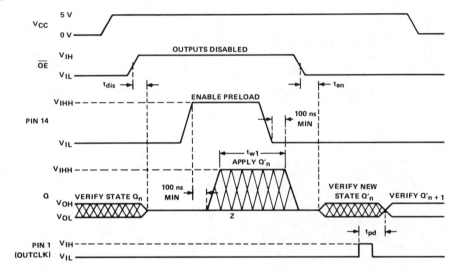

### security fuse programming

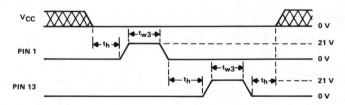

Field-Programmable Logic

3

**3**

**Field-Programmable Logic**

- Second Generation PAL Architecture

- Choice of Operating Speeds
  TIBPAL22V10AC . . . 25 ns Max
  TIBPAL22V10AM . . . 30 ns Max
  TIBPAL22V10C . . . 35 ns Max
  TIBPAL22V10M . . . 40 ns Max

- Increased Logic Power — Up to 22 Inputs and 10 Outputs

- Increased Product Terms — Average of 12 per Output

- Variable Product Term Distribution Allows More Complex Functions to be Implemented

- Each Output is User Programmable for Registered or Combinatorial Operation, Polarity, and Output Enable Control

- TTL-Level Preload for Improved Testability

- Extra Terms Provide Logical Synchronous Set and Asynchronous Reset Capability

- Fast Programming, High Programming Yield, and Unsurpassed Reliability Ensured Using Ti-W Fuses

- AC and DC Testing Done at the Factory Utilizing Special Designed-In Test Features

- Dependable Texas Instruments Quality and Reliability

- Package Options Include Plastic and Ceramic Dual-In-Line Packages and Chip Carriers

- Functionally Equivalent to AMD AMPAL22V10 and AMPAL22V10A

M SUFFIX . . . JT PACKAGE
C SUFFIX . . . NT PACKAGE
(TOP VIEW)

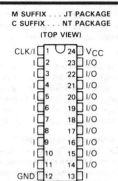

M SUFFIX . . . FK PACKAGE
C SUFFIX . . . FN PACKAGE
(TOP VIEW)

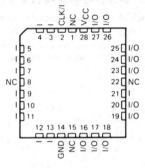

NC — No internal connection
Pin assignments in operating mode

## description

The TIBPAL22V10 and TIPPAL22V10A are programmable array logic devices featuring high speed and functional equivalency when compared to presently available devices. They are implemented with the familiar sum-of-products (AND-OR) logic structure featuring the new concept "Programmable Output Logic Macrocell". These IMPACT™ circuits combine the latest Advanced Low-Power Schottky technology with proven titanium-tungsten fuses to provide reliable high-performance substitutes for conventional TTL logic.

These devices contain up to 22 inputs and 10 outputs. They incorporate the unique capability of defining and programming the architecture of each output on an individual basis. Outputs may be registered or nonregistered and inverting or noninverting as shown in the output logic macrocell diagram. The ten potential outputs are enabled through the use of individual product terms.

Field-Programmable Logic

IMPACT is a trademark of Texas Instruments.

Copyright © 1986, Texas Instruments Incorporated

Further advantages can be seen in the introduction of variable product term distribution. This technique allocates from 8 to 16 logical product terms to each output for an average of 12 product terms per output. This variable allocation of terms allows far more complex functions to be implemented than in previously available devices.

Circuit design is enhanced by the addition of a synchronous set and an asynchronous reset product term. These functions are common to all registers. When the synchronous set product term is a logic 1, the output registers are loaded with a logic 1 on the next low-to-high clock transition. When the asynchronous reset product term is a logic 1, the output registers are loaded with a logic 0. The output logic level after set or reset depends on the polarity selected during programming. Output registers can be preloaded to any desired state during testing. Preloading permits full logical verification during product testing.

With features such as programmable output logic macrocells and variable product term distribution, the TIBPAL22V10 and TIBPAL22V10A offer quick design and development of custom LSI functions with complexities of 500 to 800 equivalent gates. Since each of the ten output pins may be individually configured as inputs on either a temporary or permanent basis, functions requiring up to 21 inputs and a single output or down to 12 inputs and 10 outputs are possible.

A power-up clear function is supplied that forces all registered outputs to a predetermined state after power is applied to the device. Registered outputs selected as active-low power-up with their outputs high. Registered outputs selected as active-high power-up with their outputs low.

A single security fuse is provided on each device to discourage unauthorized copying of fuse patterns. Once blown, the verification circuitry is disabled and all other fuses will appear to be open.

The M suffix devices are characterized for operation over the full military temperature range of −55°C to 125°C. The C suffix devices are characterized for operation from 0°C to 75°C.

**TEXAS**
**INSTRUMENTS**

## logic diagram (positive logic)

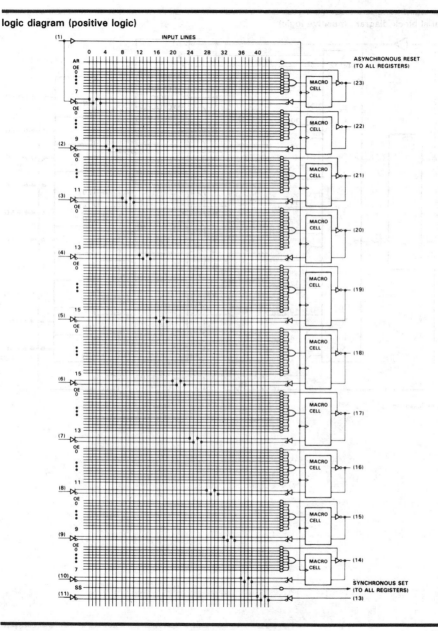

Field-Programmable Logic

3

## TIBPAL22V10, TIBPAL22V10A
## HIGH-PERFORMANCE *IMPACT*™ PROGRAMMABLE ARRAY LOGIC

**functional block diagram (positive logic)**

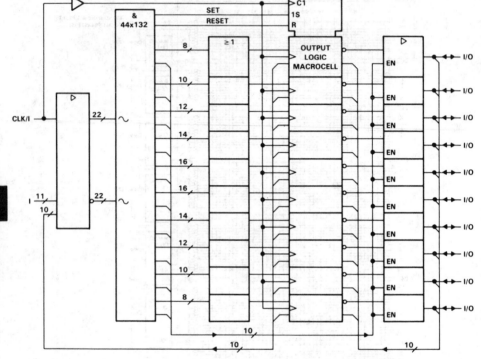

∿ denotes fused inputs

TEXAS
INSTRUMENTS

**output logic macrocell diagram**

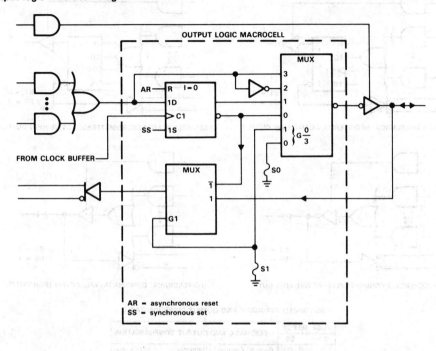

AR = asynchronous reset
SS = synchronous set

**TEXAS**
**INSTRUMENTS**

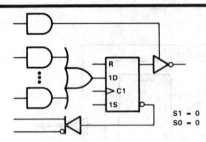

REGISTER FEEDBACK, REGISTERED, ACTIVE-LOW OUTPUT

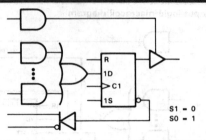

REGISTER FEEDBACK, REGISTERED, ACTIVE-HIGH OUTPUT

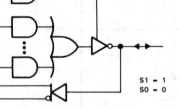

I/O FEEDBACK, COMBINATIONAL, ACTIVE-LOW OUTPUT

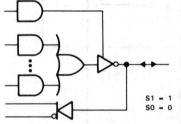

I/O FEEDBACK, COMBINATIONAL, ACTIVE-HIGH OUTPUT

### MACROCELL FEEDBACK AND OUTPUT FUNCTION TABLE

| FUSE SELECT | | FEEDBACK AND OUTPUT CONFIGURATION | | |
|---|---|---|---|---|
| S1 | S0 | | | |
| 0 | 0 | Register feedback | Registered | Active low |
| 0 | 1 | Register feedback | Registered | Active high |
| 1 | 0 | I/O feedback | Combinational | Active low |
| 1 | 1 | I/O feedback | Combinational | Active high |

0 = unblown fuse, 1 = blown fuse
S1 and S0 are select-function fuses as shown in the output logic
macrocell diagram.

### FIGURE 1. RESULTANT MACROCELL FEEDBACK AND OUTPUT LOGIC AFTER PROGRAMMING

## absolute maximum ratings over operating free-air temperature range (unless otherwise noted)

Supply voltage, $V_{CC}$ (see Note 1) . . . . . . . . . . . . . . . . . . . . . . . . . . . . . . . . . . . . . . . . . . . . . . . 7 V
Input voltage (see Note 1) . . . . . . . . . . . . . . . . . . . . . . . . . . . . . . . . . . . . . . . . . . . . . . . . . . . . 5.5 V
Voltage applied to a disabled output (see Note 1) . . . . . . . . . . . . . . . . . . . . . . . . . . . . . . . . . . 5.5 V
Operating free-air temperature range: M suffix . . . . . . . . . . . . . . . . . . . . . . . . . −55°C to 125°C
C suffix . . . . . . . . . . . . . . . . . . . . . . . . . . . . . . 0°C to 75°C
Storage temperature range . . . . . . . . . . . . . . . . . . . . . . . . . . . . . . . . . . . . . . −65°C to 150°C

NOTE 1: These ratings apply except for programming pins during a programming cycle or during a pre-load cycle.

TEXAS
INSTRUMENTS

### recommended operating conditions

| | | | TIBPAL22V10M | | | TIBPAL22V10C | | | UNIT |
|---|---|---|---|---|---|---|---|---|---|
| | | | MIN | NOM | MAX | MIN | NOM | MAX | |
| $V_{CC}$ | Supply voltage | | 4.5 | 5 | 5.5 | 4.75 | 5 | 5.25 | V |
| $V_{IH}$ | High-level input voltage | | 2 | | 5.5 | 2 | | 5.5 | V |
| $V_{IL}$ | Low-level input voltage | | | | 0.8 | | | 0.8 | V |
| $I_{OH}$ | High-level output current | | | | −2 | | | −3.2 | mA |
| $I_{OL}$ | Low-level output current | | | | 12 | | | 16 | mA |
| $f_{clock}$ | Clock frequency† | | | | 16.5 | | | 18 | MHz |
| $t_w$ | Pulse duration | Clock high or low | 30 | | | 25 | | | ns |
| | | Asynchronous Reset high or low | 40 | | | 35 | | | |
| $t_{su}$ | Setup time before clock↑ | Input | 35 | | | 30 | | | ns |
| | | Feedback | 35 | | | 30 | | | |
| | | Synchronous Set | 35 | | | 30 | | | |
| | | Asynchronous Reset low (inactive) | 40 | | | 35 | | | |
| $t_h$ | Hold time, input, set, or feedback after clock↑ | | 0 | | | 0 | | | ns |
| $T_A$ | Operating free-air temperature | | −55 | | 125 | 0 | | 75 | °C |

### electrical characteristics over recommended operating free-air temperature range

| PARAMETER | | TEST CONDITIONS‡ | | TIBPAL22V10M | | | TIBPAL22V10C | | | UNIT |
|---|---|---|---|---|---|---|---|---|---|---|
| | | | | MIN | TYP§ | MAX | MIN | TYP§ | MAX | |
| $V_{IK}$ | | $V_{CC}$ = MIN, | $I_I$ = −18 mA | | | −1.2 | | | −1.2 | V |
| $V_{OH}$ | | $V_{CC}$ = MIN, | $I_{OH}$ = MAX | 2.4 | 3.5 | | 2.4 | 3.5 | | V |
| $V_{OL}$ | | $V_{CC}$ = MIN, | $I_{OL}$ = MAX | | 0.25 | 0.5 | | 0.35 | 0.5 | V |
| $I_{OZH}$ | | $V_{CC}$ = MAX, | $V_O$ = 2.7 V | | | 0.1 | | | 0.1 | mA |
| $I_{OZL}$ | Any output | $V_{CC}$ = MAX, | $V_O$ = 0.4 V | | | −100 | | | −100 | μA |
| | Any I/O | | | | | −250 | | | −250 | |
| $I_I$ | | $V_{CC}$ = MAX, | $V_I$ = 5.5 V | | | 1 | | | 1 | mA |
| $I_{IH}$ | | $V_{CC}$ = MAX, | $V_I$ = 2.7 V | | | 25 | | | 25 | μA |
| $I_{IL}$ | | $V_{CC}$ = MAX, | $V_I$ = 0.4 V | | | −0.25 | | | −0.25 | mA |
| $I_{OS}$¶ | | $V_{CC}$ = MAX, | $V_O$ = 0.5 V | −30 | | −90 | −30 | | −90 | mA |
| $I_{CC}$ | | $V_{CC}$ = MAX, | $V_I$ = GND, Outputs open | | 120 | 180 | | 120 | 180 | mA |

### switching characteristics over recommended ranges of supply voltage and operating free-air temperature (unless otherwise noted)

| PARAMETER | FROM | TO | TEST CONDITIONS | TIBPAL22V10M | | | TIBPAL22V10C | | | UNIT |
|---|---|---|---|---|---|---|---|---|---|---|
| | | | | MIN | TYP§ | MAX | MIN | TYP§ | MAX | |
| $f_{max}$† | With feedback | | $C_L$ = 50 pF | 16.5 | | | 18 | | | MHz |
| $t_{pd}$ | I, I/O | I/O | R1 = 300 Ω for C suffix, | | 15 | 40 | | 15 | 35 | ns |
| $t_{pd}$ | I,I/O (reset) | Q | R1 = 390 Ω for M suffix, | | 15 | 45 | | 15 | 40 | ns |
| $t_{pd}$ | Clock | Q | R2 = 390 Ω for C suffix, | | 10 | 25 | | 10 | 25 | ns |
| $t_{en}$ | I, I/O | I/O, Q | R2 = 750 Ω for M suffix, | | 15 | 40 | | 15 | 35 | ns |
| $t_{dis}$ | I, I/O | I/O, Q | See Figure 2 | | 15 | 40 | | 15 | 35 | ns |

† $f_{max}$ and $f_{clock}$ (with feedback) = $\dfrac{1}{t_{su} + t_{pd} \text{ (CLK to Q)}}$, $f_{max}$ and $f_{clock}$ without feedback can be calculated as $f_{max}$ and

$f_{clock}$ (without feedback) = $\dfrac{1}{t_w \text{ high} + t_w \text{ low}}$.

‡ For conditions shown as MIN or MAX, use the appropriate value specified under recommended operating conditions.
§ All typical values are at $V_{CC}$ = 5 V, $T_A$ = 25 °C.
¶ Not more than one output should be shorted at a time and the duration of the short circuit should not exceed one second. Set $V_O$ at 0.5 V to avoid test problems caused by test equipment ground degradation.

TEXAS INSTRUMENTS

3 — Field-Programmable Logic

## TIBPAL22V10A
### HIGH-PERFORMANCE *IMPACT*™ PROGRAMMABLE ARRAY LOGIC

### recommended operating conditions

| | | | TIBPAL22V10AM | | | TIBPAL22V10AC | | | UNIT |
|---|---|---|---|---|---|---|---|---|---|
| | | | MIN | NOM | MAX | MIN | NOM | MAX | |
| $V_{CC}$ | Supply voltage | | 4.5 | 5 | 5.5 | 4.75 | 5 | 5.25 | V |
| $V_{IH}$ | High-level input voltage | | 2 | | 5.5 | 2 | | 5.5 | V |
| $V_{IL}$ | Low-level input voltage | | | | 0.8 | | | 0.8 | V |
| $I_{OH}$ | High-level output current | | | | −2 | | | −3.2 | mA |
| $I_{OL}$ | Low-level output current | | | | 12 | | | 16 | mA |
| $f_{clock}$ | Clock frequency† | | | | 22 | | | 28.5 | MHz |
| $t_w$ | Pulse duration | Clock high or low | 20 | | | 15 | | | ns |
| | | Asynchronous Reset high or low | 30 | | | 25 | | | |
| $t_{su}$ | Setup time before clock† | Input | 25 | | | 20 | | | ns |
| | | Feedback | 25 | | | 20 | | | |
| | | Synchronous Set | 25 | | | 20 | | | |
| | | Asynchronous Reset low (inactive) | 30 | | | 25 | | | |
| $t_h$ | Hold time, input, set, or feedback after clock† | | 0 | | | 0 | | | ns |
| $T_A$ | Operating free-air temperature | | −55 | | 125 | 0 | | 75 | °C |

### electrical characteristics over recommended operating free-air temperature range

| PARAMETER | | TEST CONDITIONS‡ | TIBPAL22V10AM | | | TIBPAL22V10AC | | | UNIT |
|---|---|---|---|---|---|---|---|---|---|
| | | | MIN | TYP§ | MAX | MIN | TYP§ | MAX | |
| $V_{IK}$ | | $V_{CC}$ = MIN, $I_I$ = −18 mA | | | −1.2 | | | −1.2 | V |
| $V_{OH}$ | | $V_{CC}$ = MIN, $I_{OH}$ = MAX | 2.4 | 3.5 | | 2.4 | 3.5 | | V |
| $V_{OL}$ | | $V_{CC}$ = MIN, $I_{OL}$ = MAX | | 0.25 | 0.5 | | 0.35 | 0.5 | V |
| $I_{OZH}$ | | $V_{CC}$ = MAX, $V_O$ = 2.7 V | | | 0.1 | | | 0.1 | mA |
| $I_{OZL}$ | Any output | $V_{CC}$ = MAX, $V_O$ = 0.4 V | | | −100 | | | −100 | μA |
| | Any I/O | | | | −250 | | | −250 | |
| $I_I$ | | $V_{CC}$ = MAX, $V_I$ = 5.5 V | | | 1 | | | 1 | mA |
| $I_{IH}$ | | $V_{CC}$ = MAX, $V_I$ = 2.7 V | | | 25 | | | 25 | μA |
| $I_{IL}$ | | $V_{CC}$ = MAX, $V_I$ = 0.4 V | | | −0.25 | | | −0.25 | mA |
| $I_{OS}$§ | | $V_{CC}$ = MAX, $V_O$ = 0.5 V | −30 | | −90 | −30 | | −90 | mA |
| $I_{CC}$ | | $V_{CC}$ = MAX, $V_I$ = GND, Outputs open | | 120 | 180 | | 120 | 180 | mA |

### switching characteristics over recommended ranges of supply voltage and operating free-air temperature
### (unless otherwise noted)

| PARAMETER | FROM | TO | TEST CONDITIONS | TIBPAL22V10AM | | | TIBPAL22V10AC | | | UNIT |
|---|---|---|---|---|---|---|---|---|---|---|
| | | | | MIN | TYP§ | MAX | MIN | TYP§ | MAX | |
| $f_{max}$† | With feedback | | $C_L$ = 50 pF | 22 | | | 28.5 | | | MHz |
| $t_{pd}$ | I, I/O | I/O | R1 = 300 Ω for C suffix, | | 15 | 30 | | 15 | 25 | ns |
| $t_{pd}$ | I, I/O (reset) | Q | R1 = 390 Ω for M suffix, | | 15 | 35 | | 15 | 30 | ns |
| $t_{pd}$ | Clock | Q | R2 = 390 Ω for C suffix, | | 10 | 20 | | 10 | 15 | ns |
| $t_{en}$ | I, I/O | Q | R2 = 750 Ω for M suffix, | | 15 | 30 | | 15 | 25 | ns |
| $t_{dis}$ | I, I/O | Q | See Figure 2 | | 15 | 30 | | 15 | 25 | ns |

† $f_{max}$ and $f_{clock}$ (with feedback) = $\dfrac{1}{t_{su} + t_{pd} \text{ (CLK to Q)}}$, $f_{max}$ and $f_{clock}$ without feedback can be calculated as $f_{max}$ and

$f_{clock}$ (without feedback) = $\dfrac{1}{t_w \text{ high} + t_w \text{ low}}$.

‡ For conditions shown as MIN or MAX, use the appropriate value specified under recommended operating conditions.
§ All typical values are at $V_{CC}$ = 5 V, $T_A$ = 25°C.
¶ Not more than one output should be shorted at a time and the duration of the short circuit should not exceed one second. Set $V_O$ at 0.5 V to avoid test problems caused by test equipment ground degradation.

**3**

**Field-Programmable Logic**

### preload procedure for registered outputs (see Note 2)

The output registers can be preloaded to any desired state during device testing. This permits any state to be tested without having to step through the entire state-machine sequence. Each register is preloaded individually by following the steps given below.

Step 1. With $V_{CC}$ at 5 volts and pin 1 at $V_{IL}$, raise pin 13 to $V_{IHH}$.

Step 2. Apply either $V_{IL}$ or $V_{IH}$ to the output corresponding to the register to be preloaded.

Step 3. Pulse pin 1, clocking in preload data.

Step 4. Remove output voltage, then lower pin 13 to $V_{IL}$. Preload can be verified by observing the voltage level at the output pin.

### preload waveforms (see Notes 2 and 3)

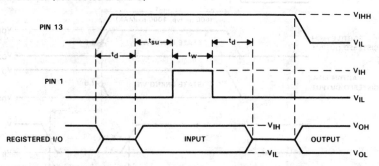

NOTES: 2. Pin numbers shown are for JT and NT packages only. If chip carrier socket adapter is not used, pin numbers must be changed accordingly.

3. $t_d = t_{su} = t_w = 100$ ns to 1000 ns. $V_{IHH} = 10.25$ V to 10.75 V.

Field-Programmable Logic

3

## TIBPAL22V10, TIBPAL22V10A
## HIGH-PERFORMANCE *IMPACT*™ PROGRAMMABLE ARRAY LOGIC

### power-up reset

Following power-up, all registers are reset to zero. The output level depends on the polarity selected during programming. This feature provides extra flexibility to the system designer and is especially valuable in simplifying state-machine initialization. To ensure a valid power-up reset, it is important that the $V_{CC}$'s rise be monotonic. Following power-up reset, a low-to-high clock transition must not occur until all applicable input and feedback setup times are met.

### power-up reset waveforms

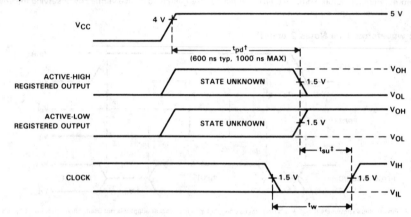

† This is the power-up reset time and applies to registered outputs only. The values shown are from characterization data.
‡ This is the setup time for input or feedback.

### programming information

Texas Instruments Programmable Logic Devices can be programmed using widely available software and inexpensive device programmers.

Complete programming specifications, algorithms, and the latest information on hardware, software, and firmware are available upon request. Information on programmers capable of programming Texas Instruments Programmable Logic is also available, upon request, from the nearest TI field sales office, local authorized TI distributor, or by calling Texas Instruments at (214) 995-2980.

TEXAS
INSTRUMENTS

## PARAMETER MEASUREMENT INFORMATION

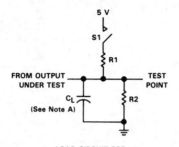

**LOAD CIRCUIT FOR
THREE-STATE OUTPUTS**

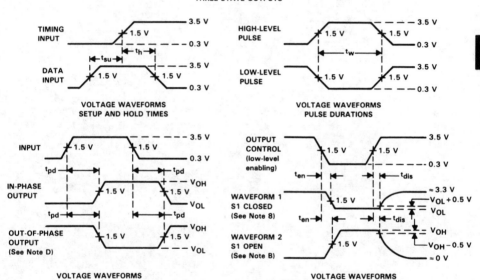

**VOLTAGE WAVEFORMS
SETUP AND HOLD TIMES**

**VOLTAGE WAVEFORMS
PULSE DURATIONS**

**VOLTAGE WAVEFORMS
PROPAGATION DELAY TIMES**

**VOLTAGE WAVEFORMS
ENABLE AND DISABLE TIMES, THREE-STATE OUTPUTS**

NOTES: A. $C_L$ includes probe and jig capacitance.
   B. Waveform 1 is for an output with internal conditions such that the output is low except when disabled by the output control.
      Waveform 2 is for an output with internal conditions such that the output is high except when disabled by the output control.
   C. All input pulses have the following characteristics: PRR ≤ 1 MHz, $t_r$ = $t_f$ = 2 ns, duty cycle = 50%.
   D. When measuring propagation delay times of 3-state outputs, switch S1 is open.

**FIGURE 2**

**3**

**Field-Programmable Logic**

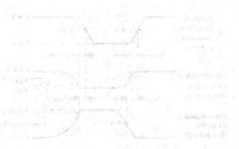

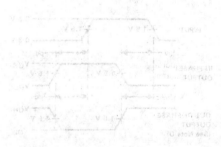

3

**Field-Programmable Logic**

- 50-MHz Clock Rate

- Power-On Preset of All Flip-Flops

- 6-Bit Internal State Register with 8-Bit Output Register

- Power Dissipation . . . 600 mW Typical

- Programmable Asynchronous Preset or Output Control

- Functionally Equivalent to, but Faster than 82S105A[†]

## description

The TIB82S105B is a TTL field-programmable state machine of the Mealy type. This state machine (logic sequencer) contains 48 product terms (AND terms) and 14 pairs of sum terms (OR terms). The product and sum terms are used to control the 6-bit internal state register and the 8-bit output register.

The outputs of the internal state register (P0—P5) are fed back and combined with the 16 inputs (I0—I15) to form the AND array. In addition a single sum term is complemented and fed back to the AND array, which allows any of the product terms to be summed, complemented, and used as an input to the AND array.

The state and output registers are positive-edge-triggered S/R flip-flops. These registers are unconditionally preset high on power-up. Pin 19 can be used to preset both registers or, by blowing the proper fuse, be converted to an output control function.

The TIB82S105BM is characterized for operation over the full military temperature range of −55 °C to 125 °C. The TIB82S105BC is characterized for operation from 0 °C to 75 °C.

[†]Power-up preset and asynchronous preset functions are not identical to 82S105A. See Recommended Operating Conditions.

M SUFFIX . . . JD PACKAGE
C SUFFIX . . . JD OR N PACKAGE
(TOP VIEW)

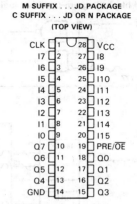

M SUFFIX . . . FK PACKAGE
C SUFFIX . . . FK OR FN PACKAGE
(TOP VIEW)

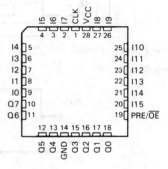

**Field-Programmable Logic**

3

**TEXAS INSTRUMENTS**

### functional block diagram (positive logic)

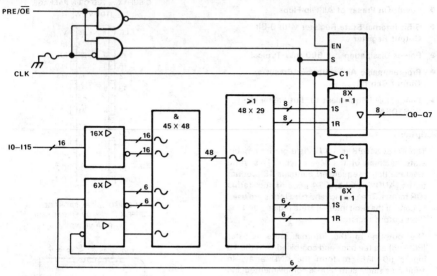

∿ denotes fused inputs.

### timing diagram

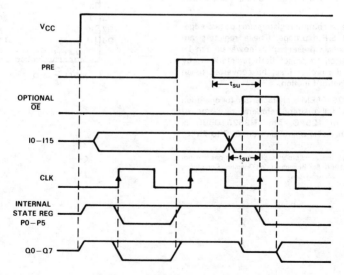

**TEXAS INSTRUMENTS**

**logic diagram (positive logic)**

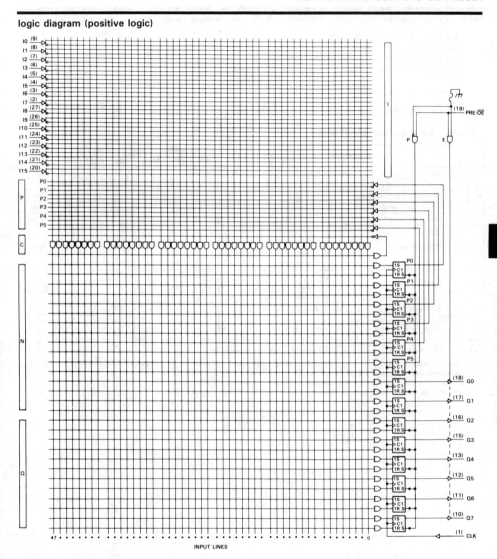

NOTES: 1. All AND gate inputs with a blown link float to a logic 1.
2. All OR gate inputs with a blown link float to a logic 0.

3

Field-Programmable Logic

![Texas Instruments logo] **TEXAS INSTRUMENTS**

**absolute maximum ratings over operating free-air temperature range (unless otherwise noted)**

Supply voltage, $V_{CC}$ (see Note 3) . . . . . . . . . . . . . . . . . . . . . . . . . . . . . . . . . . . . . . . . . . . . . . 7 V

Input voltage (see Note 3) . . . . . . . . . . . . . . . . . . . . . . . . . . . . . . . . . . . . . . . . . . . . . . . . . . . . 5.5 V

Voltage applied to a disabled output (see Note 3) . . . . . . . . . . . . . . . . . . . . . . . . . . . . . . . . . . 5.5 V

Operating free-air temperature range: TIB82S105BM . . . . . . . . . . . . . . . . . . . . . −55°C to 125°C

TIB82S105BC . . . . . . . . . . . . . . . . . . . . . . . 0°C to 75°C

Storage temperature range . . . . . . . . . . . . . . . . . . . . . . . . . . . . . . . . . . . . . . . . . . . . −65°C to 150°C

NOTE 3: These ratings apply except for programming pins during a programming cycle.

**recommended operating conditions**

| PARAMETER | | M SUFFIX | | | C SUFFIX | | | UNIT |
|-----------|---|----------|-----|-----|----------|-----|------|------|
| | | MIN | NOM | MAX | MIN | NOM | MAX | |
| $V_{CC}$ | Supply voltage | 4.5 | 5 | 5.5 | 4.75 | 5 | 5.25 | V |
| $V_{IH}$ | High-level input voltage | 2 | | 5.5 | 2 | | 5.5 | V |
| $V_{IL}$ | Low-level input voltage | | | 0.8 | | | 0.8 | V |
| $I_{OH}$ | High-level output current | | | −2 | | | −3.2 | mA |
| $I_{OL}$ | Low-level output current | | | 12 | | | 24 | mA |
| $f_{clock}$ | Clock frequency† | 1 thru 48 product terms without C-array‡ | 0 | | 40 | 0 | | 50 | MHz |
| | | 1 thru 48 product terms with C-array | 0 | | 25 | 0 | | 30 | |
| $t_w$ | Pulse duration | Clock high or low | 12 | | | 10 | | | ns |
| | | Preset | 18 | | | 15 | | | |
| $t_{su}$ | Setup time before CLK↑, 1 thru 48 product terms | Without C-array | 20 | | | 15 | | | ns |
| | | With C-array | 35 | | | 30 | | | |
| $t_{su}$ | Setup time, Preset low (inactive) before CLK↑§ | | 10 | | | 8 | | | ns |
| $t_h$ | Hold time, input after CLK↑ | | 0 | | | 0 | | | ns |
| $T_A$ | Operating free-air temperature | | −55 | | 125 | 0 | | 75 | °C |

† The maximum clock frequency is independent of the internal programmed configuration. If an output is fed back externally to an input, the maximum clock frequency must be calculated.

‡ The C-array is the single sum term that is complemented and fed back to the AND array.

§ After Preset goes inactive, normal clocking resumes on the first low-to-high clock transition.

3

Field-Programmable Logic

**TEXAS**
**INSTRUMENTS**

**electrical characteristics over recommended operating free-air temperature range (unless otherwise noted)**

| PARAMETER | TEST CONDITIONS[†] | | M SUFFIX MIN | M SUFFIX TYP[‡] | M SUFFIX MAX | C SUFFIX MIN | C SUFFIX TYP[‡] | C SUFFIX MAX | UNIT |
|---|---|---|---|---|---|---|---|---|---|
| $V_{IK}$ | $V_{CC}$ = MIN, | $I_I$ = −18 mA | | | −1.2 | | | −1.2 | V |
| $V_{OH}$ | $V_{CC}$ = MIN, | $I_{OH}$ = MAX | 2.4 | 3.2 | | 2.4 | 3 | | V |
| $V_{OL}$ | $V_{CC}$ = MIN, | $I_{OL}$ = MAX | | 0.25 | 0.4 | | 0.37 | 0.5 | V |
| $I_I$ | $V_{CC}$ = MAX, | $V_I$ = 5.5 V | | | 25 | | | 25 | µA |
| $I_{IH}$ | $V_{CC}$ = MAX, | $V_I$ = 2.7 V | | | 20 | | | 20 | µA |
| $I_{IL}$ | $V_{CC}$ = MAX, | $V_I$ = 0.4 V | | | −0.25 | | | −0.25 | mA |
| $I_O$ [§] | $V_{CC}$ = MAX, | $V_O$ = 2.25 V | −30 | | −112 | −30 | | −112 | mA |
| $I_{OZH}$ | $V_{CC}$ = MAX, | $V_O$ = 2.7 V | | | 20 | | | 20 | µA |
| $I_{OZL}$ | $V_{CC}$ = MAX, | $V_O$ = 0.4 V | | | −20 | | | −20 | µA |
| $I_{CC}$ | $V_{CC}$ = MAX, PRE/$\overline{OE}$ input at GND, | $V_I$ = 4.5 V, Outputs open | | 120 | 180 | | 120 | 180 | mA |

**switching characteristics over recommended supply voltage and operating free-air temperature ranges (unless otherwise noted)**

| PARAMETER | | FROM | TO | TEST CONDITIONS | M SUFFIX MIN | M SUFFIX TYP[‡] | M SUFFIX MAX | C SUFFIX MIN | C SUFFIX TYP[‡] | C SUFFIX MAX | UNIT |
|---|---|---|---|---|---|---|---|---|---|---|---|
| $f_{max}$[¶] | Without C-array | | | | 40 | 70 | | 50 | 70 | | MHz |
| | With C-array | | | | 25 | 45 | | 30 | 45 | | |
| $t_{pd}$ | | CLK↑ | Q | $R_L$ = 500 Ω, $C_L$ = 50 pF | | 8 | 20 | | 8 | 15 | ns |
| $t_{pd}$ | | PRE↑ | Q | | | 12 | 25 | | 12 | 20 | ns |
| $t_{pd}$ | | $V_{CC}$↑ | Q | | | 0 | 10 | | 0 | 10 | ns |
| $t_{en}$ | | $\overline{OE}$↓ | Q | | | 10 | 25 | | 10 | 20 | ns |
| $t_{dis}$ | | $\overline{OE}$↑ | Q | | | 5 | 15 | | 5 | 10 | ns |

[†] For conditions shown as MIN or MAX, use the appropriate value specified under recommended operating conditions.
[‡] All typical values are at $V_{CC}$ = 5 V, $T_A$ = 25 °C.
[§] The output conditions have been chosen to produce a current that closely approximates one half of the true short-circuit current, $I_{OS}$.
[¶] $f_{max}$ is independent of the internal programmed configuration and the number of product terms used.

3

Field-Programmable Logic

TEXAS
INSTRUMENTS

## TIB82S105B
## 16 × 48 × 8 FIELD-PROGRAMMABLE LOGIC SEQUENCER
## WITH 3-STATE OUTPUTS OR PRESET

### pin assignment in programming mode (pin 1 ≤ V$_{IHH}$)

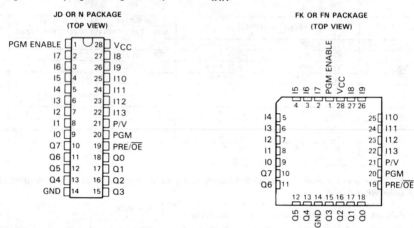

**JD OR N PACKAGE**
**(TOP VIEW)**

**FK OR FN PACKAGE**
**(TOP VIEW)**

### programming parameters, T$_A$ = 25 °C

| PARAMETER | | MIN | NOM | MAX | UNIT |
|---|---|---|---|---|---|
| V$_{CC}$ | Verify-level supply voltage | 4.75 | 5 | 5.25 | V |
| V$_{IHH}$ | Program high-level input voltage | 14.5 | 15 | 15.5 | V |
| I$_{IHH}$ | Program level input current | | 250 | 500 | mA |
| V$_{IX}$ | Program level input voltage | 10.25 | 10.5 | 10.75 | V |
| V$_{CC1}$ | Programming supply voltage | 8.25 | 8.5 | 8.75 | V |
| I$_{CC1}$ | Programming supply current | 550 | | 1000 | mA |
| V$_{IH}$ | High-level input voltage | 2 | | | V |
| V$_{IL}$ | Low-level input voltage | | | 0.8 | V |
| V$_{OH}$ | High-level output voltage | 2.4 | 3 | | V |
| V$_{OL}$ | Low-level output voltage | | 0.35 | 0.45 | V |
| t$_{w1}$ | Program-pulse duration | 10 | | 25 | µs |
| t$_{w2}$ | Verify-pulse duration | 5 | | 10 | µs |
| | Program-pulse duty cycle | | | 25% | |
| t$_d$ | Delay time | 10 | | 25 | µs |
| t$_r$ | Rise time | 17 | 20 | 25 | µs |

TEXAS
INSTRUMENTS

**array fuse addresses**

### TABLE 1. INPUT LINE AND SUM-OF-PRODUCTS LINE SELECT

| ROW HEX ADDRESS | | SELECTED VARIABLE | |
|---|---|---|---|
| I13, I12, I11 | I10, I9, I8, I7 | | |
| 0 | 0 | N0 | SET |
| 0 | 1 | N0 | RESET |
| 0 | 2 | N1 | SET |
| 0 | 3 | N1 | RESET |
| 0 | 4 | N2 | SET |
| 0 | 5 | N2 | RESET |
| 0 | 6 | N3 | SET |
| 0 | 7 | N3 | RESET |
| 0 | 8 | N4 (OR Array) | SET |
| 0 | 9 | N4 | RESET |
| 0 | A | N5 | SET |
| 0 | B | N5 | RESET |
| 0 | C | Q0 | SET |
| 0 | D | Q0 | RESET |
| 0 | E | Q1 | SET |
| 0 | F | Q1 | RESET |
| 1 | 0 | Q2 | SET |
| 1 | 1 | Q2 | RESET |
| 1 | 2 | Q3 | SET |
| 1 | 3 | Q3 | RESET |
| 1 | 4 | Q4 | SET |
| 1 | 5 | Q4 | RESET |
| 1 | 6 | Q5 | SET |
| 1 | 7 | Q5 | RESET |
| 1 | 8 | Q6 | SET |
| 1 | 9 | Q6 | RESET |
| 1 | A | Q7 | SET |
| 1 | B | Q7 | RESET |
| 1 | C | Complement Array | C |
| 1 | D | Empty Address Space | |
| ↓ | ↓ | | |
| 3 | F | | |

| ROW HEX ADDRESS | | SELECTED VARIABLE |
|---|---|---|
| I13, I12, I11 | I10, I9, I8, I7 | |
| 4 | 0 | $I_0$ |
| 4 | 1 | $\bar{I}_0$ |
| 4 | 2 | $I_1$ |
| 4 | 3 | $\bar{I}_1$ |
| 4 | 4 | $I_2$ |
| 4 | 5 | $\bar{I}_2$ |
| 4 | 6 | $I_3$ |
| 4 | 7 | $\bar{I}_3$ |
| 4 | 8 | $I_4$ |
| 4 | 9 | $\bar{I}_4$ |
| 4 | A | $I_5$ |
| 4 | B | $\bar{I}_5$ |
| 4 | C | $I_6$ |
| 4 | D | $\bar{I}_6$ |
| 4 | E | $I_7$ |
| 4 | F | $\bar{I}_7$ |
| 5 | 0 | $I_8$ |
| 5 | 1 | $\bar{I}_8$ |
| 5 | 2 | $I_9$ |
| 5 | 3 | $\bar{I}_9$ |
| 5 | 4 | $I_{10}$ (AND Array) |
| 5 | 5 | $\bar{I}_{10}$ |
| 5 | 6 | $I_{11}$ |
| 5 | 7 | $\bar{I}_{11}$ |
| 5 | 8 | $I_{12}$ |
| 5 | 9 | $\bar{I}_{12}$ |
| 5 | A | $I_{13}$ |
| 5 | B | $\bar{I}_{13}$ |
| 5 | C | $I_{14}$ |
| 5 | D | $\bar{I}_{14}$ |
| 5 | E | $I_{15}$ |
| 5 | F | $\bar{I}_{15}$ |
| 6 | 0 | $P_0$ |
| 6 | 1 | $\bar{P}_0$ |
| 6 | 2 | $P_1$ |
| 6 | 3 | $\bar{P}_1$ |
| 6 | 4 | $P_2$ |
| 6 | 5 | $\bar{P}_2$ |
| 6 | 6 | $P_3$ |
| 6 | 7 | $\bar{P}_3$ |
| 6 | 8 | $P_4$ |
| 6 | 9 | $\bar{P}_4$ |
| 6 | A | $P_5$ |
| 6 | B | $\bar{P}_5$ |
| 6 | C | Complement Array — $\bar{C}$ |

**TABLE 2. PRODUCT LINE SELECT**

| COLUMN HEX ADDRESS | | SELECTED TRANSITION TERM |
|---|---|---|
| 15, 14 | 13, 12, 11, 10 | |
| 0 | 0 | 0 |
| 0 | 1 | 1 |
| 0 | 2 | 2 |
| 0 | 3 | 3 |
| 0 | 4 | 4 |
| 0 | 5 | 5 |
| 0 | 6 | 6 |
| 0 | 7 | 7 |
| 0 | 8 | 8 |
| 0 | 9 | 9 |
| 0 | A | 10 |
| 0 | B | 11 |
| 0 | C | 12 |
| 0 | D | 13 |
| 0 | E | 14 |
| 0 | F | 15 |
| 1 | 0 | 16 |
| 1 | 1 | 17 |
| 1 | 2 | 18 |
| 1 | 3 | 19 |
| 1 | 4 | 20 |
| 1 | 5 | 21 |
| 1 | 6 | 22 |
| 1 | 7 | 23 |
| 1 | 8 | 24 |
| 1 | 9 | 25 |
| 1 | A | 26 |
| 1 | B | 27 |
| 1 | C | 28 |
| 1 | D | 29 |
| 1 | E | 30 |
| 1 | F | 31 |
| 2 | 0 | 32 |
| 2 | 1 | 33 |
| 2 | 2 | 34 |
| 2 | 3 | 35 |
| 2 | 4 | 36 |
| 2 | 5 | 37 |
| 2 | 6 | 38 |
| 2 | 7 | 39 |
| 2 | 8 | 40 |
| 2 | 9 | 41 |
| 2 | A | 42 |
| 2 | B | 43 |
| 2 | C | 44 |
| 2 | D | 45 |
| 2 | E | 46 |
| 2 | F | 47 |
| 3 | 0 | Test Col 48 |
| 3 | 1 | Test Col 49 |

TEXAS
INSTRUMENTS

## programming procedure for array fuses (see Note 4)

Array fuses are programmed using a binary select method. Each fuse can be addressed by selecting the appropriate input line or sum of products line (row address) and product line (column address). The addresses for selecting input lines, sum of products lines, and product lines are shown in Tables 1 and 2.

SETUP
Step 1: Set PGM ENABLE to GND.
Step 2: Apply address to inputs.
Step 3: Set PGM to $V_{IH}$.
Step 4: Set P/V to $V_{IL}$.
Step 5: Wait $t_d$, set $V_{CC}$ to $V_{CC1}$.

PROGRAM
Step 1: Wait $t_d$, raise P/V to $V_{IH}$.
Step 2: Wait $t_d$, raise PGM ENABLE to $V_{IHH}$.
Step 3: Wait $t_d$, pulse PGM to $V_{IL}$ for $t_{w1}$.
Step 4: Wait $t_d$, return PGM ENABLE to GND.
Step 5: Wait $t_d$, return P/V to $V_{IL}$.

VERIFY
Step 1: Wait $t_d$, lower PGM to $V_{IL}$.
Step 2: After $t_{w2}$, read sense: A $V_{IH}$ level indicates a blown fuse.
Step 3: Raise PGM to $V_{IH}$.

NEXT ADDRESS SELECT
Step 1: After $t_d$, lower $V_{CC}$ to GND.
Step 2: For the same product line wait $t_d$, then apply new input line or sum-of-products line address.
Step 3: For different product line wait $t_d$, apply new input line or sum-of-products line address, then apply new product line address.
Step 4: Wait $t_d$, set $V_{CC}$ at $V_{CC1}$.
Step 5: Continue with program or verify sequence.

NOTE 4: Input lines and sum of product lines are also referred to as variables. Product lines are also referred to as transition terms.

TEXAS
INSTRUMENTS

Field-Programmable Logic

3

**programming waveforms for array fuses**

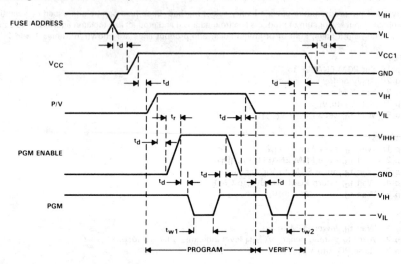

**programming procedure for PRE/OE option**

PROGRAM
Step 1: With PRE/$\overline{OE}$ at GND, raise V$_{CC}$ to V$_{CC1}$.
Step 2: Wait t$_d$, pulse PRE/$\overline{OE}$ to V$_{IX}$ for a duration of t$_{w1}$.
Step 3: A t$_d$ delay after PRE/$\overline{OE}$ has returned to GND, lower V$_{CC}$ to 5 volts or GND.

VERIFY
Step 1: With PRE/$\overline{OE}$ at GND, set V$_{CC}$ to 5 volts.
Step 2: After a delay of t$_d$, raise PRE/$\overline{OE}$ to V$_{IX}$ for a minimum duration of t$_{w2}$.
Step 3: Return PRE/$\overline{OE}$ to GND.
Step 4: Wait t$_d$, pulse PRE/$\overline{OE}$ to V$_{IH}$ for a duration of t$_{w2}$.
Step 5: After a t$_d$ delay, Q0 indicates V$_{OH}$ if the PRE option is selected and V$_{OL}$ if the $\overline{OE}$ option is programmed.

**programming waveforms for PRE/OE option**

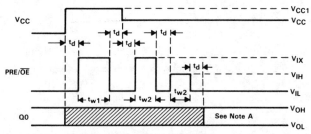

NOTE A: After programming if the preset option is selected, Q0 will be high; if the output-enable option is selected, Q0 will be low.

TEXAS
INSTRUMENTS

### diagnostics

A diagnostics mode is provided with these devices that allows the user to inspect the contents of the state register. When I0 (pin 9) is held at 10 V, the state register bits P0−P5 will appear at the Q0−Q5 outputs and Q6−Q7 will be high. The contents of the output register will remain unchanged.

### diagnostics waveforms

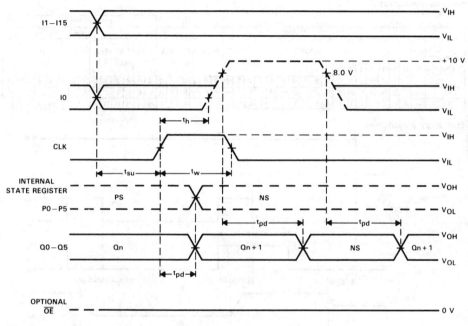

PS = Present state, NS = Next state

TEXAS
INSTRUMENTS

## test array

A test array that consists of product lines 48 and 49 has been added to these devices to allow testing prior to programming. The test array is factory programmed as shown below. Testing is accomplished by connecting Q0−Q7 to I8−I15, PRE/$\overline{OE}$ to GND, and applying the proper input signals as shown in the timing diagram. Product lines 48 and 49 MUST be deleted during user programming to avoid interference with the programmed logic function.

**TEST ARRAY PROGRAM**

| | | | | | | | | | | | | | | | | | | | | | | | | | | | OPTION PRE/$\overline{OE}$ | | | | | | | | | | H |
|---|---|---|---|---|---|---|---|---|---|---|---|---|---|---|---|---|---|---|---|---|---|---|---|---|---|---|---|---|---|---|---|---|---|---|---|---|---|
| | | | **AND** | | | | | | | | | | | | | | | | | | | | | | | | **OR** | | | | | | | | | | |
| PRODUCT LINE | C | C̄ | **INPUT (In)** | | | | | | | | | | | | | | | | **PRESENT STATE (PS)** | | | | | | **NEXT STATE (NS)** | | | | | | **OUT (Qn)** | | | | | | | |
| | | | 15 | 14 | 13 | 12 | 11 | 10 | 9 | 8 | 7 | 6 | 5 | 4 | 3 | 2 | 1 | 0 | 5 | 4 | 3 | 2 | 1 | 0 | 5 | 4 | 3 | 2 | 1 | 0 | 7 | 6 | 5 | 4 | 3 | 2 | 1 | 0 |
| 48 | X | − | H | H | H | H | H | H | H | H | H | H | H | H | H | H | H | H | H | H | H | H | H | H | L | L | L | L | L | L | L | L | L | L | L | L | L | L |
| 49 | − | X | L | L | L | L | L | L | L | L | L | L | L | L | L | L | L | L | L | L | L | L | L | H | H | H | H | H | H | H | H | H | H | H | H | H | H |

## test array waveforms

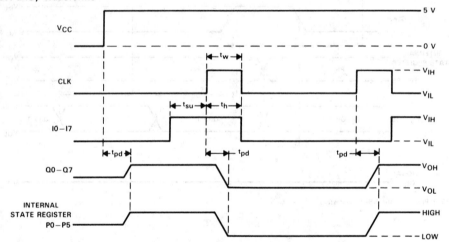

**TEST ARRAY DELETED**

| | | | | | | | | | | | | | | | | | | | | | | | | | | | OPTION PRE/$\overline{OE}$ | | | | | | | | | | H |
|---|---|---|---|---|---|---|---|---|---|---|---|---|---|---|---|---|---|---|---|---|---|---|---|---|---|---|---|---|---|---|---|---|---|---|---|---|---|
| | | | **AND** | | | | | | | | | | | | | | | | | | | | | | | | **OR** | | | | | | | | | | |
| PRODUCT LINE | C | C̄ | **INPUT (In)** | | | | | | | | | | | | | | | | **PRESENT STATE (PS)** | | | | | | **NEXT STATE (NS)** | | | | | | **OUT (Qn)** | | | | | | | |
| | | | 15 | 14 | 13 | 12 | 11 | 10 | 9 | 8 | 7 | 6 | 5 | 4 | 3 | 2 | 1 | 0 | 5 | 4 | 3 | 2 | 1 | 0 | 5 | 4 | 3 | 2 | 1 | 0 | 7 | 6 | 5 | 4 | 3 | 2 | 1 | 0 |
| 48 | − | − | H | H | H | H | H | H | H | H | H | H | H | H | H | H | H | H | H | H | H | H | H | H | − | − | − | − | − | − | − | − | − | − | − | − | − | − |
| 49 | − | X | L | L | L | L | L | L | L | L | L | L | L | L | L | L | L | L | L | L | L | L | L | − | − | − | − | − | − | − | − | − | − | − | − | − | − |

X = Fuse intact, − = Fuse blown

TEXAS
INSTRUMENTS

## TIB82S105B, 82S105A COMPARISON

The Texas Instruments 82S105A and TIB82S105B are functionally equivalent 16 × 48 × 8 Field-Programmable Logic Sequencers. The TI 82S105A is designed to be a direct replacement to the Signetics 82S105A. However, the TIB82S105B is designed for a maximum speed of 50 MHz with the preset function being made conventional. As a result the TIB82S105B differs from the 82S105A in speed and in the preset recovery function.

The TIB82S105B is a high-speed version of the original 82S105A. The TIB82S105B features increased switching speeds with no increase in power. The maximum operating frequency is increased from 20 MHz to 50 MHz and does not decrease as more product terms are connected to each sum (OR) line. For instance, if all 48 product tems were connected to a sum line on the original 82S105A, the $f_{max}$ would be about 15 MHz. The $f_{max}$ for the TIB82S105B remains at 50 MHz regardless of the programmed configuration. In addition, the preset recovery sequence was changed to a conventional recovery sequence, providing quicker clock recovery times. This is explained in the following paragraph.

The TIB82S105B and the 82S105A are equipped with power-up preset and asynchronous preset functions. The power-up preset causes the registers to go high during power-up. The asynchronous preset inhibits clocking and causes the registers to go high whenever the preset pin is taken high. After a power-up preset occurs, the minimum setup time from power-up to the first clock pulse must be met in order to assure that clocking is not inhibited. In a similar manner after an asynchronous preset, the preset input must return low (inactive) for a given time, $t_{su}$, before clocking.

The Texas Instruments 82S105A and the Signetics 82S105A were designed in such a way that after both power-up preset and asynchronous preset they require that a high-to-low clock transition occur before a clocking transition (low-to-high) will be recognized. This is shown in Figure 1. The Texas Instruments TIB82S105B does not require a high-to-low clock transition before clocking can be resumed, it only requires that the preset be inactive 8 ns (preset inactive-state setup time) before the clock rising edge. See Figure 2.

The TIB82S105B, with an $f_{max}$ of 50 MHz, is ideal for systems in which the state machine must run several times faster than the system clock. It is recommended that the TIB82S105B be used in new designs and the TI 82S105A be used as a second source to the Signetics 82S105A. *However, if the TIB82S105B is used to replace the 82S105A, then the customer must understand that clocking will begin with the first clock rising edge after preset.*

### TABLE 3. SPEED DIFFERENCES

| PARAMETER | 82S105A TI AND SIGNETICS | TIB82S105B TI ONLY |
|---|---|---|
| $f_{max}$ | 20 MHz | 50 MHz |
| $t_{pd}$, CLK to Q | 20 ns | 15 ns |

TEXAS
INSTRUMENTS

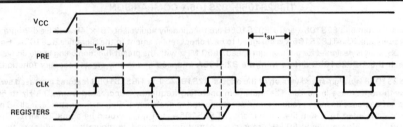

**FIGURE 1. 82S105A PRESET RECOVERY OPERATION**

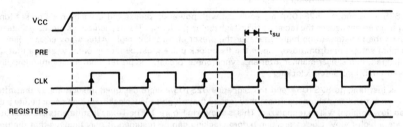

**FIGURE 2. TIB82S105B PRESET RECOVERY OPERATION**

TEXAS
INSTRUMENTS

PRODUCT
PREVIEW

82S105A
16 × 48 × 8 FIELD-PROGRAMMABLE LOGIC SEQUENCER
WITH 3-STATE OUTPUTS OR PRESET

D2897,JANUARY 1985−REVISED JUNE 1986

- Programmable Asynchronous Preset or Output Control

- Power-On Preset of All Flip-Flops

- 6-Bit Internal State Register with 8-Bit Output Register

- Power Dissipation . . . 650 mW Typical

- Programmable Asynchronous Preset or Output Control

- Designed to be Interchangeable with Signetics 82S105A

**M SUFFIX . . . JD PACKAGE**
**C SUFFIX . . . JD OR N PACKAGE**
(TOP VIEW)

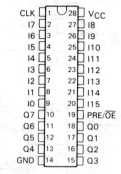

### description

The 82S105A is a TTL field-programmable state machine of the Mealy type. This state machine (logic sequencer) contains 48 product terms (AND terms) and 14 pairs of sum terms (OR terms). The product and sum terms are used to control the 6-bit internal state register and the 8-bit output register.

The outputs of the internal state register (P0—P5) are fed back and combined with the 16 inputs (I0—I15) to form the AND array. In addition a single sum term is complemented and fed back to the AND array, which allows any of the product terms to be summed, complemented, and used as an input to the AND array.

The state and output registers are positive-edge-triggered S/R flip-flops. These registers are unconditionally preset high on power-up. Pin 19 can be used to preset both registers or, by blowing the proper fuse, be converted to an output control function.

The 82S105AM is characterized for operation over the full military temperature range of −55 °C to 125 °C. The 82S105AC is characterized for operation from 0 °C to 70 °C.

**M SUFFIX . . . FK PACKAGE**
**C SUFFIX . . . FK OR FN PACKAGE**
(TOP VIEW)

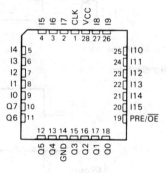

3

Field-Programmable Logic

TEXAS
INSTRUMENTS

## 82S105A
## 16 × 48 × 8 FIELD-PROGRAMMABLE LOGIC SEQUENCER
## WITH 3-STATE OUTPUTS OR PRESET

**functional block diagram (positive logic)**

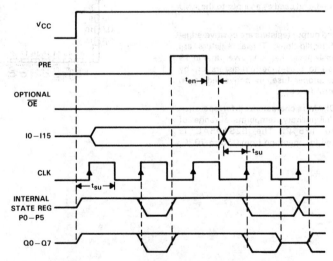

∿ denotes fused inputs.

**timing diagram**

**TEXAS INSTRUMENTS**

**logic diagram (positive logic)**

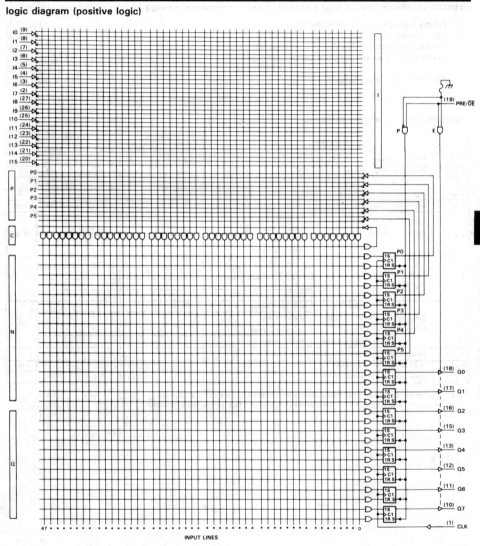

NOTES: 1. All AND gate inputs with a blown link float to a logic "1".
2. All OR gate inputs with a blown link float to a logic "0".

**TEXAS INSTRUMENTS**

## 82S105A
## 16 × 48 × 8 FIELD-PROGRAMMABLE LOGIC SEQUENCER
## WITH 3-STATE OUTPUTS OR PRESET

**absolute maximum ratings over operating free-air temperature range (unless otherwise noted)**

Supply voltage, $V_{CC}$ (see Note 3) . . . . . . . . . . . . . . . . . . . . . . . . . . . . . . . . . . . . . . . . . . . . . . . . 7 V
Input voltage (see Note 3) . . . . . . . . . . . . . . . . . . . . . . . . . . . . . . . . . . . . . . . . . . . . . . . . . . . . . . . 5.5 V
Voltage applied to a disabled output (see Note 3) . . . . . . . . . . . . . . . . . . . . . . . . . . . . . . . . . . 5.5 V
Operating free-air temperature range: 82S105AM . . . . . . . . . . . . . . . . . . . . . . . −55°C to 125°C
82S105AC . . . . . . . . . . . . . . . . . . . . . . . . . . 0°C to 70°C
Storage temperature range . . . . . . . . . . . . . . . . . . . . . . . . . . . . . . . . . . . . . . . . . . −65°C to 150°C

NOTE 3: These ratings apply except for programming pins during a programming cycle.

**recommended operating conditions**

| PARAMETER | | | M SUFFIX | | | C SUFFIX | | | UNIT |
|---|---|---|---|---|---|---|---|---|---|
| | | | MIN | NOM | MAX | MIN | NOM | MAX | |
| $V_{CC}$ | Supply voltage | | 4.5 | 5 | 5.5 | 4.75 | 5 | 5.25 | V |
| $V_{IH}$ | High-level input voltage | | 2 | | 5.5 | 2 | | 5.5 | V |
| $V_{IL}$ | Low-level input voltage | | | | 0.8 | | | 0.8 | V |
| $I_{OH}$ | High-level output current | | | | −2 | | | −3.2 | mA |
| $I_{OL}$ | Low-level output current | | | | 12 | | | 24 | mA |
| $f_{clock}$ | Clock frequency | 48 product terms without C-array† | | | | | | | MHz |
| | | 48 product terms with C-array | | | | | | | |
| $t_w$ | Pulse duration, clock high or low | Clock high | | | | | | | ns |
| | | Clock low | | | | | | | |
| | | With C-array | | | | | | | |
| | | Preset | | | | | | | |
| $t_{su}$ | Setup time before CLK↑ | 25 thru 48 product terms / Without C-array | | | | | | | ns |
| | | With C-array | | | | | | | |
| | | 1 thru 24 product terms / Without C-array | | | | | | | |
| | | With C-array | | | | | | | |
| $t_{su}$ | Setup time, Preset low (inactive) before CLK↓‡ | | | | | | | | ns |
| $t_h$ | Hold time, input after CLK↑ | | | | | | | | ns |
| $T_A$ | Operating free-air temperature | | −55 | | 125 | 0 | | 70 | °C |

† The C-array is the single sum term that is complemented and fed back to the AND array.
‡ After Preset goes inactive, normal clocking resumes following a high-to-low clock transition.

TEXAS
INSTRUMENTS

**3**
Field-Programmable Logic

**electrical characteristics over recommended operating free-air temperature range (unless otherwise noted)**

| PARAMETER | TEST CONDITIONS† | M SUFFIX MIN | M SUFFIX TYP‡ | M SUFFIX MAX | C SUFFIX MIN | C SUFFIX TYP‡ | C SUFFIX MAX | UNIT |
|---|---|---|---|---|---|---|---|---|
| $V_{IK}$ | $V_{CC}$ = MIN, $I_I$ = −18 mA | | | −1.2 | | | −1.2 | V |
| $V_{OH}$ | $V_{CC}$ = MIN, $I_{OH}$ = MAX | 2.4 | 3.2 | | 2.4 | 3 | | V |
| $V_{OL}$ | $V_{CC}$ = MIN, $I_{OL}$ = MAX | | 0.25 | 0.4 | | 0.37 | 0.5 | V |
| $I_I$ | $V_{CC}$ = MAX, $V_I$ = 5.5 V | | | 0.1 | | | 0.1 | mA |
| $I_{IH}$ | $V_{CC}$ = MAX, $V_I$ = 2.7 V | | | 20 | | | 20 | μA |
| $I_{IL}$ | $V_{CC}$ = MAX, $V_I$ = 0.4 V | | | −0.5 | | | −0.5 | mA |
| $I_O$ § | $V_{CC}$ = MAX, $V_O$ = 2.25 V | −30 | | −112 | −30 | | −112 | mA |
| $I_{OZH}$ | $V_{CC}$ = MAX, $V_O$ = 2.7 V | | | 20 | | | 20 | μA |
| $I_{OZL}$ | $V_{CC}$ = MAX, $V_O$ = 0.4 V | | | −20 | | | −20 | μA |
| $I_{CC}$ | $V_{CC}$ = MAX, $V_I$ = 4.5 V, PRE/$\overline{OE}$ input at GND, Outputs open | | 120 | | | 120 | | mA |

**switching characteristics over recommended supply voltage and operating free-air temperature ranges (unless otherwise noted)**

| PARAMETER | | FROM | TO | TEST CONDITIONS | M SUFFIX MIN | M SUFFIX TYP‡ | M SUFFIX MAX | C SUFFIX MIN | C SUFFIX TYP‡ | C SUFFIX MAX | UNIT |
|---|---|---|---|---|---|---|---|---|---|---|---|
| $f_{max}$ ¶ | Without C-array | | | | | | | 20 | | | MHz |
| | With C-array | | | | | | | 12.5 | | | |
| $t_{pd}$ | | CLK↑ | Q | $R_L$ = 500 Ω, $C_L$ = 50 pF | | | 15 | | | 15 | ns |
| $t_{pd}$ | | PRE↑ | Q | | | | 18 | | | 18 | ns |
| $t_{pd}$ | | $V_{CC}$↑ | Q | | | | 0 | | | 0 | ns |
| $t_{en}$ | | $\overline{OE}$↓ | Q | | | | 20 | | | 20 | ns |
| $t_{dis}$ | | $\overline{OE}$↑ | Q | | | | 20 | | | 20 | ns |

† For conditions shown as MIN or MAX, use the appropriate value specified under recommended operating conditions.
‡ All typical values are at $V_{CC}$ = 5 V, $T_A$ = 25 °C.
§ The output conditions have been chosen to produce a current that closely approximates one half of the true short-circuit current, $I_{OS}$.
¶ Measured with 48 product terms connected in the OR-array.

**3**

Field-Programmable Logic

**TEXAS INSTRUMENTS**

## 82S105A
## 16 × 48 × 8 FIELD-PROGRAMMABLE LOGIC SEQUENCER
## WITH 3-STATE OUTPUTS OR PRESET

### pin assignment in programming mode (pin 1 ≤ $V_{IHH}$)

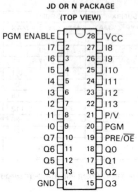

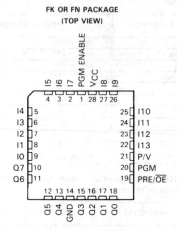

### programming parameters, $T_A = 25°C$

| | PARAMETER | MIN | NOM | MAX | UNIT |
|---|---|---|---|---|---|
| $V_{CC}$ | Verify-level supply voltage | 4.75 | 5 | 5.25 | V |
| $V_{IHH}$ | Program high-level input voltage | 14.5 | 15 | 15.5 | V |
| $I_{IHH}$ | Program level input current | | 250 | 500 | mA |
| $V_{IX}$ | Program level input voltage | 10.25 | 10.5 | 10.75 | V |
| $V_{CC1}$ | Programming supply voltage | 8.25 | 8.5 | 8.75 | V |
| $I_{CC1}$ | Programming supply current | 550 | | 1000 | mA |
| $V_{IH}$ | High-level input voltage | 2 | | | V |
| $V_{IL}$ | Low-level input voltage | | | 0.8 | V |
| $V_{OH}$ | High-level output voltage | 2.4 | 3 | | V |
| $V_{OL}$ | Low-level output voltage | | 0.35 | 0.45 | V |
| $t_{w1}$ | Program-pulse duration | 10 | | 25 | $\mu$s |
| $t_{w2}$ | Verify-pulse duration | 5 | | 10 | $\mu$s |
| | Program-pulse duty cycle | | | 25% | |
| $t_d$ | Delay time | 10 | | 25 | $\mu$s |
| $t_r$ | Rise time | 17 | 20 | 25 | $\mu$s |

TEXAS
INSTRUMENTS

**array fuse addresses**

### TABLE 1. INPUT LINE AND SUM-OF-PRODUCTS LINE SELECT

| ROW HEX ADDRESS I13, I12, I11 | ROW HEX ADDRESS I10, I9, I8, I7 | SELECTED VARIABLE | | ROW HEX ADDRESS I13, I12, I11 | ROW HEX ADDRESS I10, I9, I8, I7 | SELECTED VARIABLE |
|---|---|---|---|---|---|---|
| 0 | 0 | N0 | SET | 4 | 0 | I0 |
| 0 | 1 | | RESET | 4 | 1 | $\bar{I}0$ |
| 0 | 2 | N1 | SET | 4 | 2 | I1 |
| 0 | 3 | | RESET | 4 | 3 | $\bar{I}1$ |
| 0 | 4 | N2 | SET | 4 | 4 | I2 |
| 0 | 5 | | RESET | 4 | 5 | $\bar{I}2$ |
| 0 | 6 | N3 | SET | 4 | 6 | I3 |
| 0 | 7 | | RESET | 4 | 7 | $\bar{I}3$ |
| 0 | 8 | OR Array — N4 | SET | 4 | 8 | I4 |
| 0 | 9 | | RESET | 4 | 9 | $\bar{I}4$ |
| 0 | A | N5 | SET | 4 | A | I5 |
| 0 | B | | RESET | 4 | B | $\bar{I}5$ |
| 0 | C | Q0 | SET | 4 | C | I6 |
| 0 | D | | RESET | 4 | D | $\bar{I}6$ |
| 0 | E | Q1 | SET | 4 | E | I7 |
| 0 | F | | RESET | 4 | F | $\bar{I}7$ |
| 1 | 0 | Q2 | SET | 5 | 0 | I8 |
| 1 | 1 | | RESET | 5 | 1 | $\bar{I}8$ |
| 1 | 2 | Q3 | SET | 5 | 2 | I9 |
| 1 | 3 | | RESET | 5 | 3 | $\bar{I}9$ |
| 1 | 4 | Q4 | SET | 5 | 4 | I10 |
| 1 | 5 | | RESET | 5 | 5 | AND Array — $\bar{I}10$ |
| 1 | 6 | Q5 | SET | 5 | 6 | I11 |
| 1 | 7 | | RESET | 5 | 7 | $\bar{I}11$ |
| 1 | 8 | Q6 | SET | 5 | 8 | I12 |
| 1 | 9 | | RESET | 5 | 9 | $\bar{I}12$ |
| 1 | A | Q7 | SET | 5 | A | I13 |
| 1 | B | | RESET | 5 | B | $\bar{I}13$ |
| 1 | C | Complement Array | C | 5 | C | I14 |
| | | | | 5 | D | $\bar{I}14$ |
| 1 | D | | | 5 | E | I15 |
| | | | | 5 | F | $\bar{I}15$ |
| | | | | 6 | 0 | P0 |
| | | | | 6 | 1 | $\bar{P}0$ |
| | | | | 6 | 2 | P1 |
| | | | | 6 | 3 | $\bar{P}1$ |
| | | | | 6 | 4 | P2 |
| | | Empty Address Space | | 6 | 5 | $\bar{P}2$ |
| | | | | 6 | 6 | P3 |
| | | | | 6 | 7 | $\bar{P}3$ |
| | | | | 6 | 8 | P4 |
| | | | | 6 | 9 | $\bar{P}4$ |
| | | | | 6 | A | P5 |
| | | | | 6 | B | $\bar{P}5$ |
| 3 | F | | | 6 | C | Complement Array — $\bar{C}$ |

TEXAS INSTRUMENTS

Field-Programmable Logic

3

### TABLE 2. PRODUCT LINE SELECT

| COLUMN HEX ADDRESS | | SELECTED TRANSITION TERM |
|---|---|---|
| I5, I4 | I3, I2, I1, I0 | |
| 0 | 0 | 0 |
| 0 | 1 | 1 |
| 0 | 2 | 2 |
| 0 | 3 | 3 |
| 0 | 4 | 4 |
| 0 | 5 | 5 |
| 0 | 6 | 6 |
| 0 | 7 | 7 |
| 0 | 8 | 8 |
| 0 | 9 | 9 |
| 0 | A | 10 |
| 0 | B | 11 |
| 0 | C | 12 |
| 0 | D | 13 |
| 0 | E | 14 |
| 0 | F | 15 |
| 1 | 0 | 16 |
| 1 | 1 | 17 |
| 1 | 2 | 18 |
| 1 | 3 | 19 |
| 1 | 4 | 20 |
| 1 | 5 | 21 |
| 1 | 6 | 22 |
| 1 | 7 | 23 |
| 1 | 8 | 24 |
| 1 | 9 | 25 |
| 1 | A | 26 |
| 1 | B | 27 |
| 1 | C | 28 |
| 1 | D | 29 |
| 1 | E | 30 |
| 1 | F | 31 |
| 2 | 0 | 32 |
| 2 | 1 | 33 |
| 2 | 2 | 34 |
| 2 | 3 | 35 |
| 2 | 4 | 36 |
| 2 | 5 | 37 |
| 2 | 6 | 38 |
| 2 | 7 | 39 |
| 2 | 8 | 40 |
| 2 | 9 | 41 |
| 2 | A | 42 |
| 2 | B | 43 |
| 2 | C | 44 |
| 2 | D | 45 |
| 2 | E | 46 |
| 2 | F | 47 |
| 3 | 0 | Test Col 48 |
| 3 | 1 | Test Col 49 |

TEXAS
INSTRUMENTS

## programming procedure for array fuses

Array fuses are programmed using a binary select method. Each fuse can be addressed by selecting the appropriate input line or sum of products line (row address) and product line (column address). The addresses for selecting input lines, sum of products lines, and product lines are shown in Tables 1 and 2.

SETUP
Step 1: Set PGM ENABLE to GND.
Step 2: Apply address to inputs.
Step 3: Set PGM to $V_{IH}$.
Step 4: Set P/V to $V_{IL}$.
Step 5: Wait $t_d$, set $V_{CC}$ to $V_{CC1}$.

PROGRAM
Step 1: Wait $t_d$, raise P/V to $V_{IH}$.
Step 2: Wait $t_d$, raise PGM ENABLE to $V_{IHH}$.
Step 3: Wait $t_d$, pulse PGM to $V_{IL}$ for $t_{w1}$.
Step 4: Wait $t_d$, return PGM ENABLE to GND.
Step 5: Wait $t_d$, return P/V to $V_{IL}$.

VERIFY
Step 1: Wait $t_d$, lower PGM to $V_{IL}$.
Step 2: After $t_{w2}$, read sense: A $V_{IH}$ level indicates a blown fuse.
Step 3: Raise PGM to $V_{IH}$.

NEXT ADDRESS SELECT
Step 1: After $t_d$, lower $V_{CC}$ to GND.
Step 2: For the same product line wait $t_d$, then apply new input line or sum-of-products line address.
Step 3: For different product line wait $t_d$, apply new input line or sum-of-products line address, then apply new product line address.
Step 4: Wait $t_d$, set $V_{CC}$ at $V_{CC1}$.
Step 5: Continue with program or verify sequence.

NOTE 4: Input lines and sum of product lines are also referred to as variables. Product lines are also referred to as transition terms.

**3**

Field-Programmable Logic

**programming waveforms**

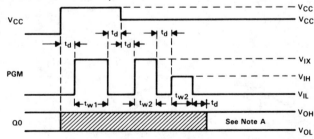

## programming procedure for PRE/$\overline{OE}$ option

PROGRAM

Step 1: With PRE/$\overline{OE}$ at GND, raise $V_{CC}$ to $V_{CC1}$.

Step 2: Wait $t_d$, pulse PRE/$\overline{OE}$ to $V_{IX}$ for a duration of $t_{w1}$.

Step 3: A $t_d$ delay after PRE/$\overline{OE}$ has returned to GND, lower $V_{CC}$ to 5 volts or GND.

VERIFY

Step 1: With PRE/$\overline{OE}$ at GND, set $V_{CC}$ to 5 volts.

Step 2: After a delay of $t_d$, raise PRE/$\overline{OE}$ to $V_{IX}$ for a minimum duration of $t_{w2}$.

Step 3: Return PRE/$\overline{OE}$ to GND.

Step 4: Wait $t_d$, pulse PRE/$\overline{OE}$ to $V_{IH}$ for a duration of $t_{w2}$.

Step 5: After a $t_d$ delay, Q0 indicates $V_{OH}$ if the PRE option is selected and $V_{OL}$ if the $\overline{OE}$ option is programmed.

## programming waveforms for PRE/$\overline{OE}$ option

NOTE A: After programming if the preset option is selected, Q0 will be high; if the output-enable option is selected, Q0 will be low.

**TEXAS INSTRUMENTS**

### diagnostics

A diagnostics mode is provided with these devices that allows the user to inspect the contents of the state register. When I0 (pin 9) is held at 10 V, the state register bits P0—P5 will appear at the Q0—Q5 outputs and Q6—Q7 will be high. The contents of the output register will remain unchanged.

### diagnostics waveforms

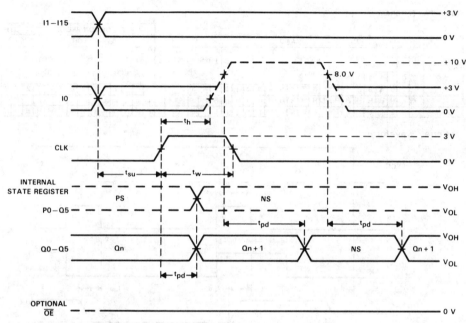

PS = Present state, NS = Next state

# 82S105A
# 16 × 48 × 8 FIELD-PROGRAMMABLE LOGIC SEQUENCER
# WITH 3-STATE OUTPUTS OR PRESET

## test array

A test array that consists of product lines 48 and 49 has been added to these devices to allow testing prior to programming. The test array is factory programmed as shown below. Testing is accomplished by connecting Q0−Q7 to I8−I15, PRE/OE to GND, and applying the proper input signals as shown in the timing diagram. Product lines 48 and 49 MUST be deleted during user programming to avoid interference with the programmed logic function.

**TEST ARRAY PROGRAM**

| | | | | | | | | | | | | | | | | | | | | | | | | | | | OPTION PRE/OE | | | | | | | H | | | | | | | | |
|---|---|---|---|---|---|---|---|---|---|---|---|---|---|---|---|---|---|---|---|---|---|---|---|---|---|---|---|---|---|---|---|---|---|---|---|---|---|---|---|---|---|
| | | | | | | AND | | | | | | | | | | | | | | | | | | OR | | | | | | | | | | | | | | | | | |
| PRODUCT LINE | C | C̄ | INPUT (In) | | | | | | | | | | | | | | | | PRESENT STATE (PS) | | | | | | NEXT STATE (NS) | | | | | | OUT (Qn) | | | | | | | |
| | | | 15 | 14 | 13 | 12 | 11 | 10 | 9 | 8 | 7 | 6 | 5 | 4 | 3 | 2 | 1 | 0 | 5 | 4 | 3 | 2 | 1 | 0 | 5 | 4 | 3 | 2 | 1 | 0 | 7 | 6 | 5 | 4 | 3 | 2 | 1 | 0 |
| 48 | X | – | H | H | H | H | H | H | H | H | H | H | H | H | H | H | H | H | H | H | H | H | H | H | L | L | L | L | L | L | L | L | L | L | L | L | L | L |
| 49 | – | X | L | L | L | L | L | L | L | L | L | L | L | L | L | L | L | L | L | L | L | L | L | L | H | H | H | H | H | H | H | H | H | H | H | H | H | H |

## test array waveforms

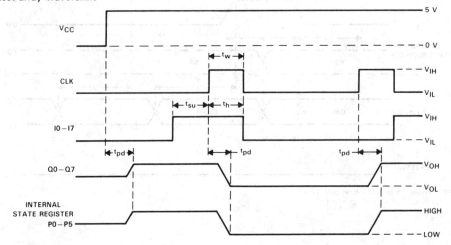

**TEST ARRAY DELETED**

| | | | | | | | | | | | | | | | | | | | | | | | | | | | OPTION PRE/OE | | | | | | | H | | | | | | | | |
|---|---|---|---|---|---|---|---|---|---|---|---|---|---|---|---|---|---|---|---|---|---|---|---|---|---|---|---|---|---|---|---|---|---|---|---|---|---|---|---|---|---|
| | | | | | | AND | | | | | | | | | | | | | | | | | | OR | | | | | | | | | | | | | | | | | |
| PRODUCT LINE | C | C̄ | INPUT (In) | | | | | | | | | | | | | | | | PRESENT STATE (PS) | | | | | | NEXT STATE (NS) | | | | | | OUT (Qn) | | | | | | | |
| | | | 15 | 14 | 13 | 12 | 11 | 10 | 9 | 8 | 7 | 6 | 5 | 4 | 3 | 2 | 1 | 0 | 5 | 4 | 3 | 2 | 1 | 0 | 5 | 4 | 3 | 2 | 1 | 0 | 7 | 6 | 5 | 4 | 3 | 2 | 1 | 0 |
| 48 | – | – | H | H | H | H | H | H | H | H | H | H | H | H | H | H | H | H | H | H | H | H | H | H | – | – | – | – | – | – | – | – | – | – | – | – | – | – |
| 49 | – | X | L | L | L | L | L | L | L | L | L | L | L | L | L | L | L | L | L | L | L | L | L | L | – | – | – | – | – | – | – | – | – | – | – | – | – | – |

X = Fuse intact, — = Fuse blown

- Programmable Asynchronous Preset or Output Control

- Power-On Preset of All Flip-Flops

- 8-Bit Internal State Register with 4-Bit Output Register

- Power Dissipation . . . 600 mW Typical

- Functionally Equivalent to,[†] but Faster than 82S167A

### description

The TIB82S167B is a TTL field-programmable state machine of the Mealy type. This state machine (logic sequencer) contains 48 product terms (AND terms) and 12 pairs of sum terms (OR terms). The product and sum terms are used to control the 8-bit internal state register and the 4-bit output register.

The outputs of the internal state register (P0-P7) are fed back and combined with the 14 inputs (I0-I13) to form the AND array. In addition the first two bits of the internal state register (P0-P1) are brought off-chip to allow the output register to be extended to 6 bits if desired. A single sum term is complemented and fed back to the AND array, which allows any of the product terms to be summed, complemented, and used as inputs to the AND array.

The state and output registers are positive-edge-triggered S/R flip-flops. These registers are unconditionally preset high on power-up. PRE/$\overline{OE}$ can be used as PRE to preset both registers or, by blowing the proper fuse, be converted to an output control function, $\overline{OE}$.

The TIB82S167BM is characterized for operation over the full military temperature range of −55°C to 125°C. The TIB82S167BC is characterized for operation from 0°C to 75°C.

[†] Power up preset and asynchronous preset functions are not identical to 82S167A.

M SUFFIX . . . JT PACKAGE
C SUFFIX . . . JT OR NT PACKAGE
(TOP VIEW)

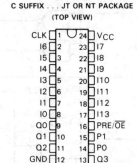

M SUFFIX . . . FK PACKAGE
C SUFFIX . . . FK OR FN PACKAGE
(TOP VIEW)

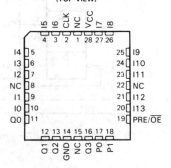

NC — No internal connection

**3**

Field-Programmable Logic

TEXAS
INSTRUMENTS

**functional block diagram (positive logic)**

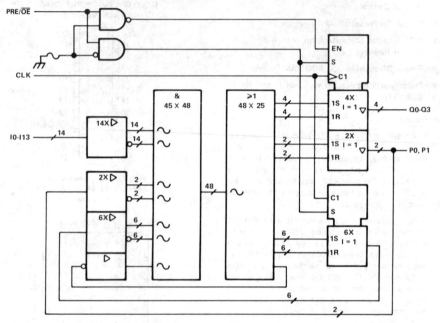

$\sim$ denotes fused inputs

**TEXAS**
**INSTRUMENTS**

**timing diagram**

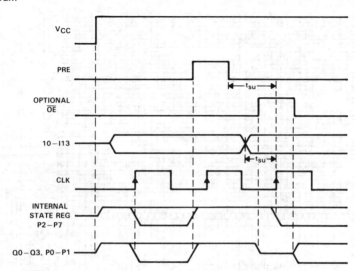

Field-Programmable Logic

3

## LOGIC DIAGRAM

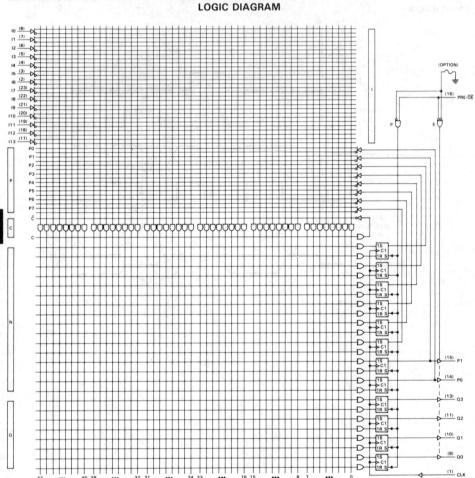

NOTES: 1. All AND gate inputs with a blown link float to the high level.
2. All OR gate inputs with a blown link float to the low level.

TEXAS
INSTRUMENTS

### absolute maximum ratings over operating free-air temperature range (unless otherwise noted)

Supply voltage, $V_{CC}$ (see Note 3) . . . . . . . . . . . . . . . . . . . . . . . . . . . . . . . . . . . . . . . . . . . . . . . . . . . . . 7 V
Input voltage (see Note 3) . . . . . . . . . . . . . . . . . . . . . . . . . . . . . . . . . . . . . . . . . . . . . . . . . . . . . . . . . . . . 5.5 V
Voltage applied to a disabled output (see Note 3) . . . . . . . . . . . . . . . . . . . . . . . . . . . . . . . . . . . . . . . 5.5 V
Operating free-air temperature range: TIB82S167BM . . . . . . . . . . . . . . . . . . . . . . −55 °C to 125 °C
TIB82S167BC . . . . . . . . . . . . . . . . . . . . . . . . 0 °C to 75 °C
Storage temperature range . . . . . . . . . . . . . . . . . . . . . . . . . . . . . . . . . . . . . . . . . . . . −65 °C to 150 °C

NOTE 3: These ratings apply except for programming pins during a programming cycle.

### recommended operating conditions

| PARAMETER | | | M SUFFIX | | | C SUFFIX | | | UNIT |
|---|---|---|---|---|---|---|---|---|---|
| | | | MIN | NOM | MAX | MIN | NOM | MAX | |
| $V_{CC}$ | Supply voltage | | 4.5 | 5 | 5.5 | 4.75 | 5 | 5.25 | V |
| $V_{IH}$ | High-level input voltage | | 2 | | 5.5 | 2 | | 5.5 | V |
| $V_{IL}$ | Low-level input voltage | | | | 0.8 | | | 0.8 | V |
| $I_{OH}$ | High-level output current | | | | −2 | | | −3.2 | mA |
| $I_{OL}$ | Low-level output current | | | | 12 | | | 24 | mA |
| $f_{clock}$ | Clock frequency[†] | 1 thru 48 product terms without C-array[‡] | 0 | | 40 | 0 | | 50 | MHz |
| | | 1 thru 48 product terms with C-array | 0 | | 25 | 0 | | 30 | |
| $t_w$ | Pulse duration | Clock high or low | 12 | | | 10 | | | ns |
| | | Preset | 18 | | | 15 | | | |
| $t_{su}$ | Setup time before CLK↑, 1 thru 48 product terms | Without C-array | 20 | | | 15 | | | ns |
| | | With C-array | 35 | | | 30 | | | |
| $t_{su}$ | Setup time, Preset low (inactive) before CLK↑[§] | | 10 | | | 8 | | | ns |
| $t_h$ | Hold time, input after CLK↑ | | 0 | | | 0 | | | ns |
| $T_A$ | Operating free-air temperature | | −55 | | 125 | 0 | | 75 | °C |

[†] The maximum clock frequency is independent of the internal programmed configuration. If an output is fed back externally to an input, the maximum clock frequency must be calculated.
[‡] The C-array is the single sum term that is complemented and fed back to the AND array.
[§] After Preset goes inactive, normal clocking resumes on the first low-to-high clock transition.

**3**

**Field-Programmable Logic**

**electrical characteristics over recommended operating free-air temperature range (unless otherwise noted)**

| PARAMETER | TEST CONDITIONS[†] | | M SUFFIX | | | C SUFFIX | | | UNIT |
|---|---|---|---|---|---|---|---|---|---|
| | | | MIN | TYP[‡] | MAX | MIN | TYP[‡] | MAX | |
| $V_{IK}$ | $V_{CC}$ = MIN, | $I_I$ = −18 mA | | | −1.2 | | | −1.2 | V |
| $V_{OH}$ | $V_{CC}$ = MIN, | $I_{OH}$ = MAX | 2.4 | 3.2 | | 2.4 | 3 | | V |
| $V_{OL}$ | $V_{CC}$ = MIN, | $I_{OL}$ = MAX | | 0.25 | 0.4 | | 0.37 | 0.5 | V |
| $I_I$ | $V_{CC}$ = MAX, | $V_I$ = 5.5 V | | | 25 | | | 25 | μA |
| $I_{IH}$ | $V_{CC}$ = MAX, | $V_I$ = 2.7 V | | | 20 | | | 20 | μA |
| $I_{IL}$ | $V_{CC}$ = MAX, | $V_I$ = 0.4 V | | | −0.25 | | | −0.25 | mA |
| $I_O$ [§] | $V_{CC}$ = MAX, | $V_O$ = 2.25 V | −30 | | −112 | −30 | | −112 | mA |
| $I_{OZH}$ | $V_{CC}$ = MAX, | $V_O$ = 2.7 V | | | 20 | | | 20 | μA |
| $I_{OZL}$ | $V_{CC}$ = MAX, | $V_O$ = 0.4 V | | | −20 | | | −20 | μA |
| $I_{CC}$ | $V_{CC}$ = MAX, PRE/$\overline{OE}$ input at GND, | $V_I$ = 4.5 V, Outputs open | | 90 | 160 | | 90 | 160 | mA |

**switching characteristics over recommended supply voltage and operating free-air temperature ranges (unless otherwise noted)**

| PARAMETER | | FROM | TO | TEST CONDITIONS | M SUFFIX | | | C SUFFIX | | | UNIT |
|---|---|---|---|---|---|---|---|---|---|---|---|
| | | | | | MIN | TYP[‡] | MAX | MIN | TYP[‡] | MAX | |
| $f_{max}$ [¶] | Without C-array | | | | 40 | 70 | | 50 | 70 | | MHz |
| | With C-array | | | | 25 | 45 | | 30 | 45 | | |
| $t_{pd}$ | | CLK↑ | Q | $R_L$ = 500 Ω, $C_L$ = 50 pF | | 10 | 20 | | 10 | 15 | ns |
| $t_{pd}$ | | PRE↑ | Q | | | 8 | 25 | | 8 | 20 | ns |
| $t_{pd}$ | | $V_{CC}$↑ | Q | | | 0 | 10 | | 0 | 10 | ns |
| $t_{en}$ | | $\overline{OE}$↓ | Q | | | 10 | 25 | | 10 | 20 | ns |
| $t_{dis}$ | | $\overline{OE}$↑ | Q | | | 5 | 15 | | 5 | 10 | ns |

[†] For conditions shown as MIN or MAX, use the appropriate value specified under recommended operating conditions.
[‡] All typical values are at $V_{CC}$ = 5 V, $T_A$ = 25 °C.
[§] The output conditions have been chosen to produce a current that closely approximates one half of the true short-circuit current, $I_{OS}$.
[¶] $f_{max}$ is independent of the internal programmed configuration and the number of product terms used.

### pin assignment in programming mode (PGM ENABLE ≤ V$_{IHH}$) top view

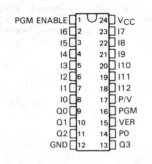 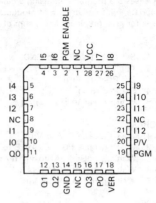

NC—No internal connection

### programming parameters, T$_A$ = 25°C

| | PARAMETER | MIN | TYP | MAX | UNIT |
|---|---|---|---|---|---|
| V$_{CC}$ | Verify-level supply voltage | 4.75 | 5 | 5.25 | V |
| V$_{IHH}$ | Program high-level input voltage | 14.5 | 15 | 15.5 | V |
| I$_{IHH}$ | Program level input current | | 250 | 500 | mA |
| V$_{IX}$ | Program level input voltage | 10.25 | 10.5 | 10.75 | V |
| V$_{CC1}$ | Programming supply voltage | 8.25 | 8.5 | 8.75 | V |
| I$_{CC1}$ | Programming supply current | 550 | | 1000 | mA |
| V$_{IH}$ | High-level input voltage | 2 | | | V |
| V$_{IL}$ | Low-level input voltage | | | 0.8 | V |
| V$_{OH}$ | High-level output voltage | 2.4 | 3 | | V |
| V$_{OL}$ | Low-level output voltage | | 0.35 | 0.45 | V |
| t$_{w1}$ | Program-pulse duration | 10 | | 25 | μs |
| t$_{w2}$ | Verify-pulse duration | 5 | | 10 | μs |
| | Program-pulse duty cycle | | | 25% | |
| t$_d$ | Delay time | 10 | | 25 | μs |
| t$_r$ | Rise time | 17 | 20 | 25 | μs |

3

Field-Programmable Logic

TEXAS
INSTRUMENTS

## programming procedure for array fuses

Array fuses are programmed using a binary select method. Each fuse can be addressed by selecting the appropriate input line or sum of products line (row address) and product line (column address). The addresses for selecting input lines, sum of products lines, and product lines are shown in Tables 1 and 2.

SETUP
Step 1: Set PGM ENABLE to GND.
Step 2: Apply address to inputs.
Step 3: Set PGM to $V_{IH}$.
Step 4: Set P/V to $V_{IL}$.
Step 5: Wait $t_d$, set $V_{CC}$ to $V_{CC1}$.

PROGRAM
Step 1: Wait $t_d$, raise P/V to $V_{IH}$.
Step 2: Wait $t_d$, raise PGM ENABLE to $V_{IHH}$.
Step 3: Wait $t_d$, pulse PGM to $V_{IL}$ for $t_{w1}$.
Step 4: Wait $t_d$, return PGM ENABLE to GND.
Step 5: Wait $t_d$, return P/V to $V_{IL}$.

VERIFY
Step 1: Wait $t_d$, lower PGM to $V_{IL}$.
Step 2: After $t_{w2}$, wait $t_d$ and read sense at Q0. A $V_{IH}$ level indicates a blown fuse. A $V_{IL}$ level indicates fuse is intact.
Step 3: Raise PGM to $V_{IH}$.

NEXT ADDRESS SELECT
Step 1: After $t_d$, lower $V_{CC}$ to GND.
Step 2: For the same product line wait $t_d$, then apply new input line or sum-of-products line address.
Step 3: For different product line wait $t_d$, apply new input line or sum-of-products line address, then apply new product line address.
Step 4: Wait $t_d$, set $V_{CC}$ at $V_{CC1}$.
Step 5: Continue with program or verify sequence.

NOTE 4: Input lines and sum of product lines are also referred to as variables. Product lines are also referred to as transition terms.

**TEXAS**
**INSTRUMENTS**

## programming waveforms

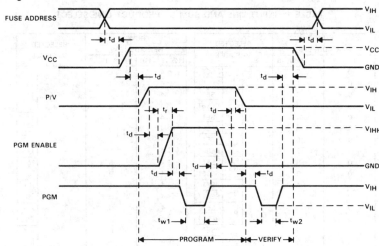

## programming procedure for PRE/$\overline{OE}$ option

PROGRAM
Step 1: With PGM at GND, raise $V_{CC}$ to $V_{CC1}$.
Step 2: Wait $t_d$, pulse PGM to $V_{IX}$ for a duration of $t_{w1}$.
Step 3: A $t_d$ delay after PGM has returned to GND, lower $V_{CC}$ to 5 volts or GND.

VERIFY
Step 1: With PGM at GND, set $V_{CC}$ to 5 volts.
Step 2: After a delay of $t_d$, raise PGM to $V_{IX}$ for a minimum duration of $t_{w2}$.
Step 3: Return PGM to GND.
Step 4: Wait $t_d$, pulse PGM to $V_{IH}$ for a duration of $t_{w2}$.
Step 5: After a $t_d$ delay, Q0 indicates $V_{OH}$ if the PRE option is selected and $V_{OL}$ if the $\overline{OE}$ option is programmed.

## programming waveforms for PRE/$\overline{OE}$ option

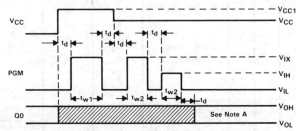

NOTE A: After programming if the PRE option is selected, Q0 will be high; if the output-enable option is selected, the output will be low.

TEXAS
INSTRUMENTS

Field-Programmable Logic

3

**array fuse addresses**

### TABLE 1. INPUT LINE AND SUM OF PRODUCT LINE SELECT

| ROW HEX ADDRESS (I12, I11, I10) | ROW HEX ADDRESS (I9, I8, I7, I6) | SELECTED VARIABLE | | |
|---|---|---|---|---|
| 0 | 0 | | N7 | SET |
| 0 | 1 | | N7 | RESET |
| 0 | 2 | | N6 | SET |
| 0 | 3 | | N6 | RESET |
| 0 | 4 | | N5 | SET |
| 0 | 5 | | N5 | RESET |
| 0 | 6 | | N4 | SET |
| 0 | 7 | | N4 | RESET |
| 0 | 8 | OR | N3 | SET |
| 0 | 9 | Array | N3 | RESET |
| 0 | A | | N2 | SET |
| 0 | B | | N2 | RESET |
| 0 | C | | P1 | SET |
| 0 | D | | P1 | RESET |
| 0 | E | | P0 | SET |
| 0 | F | | P0 | RESET |
| 1 | 0 | | Q3 | SET |
| 1 | 1 | | Q3 | RESET |
| 1 | 2 | | UNUSED | |
| 1 | 3 | | UNUSED | |
| 1 | 4 | | Q2 | SET |
| 1 | 5 | | Q2 | RESET |
| 1 | 6 | | Q1 | SET |
| 1 | 7 | | Q1 | RESET |
| 1 | 8 | | Q0 | SET |
| 1 | 9 | | Q0 | RESET |
| 1 | A | | UNUSED | |
| 1 | B | | UNUSED | |
| 1 | C | | Complement Array | C |
| 1 ↑ | D ↑ | | | |
| | | | Empty Address Space | |
| 3 ↓ | F ↓ | | | |

| ROW HEX ADDRESS (I12, I11, I10) | ROW HEX ADDRESS (I9, I8, I7, I6) | SELECTED VARIABLE | |
|---|---|---|---|
| 4 | 0 | | I0 |
| 4 | 1 | | Ī0 |
| 4 | 2 | | I1 |
| 4 | 3 | | Ī1 |
| 4 | 4 | | I2 |
| 4 | 5 | | Ī2 |
| 4 | 6 | | I3 |
| 4 | 7 | | Ī3 |
| 4 | 8 | | I4 |
| 4 | 9 | | Ī4 |
| 4 | A | | I5 |
| 4 | B | | Ī5 |
| 4 | C | | P0 |
| 4 | D | | P̄0 |
| 4 | E | | I6 |
| 4 | F | | Ī6 |
| 5 | 0 | | I7 |
| 5 | 1 | | Ī7 |
| 5 | 2 | | I8 |
| 5 | 3 | | Ī8 |
| 5 | 4 | | I9 |
| 5 | 5 | AND | Ī9 |
| 5 | 6 | Array | I10 |
| 5 | 7 | | Ī10 |
| 5 | 8 | | I11 |
| 5 | 9 | | Ī11 |
| 5 | A | | I12 |
| 5 | B | | Ī12 |
| 5 | C | | I13 |
| 5 | D | | Ī13 |
| 5 | E | | P1 |
| 5 | F | | P̄1 |
| 6 | 0 | | P7 |
| 6 | 1 | | P̄7 |
| 6 | 2 | | P6 |
| 6 | 3 | | P̄6 |
| 6 | 4 | | P5 |
| 6 | 5 | | P̄5 |
| 6 | 6 | | P4 |
| 6 | 7 | | P̄4 |
| 6 | 8 | | P3 |
| 6 | 9 | | P̄3 |
| 6 | A | | P2 |
| 6 | B | | P̄3 |
| 6 | C | Complement Array | C̄ |

TEXAS INSTRUMENTS

### TABLE 2.  PRODUCT LINE SELECT

| COLUMN HEX ADDRESS | | SELECTED TRANSITION TERM |
|---|---|---|
| I5, I4 | I3, I2, I1, I0 | |
| 0 | 0 | 0 |
| 0 | 1 | 1 |
| 0 | 2 | 2 |
| 0 | 3 | 3 |
| 0 | 4 | 4 |
| 0 | 5 | 5 |
| 0 | 6 | 6 |
| 0 | 7 | 7 |
| 0 | 8 | 8 |
| 0 | 9 | 9 |
| 0 | A | 10 |
| 0 | B | 11 |
| 0 | C | 12 |
| 0 | D | 13 |
| 0 | E | 14 |
| 0 | F | 15 |
| 1 | 0 | 16 |
| 1 | 1 | 17 |
| 1 | 2 | 18 |
| 1 | 3 | 19 |
| 1 | 4 | 20 |
| 1 | 5 | 21 |
| 1 | 6 | 22 |
| 1 | 7 | 23 |
| 1 | 8 | 24 |
| 1 | 9 | 25 |
| 1 | A | 26 |
| 1 | B | 27 |
| 1 | C | 28 |
| 1 | D | 29 |
| 1 | E | 30 |
| 1 | F | 31 |
| 2 | 0 | 32 |
| 2 | 1 | 33 |
| 2 | 2 | 34 |
| 2 | 3 | 35 |
| 2 | 4 | 36 |
| 2 | 5 | 37 |
| 2 | 6 | 38 |
| 2 | 7 | 39 |
| 2 | 8 | 40 |
| 2 | 9 | 41 |
| 2 | A | 42 |
| 2 | B | 43 |
| 2 | C | 44 |
| 2 | D | 45 |
| 2 | E | 46 |
| 2 | F | 47 |
| 3 | 0 | Test Col 48 |
| 3 | 1 | Test Col 49 |

**3**

Field-Programmable Logic

TEXAS
INSTRUMENTS

# TIB82S167B
## 14 × 48 × 6 FIELD-PROGRAMMABLE LOGIC SEQUENCER
## WITH 3-STATE OUTPUTS OR PRESET

### diagnostics

A diagnostics mode is provided with these devices that allows the user to inspect the contents of the state register. When I0 (pin 9) is held at 10 V, the state register bits P2-P7 will appear at the Q0-Q3 and P0-P1 outputs. The contents of the registers, Q0-Q3, and P0-P1 remain unchanged.

### diagnostics waveforms

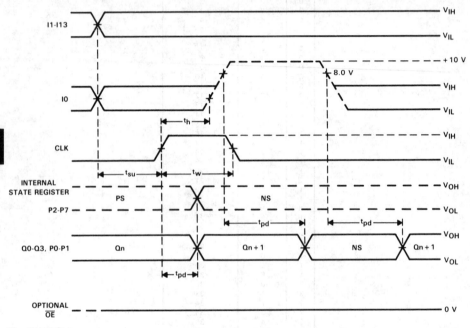

PS = Present State
NS = Next State

3
Field-Programmable Logic

TEXAS
INSTRUMENTS

## test array

A test array that consists of product lines 48 and 49 has been added to these devices to allow testing prior to programming. The test array is factory programmed as shown below. Testing is accomplished by connecting Q0-Q3 to I10-I13, PRE/$\overline{OE}$ to GND, and applying the proper input signals as shown in the timing diagram. Product lines 48 and 49 must be deleted during user programming to avoid interference with the programmed logic function.

## test array program

| | | | AND | | | | | | | | | | | | | | | | | | | | | | | | | | OPTION PRE/$\overline{OE}$ | | | | | | | | | | H |
| | | | | | | | | | | | | | | | | | | | | | | | | | | | OR | | | | | | | | | | | |
| PRODUCT LINE | C | $\overline{C}$ | INPUT (In) | | | | | | | | | | | | | | | | | PRESENT STATE (PS) | | | | | | NEXT STATE (NS) | | | | | | OUTPUT (Qn) | | | | | | | |
| | | | 15 | 14 | 13 | 12 | 11 | 10 | 9 | 8 | 7 | 6 | 5 | 4 | 3 | 2 | 1 | 0 | 5 | 4 | 3 | 2 | 1 | 0 | 5 | 4 | 3 | 2 | 1 | 0 | 7 | 6 | 5 | 4 | 3 | 2 | 1 | 0 |
| 48 | X | — | H | H | H | H | H | H | H | H | H | H | H | H | H | H | H | H | H | H | H | H | H | H | L | L | L | L | L | L | L | L | L | L | L | L | L | L |
| 49 | — | X | L | L | L | L | L | L | L | L | L | L | L | L | L | L | L | L | L | L | L | L | L | L | H | H | H | H | H | H | H | H | H | H | H | H | H | H |

## test array waveforms

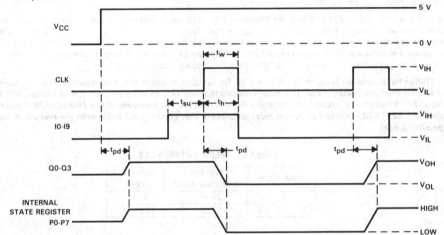

## test array deleted

| | | | AND | | | | | | | | | | | | | | | | | | | | | | | | | | OPTION PRE/$\overline{OE}$ | | | | | | | | | | H |
| | | | | | | | | | | | | | | | | | | | | | | | | | | | OR | | | | | | | | | | | |
| PRODUCT LINE | C | $\overline{C}$ | INPUT (In) | | | | | | | | | | | | | | | | | PRESENT STATE (PS) | | | | | | NEXT STATE (NS) | | | | | | OUTPUT (Qn) | | | | | | | |
| | | | 15 | 14 | 13 | 12 | 11 | 10 | 9 | 8 | 7 | 6 | 5 | 4 | 3 | 2 | 1 | 0 | 5 | 4 | 3 | 2 | 1 | 0 | 5 | 4 | 3 | 2 | 1 | 0 | 7 | 6 | 5 | 4 | 3 | 2 | 1 | 0 |
| 48 | — | — | H | H | H | H | H | H | H | H | H | H | H | H | H | H | H | H | H | H | H | H | H | H | — | — | — | — | — | — | — | — | — | — | — | — | — | — |
| 49 | — | X | L | L | L | L | L | L | L | L | L | L | L | L | L | L | L | L | L | L | L | L | L | L | — | — | — | — | — | — | — | — | — | — | — | — | — | — |

X = Fuse intact, — = Fuse blown

**3**

**Field-Programmable Logic**

## TIB82S167B, 82S167A COMPARISON

The Texas Instruments 82S167A and TIB82S167B are functionally equivalent 14 × 48 × 6 Field-Programmable Logic Sequencers. The TI 82S167A is designed to be a direct replacement to the Signetics 82S167A. However, the TIB82S167B is designed for a maximum speed of 50 MHz with the preset function being made conventional. As a result the TIB82S167B differs from the 82S167A in speed and in the preset recovery function.

The TIB82S167B is a high-speed version of the original 82S167A. The TIB82S167B features increased switching speeds with no increase in power. The maximum operating frequency is increased from 20 MHz to 50 MHz and does not decrease as more product terms are connected to each sum (OR) line. For instance, if all 48 product tems were connected to a sum line on the original 82S167A, the $f_{max}$ would be about 15 MHz. The $f_{max}$ for the TIB82S167B remains at 50 MHz regardless of the programmed configuration. In addition, the preset recovery sequence was changed to a conventional recovery sequence, providing quicker clock recovery times. This is explained in the following paragraphs.

The TIB82S167B and the 82S167A are equipped with power-up preset and asynchronous preset functions. The power-up preset causes the registers to go high during power-up. The asynchronous preset inhibits clocking and causes the registers to go high whenever the preset pin is taken high. After a power-up preset occurs, the minimum setup time from power-up to the first clock pulse must be met in order to assure that clocking is not inhibited. In a similar manner after an asynchronous preset, the preset input must return low (inactive) for a given time, $t_{su}$, before clocking.

The Texas Instruments 82S167A and the Signetics 82S167A were designed in such a way that after both power-up preset and asynchronous preset they require that a high-to-low clock transition occur before a clocking transition (low-to-high) will be recognized. This is shown in Figure 1. The Texas Instruments TIB82S167B does not require a high-to-low clock transition before clocking can be resumed, it only requires that the preset be inactive 8 ns (preset inactive-state setup time) before the clock rising edge. See Figure 2.

The TIB82S167B, with an $f_{max}$ of 50 MHz, is ideal for systems in which the state machine must run several times faster than the system clock. It is recommended that the TIB82S167B be used in new designs and the TI 82S167A be used as a second source to the Signetics 82S167A. *However, if the TIB82S167B is used to replace the 82S167A, then the customer must understand that clocking will begin with the first clock rising edge after preset.*

### TABLE 3.  SPEED DIFFERENCES

| PARAMETER | 82S167A<br>TI AND SIGNETICS | TIB82S167B<br>TI ONLY |
|:---:|:---:|:---:|
| $f_{max}$ | 20 MHz | 50 MHz |
| $t_{pd}$, CLK to Q | 20 ns | 15 ns |

TEXAS
INSTRUMENTS

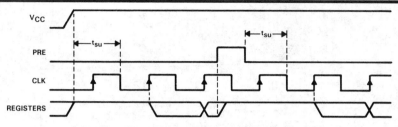

FIGURE 1. 82S167A PRESET RECOVERY OPERATION

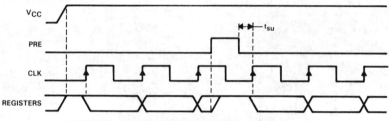

FIGURE 2. TIB82S167B PRESET RECOVERY OPERATION

**3**

Field-Programmable Logic

TEXAS
INSTRUMENTS

**PRODUCT PREVIEW**

**82S167A**
**14 × 48 × 6 FIELD-PROGRAMMABLE LOGIC SEQUENCER**
**WITH 3-STATE OUTPUTS OR PRESET**
D2896, JANUARY 1985 – REVISED OCTOBER 1985

- Programmable Asynchronous Preset or Output Control

- Power-On Preset of All Flip-Flops

- 8-Bit Internal State Register with 4-Bit Output Register

- Power Dissipation . . . 600 mW Typical

- Designed to be Interchangeable with Signetics 82S167A

**M SUFFIX . . . JT PACKAGE**
**C SUFFIX . . . JT OR NT PACKAGE**
**(TOP VIEW)**

## description

The 82S167A is a TTL field-programmable state machine of the Mealy type. This state machine (logic sequencer) contains 48 product terms (AND terms) and 12 pairs of sum terms (OR terms). The product and sum terms are used to control the 8-bit internal state register and the 4-bit output register.

The outputs of the internal state register (P0-P7) are fed back and combined with the 14 inputs (I0-I13) to form the AND array. In addition the first two bits of the internal state register (P0-P1) are brought off-chip to allow the output register to be extended to 6 bits if desired. A single sum term is complemented and fed back to the AND array, which allows any of the product terms to be summed, complemented, and used as inputs to the AND array.

The state and output registers are positive-edge-triggered S/R flip-flops. These registers are unconditionally preset high on power-up. PRE/$\overline{OE}$ can be used as $\overline{PRE}$ to preset both registers or, by blowing the proper fuse, be converted to an output control function, $\overline{OE}$.

The 82S167AM is characterized for operation over the full military temperature range of −55°C to 125°C. The 82S167AC is characterized for operation from 0°C to 75°C.

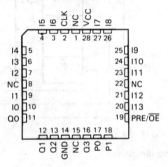

**M SUFFIX . . . FK PACKAGE**
**C SUFFIX . . . FK OR FN PACKAGE**
**(TOP VIEW)**

NC—No internal connection

**3**

**Field-Programmable Logic**

**TEXAS INSTRUMENTS**

## 14 × 48 × 6 FIELD-PROGRAMMABLE LOGIC SEQUENCER
## WITH 3-STATE OUTPUTS OR PRESET

**functional block diagram (positive logic)**

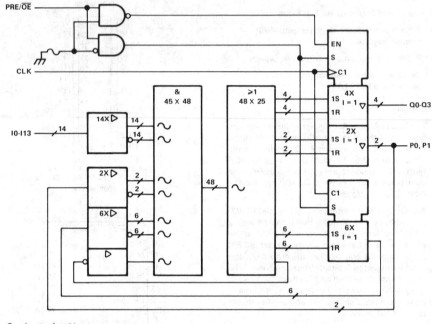

∿ denotes fused inputs

**timing diagram**

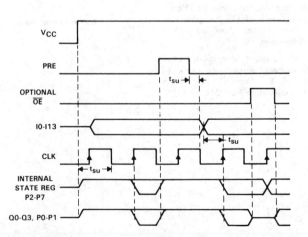

TEXAS
INSTRUMENTS

**3**

Field-Programmable Logic

**logic diagram (positive logic)**

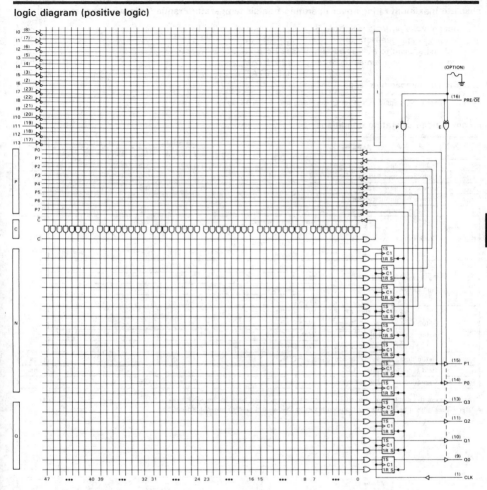

NOTES: 1. All AND gate inputs with a blown link float to the high level.
2. All OR gate inputs with a blown link float to the low level.

## 82S167A
## 14 × 48 × 6 FIELD-PROGRAMMABLE LOGIC SEQUENCER
## WITH 3-STATE OUTPUTS OR PRESET

### absolute maximum ratings over operating free-air temperature range (unless otherwise noted)

Supply voltage, $V_{CC}$ (see Note 3) . . . . . . . . . . . . . . . . . . . . . . . . . . . . . . . . . . . . . . . . . . . . . . . . 7 V
Input voltage (see Note 3) . . . . . . . . . . . . . . . . . . . . . . . . . . . . . . . . . . . . . . . . . . . . . . . . . . . . . . 5.5 V
Voltage applied to a disabled output (see Note 3) . . . . . . . . . . . . . . . . . . . . . . . . . . . . . . . . . . 5.5 V
Operating free-air temperature range: 82S167AM . . . . . . . . . . . . . . . . . . . . . . . −55°C to 125°C
                                      82S167AC . . . . . . . . . . . . . . . . . . . . . . . . . . 0°C to 75°C
Storage temperature range . . . . . . . . . . . . . . . . . . . . . . . . . . . . . . . . . . . . . . . . . . . −65°C to 150°C

NOTE 3: These ratings apply except for programming pins during a programming cycle.

### recommended operating conditions

| PARAMETER | | | M SUFFIX | | | C SUFFIX | | | UNIT |
|---|---|---|---|---|---|---|---|---|---|
| | | | MIN | NOM | MAX | MIN | NOM | MAX | |
| $V_{CC}$ | Supply voltage | | 4.5 | 5 | 5.5 | 4.75 | 5 | 5.25 | V |
| $V_{IH}$ | High-level input voltage | | 2 | | 5.5 | 2 | | 5.5 | V |
| $V_{IL}$ | Low-level input voltage | | | | 0.8 | | | 0.8 | V |
| $I_{OH}$ | High-level output current | | | | −2 | | | −3.2 | mA |
| $I_{OL}$ | Low-level output current | | | | 12 | | | 24 | mA |
| $f_{clock}$ | Clock frequency | 48 product terms without C-array [†] | | | | | | | MHz |
| | | 48 product terms with C-array | | | | | | | |
| $t_w$ | Pulse duration, clock high or low | Clock high | | | | | | | ns |
| | | Clock low | | | | | | | |
| | | With C-array | | | | | | | |
| | | Preset | | | | | | | |
| $t_{su}$ | Setup time before CLK↑ | 25 thru 48 product terms | Without C-array | | | | | | | ns |
| | | | With C-array | | | | | | |
| | | 1 thru 24 product terms | Without C-array | | | | | | |
| | | | With C-array | | | | | | |
| $t_{su}$ | Setup time, Preset low (inactive) before CLK↓ [‡] | | | | | | | | ns |
| $t_h$ | Hold time, input after CLK↑ | | | | | | | | ns |
| $T_A$ | Operating free-air temperature | | −55 | | 125 | 0 | | 70 | °C |

[†] The C-array is the single sum term that is complemented and fed back to the AND array.
[‡] After Preset goes inactive, normal clocking resumes following a high-to-low clock transition.

TEXAS
INSTRUMENTS

**electrical characteristics over recommended operating free-air temperature range (unless otherwise noted)**

| PARAMETER | TEST CONDITIONS[†] | | M SUFFIX | | | C SUFFIX | | | UNIT |
|---|---|---|---|---|---|---|---|---|---|
| | | | MIN | TYP[‡] | MAX | MIN | TYP[‡] | MAX | |
| $V_{IK}$ | $V_{CC}$ = MIN, | $I_I$ = −18 mA | | | −1.5 | | | −1.5 | V |
| $V_{OH}$ | $V_{CC}$ = MIN, | $I_{OH}$ = MAX | 2.4 | 3.2 | | 2.4 | 3 | | V |
| $V_{OL}$ | $V_{CC}$ = MIN, | $I_{OL}$ = MAX | | 0.25 | 0.5 | | 0.37 | 0.5 | V |
| $I_I$ | $V_{CC}$ = MAX, | $V_I$ = 5.5 V | | | 0.1 | | | 0.1 | mA |
| $I_{IH}$ | $V_{CC}$ = MAX, | $V_I$ = 2.7 V | | | 20 | | | 20 | μA |
| $I_{IL}$ | $V_{CC}$ = MAX, | $V_I$ = 0.4 V | | | −0.5 | | | −0.5 | mA |
| $I_{OS}$[§] | $V_{CC}$ = MAX, | $V_O$ = 0 | −20 | | −70 | −20 | | −70 | mA |
| $I_{OZH}$ | $V_{CC}$ = MAX, | $V_O$ = 2.7 V | | | 20 | | | 20 | μA |
| $I_{OZL}$ | $V_{CC}$ = MAX, | $V_O$ = 0.4 V | | | −20 | | | −20 | μA |
| $I_{CC}$ | $V_{CC}$ = MAX, PRE/$\overline{OE}$ input at GND, | $V_I$ = 4.5 V Outputs open | | 120 | | | 120 | | mA |

**switching characteristics over recommended supply voltage and operating free-air temperature ranges (unless otherwise noted)**

| PARAMETER | | FROM | TO | TEST CONDITIONS | M SUFFIX | | | C SUFFIX | | | UNIT |
|---|---|---|---|---|---|---|---|---|---|---|---|
| | | | | | MIN | TYP[‡] | MAX | MIN | TYP[‡] | MAX | |
| $f_{max}$[¶] | With C-array | | | | | | | 12.5 | | | MHz |
| | Without C-array | | | | | | | 20 | | | |
| $t_{pd}$ | | CLK↑ | Q | R1 = 470 Ω, | | | | | | 15 | ns |
| $t_{pd}$ | | PRE↑ | Q | R2 = 1 kΩ, | | | | | | 18 | ns |
| $t_{pd}$ | | $V_{CC}$↑ | Q | $C_L$ = 30 pF | | | | | | 0 | ns |
| $t_{en}$ | | $\overline{OE}$↓ | Q | | | | | | | 20 | ns |
| $t_{dis}$ | | $\overline{OE}$↑ | Q | | | | | | | 20 | ns |

[†] For conditions shown as MIN or MAX, use the appropriate value specified under recommended operating conditions.
[‡] All typical values are at $V_{CC}$ = 5 V, $T_A$ = 25 °C.
[§] Not more than one output should be shorted at a time and duration of the short-circuit should not exceed one second.
[¶] $f_{max}$ is measured with 48 product terms connected in the OR-array and is independent of internal registered feedback.

**3**

**Field-Programmable Logic**

TEXAS
INSTRUMENTS

## 82S167A
## 14 × 48 × 6 FIELD-PROGRAMMABLE LOGIC SEQUENCER
## WITH 3-STATE OUTPUTS OR PRESET

pin assignment in programming mode (PGM ENABLE ≤ V$_{IHH}$) top view

```
PGM ENABLE [ 1    24 ] VCC
        I6 [ 2    23 ] I7
        I5 [ 3    22 ] I8
        I4 [ 4    21 ] I9
        I3 [ 5    20 ] I10
        I2 [ 6    19 ] I11
        I1 [ 7    18 ] I12
        I0 [ 8    17 ] P/V
        Q0 [ 9    16 ] PGM
        Q1 [ 10   15 ] VER
        Q2 [ 11   14 ] P0
       GND [ 12   13 ] Q3
```

```
              I5  I6 PGM NC VCC I7 I8
                       ENABLE
                4   3   2   1  28 27 26
        I4 [ 5                      25 ] I9
        I3 [ 6                      24 ] I10
        I2 [ 7                      23 ] I11
        NC [ 8                      22 ] NC
        I1 [ 9                      21 ] I12
        I0 [ 10                     20 ] P/V
        Q0 [ 11                     19 ] PGM
               12 13 14 15 16 17 18
               Q1 Q2 GND NC Q3 P0 VER
```

NC—No internal connection

## programming parameters, T$_A$ = 25 °C

| | PARAMETER | MIN | TYP | MAX | UNIT |
|---|---|---|---|---|---|
| V$_{CC}$ | Verify-level supply voltage | | 5 | | V |
| V$_{IHH}$ | Program high-level input voltage | 14.5 | 15 | 15.5 | V |
| I$_{IHH}$ | Program level input current | | 250 | 500 | mA |
| V$_{IX}$ | Program level input voltage | 10.25 | 10.5 | 10.75 | V |
| V$_{CC1}$ | Programming supply voltage | 8.25 | 8.5 | 8.75 | V |
| I$_{CC1}$ | Programming supply current | 550 | | 1000 | mA |
| V$_{IH}$ | High-level input voltage | 2 | | | V |
| V$_{IL}$ | Low-level input voltage | | | 0.8 | V |
| V$_{OH}$ | High-level output voltage | 2.4 | 3 | | V |
| V$_{OL}$ | Low-level output voltage | | 0.35 | 0.45 | V |
| t$_{w1}$ | Program-pulse duration | 10 | | 25 | $\mu$s |
| t$_{w2}$ | Verify-pulse duration | 5 | | 10 | $\mu$s |
| | Program-pulse duty cycle | | | 25% | |
| t$_d$ | Delay time | 10 | | 25 | $\mu$s |
| t$_r$ | Rise time | 17 | 20 | 25 | $\mu$s |

**3**

**Field-Programmable Logic**

TEXAS
INSTRUMENTS

## programming procedure for array fuses

Array fuses are programmed using a binary select method. Each fuse can be addressed by selecting the appropriate input line or sum of products line (row address) and product line (column address). The addresses for selecting input lines, sum of products lines, and product lines are shown in Tables 1 and 2.

SETUP
Step 1: Set PGM ENABLE to GND.
Step 2: Apply address to inputs.
Step 3: Set PGM to $V_{IH}$.
Step 4: Set P/V to $V_{IL}$.
Step 5: Wait $t_d$, set $V_{CC}$ to $V_{CC1}$.

PROGRAM
Step 1: Wait $t_d$, raise P/V to $V_{IH}$.
Step 2: Wait $t_d$, raise PGM ENABLE to $V_{IHH}$.
Step 3: Wait $t_d$, pulse PGM to $V_{IL}$ for $t_{w1}$.
Step 4: Wait $t_d$, return PGM ENABLE to GND.
Step 5: Wait $t_d$, return P/V to $V_{IL}$.

VERIFY
Step 1: Wait $t_d$, lower PGM to $V_{IL}$.
Step 2: After $t_{w2}$, wait $t_d$ and read sense at Q0. A $V_{IH}$ level indicates a blown fuse. A $V_{IL}$ level indicates fuse is intact.
Step 3: Raise PGM to $V_{IH}$.

NEXT ADDRESS SELECT
Step 1: After $t_d$, lower $V_{CC}$ to GND.
Step 2: For the same product line wait $t_d$, then apply new input line or sum-of-products line address.
Step 3: For different product line wait $t_d$, apply new input line or sum-of-products line address, then apply new product line address.
Step 4: Wait $t_d$, set $V_{CC}$ at $V_{CC1}$.
Step 5: Continue with program or verify sequence.

NOTE 4: Input lines and sum of product lines are also referred to as variables. Product lines are also referred to as transition terms.

**TEXAS**
**INSTRUMENTS**

## 82S167A
## 14 × 48 × 6 FIELD-PROGRAMMABLE LOGIC SEQUENCER
## WITH 3-STATE OUTPUTS OR PRESET

### programming waveforms

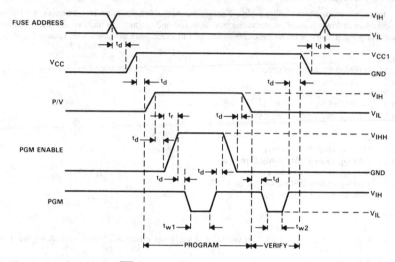

### programming procedure for PRE/$\overline{OE}$ option

PROGRAM
Step 1: With PGM at GND, raise $V_{CC}$ to $V_{CC1}$.
Step 2: Wait $t_d$, pulse PGM to $V_{IX}$ for a duration of $t_{w1}$.
Step 3: A $t_d$ delay after PGM has returned to GND, lower $V_{CC}$ to 5 volts or GND.

VERIFY
Step 1: With PGM at GND, set $V_{CC}$ to 5 volts.
Step 2: After a delay of $t_d$, raise PGM to $V_{IX}$ for a minimum duration of $t_{w2}$.
Step 3: Return PGM to GND.
Step 4: Wait $t_d$, pulse PGM to $V_{IH}$ for a duration of $t_{w2}$.
Step 5: After a $t_d$ delay, Q0 indicates $V_{OH}$ if the PRE option is selected and $V_{OL}$ if the $\overline{OE}$ option is programmed.

### programming waveforms for PRE/$\overline{OE}$ option

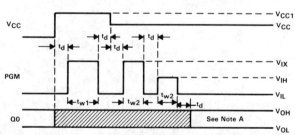

NOTE A: After programming if the PRE option is selected, Q0 will be high; if the output-enable option is selected, the output will be low.

TEXAS
INSTRUMENTS

**array fuse addresses**

## TABLE 1. INPUT LINE AND SUM-OF-PRODUCTS LINE SELECT

| ROW HEX ADDRESS $I12, I11, I10$ | $I9, I8, I7, I6$ | SELECTED VARIABLE | | | ROW HEX ADDRESS $I12, I11, I10$ | $I9, I8, I7, I6$ | SELECTED VARIABLE |
|---|---|---|---|---|---|---|---|
| 0 | 0 | | N7 | SET | 4 | 0 | I0 |
| 0 | 1 | | N7 | RESET | 4 | 1 | $\bar{I}0$ |
| 0 | 2 | | N6 | SET | 4 | 2 | I1 |
| 0 | 3 | | N6 | RESET | 4 | 3 | $\bar{I}1$ |
| 0 | 4 | | N5 | SET | 4 | 4 | I2 |
| 0 | 5 | | N5 | RESET | 4 | 5 | $\bar{I}2$ |
| 0 | 6 | | N4 | SET | 4 | 6 | I3 |
| 0 | 7 | | N4 | RESET | 4 | 7 | $\bar{I}3$ |
| 0 | 8 | OR Array | N3 | SET | 4 | 8 | I4 |
| 0 | 9 | | N3 | RESET | 4 | 9 | $\bar{I}4$ |
| 0 | A | | N2 | SET | 4 | A | I5 |
| 0 | B | | N2 | RESET | 4 | B | $\bar{I}5$ |
| 0 | C | | P1 | SET | 4 | C | P0 |
| 0 | D | | P1 | RESET | 4 | D | $\bar{P}0$ |
| 0 | E | | P0 | SET | 4 | E | I6 |
| 0 | F | | P0 | RESET | 4 | F | $\bar{I}6$ |
| 1 | 0 | | Q3 | SET | 5 | 0 | I7 |
| 1 | 1 | | Q3 | RESET | 5 | 1 | $\bar{I}7$ |
| 1 | 2 | | UNUSED | | 5 | 2 | I8 |
| 1 | 3 | | UNUSED | | 5 | 3 | $\bar{I}8$ |
| 1 | 4 | | Q2 | SET | 5 | 4 | I9 |
| 1 | 5 | | Q2 | RESET | 5 | 5 | $\bar{I}9$ |
| 1 | 6 | | Q1 | SET | 5 | 6 | I10 |
| 1 | 7 | | Q1 | RESET | 5 | 7 | $\bar{I}10$ |
| 1 | 8 | | Q0 | SET | 5 | 8 | I11 |
| 1 | 9 | | Q0 | RESET | 5 | 9 | $\bar{I}11$ |
| 1 | A | | UNUSED | | 5 | A | I12 |
| 1 | B | | UNUSED | | 5 | B | $\bar{I}12$ |
| 1 | C | Complement Array | C | | 5 | C | I13 |
| | | | | | 5 | D | $\bar{I}13$ |
| 1 | D | | | | 5 | E | P1 |
| | | | | | 5 | F | $\bar{P}1$ |
| | | | | | 6 | 0 | P7 |
| | | | | | 6 | 1 | $\bar{P}7$ |
| | | | | | 6 | 2 | P6 |
| | | | | | 6 | 3 | $\bar{P}6$ |
| | | | | | 6 | 4 | P5 |
| | | Empty Address Space | | | 6 | 5 | $\bar{P}5$ |
| | | | | | 6 | 6 | P4 |
| | | | | | 6 | 7 | $\bar{P}4$ |
| | | | | | 6 | 8 | P3 |
| | | | | | 6 | 9 | $\bar{P}3$ |
| | | | | | 6 | A | P2 |
| | | | | | 6 | B | $\bar{P}3$ |
| 3 | F | | | | 6 | C | Complement Array $\bar{C}$ |

TABLE 2.  PRODUCT LINE SELECT

| COLUMN HEX ADDRESS | | SELECTED TRANSITION TERM |
|---|---|---|
| I5, I4 | I3, I2, I1, I0 | |
| 0 | 0 | 0 |
| 0 | 1 | 1 |
| 0 | 2 | 2 |
| 0 | 3 | 3 |
| 0 | 4 | 4 |
| 0 | 5 | 5 |
| 0 | 6 | 6 |
| 0 | 7 | 7 |
| 0 | 8 | 8 |
| 0 | 9 | 9 |
| 0 | A | 10 |
| 0 | B | 11 |
| 0 | C | 12 |
| 0 | D | 13 |
| 0 | E | 14 |
| 0 | F | 15 |
| 1 | 0 | 16 |
| 1 | 1 | 17 |
| 1 | 2 | 18 |
| 1 | 3 | 19 |
| 1 | 4 | 20 |
| 1 | 5 | 21 |
| 1 | 6 | 22 |
| 1 | 7 | 23 |
| 1 | 8 | 24 |
| 1 | 9 | 25 |
| 1 | A | 26 |
| 1 | B | 27 |
| 1 | C | 28 |
| 1 | D | 29 |
| 1 | E | 30 |
| 1 | F | 31 |
| 2 | 0 | 32 |
| 2 | 1 | 33 |
| 2 | 2 | 34 |
| 2 | 3 | 35 |
| 2 | 4 | 36 |
| 2 | 5 | 37 |
| 2 | 6 | 38 |
| 2 | 7 | 39 |
| 2 | 8 | 40 |
| 2 | 9 | 41 |
| 2 | A | 42 |
| 2 | B | 43 |
| 2 | C | 44 |
| 2 | D | 45 |
| 2 | E | 46 |
| 2 | F | 47 |
| 3 | 0 | Test Col 48 |
| 3 | 1 | Test Col 49 |

**TEXAS INSTRUMENTS**

## diagnostics

A diagnostics mode is provided with these devices that allows the user to inspect the contents of the state register. When I0 (pin 9) is held at 10 V, the state register bits P2-P5 and P6-P7 will appear at the Q0-Q3 and P0-P1 outputs. The contents of the registers, Q0-Q3, and P0-P1 remain unchanged.

## diagnostics waveforms

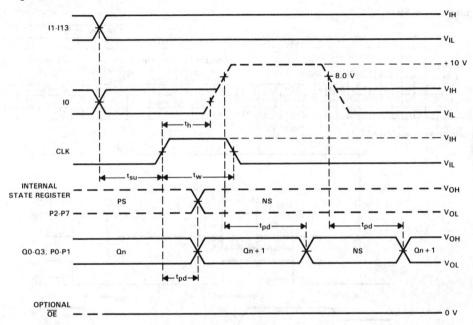

PS = Present State
NS = Next State

Field-Programmable Logic

3

## 82S167A
## 14 × 48 × 6 FIELD-PROGRAMMABLE LOGIC SEQUENCER
## WITH 3-STATE OUTPUTS OR PRESET

### test array

A test array that consists of product lines 48 and 49 has been added to these devices to allow testing prior to programming. The test array is factory programmed as shown below. Testing is accomplished by connecting Q0-Q3 to I10-I13, PRE/OE to GND, and applying the proper input signals as shown in the timing diagram. Product lines 48 and 49 must be deleted during user programming to avoid interference with the programmed logic function.

### test array program

| PRODUCT LINE | C | C̄ | INPUT (In) | | | | | | | | | | | | | | | | PRESENT STATE (PS) | | | | | | NEXT STATE (NS) | | | | | | OUTPUT (Qn) | | | | | | | | OPTION PRE/OE | H |
|---|---|---|---|---|---|---|---|---|---|---|---|---|---|---|---|---|---|---|---|---|---|---|---|---|---|---|---|---|---|---|---|---|---|---|---|---|---|---|---|---|
| | | | 15 | 14 | 13 | 12 | 11 | 10 | 9 | 8 | 7 | 6 | 5 | 4 | 3 | 2 | 1 | 0 | 5 | 4 | 3 | 2 | 1 | 0 | 5 | 4 | 3 | 2 | 1 | 0 | 7 | 6 | 5 | 4 | 3 | 2 | 1 | 0 | | |
| 48 | X | — | H | H | H | H | H | H | H | H | H | H | H | H | H | H | H | H | H | H | H | H | H | H | L | L | L | L | L | L | L | L | L | L | L | L | L | L | | |
| 49 | — | X | L | L | L | L | L | L | L | L | L | L | L | L | L | L | L | L | L | L | L | L | L | L | H | H | H | H | H | H | H | H | H | H | H | H | H | H | | |

### test array waveforms

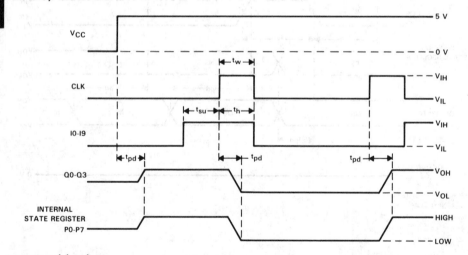

### test array deleted

| PRODUCT LINE | C | C̄ | INPUT (In) | | | | | | | | | | | | | | | | PRESENT STATE (PS) | | | | | | NEXT STATE (NS) | | | | | | OUTPUT (Qn) | | | | | | | | OPTION PRE/OE | H |
|---|---|---|---|---|---|---|---|---|---|---|---|---|---|---|---|---|---|---|---|---|---|---|---|---|---|---|---|---|---|---|---|---|---|---|---|---|---|---|---|---|
| | | | 15 | 14 | 13 | 12 | 11 | 10 | 9 | 8 | 7 | 6 | 5 | 4 | 3 | 2 | 1 | 0 | 5 | 4 | 3 | 2 | 1 | 0 | 5 | 4 | 3 | 2 | 1 | 0 | 7 | 6 | 5 | 4 | 3 | 2 | 1 | 0 | | |
| 48 | — | — | H | H | H | H | H | H | H | H | H | H | H | H | H | H | H | H | H | H | H | H | H | H | — | — | — | — | — | — | — | — | — | — | — | — | — | — | | |
| 49 | — | X | L | L | L | L | L | L | L | L | L | L | L | L | L | L | L | L | L | L | L | L | L | L | — | — | — | — | — | — | — | — | — | — | — | — | — | — | | |

X = Fuse intact,  — = Fuse blown

TEXAS
INSTRUMENTS

**PARAMETER MEASUREMENT INFORMATION**

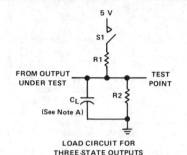

LOAD CIRCUIT FOR
THREE-STATE OUTPUTS

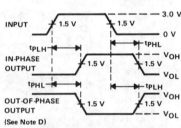

VOLTAGE WAVEFORMS
SETUP AND HOLD TIMES

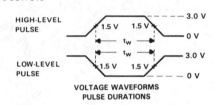

VOLTAGE WAVEFORMS
PULSE DURATIONS

VOLTAGE WAVEFORMS
PROPAGATION DELAY TIMES

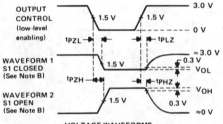

VOLTAGE WAVEFORMS
ENABLE AND DISABLE TIMES, THREE-STATE OUTPUTS

NOTES: A. $C_L$ includes probe and jig capacitance.
   B. Waveform 1 is for an output with internal conditions such that the output is low except when disabled by the output control.
   Waveform 2 is for an output with internal conditions such that the output is high except when disabled by the output control.
   C. All input pulses have the following characteristics: PRR ≤ 1 MHz, $t_r = t_f = 2$ ns, duty cycle = 50%.
   D. When measuring propagation delay times of 3-state outputs, switch S1 is closed.

**3**

**Field-Programmable Logic**

- High Speed . . . t<sub>pd</sub> 12 ns Typical, 20 ns Maximum

- Low Power . . . I<sub>CC</sub> 28 mA Typical, 45 mA Maximum

- Ideal for High-Speed Decoding

- Package Options Include Both Plastic and Ceramic Chip Carriers in Addition to Plastic and Ceramic DIPs

### description

This field-programmable gate array device features a high-speed AND array. It combines Advanced Low-Power Schottky technology with proven titannium-tungsten fuses. These devices will provide reliable high-performance substitutes for conventional TTL logic. Applications include address decoders, code detectors, peripheral selectors, fault monitors, and machine-state decoders. Their easy programmability allows for quick design of custom functions and typically result in a more compact circuit board.

The TIFPGA529 M suffix is characterized for operation over the full military temperature range of −55 °C to 125 °C. The TIFPGA529 C suffix is characterized for operation from 0 °C to 70 °C.

M SUFFIX . . . J PACKAGE
C SUFFIX . . . J OR N PACKAGE
(TOP VIEW)

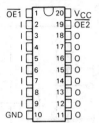

M SUFFIX . . . FK PACKAGE
C SUFFIX . . . FN PACKAGE
(TOP VIEW)

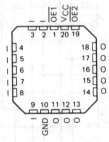

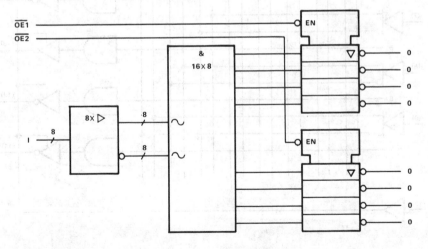

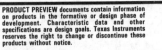 denotes fused inputs.

TEXAS
INSTRUMENTS

**Field-Programmable Logic**

3

## TIFPGA529
## FIELD-PROGRAMMABLE GATE ARRAY (8 × 8 × 8)

logic diagram (positive logic)

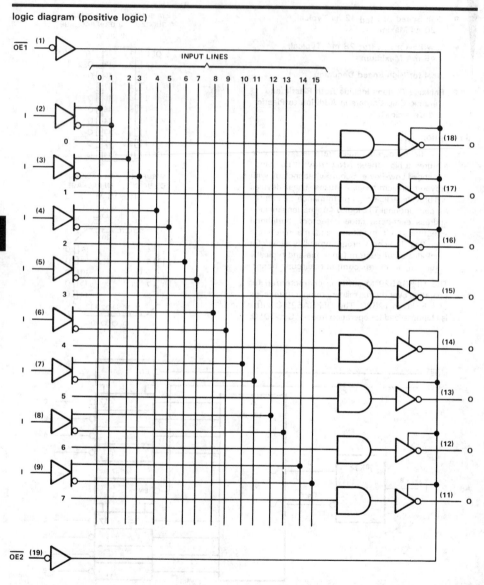

TEXAS
INSTRUMENTS

Field-Programmable Logic

### absolute maximum ratings over operating free-air temperature range (unless otherwise noted)

Supply voltage, $V_{CC}$ (see Note 1) . . . . . . . . . . . . . . . . . . . . . . . . . . . . . . . . . . . . . . . . . . . . . 7 V
Input voltage, $V_I$ (see Note 1) . . . . . . . . . . . . . . . . . . . . . . . . . . . . . . . . . . . . . . . . . . . . . . 5.5 V
Voltage applied to a disabled output (see Note 1) . . . . . . . . . . . . . . . . . . . . . . . . . . . . . . . . 5.5 V
Operating free-air temperature range: M suffix . . . . . . . . . . . . . . . . . . . . . . . . . . −55°C to 125°C
C suffix . . . . . . . . . . . . . . . . . . . . . . . . . . . 0°C to 70°C
Storage temperature range . . . . . . . . . . . . . . . . . . . . . . . . . . . . . . . . . . . . . . . −65°C to 150°C

NOTE 1: These ratings apply except for programming pins during a programming cycle.

### recommended operating conditions

|  |  | M SUFFIX | | | C SUFFIX | | | UNIT |
|---|---|---|---|---|---|---|---|---|
|  |  | MIN | NOM | MAX | MIN | NOM | MAX |  |
| $V_{CC}$ | Supply voltage | 4.5 | 5 | 5.5 | 4.75 | 5 | 5.25 | V |
| $V_{IH}$ | High-level input voltage | 2 |  | 5.5 | 2 |  | 5.5 | V |
| $V_{IL}$ | Low-level input voltage |  |  | 0.8 |  |  | 0.8 | V |
| $I_{OH}$ | High-level output current |  |  | −2 |  |  | −3.2 | mA |
| $I_{OL}$ | Low-level output current |  |  | 12 |  |  | 24 | mA |
| $T_A$ | Operating free-air temperature | −55 |  | 125 | 0 |  | 70 | °C |

### programming parameters, $T_A = 25°C$

|  |  |  | MIN | NOM | MAX | UNIT |
|---|---|---|---|---|---|---|
| $V_{CC}$ | Verify supply voltage |  | 4.75 | 5 | 5.25 | V |
| $V_{CCP}$ | Programming supply voltage |  | 8.75 | 9 | 9.25 | V |
| $V_{IH}$ | High-level input voltage |  | 4 | 4.5 | 5 | V |
| $V_{IL}$ | Low-level input voltage |  | 0 | 0 | 0.5 | V |
| $V_{IHH}$ | Program pulse input voltage |  | 11.75 | 12 | 12.25 | V |
| $I_{IHH}$ | Program pulse input current | I0 through I7 |  | 2 | 5 | mA |
|  |  | O0 through O7 |  | 2 | 5 |  |
| $I_{CCP}$ | Programming supply current |  |  |  | 200 | mA |
| $t_{w1}$ | Pulse duration, $V_{CC}$ |  | 50 |  | 200 | μs |
| $t_{w2}$ | Pulse duration, O0 through O7 |  | 10 |  | 50 | μs |
|  | $V_{CC}$ pulse duty cycle |  |  | 10% | 20% |  |
| $t_{su}$ | Setup time |  | 100 |  |  | ns |
| $t_h$ | Hold time |  | 100 |  |  | ns |

**3**

**Field-Programmable Logic**

## TIFPGA529
## FIELD-PROGRAMMABLE GATE ARRAY (8 × 8 × 8)

**electrical characteristics over recommended operating free-air temperature range**

| PARAMETER | TEST CONDTIONS | M SUFFIX | | | C SUFFIX | | | UNIT |
|---|---|---|---|---|---|---|---|---|
| | | MIN | TYP† | MAX | MIN | TYP† | MAX | |
| $V_{IK}$ | $V_{CC}$ = MIN, $I_I$ = −18 mA | | | −1.5 | | | −1.5 | V |
| $V_{OH}$ | $V_{CC}$ = MIN, $I_{OH}$ = MAX | 2.4 | 3.3 | | 2.4 | 3.3 | | V |
| $V_{OL}$ | $V_{CC}$ = MIN, $I_{OL}$ = MAX | | 0.35 | 0.4 | | 0.35 | 0.5 | V |
| $I_{OZH}$ | $V_{CC}$ = MAX, $V_O$ = 2.7 V | | | 20 | | | 20 | $\mu$A |
| $I_{OZL}$ | $V_{CC}$ = MAX, $V_O$ = 0.4 V | | | −20 | | | −20 | $\mu$A |
| $I_I$ | $V_{CC}$ = MAX, $V_I$ = 5.5 V | | | 0.1 | | | 0.1 | mA |
| $I_{IH}$ | $V_{CC}$ = MAX, $V_I$ = 2.7 V | | | 20 | | | 20 | $\mu$A |
| $I_{IL}$ | $V_{CC}$ = MAX, $V_I$ = 0.4 V | | | −0.2 | | | −0.2 | mA |
| $I_O$ | $V_{CC}$ = MAX, $V_O$ = 2.25 V | −30 | | −112 | −30 | | −112 | mA |
| $I_{CC}$ | $V_{CC}$ = MAX, $V_I$ = 4.5 V, Outputs open | | 28 | 45 | | 28 | 45 | mA |

**switching characteristics over recommended supply voltage and operating free-air temperature ranges,**
$R_L$ = 500 Ω, $C_L$ = 50 pF (unless otherwise noted)

| PARAMETER | FROM (INPUT) | TO (OUTPUT) | M SUFFIX | | | C SUFFIX | | | UNIT |
|---|---|---|---|---|---|---|---|---|---|
| | | | MIN | TYP† | MAX | MIN | TYP† | MAX | |
| $t_{pd}$ | I | O | | 12 | | | 12 | | ns |
| $t_{en}$ | $\overline{OE}$ | Q | | 12 | | | 12 | | ns |
| $t_{dis}$ | $\overline{OE}$ | Q | | 8 | | | 8 | | ns |

†All typical values are at $V_{CC}$ = 5 V, $T_A$ = 25 °C.

## PROGRAMMING PROCEDURE

**pin assignments in programming mode**

DUAL-IN-LINE PACKAGE

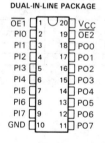

CHIP CARRIER

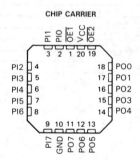

**TEXAS INSTRUMENTS**

## PROGRAMMING PROCEDURE (Continued)

A linear select method is used to program array fuses. Each fuse can be opened by selecting the appropriate (one to 16) input line and then pulsing the correct (one of 8) product line. The levels for selecting input and product lines are shown in Tables 1 and 2.

Step 1: Raise $\overline{OE1}$ and $\overline{OE2}$ to $V_{IH}$.
Step 2: Raise not-selected inputs to $V_{IH}$.
Step 3: Raise the selected input to $V_{IH}$ or $V_{IL}$ in accordance with Table 1.
Step 4: Raise $V_{CC}$ from 5 V to $V_{CCP}$.
Step 5: Blow the fuse by pulsing the appropriate output to $V_{IHH}$ in accordance with Table 2.
Step 6: Return $V_{CC}$ to 5 V and pulse the selected input. The appropriate output will switch from $V_{OL}$ to $V_{OH}$.
Step 7: Return $\overline{OE1}$ and $\overline{OE2}$ to $V_{IL}$.

Steps 1 through 7 may be repeated if the verification does not indicate that the fuse was successfully programmed (blown), but no more than four times.

### TABLE 1. INPUT SELECT LINE

| INPUT LINE | PIN NAME | | | | | | | | | |
|---|---|---|---|---|---|---|---|---|---|---|
| | PIO | PI1 | PI2 | PI3 | PI4 | PI5 | PI6 | PI7 | $\overline{OE1}$ | $\overline{OE2}$ |
| 0 | L | HH | HH | HH | HH | HH | HH | HH | H | H |
| 1 | H | HH | HH | HH | HH | HH | HH | HH | H | H |
| 2 | HH | L | HH | HH | HH | HH | HH | HH | H | H |
| 3 | HH | H | HH | HH | HH | HH | HH | HH | H | H |
| 4 | HH | HH | L | HH | HH | HH | HH | HH | H | H |
| 5 | HH | HH | H | HH | HH | HH | HH | HH | H | H |
| 6 | HH | HH | HH | L | HH | HH | HH | HH | H | H |
| 7 | HH | HH | HH | HH | HH | HH | HH | HH | H | H |
| 8 | HH | HH | HH | HH | L | HH | HH | HH | H | H |
| 9 | HH | HH | HH | HH | H | HH | HH | HH | H | H |
| 10 | HH | HH | HH | HH | HH | L | HH | HH | H | H |
| 11 | HH | HH | HH | HH | HH | H | HH | HH | H | H |
| 12 | HH | HH | HH | HH | HH | HH | L | HH | H | H |
| 13 | HH | HH | HH | HH | HH | HH | H | HH | H | H |
| 14 | HH | HH | HH | HH | HH | HH | HH | L | H | H |
| 15 | HH | HH | HH | HH | HH | HH | HH | H | H | H |

### TABLE 2. PRODUCT TERM SELECT

| PRODUCT TERM | PIN NAME | | | | | | | |
|---|---|---|---|---|---|---|---|---|
| | POO | PO1 | PO2 | PO3 | PO4 | PO5 | PO6 | PO7 |
| 0 | HH | X | X | X | X | X | X | X |
| 1 | X | HH | X | X | X | X | X | X |
| 2 | X | X | HH | X | X | X | X | X |
| 3 | X | X | X | HH | X | X | X | X |
| 4 | X | X | X | X | HH | X | X | X |
| 5 | X | X | X | X | X | HH | X | X |
| 6 | X | X | X | X | X | X | HH | X |
| 7 | X | X | X | X | X | X | X | HH |

$H = V_{IH}$
$L = V_{IL}$
HH = Program pulse input voltage
X = Don't care

TEXAS
INSTRUMENTS

Field-Programmable Logic

3

# TIFPGA529
## FIELD-PROGRAMMABLE GATE ARRAY (8 × 8 × 8)

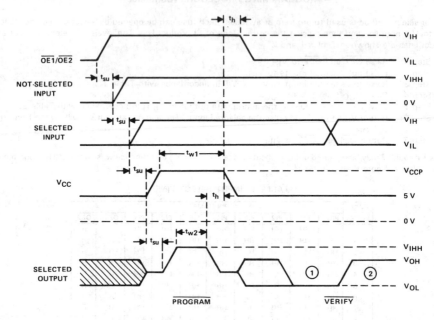

① Selected output will be low
② Selected output will go high when selected input is switched

**FIGURE 1. PROGRAMMING WAVEFORMS**

3

Field-Programmable Logic

TEXAS
INSTRUMENTS

# TIFPLA839, TIFPLA840
## 14 × 32 × 6 FIELD-PROGRAMMABLE LOGIC ARRAYS

JUNE 1984—REVISED NOVEMBER 1984

- **Input-to-Output Propagation Delay . . . 10 ns Typical**
- **24-Pin, 300-mil Slim Line Packages**
- **Power Dissipation . . . 650 mW Typical**
- **Programmable Output Polarity**

**LOGIC FUNCTION**

$f(I) = P0 + P1 \ldots P31$ for polarity link intact

$f(I) = \overline{P0} * \overline{P1} * \ldots * \overline{P31}$ for polarity link open

where P0 through P31 are product terms

### description

The 'FPLA839 (3-state outputs) and the 'FPLA840 (open-collector outputs) are TTL field-programmable logic arrays containing 32 product terms (AND terms) and six sum terms (OR terms). Each of the sum-of-products output functions can be programmed either high true or low true. The true condition of each output function is activated by the programmed logical minterms of 14 input variables. The outputs are controlled by two chip-enable pins to allow output inhibit and expansion of terms.

These devices provide high-speed data-path logic replacement where several conventional SSI functions can be designed into a single package.

The 'FPLA839M and 'FPLA840M are characterized for operation over the full military temperature range of −55°C to 125°C. The 'FPLA839C and 'FPLA840C are characterized for operation from 0°C to 70°C.

TIFPLA839M, TIFPLA840M . . . JT PACKAGE
TIFPLA839C, TIFPLA840C . . . JT OR NT PACKAGE
(TOP VIEW)

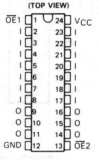

TIFPLA839M, TIFPLA840M . . . FH OR FK PACKAGE
TIFPLA839C, TIFPLA840C . . . FN PACKAGE
(TOP VIEW)

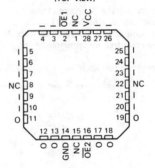

Pin assignments in operating mode (pin 1 is less positive than $V_{IHH}$)

**3**

**Field-Programmable Logic**

TEXAS
INSTRUMENTS

**functional block diagram (positive logic)**

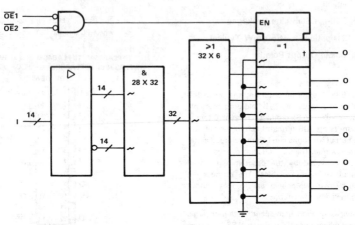

~denotes fused inputs.

†FPLA839 has 3-state (▽) outputs; FPLA840 has open-collector (◇) outputs.

**absolute maximum ratings**

Supply voltage, $V_{CC}$ (see Note 1) . . . . . . . . . . . . . . . . . . . . . . . . . . . . . . . . . . . . . . . . . . . . 7 V

Input voltage (see Note 1) . . . . . . . . . . . . . . . . . . . . . . . . . . . . . . . . . . . . . . . . . . . . . . . . . . . . 5.5 V

Off-state output voltage (see Note 1) . . . . . . . . . . . . . . . . . . . . . . . . . . . . . . . . . . . . . . . . . . 5.5 V

Operating free-air temperature range: 'FPLA839M, 'FPLA840M . . . . . . . . . . . . . . −55 °C to 125 °C

'FPLA839C, 'FPLA840C . . . . . . . . . . . . . . . . . 0 °C to 70 °C

Storage temperature . . . . . . . . . . . . . . . . . . . . . . . . . . . . . . . . . . . . . . . . . . . . . . −65 °C to 150 °C

NOTE 1: These ratings apply except for programming pins during a programming cycle.

**3**

**Field-Programmable Logic**

TEXAS
INSTRUMENTS

## LOGIC DIAGRAM

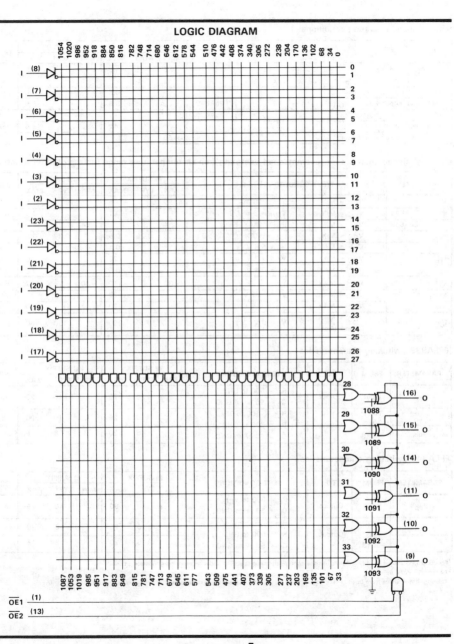

Field-Programmable Logic

TEXAS
INSTRUMENTS

## TIFPLA839, TIFPLA840
## 14 × 32 × 6 FIELD-PROGRAMMABLE LOGIC ARRAYS

**recommended operating conditions**

| | | M SUFFIX | | | C SUFFIX | | | UNIT |
|---|---|---|---|---|---|---|---|---|
| | | MIN | NOM | MAX | MIN | NOM | MAX | |
| Supply voltage, $V_{CC}$ | | 4.5 | 5 | 5.5 | 4.75 | 5 | 5.25 | V |
| High-level input voltage, $V_{IH}$ | | 2 | | | 2 | | | V |
| Low-level input voltage, $V_{IL}$ | | | | 0.8 | | | 0.8 | V |
| High-level output voltage, $V_{OH}$ | 'FPLA840 | | | 5.5 | | | 5.5 | V |
| High-level output current, $I_{OH}$ | 'FPLA839 | | | −2 | | | −3.2 | mA |
| Low-level output current, $I_{OL}$ | | | | 12 | | | 24 | mA |
| Operating free-air temperature, $T_A$ | | −55 | | 125 | 0 | | 70 | °C |

**electrical characteristics over recommended operating free-air temperature range (unless otherwise noted)**

| PARAMETER | | TEST CONDITIONS[†] | | M SUFFIX | | | C SUFFIX | | | UNIT |
|---|---|---|---|---|---|---|---|---|---|---|
| | | | | MIN | TYP[‡] | MAX | MIN | TYP[‡] | MAX | |
| $V_{IK}$ | | $V_{CC}$ = MIN, | $I_I$ = −18 mA | | | −1.5 | | | −1.5 | V |
| $I_{OH}$ 'FPLA840 | | $V_{CC}$ = MIN, | $V_{OH}$ = 5.5 V | | | 0.1 | | | 0.1 | mA |
| $V_{OH}$ 'FPLA839 | | $V_{CC}$ = MIN, | $I_{OH}$ = MAX | 2.4 | 3.2 | | 2.4 | 3 | | V |
| $V_{OL}$ | | $V_{CC}$ = MIN, | $I_{OL}$ = MAX | | 0.25 | 0.5 | | 0.37 | 0.5 | V |
| $I_I$ | | $V_{CC}$ = MAX, | $V_I$ = 5.5 V | | | 0.1 | | | 0.1 | mA |
| $I_{IH}$ | | $V_{CC}$ = MAX, | $V_I$ = 2.7 V | | | 20 | | | 20 | μA |
| $I_{IL}$ | | $V_{CC}$ = MAX, | $V_I$ = 0.4 V | | | −0.5 | | | −0.5 | mA |
| $I_O$ [§] | | $V_{CC}$ = MAX, | $V_O$ = 2.25 V | −30 | | −112 | −30 | | −112 | mA |
| $I_{OZH}$ | | $V_{CC}$ = MAX, | $V_O$ = 2.7 V | | | 20 | | | 20 | μA |
| $I_{OZL}$ | | $V_{CC}$ = MAX, | $V_O$ = 0.4 V | | | −20 | | | −20 | μA |
| $I_{CC}$ | | $V_{CC}$ = MAX, $\overline{OE}$ inputs at $V_{IH}$ | $V_I$ = 0 V, | | 130 | 190 | | 130 | 180 | mA |

**'FPLA839 switching characteristics**

| PARAMETER | FROM | TO | TEST CONDITIONS | M SUFFIX | | | C SUFFIX | | | UNIT |
|---|---|---|---|---|---|---|---|---|---|---|
| | | | | MIN | TYP[‡] | MAX | MIN | TYP[‡] | MAX | |
| $t_{pd}$ | Input | Output | $R_L$ = 500 to GND, $C_L$ = 50 pF to GND | | 10 | 25 | | 10 | 20 | ns |
| $t_{en}$ | Pin 1 or Pin 13 | Output | $R_{L1}$ = 500 to 7 V, $R_L$ = 500 to GND, $C_L$ = 50 pF to GND | | 10 | 25 | | 10 | 20 | ns |
| $t_{dis}$ | | | | | 8 | 20 | | 8 | 15 | |

**'FPLA840 switching characteristics**

| PARAMETER | FROM | TO | TEST CONDITIONS | M SUFFIX | | | C SUFFIX | | | UNIT |
|---|---|---|---|---|---|---|---|---|---|---|
| | | | | MIN | TYP[‡] | MAX | MIN | TYP[‡] | MAX | |
| $t_{pd}$ | Input | Output | $R_L$ = 500 to $V_{CC}$, $C_L$ = 50 pF to GND | | 10 | 30 | | 10 | 25 | ns |
| $t_{en}$ | Pin 1 or Pin 13 | Output | $R_{L1}$ = 500 to 7 V, $R_L$ = 500 to GND, $C_L$ = 50 pF to GND | | 10 | 25 | | 10 | 20 | ns |
| $t_{dis}$ | | | | | 8 | 20 | | 8 | 15 | |

[†]For conditions shown as MIN or MAX, use the appropriate value specified under recommended operating conditions.

[‡]All typical values are at $V_{CC}$ = 5 V, $T_A$ = 25°C.

[§]The output conditions have been chosen to produce a current that closely approximates one half of the true short-circuit current, $I_{OS}$.

**TEXAS INSTRUMENTS**

# TIFPLA839, TIFPLA840
## 14 × 32 × 6 FIELD-PROGRAMMABLE LOGIC ARRAYS

**OUTPUT POLARITY**
(PGM ENABLE = $V_{ILL}$)

| | | |
|---|---|---|
| PGM ENABLE | 1 | 24 | $V_{CC}$† |
| PI1 | 2 | 23 | PI0 |
| PI2 | 3 | 22 | PI13 |
| PI3 | 4 | 21 | PI12 |
| PI4 | 5 | 20 | PI11 |
| PI5 | 6 | 19 | PI10 |
| PI6 | 7 | 18 | PI9 |
| PI7 | 8 | 17 | PI8 |
| PO5 | 9 | 16 | PO0 |
| PO4 | 10 | 15 | PO1 |
| PO3 | 11 | 14 | PO2 |
| GND | 12 | 13 | $\overline{OE2}$ |

**AND MATRIX**
($V_{CC3}$)

| | | |
|---|---|---|
| PGM ENABLE | 1 | 24 | $V_{CC}$ |
| PI1 | 2 | 23 | PI0 |
| PI2 | 3 | 22 | PI13 |
| PI3 | 4 | 21 | PI12 |
| PI4 | 5 | 20 | PI11 |
| PI5 | 6 | 19 | PI10 |
| PI6 | 7 | 18 | PI9 |
| PI7 | 8 | 17 | PI8 |
| PO | 9 | 16 | PA0 |
| PA4 | 10 | 15 | PA1 |
| PA3 | 11 | 14 | PA2 |
| GND | 12 | 13 | PGM |

**OR MATRIX**
($V_{CC1}$, PA5 = $V_{IL}$)

| | | |
|---|---|---|
| PGM ENABLE | 1 | 24 | $V_{CC}$ |
| PA1 | 2 | 23 | PA0 |
| PA2 | 3 | 22 | PI13 |
| PA3 | 4 | 21 | PI12 |
| PA4 | 5 | 20 | PI11 |
| PA5 | 6 | 19 | PI10 |
| PI6 | 7 | 18 | PI9 |
| PI7 | 8 | 17 | PI8 |
| PO5 | 9 | 16 | PO0 |
| PO4 | 10 | 15 | PO1 |
| PO3 | 11 | 14 | PO2 |
| GND | 12 | 13 | PGM |

†$V_{CC}$ = $V_{CC2}$ for program and $V_{CC1}$ for verify
Pin assignment in programming mode (pin 1 ≤ $V_{IHH}$) top views

## programming parameters, $T_A$ = 25°C

| PARAMETER | | MEASURED AT | PROGRAMMING MODE | MIN | TYP | MAX | UNIT |
|---|---|---|---|---|---|---|---|
| $V_{IHH}$ | Program high-level input voltage | PGM ENABLE | AND, OR | 16.5 | 17 | 17.5 | V |
| | | PO pins | Polarity | | | | |
| $V_{ILL}$ | Program low-level input voltage | PGM ENABLE | Any | 0 | | 0.4 | V |
| $I_{IHH}$ | Program-level input current | PO pins | Polarity | | 100 | | mA |
| | | PGM ENABLE | AND, OR | | 150 | | |
| $V_{IX}$ | Program-level input voltage | POO thru PO5 | Polarity | 9.5 | 10 | 10.5 | V |
| | | PGM | AND, OR | | | | |
| $I_{IX}$ | Program-level input current | PI pins | AND | | 0.6 | 2 | mA |
| | | $\overline{OE2}$ | Polarity | | | 5 | |
| | | POO thru PO5 | OR | | 5 | 10 | |
| $V_{CC1}$ | Programming supply voltage | $V_{CC}$ | OR | 8.5 | 8.75 | 9 | V |
| $I_{CC1}$ | Programming supply current | $V_{CC}$ | OR | | 250 | 400 | mA |
| $V_{CC2}$ | Programming supply voltage | $V_{CC}$ | Polarity | | 0 | 0.4 | V |
| $V_{CC3}$ | Programming supply voltage | $V_{CC}$ | AND | 4.75 | 5 | 5.25 | V |
| $V_{IH}$ | High-level input voltage | Any | Any | 2 | | | V |
| $V_{IL}$ | Low-level input voltage | Any | Any | 0 | | 0.8 | V |
| $V_{OH}$ | High-level output voltage | Any | Any | 2.4 | 3.2 | | V |
| $V_{OL}$ | Low-level output voltage | Any | Any | | 0.25 | 0.5 | V |
| $t_w$ | Program pulse duration | POO thru PO5 | Polarity | | 50 | 1000 | µs |
| | | PGM | AND, OR | | | | |
| | Program pulse duty cycle | POO thru PO5 | Polarity | | 10 | 50 | % |
| | | PGM | AND, OR | | | | |
| $t_d$ | Delay time | Any | Any | 10 | | | µs |
| $t_r$ | Rise time | Any | Any | | 25 | | µs |

**3**

**Field-Programmable Logic**

TEXAS
INSTRUMENTS

### PROGRAMMING PROCEDURE

## OUTPUT POLARITY

### Program

Load all output pins with a 10-kΩ resistor to 5 V and set pin 12 (GND) to 0 V. Program the output polarity before programming either the AND matrix or the OR matrix. An unprogrammed device has all six outputs noninverting. When the polarity link of an output is opened, the output function becomes inverting. Program one output at a time as follows:

Step 1: Set PGM ENABLE (pin 1) to $V_{ILL}$.
Step 2: Set $V_{CC}$ (pin 24) to $V_{CC2}$; set $\overline{OE}2$ (pin 13) to $V_{IH}$ and PI0 through PI13 to $V_{IH}$.
Step 3: Ramp the appropriate output to $V_{IHH}$ and remove after $t_w$.
Step 4: Repeat step 3 for each output to be programmed low.

### Verify

Step 1: Set PGM ENABLE (pin 1) to $V_{ILL}$; set $V_{CC}$ (pin 24) to $V_{CC2}$; set PI0 through PI13 to $V_{IH}$.
Step 2: Wait $t_d$ and raise $V_{CC}$ (pin 24) to $V_{CC1}$.
Step 3: Enable the device by applying $V_{IL}$ to $\overline{OE}2$ (pin 13).
Step 4: Sense the logic state of all six outputs. An output at $V_{OH}$ has been programmed to be inverting, while an output at $V_{OL}$ has remained noninverting.
Step 5: Remove $V_{CC1}$.

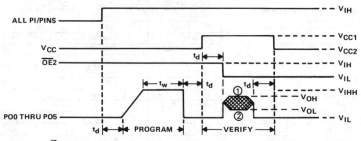

① A high level during the verify interval indicates that programming has been successful.
② A low level during the verify interval indicates that programming has not been successful.

### FIGURE 1. OUTPUT POLARITY PROGRAMMING WAVEFORMS

## AND MATRIX

### Program

Program the output polarity before programming either the AND matrix or the OR matrix. Load all output pins with a 10-kΩ resistor to 5 V and set pin 12 (GND) to $V_{IL}$. Program each input separately for each product term, one fuse at a time. Unused terms do not require fusing, however, all input variables of a selected product term must be programmed either true, complement, or don't care (both links are blown), as follows:

Step 1: Set PGM ENABLE (pin 1) to $V_{ILL}$; set $V_{CC}$ (pin 24) to $V_{CC3}$.
Step 2: Disable all outputs by applying $V_{IH}$ to PGM (pin 13).
Step 3: Disable all inputs by applying $V_{IX}$ to the I inputs.
Step 4: Address the product term to be programmed (0 through 31) by applying its binary code ($V_{IH}$ for a high and $V_{IL}$ for a low) to outputs PA0 through PA4 with PA0 as the least significant bit.

### PROGRAMMING PROCEDURE

Step 5: Lower the voltage on the first input to $V_{IH}$ for a true, or to $V_{IL}$ for the complement.
Step 6: After $t_d$, raise PGM ENABLE to $V_{IHH}$.
Step 7: After additional $t_d$, pulse the PGM input to $V_{IH}$ for $t_w$.
Step 8: After additional $t_d$ delay, lower PGM ENABLE to $V_{ILL}$.
Step 9: Disable programmed input by raising it back to $V_{IH}$.
Step 10: Repeat steps 5 through 9 for each input.
Step 11: Repeat steps 4 through 10 for each product term.

**Verify**

Step 1: Set PGM ENABLE (pin 1) to $V_{ILL}$; set $V_{CC}$ (pin 24) to $V_{CC3}$.
Step 2: Enable PO output by setting PGM to $V_{IX}$.
Step 3: Disable all inputs by applying $V_{IX}$ to the I inputs.
Step 4: Address the product term to be verified (0 through 31) by applying its binary code on outputs PA0 through PA4.
Step 5: Lower the input voltage on the first input to $V_{IH}$ and check the logic level of output PO, then lower the same input to $V_{IL}$ and again check the level of PO. The input variable state contained in the product term is determined from the following table. Two tests are required to verify the programmed state of each variable.

| STATE | I | PO |
|---|---|---|
| TRUE | L | L |
|  | H | H |
| COMPLEMENT | L | H |
|  | H | L |
| DON'T CARE | L | H |
|  | H | H |
| INACTIVE | L | L |
|  | H | L |

Step 6: Disable verified input by raising it back to $V_{IX}$.
Step 7: Repeat steps 5 and 6 for all other inputs.
Step 8: Repeat steps 4 through 7 for all other product terms.

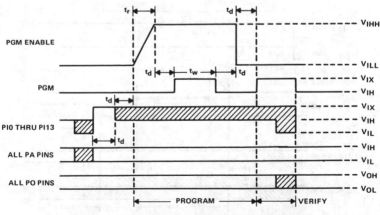

### FIGURE 2. AND MATRIX PROGRAMMING WAVEFORMS

Field-Programmable Logic

3

3

Field-Programmable Logic

### PROGRAMMING PROCEDURE

#### OR MATRIX

**Program**

Program the output polarity before programming either the AND matrix or the OR matrix. Load all output pins with a 10-kΩ resistor to 5 V and set pin 12 (GND) to 0 V. If the product term is contained in the output function, no fusing is required. Unwanted terms are deleted by programming one at a time, as follows:

Step 1: Set PGM ENABLE (pin 1) to $V_{ILL}$. Disable the outputs by setting PGM (pin 13) to $V_{IH}$. Set $V_{CC}$ to $V_{CC3}$. Set PI6 through PI13 and PA0 through PA5 to $V_{IH}$.

Step 2: Wait $t_d$ and raise $V_{CC}$ (pin 24) to the program level, $V_{CC1}$.

Step 3: Use the inputs PA0 through PA5 to address the product term (0 through 31) that is to be removed by applying the corresponding binary code with input PA0 as the least significant bit.

Step 4: Raise the output pin to $V_{IX}$.

Step 5: Wait $t_d$, then raise PGM ENABLE to $V_{IHH}$.

Step 6: Wait $t_d$, then pulse PGM to $V_{IX}$ for a period of $t_p$.

Step 7: Wait $t_d$, then lower PGM ENABLE to $V_{ILL}$.

Step 8: Wait $t_d$, then remove $V_{IX}$ from output pin.

Step 9: Repeat steps 4 through 8 for all other output functions.

Step 10: Repeat steps 3 through 9 for all other product terms.

Step 11: Lower $V_{CC}$ to $V_{CC3}$.

**Verify**

Step 1: Set PGM ENABLE (pin 1) to $V_{ILL}$. Disable the outputs by setting PGM (pin 13) to $V_{IH}$. Set $V_{CC}$ to $V_{CC3}$. Set PI6 through PI13 and PA0 through PA5 to $V_{IH}$.

Step 2: Wait $t_d$ and set $V_{CC}$ (pin 24) to the verify level, $V_{CC1}$.

Step 3: Address the product term to be verified (0 through 31) by applying its binary code to inputs PA0 through PA5.

Step 4: Wait $t_d$, and set PGM (pin 13) to $V_{IL}$.

Step 5: Monitor the state of all six outputs (PO0 through PO5) and determine the status of the OR matrix from the following table:

| OUTPUT | | OR FUSE LINK |
|---|---|---|
| ACTIVE HIGH | ACTIVE LOW | |
| L | H | FUSED |
| H | L | PRESENT |

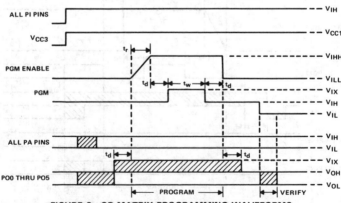

**FIGURE 3. OR MATRIX PROGRAMMING WAVEFORMS**

TEXAS
INSTRUMENTS

General Information 1

Functional Index 2

Field-Programmable Logic 3

PROMs 4

RAMs and Memory-Based
Code Converters 5

Designing with Texas Instruments
Field-Programmable Logic 6

Mechanical Data 7

4-1

4

PROMs

# BIPOLAR PROM CROSS-REFERENCE GUIDE

| DEVICE | MANUFACTURER | TI | DEVICE | MANUFACTURER | TI |
|--------|--------------|-----|--------|--------------|-----|
| 27S18 | AMD | TBP18SA030 | 7122 | FUJITSU | TBP24S41 |
| 27S18A | AMD | TBP38SA030 | 7123 | FUJITSU | TBP28SA42 |
| 27S19 | AMD | TBP18S030 | 7124 | FUJITSU | TBP28S42 |
| 27S19A | AMD | TBP38S030 | 7127 | FUJITSU | TBP24SA81 |
| 27S20 | AMD | TBP24SA10 | 7128 | FUJITSU | TBP24S81 |
| 27S21 | AMD | TBP24S10 | 7131 | FUJITSU | TBP28SA86A |
| 27S28 | AMD | TBP28SA42 | 7132 | FUJITSU | TBP28S86A |
| 27S29 | AMD | TBP28S42 | 7138 | FUJITSU | TBP28S166 |
| 27S30 | AMD | TBP28SA46 | 74S188 | NATIONAL | TBP18SA030 |
| 27S31 | AMD | TBP28S46 | 74S287 | NATIONAL | TBP24S10 |
| 27S32 | AMD | TBP24SA41 | 74S288 | NATIONAL | TBP18S030 |
| 27S33 | AMD | TBP24S41 | 74S387 | NATIONAL | TBP24SA10 |
| 27S180 | AMD | TBP28SA86A | 74S470 | NATIONAL | TBP28LA22 |
| 27S181 | AMD | TBP28S86A | 74S471 | NATIONAL | TBP28L22 |
| 27S184 | AMD | TBP24SA81 | 74S472 | NATIONAL | TBP28S42 |
| 27S185 | AMD | TBP24S81 | 74S473 | NATIONAL | TBP28SA42 |
| 27S191 | AMD | TBP38S166-45 | 74S474 | NATIONAL | TBP28S46 |
| 27S191A | AMD | TBP38L166-35 | 74S475 | NATIONAL | TBP28SA46 |
| 3601 | INTEL | TBP24SA10 | 74S572 | NATIONAL | TBP24SA41 |
| 3604 | INTEL | TBP28SA46 | 74S573 | NATIONAL | TBP24S41 |
| 3605 | INTEL | TBP24SA41 | 7602 | HARRIS | TBP18SA030 |
| 3608 | INTEL | TBP28SA86A | 7603 | HARRIS | TBP18S030 |
| 3621 | INTEL | TBP24S10 | 7608 | HARRIS | TBP28S2708A |
| 3624 | INTEL | TBP28S46 | 7610 | HARRIS | TBP24SA10 |
| 3625 | INTEL | TBP24S41 | 7611 | HARRIS | TBP24S10 |
| 3628 | INTEL | TBP28S86A | 76161 | HARRIS | TBP28S166 |
| 3636 | INTEL | TBP28S166 | 76161 | MOTOROLA | TBP28S166 |
| 6300-1 | MMI | TBP24SA10 | 7640 | HARRIS | TBP28SA46 |
| 6301-1 | MMI | TBP24S10 | 7640 | MOTOROLA | TBP28SA46 |
| 6308-1 | MMI | TBP28LA22 | 7641 | HARRIS | TBP28S46 |
| 6309-1 | MMI | TBP28L22 | 7641 | MOTOROLA | TBP28S46 |
| 6330-1 | MMI | TBP18SA030 | 7642 | HARRIS | TBP24SA41 |
| 6331-1 | MMI | TBP18S030 | 7642 | MOTOROLA | TBP24SA41 |
| 6340-1 | MMI | TBP28SA46 | 7643 | HARRIS | TBP24S41 |
| 6341-1 | MMI | TBP28S46 | 7643 | MOTOROLA | TBP24S41 |
| 6348-1 | MMI | TBP28SA42 | 7648 | HARRIS | TBP28SA42 |
| 6349-1 | MMI | TBP28S42 | 7649 | HARRIS | TBP28S42 |
| 6352-1 | MMI | TBP24SA41 | 7680 | MOTOROLA | TBP28SA86A |
| 6353-1 | MMI | TBP24S41 | 7680 | HARRIS | TBP28SA86A |
| 6380-1 | MMI | TBP28SA86A | 7681 | HARRIS | TBP28S86A |
| 6381-1 | MMI | TBP28S86A | 7681 | MOTOROLA | TBP28S86A |
| 6388-1 | MMI | TBP24SA81 | 7684 | HARRIS | TBP24SA81 |
| 6389-1 | MMI | TBP24S81 | 7684 | MOTOROLA | TBP24SA81 |
| 63S081 | MMI | TBP38S030 | 7685 | HARRIS | TBP24S81 |
| 63S1681 | MMI | TBP28S166 | 7685 | MOTOROLA | TBP24S81 |
| 63S1681A | MMI | TBP38L166-35 | 82S23 | SIGNETICS | TBP18SA030 |
| 7117 | FUJITSU | TBP28LA22 | 82S23A | SIGNETICS | TBP38SA030 |
| 7118 | FUJITSU | TBP28L22 | 82S123 | SIGNETICS | TBP18S030 |
| 7121 | FUJITSU | TBP24SA41 | 82S123A | SIGNETICS | TBP38S030 |

**4**

**PROMs**

# BIPOLAR PROM CROSS-REFERENCE GUIDE

| DEVICE | MANUFACTURER | TI | DEVICE | MANUFACTURER | TI |
|--------|--------------|-----|--------|--------------|-----|
| 82S126 | SIGNETICS | TBP24SA10 | 87S184 | NATIONAL | TBP24SA81 |
| 82S129 | SIGNETICS | TBP24S10 | 87S185 | NATIONAL | TBP24S81 |
| 82S136 | SIGNETICS | TBP24SA41 | 87S191 | NATIONAL | TBP28S166 |
| 82S137 | SIGNETICS | TBP24S41 | 87S191A | NATIONAL | TBP38S166-45 |
| 82S140 | SIGNETICS | TBP28SA46 | 87S191B | NATIONAL | TBP38S166-35 |
| 82S141 | SIGNETICS | TBP28S46 | 93417 | FAIRCHILD | TBP24SA10 |
| 82S146 | SIGNETICS | TBP28SA42 | 93427 | FAIRCHILD | TBP24S10 |
| 82S147 | SIGNETICS | TBP28S42 | 93438 | FAIRCHILD | TBP28SA46 |
| 82S180 | SIGNETICS | TBP28SA86A | 93448 | FAIRCHILD | TBP28S46 |
| 82S181 | SIGNETICS | TBP28S86A | 93450 | FAIRCHILD | TBP28SA86A |
| 82LS181 | SIGNETICS | TBP28L86A | 93451 | FAIRCHILD | TBP28S86A |
| 82S184 | SIGNETICS | TBP24SA81 | 93452 | FAIRCHILD | TBP24SA41 |
| 82S185 | SIGNETICS | TBP24S81 | 93453 | FAIRCHILD | TBP24S41 |
| 82S191 | SIGNETICS | TBP28S166 | 93511 | FAIRCHILD | TBP28S166 |
| 82S191B | SIGNETICS | TBP38L166-45 | 93511C | FAIRCHILD | TBP38L166-45 |
| 82S2708 | SIGNETICS | TBP28S2708A | 93514 | FAIRCHILD | TBP24SA81 |
| 87S180 | NATIONAL | TBP28SA86A | 93515 | FAIRCHILD | TBP24S81 |
| 87S181 | NATIONAL | TBP28S86A | | | |

4

PROMS

- Titanium-Tungsten (Ti-W) Fuse Link for Reliable Low-Voltage Full Family Compatible Programming

- Full Decoding and Fast Chip Select Simplify System Design

- P-N-P Inputs for Reduced Loading on System Buffers/Drivers

- Applications Include:
  Microprogramming/Firmware Loaders
  Code Converters/Character Generators
  Translators/Emulators
  Address Mapping/Look-Up Tables

- Choice of 3-State or Open-Collector Outputs

**TBP18SA030, TBP18S030 . . . J OR N PACKAGE**

(TOP VIEW)

| | |
|---|---|
| Q0 [ 1 | 16 ] $V_{CC}$ |
| Q1 [ 2 | 15 ] $\overline{G}$ |
| Q2 [ 3 | 14 ] A4 |
| Q3 [ 4 | 13 ] A3 |
| Q4 [ 5 | 12 ] A2 |
| Q5 [ 6 | 11 ] A1 |
| Q6 [ 7 | 10 ] A0 |
| GND [ 8 | 9 ] Q7 |

## description

These monolithic TTL programmable read-only memories (PROMs) feature titanium-tungsten (Ti-W) fuse links with each link designed to program in 20 microseconds. The Schottky-clamped versions of these PROMs offer considerable flexibility for upgrading existing designs or improving new designs as they feature full Schottky clamping for improved performance, low-current MOS-compatible p-n-p inputs, choice of bus-driving three-state or open-collector outputs, and improved chip-select access times.

Data can be electronically programmed, as desired, at any bit location in accordance with the programming procedure specified. All PROMs are supplied with a low-logic level output condition stored at each bit location. The programming procedure open-circuits Ti-W metal links, which reverses the stored logic level at selected locations. The procedure is irreversible; once altered, the output for that bit location is permanently programmed. Outputs that have never been altered may later be programmed to supply the opposite output level. Operation of the unit within the recommended operating conditions will not alter the memory content.

A low level at the chip-select input(s) enables each PROM. The opposite level at any chip-select input causes the outputs to be off.

The three-state output offers the convenience of an open-collector with the speed of a totem-pole output; it can be bus-connected to other similar outputs yet it retains the fast rise time characteristic of the TTL totem-pole output. The open-collector output offers the capability of direct interface with a data line having a passive pull up.

A MJ suffix designates full-temperature circuits (formerly 54 Family) and are characterized for operation over the full military temperature range of −55°C to 125°C. A J or N suffix designates commercial-temperature circuits (formerly 74 Family) and are characterized for operation from 0°C to 70°C.

**4**

**PROMs**

**TEXAS INSTRUMENTS**

## TBP18S030, TBP18SA030
## 256 BITS (32 WORDS BY 8 BITS)
## PROGRAMMABLE READ-ONLY MEMORIES

### logic symbol

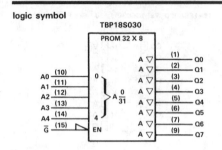
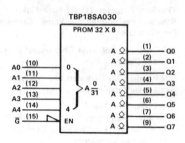

### schematics of inputs and outputs

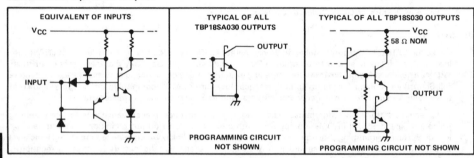

| EQUIVALENT OF INPUTS | TYPICAL OF ALL TBP18SA030 OUTPUTS | TYPICAL OF ALL TBP18S030 OUTPUTS |

PROGRAMMING CIRCUIT NOT SHOWN

PROGRAMMING CIRCUIT NOT SHOWN

### absolute maximum ratings over operating free-air temperature range (unless otherwise noted)

Supply voltage (see Note 1) ................................................................ 7V
Input voltage .............................................................................. 5.5V
Off-state output voltage ................................................................... 5.5V
Operating free-air temperature range: Full-temperature-range circuits ........................ −55°C to 125°C
Commercial-temperature-range circuits ..................... 0°C to 70°C
Storage temperature range .............................................................. −65°C to 150°C

### recommended conditions for programming TBP18S', TBP18SA PROMs

| | | MIN | NOM | MAX | UNIT |
|---|---|---|---|---|---|
| Supply voltage, V_CC (see Note 1) | Steady state | 4.75 | 5 | 5.25 | V |
| | Program pulse | 9 | 9.25 | 9.5 | |
| Input voltage | High level, V_IH | 2.4 | | 5 | V |
| | Low level, V_IL | 0 | | 0.5 | |
| Termination of all outputs except the one to be programmed | | See load circuit (Figure 1) | | | |
| Voltage applied to output to be programmed, V_O(pr) (see Note 2) | | 0 | 0.25 | 0.3 | V |
| Duration of V_CC programming pulse X (see Figure 2 and Note 3) | | 15 | 25 | 100 | μs |
| Programming duty cycle for Y pulse | | | 25 | 35 | % |
| Free-air temperature | | 20 | 25 | 30 | °C |

NOTES: 1. Voltage values are with respect to network ground terminal. The supply voltage rating does not apply during programming.
2. The TBP18S030, TBP18SA030 are supplied with all bit locations containing a low logic level, and programming a bit changes the output of the bit to high logic level.
3. Programming is guaranteed if the pulse applied is 98 μs in duration.

TEXAS
INSTRUMENTS

## programming procedure

1. Apply steady-state supply voltage ($V_{CC}$ = 5 V) and address the word to be programmed.

2. Verify that the bit location needs to be programmed. If not, proceed to the next bit.

3. If the bit requires programming, disable the outputs by applying a high-logic level voltage to the chip-select input(s).

4. Only one bit location is programmed at a time. Connect each output not being programmed to 5 V through 3.9 kΩ and apply the voltage specified in the table to the output to be programmed. Maximum current into the programmer output is 150 mA.

5. Step $V_{CC}$ to 9.25 nominal. Maximum supply current required during programming is 750 mA.

6. Apply a low-logic-level voltage to the chip-select input(s). This should occur between 1 μs and 1 ms after $V_{CC}$ has reached its 9.25 level. See programming sequence of Figure 2.

7. After the X pulse time is reached, a high logic level is applied to the chip-select inputs to disable the outputs.

8. Within the range of 1 μs to 1 ms after the chip-select input(s) reach a high logic level, $V_{CC}$ should be stepped down to 5 V at which level verification can be accomplished.

9. The chip-select input(s) may be taken to a low logic level (to permit program verification) 1 μs or more after $V_{CC}$ reaches its steady-state value of 5 V.

10. At a Y pulse duty cycle of 35% or less, repeat steps 1 through 8 for each output where it is desired to program a bit.

11. Verify accurate programming of every word after all words have been programmed using $V_{CC}$ values of 4.5 and 5.5 volts.

**LOAD CIRCUIT FOR EACH OUTPUT
NOT BEING PROGRAMMED OR FOR
PROGRAM VERIFICATION**

**FIGURE 1 – LOAD CIRCUIT**

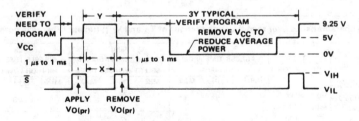

**FIGURE 2 – VOLTAGE WAVEFORMS FOR PROGRAMMING**

**4**

**PROMs**

TEXAS
INSTRUMENTS

## TBP18S030
## 256 BITS (32 WORDS BY 8 BITS)
## PROGRAMMABLE READ-ONLY MEMORIES WITH 3-STATE OUTPUTS

**recommended operating conditions (see Note 4)**

| PARAMETER | | TBP18S030 | | | UNIT |
|---|---|---|---|---|---|
| | | MIN | NOM | MAX | |
| Supply voltage, $V_{CC}$ | MJ | 4.5 | 5 | 5.5 | V |
| | J, N | 4.75 | 5 | 5.25 | |
| High-level output current, $I_{OH}$ | MJ | | | −2 | mA |
| | J,N | | | −6.5 | |
| Low-level output current, $I_{OL}$ | | | | 20 | mA |
| Operating free-air temperature, $T_A$ | MJ | −55 | | 125 | °C |
| | J ,N | 0 | | 70 | |

**electrical characteristics over recommended operating free-air temperature range (unless otherwise noted) (see Note 4)**

| | PARAMETER | TEST CONDITIONS† | FULL TEMP (MJ) | | | COMM. TEMP (J,N) | | | UNIT |
|---|---|---|---|---|---|---|---|---|---|
| | | | MIN | TYP‡ | MAX | MIN | TYP‡ | MAX | |
| $V_{IH}$ | High-level input voltage | | 2 | | | 2 | | | V |
| $V_{IL}$ | Low-level input voltage | | | | 0.8 | | | 0.8 | V |
| $V_{IK}$ | Input clamp voltage | $V_{CC}$ = MIN,   $I_I$ = −18 mA | | | −1.2 | | | −1.2 | V |
| $V_{OH}$ | High-level output voltage | $V_{CC}$ = MIN,   $V_{IH}$ = 2V, $V_{IL}$ = 0.8V,   $I_{OH}$ = MAX | 2.4 | 3.4 | | 2.4 | 3.2 | | V |
| $V_{OL}$ | Low-level output voltage | $V_{CC}$ = MIN,   $V_{IH}$ = 2V, $V_{IL}$ = 0.8V,   $I_{OL}$ = MAX | | | 0.5 | | | 0.5 | V |
| $I_{OZH}$ | Off-state output current, high-level voltage applied | $V_{CC}$ = MAX,   $V_{IH}$ = 2 V, $V_O$ = 2.4 V | | | 50 | | | 50 | μA |
| $I_{OZL}$ | Off-state output current, low-level voltage applied | $V_{CC}$ = MAX,   $V_{IH}$ = 2 V, $V_O$ = 0.5 V | | | −50 | | | −50 | μA |
| $I_I$ | Input current at maximum input voltage | $V_{CC}$ = MAX,   $V_I$ = 5.5 V, | | | 1 | | | 1 | mA |
| $I_{IH}$ | High-level input current | $V_{CC}$ = MAX,   $V_I$ = 2.7 V | | | 25 | | | 25 | μA |
| $I_{IL}$ | Low-level input current | $V_{CC}$ = MAX,   $V_I$ = 0.5 V | | | −0.25 | | | −0.25 | mA |
| $I_{OS}$ | Short-circuit output current§ | $V_{CC}$ = MAX, | −30 | | −100 | −30 | | −100 | mA |
| $I_{CC}$ | Supply current | $V_{CC}$ = MAX, Chip select(s) at 0 V, Outputs open, See Note 5 | | 80 | 110 | | 80 | 110 | mA |

**switching characteristics over recommended ranges of $T_A$ and $V_{CC}$ (unless otherwise noted)**

| TYPE | TEST CONDITIONS | $t_{a(A)}$ ACCESS TIME FROM ADDRESS | | | $t_{a(S)}$ ACCESS TIME FROM CHIP SELECT (ENABLE TIME) | | | $t_{dis}$ DISABLE TIME FROM HIGH OR LOW LEVEL | | | UNIT |
|---|---|---|---|---|---|---|---|---|---|---|---|
| | | MIN | TYP‡ | MAX | MIN | TYP‡ | MAX | MIN | TYP‡ | MAX | |
| TBP18S030MJ | $C_L$ = 30 pF for $t_{a(A)}$ and $t_{a(S)}$, 5 pF for $t_{dis}$, See Note 6 | | 25 | 50 | | 12 | 30 | | 8 | 30 | ns |
| TBP18S030 | | | 25 | 40 | | 12 | 25 | | 8 | 20 | ns |

†For conditions shown as MIN or MAX, use the appropriate value specified under recommended operating conditions.
‡All typical values are at $V_{CC}$ = 5 V, $T_A$ = 25 °C.
§Not more than one output should be shorted at a time and duration of the short circuit should not exceed one second.
NOTES: 4. MJ designates full-temperature circuits (formerly 54 Family), J and N designate commercial-temperature circuits (formerly 74 Family).
      5. The typical values of $I_{CC}$ are with all outputs low.
      6. Load circuits and voltage waveforms are shown in Section 1.

**4**

**PROMS**

TEXAS
INSTRUMENTS

## recommended operating conditions (see Note 4)

| PARAMETER | | | TBP18SA030 | | | UNIT |
|---|---|---|---|---|---|---|
| | | | MIN | NOM | MAX | |
| Supply voltage, $V_{CC}$ | | MJ | 4.5 | 5 | 5.5 | V |
| | | J, N | 4.75 | 5 | 5.25 | |
| High-level output voltage, $V_{OH}$ | | | | | 5.5 | V |
| Low-level output current, $I_{OL}$ | | | | | 20 | mA |
| Operating free-air temperature, $T_A$ | | MJ | −55 | | 125 | °C |
| | | J, N | 0 | | 70 | |

## electrical characteristics over recommended operating free-air temperature range (unless otherwise noted)

| | PARAMETER | TEST CONDITIONS[†] | | MIN | TYP[‡] | MAX | UNIT |
|---|---|---|---|---|---|---|---|
| $V_{IH}$ | High-level input voltage | | | 2 | | | V |
| $V_{IL}$ | Low-level input voltage | | | | | 0.8 | V |
| $V_{IK}$ | Input clamp voltage | $V_{CC}$ = MIN, | $I_I$ = −18mA | | | −1.2 | V |
| $I_{OH}$ | High-level output current | $V_{CC}$ = MIN, $V_{IH}$ = 2 V, $V_{IL}$ = 0.8 V | $V_{OH}$ = 2.4 V | | | 50 | µA |
| | | | $V_{OH}$ = 5.5 V | | | 100 | |
| $V_{OL}$ | Low-level output voltage | $V_{CC}$ = MIN, $V_{IL}$ = 0.8 V, | $V_{IH}$ = 2 V, $I_{OL}$ = MAX | | | 0.5 | V |
| $I_I$ | Input current at maximum input voltage | $V_{CC}$ = MAX, | $V_I$ = 5.5 V | | | 1 | mA |
| $I_{IH}$ | High-level input current | $V_{CC}$ = MAX, | $V_I$ = 2.7 V | | | 25 | µA |
| $I_{IL}$ | Low-level input current | $V_{CC}$ = MAX, | $V_I$ = 0.5 V | | | −0.25 | mA |
| $I_{CC}$ | Supply current | $V_{CC}$ = MAX, Chip select(s) at 0 V, Outputs open, See Note 5 | | | 80 | 110 | mA |

## switching characteristics over recommended ranges of $T_A$ and $V_{CC}$ (unless otherwise noted)

| TYPE | TEST CONDITIONS | t(A) ACCESS TIME FROM ADDRESS | | | ta(S) ACCESS TIME FROM CHIP SELECT (ENABLE TIME) | | | tPLH PROPAGATION DELAY TIME, LOW-TO-HIGH-LEVEL OUTPUT FROM CHIP SELECT (DISABLE TIME) | | | UNIT |
|---|---|---|---|---|---|---|---|---|---|---|---|
| | | MIN | TYP[‡] | MAX | MIN | TYP[‡] | MAX | MIN | TYP[‡] | MAX | |
| TBP18SA030MJ | $C_L$ = 30pF, $R_{L1}$ = 300 Ω, $R_{L2}$ = 600 Ω, See Note 6 | | 25 | 50 | | 12 | 30 | | 12 | 30 | ns |
| TBP18SA030 | | | 25 | 40 | | 12 | 25 | | 12 | 25 | ns |

[†]For conditions shown as MIN or MAX, use the appropriate value specified under recommended operating conditions.
[‡]All typical values are at $V_{CC}$ = 5 V, $T_A$ = 25 °C.
NOTES:  4. MJ designates full-temperature circuits (formerly 54 Family), J and N designate commercial-temperature circuits (formerly 74 Family).
     5. The typical values of $I_{CC}$ are with all outputs low.
     6. Load circuits and voltage waveforms are shown in Section 1.

**4**

**PROMs**

- Expanded Family of Standard and Low Power PROMs

- Titanium-Tungsten (Ti-W) Fuse Links for Reliable Low-Voltage Full-Family-Compatible Programming

- Full Decoding and Fast Chip Select Simplify System Design

- P-N-P Inputs for Reduced Loading On System Buffers/Drivers

- Each PROM Supplied With a High Logic Level Stored at Each Bit Location

- Applications Include:
  Microprogramming/Firmware Loaders
  Code Converters/Character Generators
  Translators/Emulators
  Address Mapping/Look-Up Tables

## description

The 24 and 28 Series of monolithic TTL programmable read-only memories (PROMs) feature an expanded selection of standard and low-power PROMs. This expanded PROM family provides the system designer with considerable flexibility in upgrading existing designs or optimizing new designs. Featuring proven titanium-tungsten (Ti-W) fuse links with low-current MOS-compatible p-n-p inputs, all family members utilize a common programming technique designed to program each link with a 20-microsecond pulse.

The 4096-bit and 8192-bit PROMs are offered in a wide variety of packages ranging from 18-pin 300 mil-wide thru 24 pin 600 mil-wide. The 16,384-bit PROMs provide twice the bit density of the 8192-bit PROMs and are provided in a 24 pin 600 mil-wide package.

All PROMs are supplied with a logic-high output level stored at each bit location. The programming procedure will produce open-circuits in the Ti-W metal links, which reverses the stored logic level at the selected location. The procedure is irreversible; once altered, the output for that bit location is permanently programmed. Outputs that have never been altered may later be programmed to supply the opposite output level. Operation of the unit within the recommended operating conditions will not alter the memory content.

Active level(s) at the chip-select input(s) (S or $\overline{S}$) enables all of the outputs. An inactive level at any chip-select input causes all outputs to be in the three-state, or off condition.

## standard PROMs

The standard PROM members of Series 24 and 28 offer high performance for applications which require the uncompromised speed of Schottky technology. The fast chip-select access times allow additional decoding delays to occur without degrading speed performance.

| TYPE NUMBER | PACKAGE† AND TEMPERATURE RANGE DESIGNATORS | OUTPUT CONFIGURATION‡ | BIT SIZE (ORGANIZATION) | TYPICAL PERFORMANCE | | |
|---|---|---|---|---|---|---|
| | | | | ACCESS TIMES | | POWER |
| | | | | ADDRESS | SELECT | DISSIPATION |
| TBP24S10 | MJ, J, N | ▽ | 1024 Bits | 35 ns | 20 ns | 375 mW |
| TBP24SA10 | MJ, J, N | ☖ | (256W × 4B) | | | |
| TBP28S42 | MJ, J, N | ▽ | | | | |
| TBP28SA42 | MJ, J, N | ☖ | 4096 Bits | 35 ns | 20 ns | 500 mW |
| TBP28S46 | MJW, JW, NW | ▽ | (512W × 8B) | | | |
| TBP28SA46 | MJW, JW, NW | ☖ | | | | |
| TBP24S41 | MJ, J, N | ▽ | 4096 Bits | 40 ns | 20 ns | 475 mW |
| TBP24SA41 | MJ, J, N | ☖ | (1024 × 4B) | | | |
| TBP24S81 | MJ, J, N | ▽ | 8192 Bits | 45 ns | 20 ns | 625 mW |
| TBP24SA81 | MJ, J, N | ☖ | (2048 × 4B) | | | |
| TBP28S86A | MJW, JW, NW | ▽ | | | | |
| TBP28SA86A | MJW, JW, NW | ☖ | 8192 Bits | 45 ns | 20 ns | 625 mW |
| TBP28S2708A | NW | ▽ | (1024 × 8B) | | | |
| TBP28S166 | NW | ▽ | 16,384 Bits (2048W × 8B) | 35 ns | 15 ns | 650 mW |

†MJ and MJW designates full-temperature-range circuits (formerly 54 Family), J, JW, N, and NW designates commercial-temperature-range circuits (formerly 74 Family).
‡ ▽ = three state, ☖ = open collector.

TEXAS INSTRUMENTS

4

PROMs

### low power PROMs

To upgrade systems utilizing MOS EPROMs or MOS PROMs, or when designing new systems which do not require maximum speed, the low-power PROM family offers the output drive and speed performance of bipolar technology, plus reduced power dissipation.

| TYPE NUMBER | PACKAGE† AND TEMPERATURE RANGE DESIGNATORS | OUTPUT CONFIGURATION‡ | BIT SIZE (ORGANIZATION) | TYPICAL PERFORMANCE | | |
|---|---|---|---|---|---|---|
| | | | | ACCESS TIMES | | POWER DISSIPATION |
| | | | | ADDRESS | SELECT | |
| TBP28L22 | MJ, J,N | ▽ | 2048 Bits (256W × 8B) | 45 ns | 20 ns | 375 mW |
| TBP28LA22 | MJ, J, N | ⋄ | | | | |
| TBP28L42 | MJ, J, N | ▽ | 4096 Bits (512W × 8B) | 60 ns | 30 ns | 250 mW |
| TBP28L46 | MJW, JW, NW | ▽ | | | | |
| TBP28L86A | MJW, JW, NW | ▽ | 8192 Bits (1024W × 8B) | 80 ns | 35 ns | 350 mW |
| TBP28L166 | NW | ▽ | 16,384 Bits (2084W × 8B) | 65 ns | 30 ns | 350 mW |

†MJ and MJW designates full-temperature-range circuits (formerly 54 Family), J, JW, N, and NW designates commercial-temperature-range circuits (formerly 74 Family).
‡ ▽ = three state, ⋄ = open collector.

### schematics of inputs and outputs

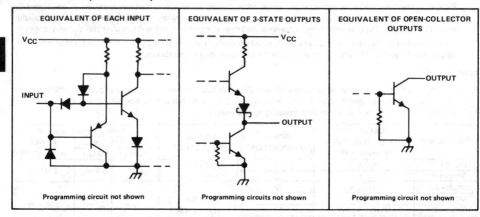

| EQUIVALENT OF EACH INPUT | EQUIVALENT OF 3-STATE OUTPUTS | EQUIVALENT OF OPEN-COLLECTOR OUTPUTS |
|---|---|---|
| Programming circuit not shown | Programming circuits not shown | Programming circuit not shown |

### absolute maximum ratings over operating free-air temperature range (unless otherwise noted)

Supply voltage (see Note 1) . . . . . . . . . . . . . . . . . . . . . . . . . . . . . . . . . . . . . . . . . . . . . . . . . . . . . . 7 V
Input voltage . . . . . . . . . . . . . . . . . . . . . . . . . . . . . . . . . . . . . . . . . . . . . . . . . . . . . . . . . . . . . . . . 5.5 V
Chip-select peak input voltage (S, S1, S2) (see Note 2) . . . . . . . . . . . . . . . . . . . . . . . . . . . . . . . 11 V
Off-state output voltage . . . . . . . . . . . . . . . . . . . . . . . . . . . . . . . . . . . . . . . . . . . . . . . . . . . . . . . . . 5.5 V
Off-state peak output voltage (see Note 2) . . . . . . . . . . . . . . . . . . . . . . . . . . . . . . . . . . . . . . . . 16.25 V
Operating free-air temperature range: Full-temperature-range circuits (M suffix) . . −55 °C to 125 °C
Commercial-temperature-range circuits . . . . . . . . 0 °C to 70 °C
Storage temperature range . . . . . . . . . . . . . . . . . . . . . . . . . . . . . . . . . . . . . . . . . . . . −65 °C to 150 °C

NOTES: 1. Voltage values are with respect to network ground terminal.
2. These ratings apply only under the conditions described in the programming procedure.

TEXAS
INSTRUMENTS

## logic symbol

TBP24S10

PROM 256 X 4

| | | |
|---|---|---|
| A0 (5) | 0 | |
| A1 (6) | | |
| A2 (7) | | A ▽ (12) Q0 |
| A3 (4) | | A ▽ (11) Q1 |
| A4 (3) | A $\frac{0}{255}$ | A ▽ (10) Q2 |
| A5 (2) | | A ▽ (9) Q3 |
| A6 (1) | | |
| A7 (15) | 7 | |
| $\overline{G2}$ (14) | & EN | |
| $\overline{G1}$ (13) | | |

## pin assignment

TBP24S10
J or N PACKAGE
(TOP VIEW)

| A6 | 1 | 16 | $V_{CC}$ |
|---|---|---|---|
| A5 | 2 | 15 | A7 |
| A4 | 3 | 14 | $\overline{G2}$ |
| A3 | 4 | 13 | $\overline{G1}$ |
| A0 | 5 | 12 | Q0 |
| A1 | 6 | 11 | Q1 |
| A2 | 7 | 10 | Q2 |
| GND | 8 | 9 | Q3 |

## recommended operating conditions

| | PARAMETER | MJ MIN | MJ NOM | MJ MAX | J OR N MIN | J OR N NOM | J OR N MAX | UNIT |
|---|---|---|---|---|---|---|---|---|
| $V_{CC}$ | Supply voltage | 4.5 | 5 | 5.5 | 4.75 | 5 | 5.25 | V |
| $V_{IH}$ | High-level input voltage | 2 | | | 2 | | | V |
| $V_{IL}$ | Low-level input voltage | | | 0.8 | | | 0.8 | V |
| $I_{OH}$ | High-level output current | | | $-2$ | | | $-6.5$ | mA |
| $I_{OL}$ | Low-level output current | | | 16 | | | 16 | mA |
| $T_A$ | Operating free-air temperature range | $-55$ | | 125 | 0 | | 70 | °C |

## electrical characteristics over recommended operating free-air temperature range (unless otherwise noted)

| PARAMETER | TEST CONDITIONS[†] | | MJ MIN | MJ TYP[‡] | MJ MAX | J OR N MIN | J OR N TYP[‡] | J OR N MAX | UNIT |
|---|---|---|---|---|---|---|---|---|---|
| $V_{IK}$ | $V_{CC}$ = MIN, | $I_I = -18$ mA | | | $-1.2$ | | | $-1.2$ | V |
| $V_{OH}$ | $V_{CC}$ = MIN, | $I_{OH}$ = MAX | 2.4 | 3.1 | | 2.4 | 3.1 | | V |
| $V_{OL}$ | $V_{CC}$ = MIN, | $I_{OL}$ = 16 mA | | | 0.5 | | | 0.5 | V |
| $I_{OZH}$ | $V_{CC}$ = MAX, | $V_O$ = 2.4 V | | | 50 | | | 50 | $\mu$A |
| $I_{OZL}$ | $V_{CC}$ = MAX, | $V_O$ = 0.5 V | | | $-50$ | | | $-50$ | $\mu$A |
| $I_I$ | $V_{CC}$ = MAX, | $V_I$ = 5.5 V | | | 1 | | | 1 | mA |
| $I_{IH}$ | $V_{CC}$ = MAX, | $V_I$ = 2.7 V | | | 25 | | | 25 | $\mu$A |
| $I_{IL}$ | $V_{CC}$ = MAX, | $V_I$ = 0.5 V | | | $-0.25$ | | | $-0.25$ | mA |
| $I_{OS}$[§] | $V_{CC}$ = MAX | | $-30$ | | $-100$ | $-30$ | | $-100$ | mA |
| $I_{CC}$ | $V_{CC}$ = MAX | | | 75 | 100 | | 75 | 100 | mA |

## switching characteristics over recommended ranges of $T_A$ and $V_{CC}$ (unless otherwise noted)

| | PARAMETER | TEST CONDITIONS | MJ MIN | MJ TYP[‡] | MJ MAX | J OR N MIN | J OR N TYP[‡] | J OR N MAX | UNIT |
|---|---|---|---|---|---|---|---|---|---|
| $t_{a(A)}$ | Access time from address | $C_L$ = 30 pF | | 35 | 75 | | 35 | 55 | ns |
| $t_{a(S)}$ | Access time from chip select (enable time) | See Note 3 | | 20 | 40 | | 20 | 35 | ns |
| $t_{dis}$ | Disable time | $C_L$ = 5 pF See Note 3 | | 15 | 40 | | 15 | 35 | ns |

[†]For conditions shown as MIN or MAX, use appropriate value specified under recommended operating conditions.
[‡]All typical values are at $V_{CC}$ = 5 V, $T_A$ = 25 °C.
[§]Not more than one output should be shorted at a time, and duration of the short circuit should not exceed one second.
NOTE 3: Load circuits and voltage waveforms are shown in Section 1.

### TEXAS
### INSTRUMENTS

4

PROMs

# TBP24SA10
# 1024 BITS (256 WORDS BY 4 BITS)
## STANDARD PROGRAMMABLE READ-ONLY MEMORIES WITH OPEN-COLLECTOR OUTPUTS

## logic symbol

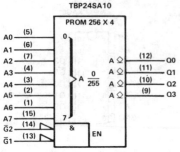

## pin assignment

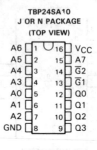

### recommended operating conditions

| | PARAMETER | MJ MIN | MJ NOM | MJ MAX | J OR N MIN | J OR N NOM | J OR N MAX | UNIT |
|---|---|---|---|---|---|---|---|---|
| $V_{CC}$ | Supply voltage | 4.5 | 5 | 5.5 | 4.75 | 5 | 5.25 | V |
| $V_{IH}$ | High-level input voltage | 2 | | | 2 | | | V |
| $V_{IL}$ | Low-level input voltage | | | 0.8 | | | 0.8 | V |
| $V_{OH}$ | High-level output voltage | | | 5.5 | | | 5.5 | V |
| $I_{OL}$ | Low-level output current | | | 16 | | | 16 | mA |
| $T_A$ | Operating free-air temperature range | −55 | | 125 | 0 | | 70 | °C |

### electrical characteristics over recommended operating free-air temperature range (unless otherwise noted)

| PARAMETER | TEST CONDITIONS[†] | | MJ MIN | MJ TYP[‡] | MJ MAX | J OR N MIN | J OR N TYP[‡] | J OR N MAX | UNIT |
|---|---|---|---|---|---|---|---|---|---|
| $V_{IK}$ | $V_{CC}$ = MIN, | $I_I$ = −18 mA | | | −1.2 | | | −1.2 | V |
| $I_{OH}$ | $V_{CC}$ = MIN, | $V_{OH}$ = 2.4 V | | | 0.05 | | | 0.05 | mA |
| | | $V_{OH}$ = 5.5 V | | | 0.1 | | | 0.1 | |
| $V_{OL}$ | $V_{CC}$ = MIN, | $I_{OL}$ = 16 mA | | | 0.5 | | | 0.45 | V |
| $I_I$ | $V_{CC}$ = MAX, | $V_I$ = 5.5 V | | | 1 | | | 1 | mA |
| $I_{IH}$ | $V_{CC}$ = MAX, | $V_I$ = 2.7 V | | | 25 | | | 25 | µA |
| $I_{IL}$ | $V_{CC}$ = MAX, | $V_I$ = 0.5 V | | | −0.25 | | | −0.25 | mA |
| $I_{CC}$ | $V_{CC}$ = MAX | | | 75 | 100 | | 75 | 100 | mA |

### switching characteristics over recommended ranges of $T_A$ and $V_{CC}$ (unless otherwise noted)

| | PARAMETER | TEST CONDITIONS | MJ MIN | MJ TYP[‡] | MJ MAX | J OR N MIN | J OR N TYP[‡] | J OR N MAX | UNIT |
|---|---|---|---|---|---|---|---|---|---|
| $t_{a(A)}$ | Access time from address | $C_L$ = 30 pF | | 35 | 75 | | 35 | 65 | ns |
| $t_{a(S)}$ | Access time from chip select (enable time) | $R_{L1}$ = 300 Ω | | 20 | 40 | | 20 | 35 | ns |
| $t_{PLH}$ | Propagation delay time low-to-high-level output from chip select | $R_{L2}$ = 600 Ω See Note 3 | | 15 | 40 | | 20 | 35 | ns |

[†]For conditions shown as MIN or MAX, use appropriate value specified under recommended operating conditions.
[‡]All typical values are at $V_{CC}$ = 5 V, $T_A$ = 25 °C.
NOTE 3: Load circuits and voltage waveforms are shown in Section 1.

TEXAS
INSTRUMENTS

## logic symbol

**TBP28S42**

PROM 512 X 8

| | | | |
|---|---|---|---|
| A0 | (1) | 0 | A ▽ (6) Q0 |
| A1 | (2) | | A ▽ (7) Q1 |
| A2 | (3) | | A ▽ (8) Q2 |
| A3 | (4) | | A ▽ (9) Q3 |
| A4 | (5) | A 0/511 | A ▽ (11) Q4 |
| A5 | (16) | | A ▽ (12) Q5 |
| A6 | (17) | | A ▽ (13) Q6 |
| A7 | (18) | | A ▽ (14) Q7 |
| A8 | (19) | 8 | |
| G̅ | (15) | EN | |

## pin assignment

**TBP28S42**
**J OR N PACKAGE**
**(TOP VIEW)**

| | | | |
|---|---|---|---|
| A0 | 1 | 20 | V_CC |
| A1 | 2 | 19 | A8 |
| A2 | 3 | 18 | A7 |
| A3 | 4 | 17 | A6 |
| A4 | 5 | 16 | A5 |
| Q0 | 6 | 15 | G̅ |
| Q1 | 7 | 14 | Q7 |
| Q2 | 8 | 13 | Q6 |
| Q3 | 9 | 12 | Q5 |
| GND | 10 | 11 | Q4 |

## recommended operating conditions

| | PARAMETER | MJ MIN | MJ NOM | MJ MAX | J OR N MIN | J OR N NOM | J OR N MAX | UNIT |
|---|---|---|---|---|---|---|---|---|
| $V_{CC}$ | Supply voltage | 4.5 | 5 | 5.5 | 4.75 | 5 | 5.25 | V |
| $V_{IH}$ | High-level input voltage | 2 | | | 2 | | | V |
| $V_{IL}$ | Low-level input voltage | | | 0.8 | | | 0.8 | V |
| $I_{OH}$ | High-level output current | | | $-2$ | | | $-6.5$ | mA |
| $I_{OL}$ | Low-level output current | | | 16 | | | 16 | mA |
| $T_A$ | Operating free-air temperature range | $-55$ | | 125 | 0 | | 70 | °C |

## electrical characteristics over recommended operating free-air temperature range (unless otherwise noted)

| PARAMETER | TEST CONDITIONS[†] | | MJ MIN | MJ TYP[‡] | MJ MAX | J OR N MIN | J OR N TYP[‡] | J OR N MAX | UNIT |
|---|---|---|---|---|---|---|---|---|---|
| $V_{IK}$ | $V_{CC}$ = MIN, | $I_I$ = $-18$ mA | | | $-1.2$ | | | $-1.2$ | V |
| $V_{OH}$ | $V_{CC}$ = MIN, | $I_{OH}$ = MAX | 2.4 | 3.1 | | 2.4 | 3.1 | | V |
| $V_{OL}$ | $V_{CC}$ = MIN, | $I_{OL}$ = 16 mA | | | 0.5 | | | 0.5 | V |
| $I_{OZH}$ | $V_{CC}$ = MAX, | $V_O$ = 2.4 V | | | 50 | | | 50 | μA |
| $I_{OZL}$ | $V_{CC}$ = MAX, | $V_O$ = 0.5 V | | | $-50$ | | | $-50$ | μA |
| $I_I$ | $V_{CC}$ = MAX, | $V_I$ = 5.5 V | | | 1 | | | 1 | mA |
| $I_{IH}$ | $V_{CC}$ = MAX, | $V_I$ = 2.7 V | | | 25 | | | 25 | μA |
| $I_{IL}$ | $V_{CC}$ = MAX, | $V_I$ = 0.5 V | | | $-0.25$ | | | $-0.25$ | mA |
| $I_{OS}$[§] | $V_{CC}$ = MAX | | $-30$ | | $-100$ | $-30$ | | $-100$ | mA |
| $I_{CC}$ | $V_{CC}$ = MAX | | | 100 | 135 | | 100 | 135 | mA |

## switching characteristics over recommended ranges of $T_A$ and $V_{CC}$ (unless otherwise noted)

| | PARAMETER | TEST CONDITIONS | MJ MIN | MJ TYP[‡] | MJ MAX | J OR N MIN | J OR N TYP[‡] | J OR N MAX | UNIT |
|---|---|---|---|---|---|---|---|---|---|
| $t_{a(A)}$ | Access time from address | $C_L$ = 30 pF | | 35 | 70 | | 35 | 60 | ns |
| $t_{a(S)}$ | Access time from chip select (enable time) | See Note 3 | | 20 | 45 | | 20 | 45 | ns |
| $t_{dis}$ | Disable time | $C_L$ = 5 pF See Note 3 | | 15 | 45 | | 15 | 40 | ns |

[†]For conditions shown as MIN or MAX, use appropriate value specified under recommended operating conditions.
[‡]All typical values are at $V_{CC}$ = 5 V, $T_A$ = 25°C.
[§]Not more than one output should be shorted at a time, and duration of the short circuit should not exceed one second.
NOTE 3: Load circuits and voltage waveforms are shown in Section 1.

4

PROMs

TEXAS
INSTRUMENTS

**logic symbol**

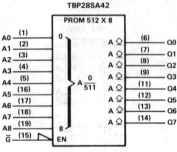

**pin assignment**

TBP28SA42
J OR N PACKAGE
(TOP VIEW)

| | | | |
|---|---|---|---|
| A0 | 1 | 20 | VCC |
| A1 | 2 | 19 | A8 |
| A2 | 3 | 18 | A7 |
| A3 | 4 | 17 | A6 |
| A4 | 5 | 16 | A5 |
| Q0 | 6 | 15 | $\overline{G}$ |
| Q1 | 7 | 14 | Q7 |
| Q2 | 8 | 13 | Q6 |
| Q3 | 9 | 12 | Q5 |
| GND | 10 | 11 | Q4 |

**recommended operating conditions**

| PARAMETER | | MJ | | | J OR N | | | UNIT |
|---|---|---|---|---|---|---|---|---|
| | | MIN | NOM | MAX | MIN | NOM | MAX | |
| $V_{CC}$ | Supply voltage | 4.5 | 5 | 5.5 | 4.75 | 5 | 5.25 | V |
| $V_{IH}$ | High-level input voltage | 2 | | | 2 | | | V |
| $V_{IL}$ | Low-level input voltage | | | 0.8 | | | 0.8 | V |
| $V_{OH}$ | High-level output voltage | | | 5.5 | | | 5.5 | V |
| $I_{OL}$ | Low-level output current | | | 16 | | | 16 | mA |
| $T_A$ | Operating free-air temperature range | -55 | | 125 | 0 | | 70 | °C |

**electrical characteristics over recommended operating free-air temperature range (unless otherwise noted)**

| PARAMETER | TEST CONDITIONS† | | MJ | | | J OR N | | | UNIT |
|---|---|---|---|---|---|---|---|---|---|
| | | | MIN | TYP‡ | MAX | MIN | TYP‡ | MAX | |
| $V_{IK}$ | $V_{CC}$ = MIN, | $I_I$ = -18 mA | | | -1.2 | | | -1.2 | V |
| $I_{OH}$ | $V_{CC}$ = MIN, | $V_{OH}$ = 2.4 V | | | 0.05 | | | 0.05 | mA |
| | | $V_{OH}$ = 5.5 V | | | 0.1 | | | 0.1 | |
| $V_{OL}$ | $V_{CC}$ = MIN, | $I_{OL}$ = 16 mA | | | 0.5 | | | 0.5 | V |
| $I_I$ | $V_{CC}$ = MAX, | $V_I$ = 5.5 V | | | 1 | | | 1 | mA |
| $I_{IH}$ | $V_{CC}$ = MAX, | $V_I$ = 2.7 V | | | 25 | | | 25 | $\mu$A |
| $I_{IL}$ | $V_{CC}$ = MAX, | $V_I$ = 0.5 V | | | -0.25 | | | -0.25 | mA |
| $I_{CC}$ | $V_{CC}$ = MAX | | | 105 | 135 | | 105 | 135 | mA |

**switching characteristics over recommended ranges of $T_A$ and $V_{CC}$ (unless otherwise noted)**

| PARAMETER | | TEST CONDITIONS | MJ | | | J OR N | | | UNIT |
|---|---|---|---|---|---|---|---|---|---|
| | | | MIN | TYP‡ | MAX | MIN | TYP‡ | MAX | |
| $t_{a(A)}$ | Access time from address | $C_L$ = 30 pF | | 35 | 75 | | 35 | 65 | ns |
| $t_{a(S)}$ | Access time from chip select (enable time) | $R_{L1}$ = 300 Ω | | 20 | 45 | | 20 | 35 | ns |
| $t_{PLH}$ | Propagation delay time low-to-high-level output from chip select | $R_{L2}$ = 600 Ω See Note 3 | | 15 | 45 | | 15 | 35 | ns |

†For conditions shown as MIN or MAX, use appropriate value specified under recommended operating conditions.
‡All typical values are at $V_{CC}$ = 5 V, $T_A$ = 25°C.
NOTE 3: Load circuits and voltage waveforms are shown in Section 1.

TEXAS
INSTRUMENTS

logic symbol        pin assignment

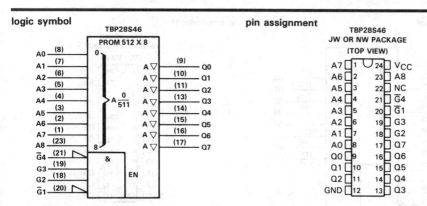

### recommended operating conditions

| | PARAMETER | MJW MIN | MJW NOM | MJW MAX | JW OR NW MIN | JW OR NW NOM | JW OR NW MAX | UNIT |
|---|---|---|---|---|---|---|---|---|
| $V_{CC}$ | Supply voltage | 4.5 | 5 | 5.5 | 4.75 | 5 | 5.25 | V |
| $V_{IH}$ | High-level input voltage | 2 | | | 2 | | | V |
| $V_{IL}$ | Low-level input voltage | | | 0.8 | | | 0.8 | V |
| $I_{OH}$ | High-level output current | | | $-2$ | | | $-6.5$ | mA |
| $I_{OL}$ | Low-level output current | | | 16 | | | 16 | mA |
| $T_A$ | Operating free-air temperature range | $-55$ | | 125 | 0 | | 70 | °C |

### electrical characteristics over recommended operating free-air temperature range (unless otherwise noted)

| PARAMETER | TEST CONDITIONS[†] | MJW MIN | MJW TYP[‡] | MJW MAX | JW OR NW MIN | JW OR NW TYP[‡] | JW OR NW MAX | UNIT |
|---|---|---|---|---|---|---|---|---|
| $V_{IK}$ | $V_{CC}$ = MIN, $I_I$ = $-18$ mA | | | $-1.2$ | | | $-1.2$ | V |
| $V_{OH}$ | $V_{CC}$ = MIN, $I_{OH}$ = MAX | 2.4 | 3.1 | | 2.4 | 3.1 | | V |
| $V_{OL}$ | $V_{CC}$ = MIN, $I_{OL}$ = 16 mA | | | 0.5 | | | 0.5 | V |
| $I_{OZH}$ | $V_{CC}$ = MAX, $V_O$ = 2.4 V | | | 50 | | | 50 | µA |
| $I_{OZL}$ | $V_{CC}$ = MAX, $V_O$ = 0.5 V | | | $-50$ | | | $-50$ | µA |
| $I_I$ | $V_{CC}$ = MAX, $V_I$ = 5.5 V | | | 1 | | | 1 | mA |
| $I_{IH}$ | $V_{CC}$ = MAX, $V_I$ = 2.7 V | | | 25 | | | 25 | µA |
| $I_{IL}$ | $V_{CC}$ = MAX, $V_I$ = 0.5 V | | | $-0.25$ | | | $-0.25$ | mA |
| $I_{OS}$[§] | $V_{CC}$ = MAX | $-15$ | | $-100$ | $-20$ | | $-100$ | mA |
| $I_{CC}$ | $V_{CC}$ = MAX | | 100 | 135 | | 100 | 135 | mA |

### switching characteristics over recommended ranges of $T_A$ and $V_{CC}$ (unless otherwise noted)

| | PARAMETER | TEST CONDITIONS | MJW MIN | MJW TYP[‡] | MJW MAX | JW OR NW MIN | JW OR NW TYP[‡] | JW OR NW MAX | UNIT |
|---|---|---|---|---|---|---|---|---|---|
| $t_{a(A)}$ | Access time from address | $C_L$ = 30 pF | | 35 | 70 | | 35 | 60 | ns |
| $t_{a(S)}$ | Access time from chip select (enable time) | See Note 3 | | 20 | 45 | | 20 | 35 | ns |
| $t_{dis}$ | Disable time | $C_L$ = 5 pF See Note 3 | | 15 | 40 | | 15 | 35 | ns |

[†]For conditions shown as MIN or MAX, use appropriate value specified under recommended operating conditions.
[‡]All typical values are at $V_{CC}$ = 5 V, $T_A$ = 25 °C.
[§]Not more than one output should be shorted at a time, and duration of the short circuit should not exceed one second.
NOTE 3: Load circuits and voltage waveforms are shown in Section 1.

TEXAS
INSTRUMENTS

4

PROMs

## TBP28SA46
## 4096 BITS (512 WORDS BY 8 BITS)
## STANDARD PROGRAMMABLE READ-ONLY MEMORIES WITH OPEN-COLLECTOR OUTPUTS

**logic symbol**                              **pin assignment**

TBP28SA46

PROM 512 X 8

| | |
|---|---|
| A0 (8) | 0 |
| A1 (7) | |
| A2 (6) | A ◇ (9) Q0 |
| A3 (5) | A ◇ (10) Q1 |
| A4 (4) | A ◇ (11) Q2 |
| A5 (3) | A $\frac{0}{511}$  A ◇ (13) Q3 |
| A6 (2) | A ◇ (14) Q4 |
| A7 (1) | A ◇ (15) Q5 |
| A8 (23) | A ◇ (16) Q6 |
| | 8  A ◇ (17) Q7 |
| $\overline{G}4$ (21) | & |
| G3 (19) | |
| G2 (18) | EN |
| $\overline{G}1$ (20) | |

TBP28SA46
JW OR NW PACKAGE
(TOP VIEW)

| | | | | |
|---|---|---|---|---|
| A7 | 1 | | 24 | VCC |
| A6 | 2 | | 23 | A8 |
| A5 | 3 | | 22 | NC |
| A4 | 4 | | 21 | $\overline{G}4$ |
| A3 | 5 | | 20 | $\overline{G}1$ |
| A2 | 6 | | 19 | G3 |
| A1 | 7 | | 18 | G2 |
| A0 | 8 | | 17 | Q7 |
| Q0 | 9 | | 16 | Q6 |
| Q1 | 10 | | 15 | Q5 |
| Q2 | 11 | | 14 | Q4 |
| GND | 12 | | 13 | Q3 |

### recommended operating conditions

| PARAMETER | | MJW | | | JW OR NW | | | UNIT |
|---|---|---|---|---|---|---|---|---|
| | | MIN | NOM | MAX | MIN | NOM | MAX | |
| $V_{CC}$ | Supply voltage | 4.5 | 5 | 5.5 | 4.75 | 5 | 5.25 | V |
| $V_{IH}$ | High-level input voltage | 2 | | | 2 | | | V |
| $V_{IL}$ | Low-level input voltage | | | 0.8 | | | 0.8 | V |
| $V_{OH}$ | High-level output voltage | | | 5.5 | | | 5.5 | V |
| $I_{OL}$ | Low-level output current | | | 16 | | | 16 | mA |
| $T_A$ | Operating free-air temperature range | -55 | | 125 | 0 | | 70 | °C |

### electrical characteristics over recommended operating free-air temperature range (unless otherwise noted)

| PARAMETER | TEST CONDITIONS[†] | | MJW | | | JW OR NW | | | UNIT |
|---|---|---|---|---|---|---|---|---|---|
| | | | MIN | TYP[‡] | MAX | MIN | TYP[‡] | MAX | |
| $V_{IK}$ | $V_{CC}$ = MIN, | $I_I$ = -18 mA | | | -1.2 | | | -1.2 | V |
| $I_{OH}$ | $V_{CC}$ = MIN, | $V_{OH}$ = 2.4 V | | | 0.05 | | | 0.05 | mA |
| | | $V_{OH}$ = 5.5 V | | | 0.1 | | | 0.1 | |
| $V_{OL}$ | $V_{CC}$ = MIN, | $I_{OL}$ = 16 mA | | | 0.5 | | | 0.5 | V |
| $I_I$ | $V_{CC}$ = MAX, | $V_I$ = 5.5 V | | | 1 | | | 1 | mA |
| $I_{IH}$ | $V_{CC}$ = MAX, | $V_I$ = 2.7 V | | | 25 | | | 25 | μA |
| $I_{IL}$ | $V_{CC}$ = MAX, | $V_I$ = 0.5 V | | | -0.25 | | | -0.25 | mA |
| $I_{CC}$ | $V_{CC}$ = MAX | | | 100 | 135 | | 100 | 135 | mA |

### switching characteristics over recommended ranges of $T_A$ and $V_{CC}$ (unless otherwise noted)

| PARAMETER | | TEST CONDITIONS | MJW | | | JW OR NW | | | UNIT |
|---|---|---|---|---|---|---|---|---|---|
| | | | MIN | TYP[‡] | MAX | MIN | TYP[‡] | MAX | |
| $t_{a(A)}$ | Access time from address | $C_L$ = 30 pF | | 35 | 75 | | 35 | 65 | ns |
| $t_{a(S)}$ | Access time from chip select (enable time) | $R_{L1}$ = 300 Ω | | 20 | 45 | | 20 | 35 | ns |
| $t_{PLH}$ | Propagation delay time low-to-high-level output from chip select | $R_{L2}$ = 600 Ω  See Note 3 | | 15 | 40 | | 15 | 35 | ns |

[†]For conditions shown as MIN or MAX, use appropriate value specified under recommended operating conditions.
[‡]All typical values are at $V_{CC}$ = 5 V, $T_A$ = 25°C.
NOTE 3: Load circuits and voltage waveforms are shown in Section 1.

4

PROMS

## logic symbol

TBP24S41
PROM 1024 X 4

| | | |
|---|---|---|
| A0 | (5) | 0 |
| A1 | (6) | |
| A2 | (7) | |
| A3 | (4) | |
| A4 | (3) | |
| A5 | (2) | A $\frac{0}{1023}$ |
| A6 | (1) | |
| A7 | (17) | |
| A8 | (16) | |
| A9 | (15) | 9 |
| $\overline{G2}$ | (10) | & |
| $\overline{G1}$ | (8) | EN |

A ▽ (14) Q0
A ▽ (13) Q1
A ▽ (12) Q2
A ▽ (11) Q3

## pin assignment

TBP24S41
J OR N PACKAGE
(TOP VIEW)

| | | | | |
|---|---|---|---|---|
| A6 | 1 | | 18 | $V_{CC}$ |
| A5 | 2 | | 17 | A7 |
| A4 | 3 | | 16 | A8 |
| A3 | 4 | | 15 | A9 |
| A0 | 5 | | 14 | Q0 |
| A1 | 6 | | 13 | Q1 |
| A2 | 7 | | 12 | Q2 |
| $\overline{G1}$ | 8 | | 11 | Q3 |
| GND | 9 | | 10 | $\overline{G2}$ |

## recommended operating conditions

| | PARAMETER | MJ MIN | MJ NOM | MJ MAX | J OR N MIN | J OR N NOM | J OR N MAX | UNIT |
|---|---|---|---|---|---|---|---|---|
| $V_{CC}$ | Supply voltage | 4.5 | 5 | 5.5 | 4.75 | 5 | 5.25 | V |
| $V_{IH}$ | High-level input voltage | 2 | | | 2 | | | V |
| $V_{IL}$ | Low-level input voltage | | | 0.8 | | | 0.8 | V |
| $I_{OH}$ | High-level output current | | | −2 | | | −3.2 | mA |
| $I_{OL}$ | Low-level output current | | | 16 | | | 16 | mA |
| $T_A$ | Operating free-air temperature range | −55 | | 125 | 0 | | 70 | °C |

## electrical characteristics over recommended operating free-air temperature range (unless otherwise noted)

| PARAMETER | TEST CONDITIONS[†] | | MJ MIN | MJ TYP[‡] | MJ MAX | J OR N MIN | J OR N TYP[‡] | J OR N MAX | UNIT |
|---|---|---|---|---|---|---|---|---|---|
| $V_{IK}$ | $V_{CC}$ = MIN, | $I_I$ = −18 mA | | | −1.2 | | | −1.2 | V |
| $V_{OH}$ | $V_{CC}$ = MIN, | $I_{OH}$ = MAX | 2.4 | 3.1 | | 2.4 | 3.1 | | V |
| $V_{OL}$ | $V_{CC}$ = MIN, | $I_{OL}$ = 16 mA | | | 0.5 | | | 0.5 | V |
| $I_{OZH}$ | $V_{CC}$ = MAX, | $V_O$ = 2.4 V | | | 50 | | | 50 | μA |
| $I_{OZL}$ | $V_{CC}$ = MAX, | $V_O$ = 0.5 V | | | −50 | | | −50 | μA |
| $I_I$ | $V_{CC}$ = MAX, | $V_I$ = 5.5 V | | | 1 | | | 1 | mA |
| $I_{IH}$ | $V_{CC}$ = MAX, | $V_I$ = 2.7 V | | | 25 | | | 25 | μA |
| $I_{IL}$ | $V_{CC}$ = MAX, | $V_I$ = 0.5 V | | | −0.25 | | | −0.25 | mA |
| $I_{OS}$[§] | $V_{CC}$ = MAX | | −15 | | −100 | −20 | | −100 | mA |
| $I_{CC}$ | $V_{CC}$ = MAX | | | 95 | 140 | | 95 | 140 | mA |

## switching characteristics over recommended ranges of $T_A$ and $V_{CC}$ (unless otherwise noted)

| | PARAMETER | TEST CONDITIONS | MJ MIN | MJ TYP[‡] | MJ MAX | J OR N MIN | J OR N TYP[‡] | J OR N MAX | UNIT |
|---|---|---|---|---|---|---|---|---|---|
| $t_{a(A)}$ | Access time from address | $C_L$ = 30 pF | | 40 | 75 | | 40 | 60 | ns |
| $t_{a(S)}$ | Access time from chip select (enable time) | See Note 3 | | 20 | 40 | | 20 | 30 | ns |
| $t_{dis}$ | Disable time | $C_L$ = 5 pF See Note 3 | | 20 | 40 | | 20 | 30 | ns |

[†]For conditions shown as MIN or MAX, use appropriate value specified under recommended operating conditions.
[‡]All typical values are at $V_{CC}$ = 5 V, $T_A$ = 25 °C.
[§]Not more than one output should be shorted at a time, and duration of the short circuit should not exceed one second.
NOTE 3: Load circuits and voltage waveforms are shown in Section 1.

4

PROMs

TEXAS
INSTRUMENTS

# TBP24SA41
# 4096 BITS (1024 WORDS BY 4 BITS)
# STANDARD PROGRAMMABLE READ-ONLY MEMORIES WITH OPEN-COLLECTOR OUTPUTS

## logic symbol

TBP24SA41

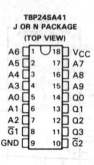

## pin assignment

TBP24SA41
J OR N PACKAGE
(TOP VIEW)

```
A6 [ 1   U 18 ] VCC
A5 [ 2     17 ] A7
A4 [ 3     16 ] A8
A3 [ 4     15 ] A9
A0 [ 5     14 ] Q0
A1 [ 6     13 ] Q1
A2 [ 7     12 ] Q2
G1 [ 8     11 ] Q3
GND [ 9    10 ] G2
```

## recommended operating conditions

| | PARAMETER | MJ | | | J OR N | | | UNIT |
|---|---|---|---|---|---|---|---|---|
| | | MIN | NOM | MAX | MIN | NOM | MAX | |
| $V_{CC}$ | Supply voltage | 4.5 | 5 | 5.5 | 4.75 | 5 | 5.25 | V |
| $V_{IH}$ | High-level input voltage | 2 | | | 2 | | | V |
| $V_{IL}$ | Low-level input voltage | | | 0.8 | | | 0.8 | V |
| $V_{OH}$ | High-level output voltage | | | 5.5 | | | 5.5 | V |
| $I_{OL}$ | Low-level output current | | | 16 | | | 16 | mA |
| $T_A$ | Operating free-air temperature range | -55 | | 125 | 0 | | 70 | °C |

## electrical characteristics over recommended operating free-air temperature range (unless otherwise noted)

| PARAMETER | TEST CONDITIONS† | | MJ | | | J OR N | | | UNIT |
|---|---|---|---|---|---|---|---|---|---|
| | | | MIN | TYP‡ | MAX | MIN | TYP‡ | MAX | |
| $V_{IK}$ | $V_{CC}$ = MIN, | $I_I$ = -18 mA | | | -1.2 | | | -1.2 | V |
| $I_{OH}$ | $V_{CC}$ = MIN, | $V_{OH}$ = 2.4 V | | | 0.05 | | | 0.05 | mA |
| | | $V_{OH}$ = 5.5 V | | | 0.1 | | | 0.1 | |
| $V_{OL}$ | $V_{CC}$ = MIN, | $I_{OL}$ = 16 mA | | | 0.5 | | | 0.5 | V |
| $I_I$ | $V_{CC}$ = MAX, | $V_I$ = 5.5 V | | | 1 | | | 1 | mA |
| $I_{IH}$ | $V_{CC}$ = MAX, | $V_I$ = 2.7 V | | | 25 | | | 25 | μA |
| $I_{IL}$ | $V_{CC}$ = MAX, | $V_I$ = 0.5 V | | | -0.25 | | | -0.25 | mA |
| $I_{CC}$ | $V_{CC}$ = MAX | | | 95 | 140 | | 95 | 140 | mA |

## switching characteristics over recommended ranges of $T_A$ and $V_{CC}$ (unless otherwise noted)

| | PARAMETER | TEST CONDITIONS | MJ | | | J OR N | | | UNIT |
|---|---|---|---|---|---|---|---|---|---|
| | | | MIN | TYP‡ | MAX | MIN | TYP‡ | MAX | |
| $t_{a(A)}$ | Access time from address | $C_L$ = 30 pF | | 40 | 75 | | 40 | 60 | ns |
| $t_{a(S)}$ | Access time from chip select (enable time) | $R_{L1}$ = 300 Ω | | 20 | 40 | | 20 | 30 | ns |
| $t_{PLH}$ | Propagation delay time low-to-high-level output from chip select | $R_{L2}$ = 600 Ω See Note 3 | | 20 | 40 | | 20 | 30 | ns |

†For conditions shown as MIN or MAX, use appropriate value specified under recommended operating conditions.
‡All typical values are at $V_{CC}$ = 5 V, $T_A$ = 25 °C.
NOTE 3: Load circuits and voltage waveforms are shown in Section 1.

**TEXAS INSTRUMENTS**

**logic symbol**                                         **pin assignment**

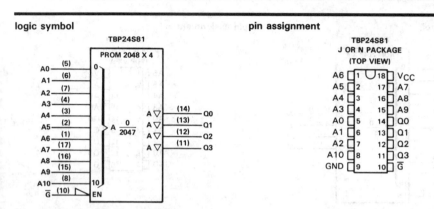

## recommended operating conditions

| | PARAMETER | MJ MIN | MJ NOM | MJ MAX | J OR N MIN | J OR N NOM | J OR N MAX | UNIT |
|---|---|---|---|---|---|---|---|---|
| $V_{CC}$ | Supply voltage | 4.5 | 5 | 5.5 | 4.75 | 5 | 5.25 | V |
| $V_{IH}$ | High-level input voltage | 2 | | | 2 | | | V |
| $V_{IL}$ | Low-level input voltage | | | 0.8 | | | 0.8 | V |
| $I_{OH}$ | High-level output current | | | −2 | | | −3.2 | mA |
| $I_{OL}$ | Low-level output current | | | 16 | | | 16 | mA |
| $T_A$ | Operating free-air temperature range | −55 | | 125 | 0 | | 70 | °C |

## electrical characteristics over recommended operating free-air temperature range (unless otherwise noted)

| PARAMETER | TEST CONDITIONS† | MJ MIN | MJ TYP‡ | MJ MAX | J OR N MIN | J OR N TYP‡ | J OR N MAX | UNIT |
|---|---|---|---|---|---|---|---|---|
| $V_{IK}$ | $V_{CC}$ = MIN, $I_I$ = −18 mA | | | −1.2 | | | −1.2 | V |
| $V_{OH}$ | $V_{CC}$ = MIN, $I_{OH}$ = MAX | 2.4 | 3.1 | | 2.4 | 3.1 | | V |
| $V_{OL}$ | $V_{CC}$ = MIN, $I_{OL}$ = 16 mA | | | 0.5 | | | 0.5 | V |
| $I_{OZH}$ | $V_{CC}$ = MAX, $V_O$ = 2.4 V | | | 50 | | | 50 | µA |
| $I_{OZL}$ | $V_{CC}$ = MAX, $V_O$ = 0.5 V | | | −50 | | | −50 | µA |
| $I_I$ | $V_{CC}$ = MAX, $V_I$ = 5.5 V | | | 1 | | | 1 | mA |
| $I_{IH}$ | $V_{CC}$ = MAX, $V_I$ = 2.7 V | | | 25 | | | 25 | µA |
| $I_{IL}$ | $V_{CC}$ = MAX, $V_I$ = 0.5 V | | | −0.25 | | | −0.25 | mA |
| $I_{OS}$§ | $V_{CC}$ = MAX | −15 | | −100 | −20 | | −100 | mA |
| $I_{CC}$ | $V_{CC}$ = MAX | | 125 | 175 | | 125 | 175 | mA |

## switching characteristics over recommended ranges of $T_A$ and $V_{CC}$ (unless otherwise noted)

| | PARAMETER | TEST CONDITIONS | MJ MIN | MJ TYP‡ | MJ MAX | J OR N MIN | J OR N TYP‡ | J OR N MAX | UNIT |
|---|---|---|---|---|---|---|---|---|---|
| $t_{a(A)}$ | Access time from address | $C_L$ = 30 pF | | 45 | 85 | | 45 | 70 | ns |
| $t_{a(S)}$ | Access time from chip select (enable time) | See Note 3 | | 20 | 50 | | 20 | 40 | ns |
| $t_{dis}$ | Disable time | $C_L$ = 5 pF See Note 3 | | 20 | 50 | | 20 | 40 | ns |

†For conditions shown as MIN or MAX, use appropriate value specified under recommended operating conditions.
‡All typical values are at $V_{CC}$ = 5 V, $T_A$ = 25°C.
§Not more than one output should be shorted at a time, and duration of the short circuit should not exceed one second.
NOTE 3: Load circuits and voltage waveforms are shown in Section 1.

**4**

**PROMs**

# TBP24SA81
# 8192 BITS (2048 WORDS BY 4 BITS)
## STANDARD PROGRAMMABLE READ-ONLY MEMORIES WITH OPEN-COLLECTOR OUTPUTS

### logic symbol

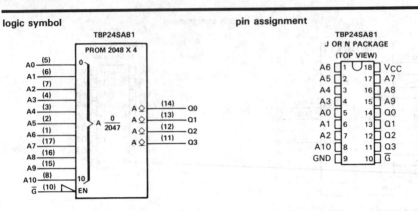

### pin assignment

TBP24SA81
J OR N PACKAGE
(TOP VIEW)

| | | | | |
|---|---|---|---|---|
| A6 | 1 | | 18 | V$_{CC}$ |
| A5 | 2 | | 17 | A7 |
| A4 | 3 | | 16 | A8 |
| A3 | 4 | | 15 | A9 |
| A0 | 5 | | 14 | Q0 |
| A1 | 6 | | 13 | Q1 |
| A2 | 7 | | 12 | Q2 |
| A10 | 8 | | 11 | Q3 |
| GND | 9 | | 10 | $\overline{G}$ |

### recommended operating conditions

| | PARAMETER | MJ | | | J OR N | | | UNIT |
|---|---|---|---|---|---|---|---|---|
| | | MIN | NOM | MAX | MIN | NOM | MAX | |
| V$_{CC}$ | Supply voltage | 4.5 | 5 | 5.5 | 4.75 | 5 | 5.25 | V |
| V$_{IH}$ | High-level input voltage | 2 | | | 2 | | | V |
| V$_{IL}$ | Low-level input voltage | | | 0.8 | | | 0.8 | V |
| V$_{OH}$ | High-level output voltage | | | 5.5 | | | 5.5 | V |
| I$_{OL}$ | Low-level output current | | | 16 | | | 16 | mA |
| T$_A$ | Operating free-air temperature range | -55 | | 125 | 0 | | 70 | °C |

### electrical characteristics over recommended operating free-air temperature range (unless otherwise noted)

| PARAMETER | TEST CONDITIONS† | | MJ | | | J OR N | | | UNIT |
|---|---|---|---|---|---|---|---|---|---|
| | | | MIN | TYP‡ | MAX | MIN | TYP‡ | MAX | |
| V$_{IK}$ | V$_{CC}$ = MIN, | I$_I$ = -18 mA | | | -1.2 | | | -1.2 | V |
| I$_{OH}$ | V$_{CC}$ = MIN, | V$_{OH}$ = 2.4 V | | | 0.05 | | | 0.05 | VmA |
| | | V$_{OH}$ = 5.5 V | | | 0.1 | | | 0.1 | |
| V$_{OL}$ | V$_{CC}$ = MIN, | I$_{OL}$ = 16 mA | | | 0.5 | | | 0.5 | V |
| I$_I$ | V$_{CC}$ = MAX, | V$_I$ = 5.5 V | | | 1 | | | 1 | mA |
| I$_{IH}$ | V$_{CC}$ = MAX, | V$_I$ = 2.7 V | | | 25 | | | 25 | µA |
| I$_{IL}$ | V$_{CC}$ = MAX, | V$_I$ = 0.5 V | | | -0.25 | | | -0.25 | mA |
| I$_{CC}$ | V$_{CC}$ = MAX | | | 125 | 175 | | 125 | 175 | mA |

### switching characteristics over recommended ranges of T$_A$ and V$_{CC}$ (unless otherwise noted)

| | PARAMETER | TEST CONDITIONS | MJ | | | J OR N | | | UNIT |
|---|---|---|---|---|---|---|---|---|---|
| | | | MIN | TYP‡ | MAX | MIN | TYP‡ | MAX | |
| t$_{a(A)}$ | Access time from address | C$_L$ = 30 pF | | 45 | 95 | | 45 | 70 | ns |
| t$_{a(S)}$ | Access time from chip select (enable time) | R$_{L1}$ = 300 Ω | | 20 | 50 | | 20 | 40 | ns |
| t$_{PLH}$ | Propagation delay time low-to-high-level output from chip select | R$_{L2}$ = 600 Ω See Note 3 | | 20 | 50 | | 20 | 40 | ns |

†For conditions shown as MIN or MAX, use appropriate value specified under recommended operating conditions.
‡All typical values are at V$_{CC}$ = 5 V, T$_A$ = 25 °C.
NOTE 3: Load circuits and voltage waveforms are shown in Section 1.

TEXAS
INSTRUMENTS

## logic symbol

**TBP28S86A**

PROM 1024 X 8

| Input | Pin | | Output | Pin |
|---|---|---|---|---|
| A0 | (8) | 0 | A▽ (9) | Q0 |
| A1 | (7) | | A▽ (10) | Q1 |
| A2 | (6) | | A▽ (11) | Q2 |
| A3 | (5) | | A▽ (13) | Q3 |
| A4 | (4) | A 0/1023 | A▽ (14) | Q4 |
| A5 | (3) | | A▽ (15) | Q5 |
| A6 | (2) | | A▽ (16) | Q6 |
| A7 | (1) | | A▽ (17) | Q7 |
| A8 | (23) | | | |
| A9 | (22) | 9 | | |
| G̅4 | (21) | & | | |
| G3 | (19) | EN | | |
| G2 | (18) | | | |
| G̅1 | (20) | | | |

## pin assignment

**TBP28S86A**
**JW OR NW PACKAGE**
**(TOP VIEW)**

| Left | Pin | | Pin | Right |
|---|---|---|---|---|
| A7 | 1 | ⌴ | 24 | VCC |
| A6 | 2 | | 23 | A8 |
| A5 | 3 | | 22 | A9 |
| A4 | 4 | | 21 | G̅4 |
| A3 | 5 | | 20 | G̅1 |
| A2 | 6 | | 19 | G3 |
| A1 | 7 | | 18 | G2 |
| A0 | 8 | | 17 | Q7 |
| Q0 | 9 | | 16 | Q6 |
| Q1 | 10 | | 15 | Q5 |
| Q2 | 11 | | 14 | Q4 |
| GND | 12 | | 13 | Q3 |

## recommended operating conditions

| PARAMETER | | MJW MIN | MJW NOM | MJW MAX | JW OR NW MIN | JW OR NW NOM | JW OR NW MAX | UNIT |
|---|---|---|---|---|---|---|---|---|
| $V_{CC}$ | Supply voltage | 4.5 | 5 | 5.5 | 4.75 | 5 | 5.25 | V |
| $V_{IH}$ | High-level input voltage | 2 | | | 2 | | | V |
| $V_{IL}$ | Low-level input voltage | | | 0.8 | | | 0.8 | V |
| $I_{OH}$ | High-level output current | | | −2 | | | −3.2 | mA |
| $I_{OL}$ | Low-level output current | | | 12 | | | 12 | mA |
| $T_A$ | Operating free-air temperature range | −55 | | 125 | 0 | | 70 | °C |

## electrical characteristics over recommended operating free-air temperature range (unless otherwise noted)

| PARAMETER | TEST CONDITIONS[†] | | MJW MIN | MJW TYP[‡] | MJW MAX | JW OR NW MIN | JW OR NW TYP[‡] | JW OR NW MAX | UNIT |
|---|---|---|---|---|---|---|---|---|---|
| $V_{IK}$ | $V_{CC}$ = MIN, | $I_I$ = −18 mA | | | −1.2 | | | −1.2 | V |
| $V_{OH}$ | $V_{CC}$ = MIN, | $I_{OH}$ = MAX | 2.4 | 3.1 | | 2.4 | 3.1 | | V |
| $V_{OL}$ | $V_{CC}$ = MIN, | $I_{OL}$ = 12 mA | | | 0.5 | | | 0.5 | V |
| $I_{OZH}$ | $V_{CC}$ = MAX, | $V_O$ = 2.4 V | | | 50 | | | 50 | μA |
| $I_{OZL}$ | $V_{CC}$ = MAX, | $V_O$ = 0.5 V | | | −50 | | | −50 | μA |
| $I_I$ | $V_{CC}$ = MAX, | $V_I$ = 5.5 V | | | 1 | | | 1 | mA |
| $I_{IH}$ | $V_{CC}$ = MAX, | $V_I$ = 2.7 V | | | 25 | | | 25 | μA |
| $I_{IL}$ | $V_{CC}$ = MAX, | $V_I$ = 0.5 V | | | −0.25 | | | −0.25 | mA |
| $I_{OS}$[§] | $V_{CC}$ = MAX | | −15 | | −100 | −20 | | −100 | mA |
| $I_{CC}$ | $V_{CC}$ = MAX | | | 110 | 170 | | 110 | 165 | mA |

## switching characteristics over recommended ranges of $T_A$ and $V_{CC}$ (unless otherwise noted)

| PARAMETER | | TEST CONDITIONS | MJW MIN | MJW TYP[‡] | MJW MAX | JW OR NW MIN | JW OR NW TYP[‡] | JW OR NW MAX | UNIT |
|---|---|---|---|---|---|---|---|---|---|
| $t_{aA}$ | Access time from address | $C_L$ = 30 pF | | 35 | 80 | | 35 | 65 | ns |
| $t_{a(S)}$ | Access time from chip select (enable time) | See Note 3 | | 20 | 50 | | 20 | 40 | ns |
| $t_{dis}$ | Disable time | $C_L$ = 5 pF See Note 3 | | 15 | 40 | | 15 | 35 | ns |

[†]For conditions shown as MIN or MAX, use appropriate value specified under recommended operating conditions.
[‡]All typical values are at $V_{CC}$ = 5 V, $T_A$ = 25°C.
[§]Not more than one output should be shorted at a time, and duration of the short circuit should not exceed one second.
NOTE 3: Load circuits and voltage waveforms are shown in Section 1.

**TEXAS INSTRUMENTS**

4

**PROMs**

## TBP28SA86A
## 8192 BITS (1024 WORDS BY 8 BITS)
## STANDARD PROGRAMMABLE READ-ONLY MEMORIES WITH OPEN-COLLECTOR OUTPUTS

**logic symbol**

**pin assignment**

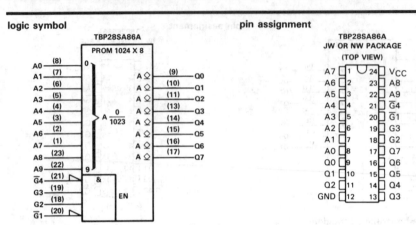

### recommended operating conditions

| | PARAMETER | MJW | | | JW OR NW | | | UNIT |
|---|---|---|---|---|---|---|---|---|
| | | MIN | NOM | MAX | MIN | NOM | MAX | |
| $V_{CC}$ | Supply voltage | 4.5 | 5 | 5.5 | 4.75 | 5 | 5.25 | V |
| $V_{IH}$ | High-level input voltage | 2 | | | 2 | | | V |
| $V_{IL}$ | Low-level input voltage | | | 0.8 | | | 0.8 | V |
| $V_{OH}$ | High-level output voltage | | | 5.5 | | | 5.5 | V |
| $I_{OL}$ | Low-level output current | | | 12 | | | 12 | mA |
| $T_A$ | Operating free-air temperature range | −55 | | 125 | 0 | | 70 | °C |

### electrical characteristics over recommended operating free-air temperature range (unless otherwise noted)

| PARAMETER | TEST CONDITIONS[†] | | MJW | | | JW OR NW | | | UNIT |
|---|---|---|---|---|---|---|---|---|---|
| | | | MIN | TYP[‡] | MAX | MIN | TYP[‡] | MAX | |
| $V_{IK}$ | $V_{CC}$ = MIN, | $I_I$ = −18 mA | | | −1.2 | | | −1.2 | V |
| $I_{OH}$ | $V_{CC}$ = MIN, | $V_{OH}$ = 2.4 V | | | 0.05 | | | 0.05 | mA |
| | | $V_{OH}$ = 5.5 V | | | 0.1 | | | 0.1 | |
| $V_{OL}$ | $V_{CC}$ = MIN, | $I_{OL}$ = 12 mA | | | 0.5 | | | 0.5 | V |
| $I_I$ | $V_{CC}$ = MAX, | $V_I$ = 5.5 V | | | 1 | | | 1 | mA |
| $I_{IH}$ | $V_{CC}$ = MAX, | $V_I$ = 2.7 V | | | 25 | | | 25 | μA |
| $I_{IL}$ | $V_{CC}$ = MAX, | $V_I$ = 0.5 V | | | −0.25 | | | −0.25 | mA |
| $I_{CC}$ | $V_{CC}$ = MAX | | | 125 | 175 | | 125 | 175 | mA |

### switching characteristics over recommended ranges of $T_A$ and $V_{CC}$ (unless otherwise noted)

| | PARAMETER | TEST CONDITIONS | MJW | | | JW OR NW | | | UNIT |
|---|---|---|---|---|---|---|---|---|---|
| | | | MIN | TYP[‡] | MAX | MIN | TYP[‡] | MAX | |
| $t_{a(A)}$ | Access time from address | $C_L$ = 30 pF | | 35 | 80 | | 35 | 70 | ns |
| $t_{a(S)}$ | Access time from chip select (enable time) | $R_{L1}$ = 300 Ω | | 20 | 50 | | 20 | 40 | ns |
| $t_{PLH}$ | Propagation delay time low-to-high-level output from chip select | $R_{L2}$ = 600 Ω See Note 3 | | 15 | 40 | | 15 | 35 | ns |

[†]For conditions shown as MIN or MAX, use appropriate value specified under recommended operating conditions.
[‡]All typical values are at $V_{CC}$ = 5 V, $T_A$ = 25 °C.
NOTE 3: Load circuits and voltage waveforms are shown in Section 1.

TEXAS
INSTRUMENTS

**logic symbol**

**pin assignment**

TBP28S2708A

PROM 1024 X 8

| A0 | (8) | 0 | | | |
| A1 | (7) | | A ▽ | (9) | Q0 |
| A2 | (6) | | A ▽ | (10) | Q1 |
| A3 | (5) | | A ▽ | (11) | Q2 |
| A4 | (4) | $A \frac{0}{1023}$ | A ▽ | (13) | Q3 |
| A5 | (3) | | A ▽ | (14) | Q4 |
| A6 | (2) | | A ▽ | (15) | Q5 |
| A7 | (1) | | A ▽ | (16) | Q6 |
| A8 | (23) | | A ▽ | (17) | Q7 |
| A9 | (22) | 9 | | | |
| $\overline{G}$ | (20) | EN | | | |

TBP28S2708A
NW PACKAGE
(TOP VIEW)

| A7 | 1 | 24 | $V_{CC}$ |
| A6 | 2 | 23 | A8 |
| A5 | 3 | 22 | A9 |
| A4 | 4 | 21 | NC |
| A3 | 5 | 20 | $\overline{G}$ |
| A2 | 6 | 19 | NC |
| A1 | 7 | 18 | NC |
| A0 | 8 | 17 | Q7 |
| Q0 | 9 | 16 | Q6 |
| Q1 | 10 | 15 | Q5 |
| Q2 | 11 | 14 | Q4 |
| GND | 12 | 13 | Q3 |

**recommended operating conditions**

| | PARAMETER | NW MIN | NW NOM | NW MAX | UNIT |
|---|---|---|---|---|---|
| $V_{CC}$ | Supply voltage | 4.75 | 5 | 5.25 | V |
| $V_{IH}$ | High-level input voltage | 2 | | | V |
| $V_{IL}$ | Low-level input voltage | | | 0.8 | V |
| $I_{OH}$ | High-level output current | | | −3.2 | mA |
| $I_{OL}$ | Low-level output current | | | 12 | mA |
| $T_A$ | Operating free-air temperature range | 0 | | 70 | °C |

**electrical characteristics over recommended operating free-air temperature range (unless otherwise noted)**

| PARAMETER | TEST CONDITIONS | | NW MIN | NW TYP[†] | NW MAX | UNIT |
|---|---|---|---|---|---|---|
| $V_{IK}$ | $V_{CC} = 4.75$, | $I_I = -18$ mA | | | −1.2 | V |
| $V_{OH}$ | $V_{CC} = 4.75$, | $I_{OH} = -3.2$ mA | 2.4 | 3.1 | | V |
| $V_{OL}$ | $V_{CC} = 4.75$, | $I_{OL} = 12$ mA | | | 0.5 | V |
| $I_{OZH}$ | $V_{CC} = 5.25$, | $V_O = 2.4$ V | | | 50 | μA |
| $I_{OZL}$ | $V_{CC} = 5.25$, | $V_O = 0.5$ V | | | −50 | μA |
| $I_I$ | $V_{CC} = 5.25$, | $V_I = 5.5$ V | | | 1 | mA |
| $I_{IH}$ | $V_{CC} = 5.25$, | $V_I = 2.7$ V | | | 25 | μA |
| $I_{IL}$ | $V_{CC} = 5.25$, | $V_I = 0.5$ V | | | −0.25 | mA |
| $I_{OS}$[‡] | $V_{CC} = 5.25$ | | −20 | | −100 | mA |
| $I_{CC}$ | $V_{CC} = 5.25$ | | | 110 | 165 | mA |

**switching characteristics over recommended ranges of $T_A$ and $V_{CC}$ (unless otherwise noted)**

| | PARAMETER | TEST CONDITIONS | NW MIN | NW TYP[†] | NW MAX | UNIT |
|---|---|---|---|---|---|---|
| $t_{a(A)}$ | Access time from address | $C_L = 30$ pF | | 45 | 70 | ns |
| $t_{a(S)}$ | Access time from chip select (enable time) | See Note 3 | | 20 | 40 | ns |
| $t_{dis}$ | Disable time | $C_L = 5$ pF<br>See Note 3 | | 20 | 40 | ns |

[†]All typical values are at $V_{CC} = 5$ V, $T_A = 25$°C.
[‡]Not more than one output should be shorted at a time, and duration of the short circuit should not exceed one second.
NOTE 3: Load circuits and voltage waveforms are shown in Section 1.

TEXAS
INSTRUMENTS

4

PROMs

## TBP28S166
## 16,384 BITS (2084 WORDS BY 8 BITS)
## STANDARD PROGRAMMABLE READ-ONLY MEMORIES WITH 3-STATE OUTPUTS

**logic symbol**          **pin assignment**

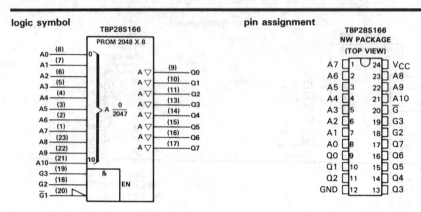

### recommended operating conditions

| | PARAMETER | NW MIN | NW NOM | NW MAX | UNIT |
|---|---|---|---|---|---|
| $V_{CC}$ | Supply voltage | 4.75 | 5 | 5.25 | V |
| $V_{IH}$ | High-level input voltage | 2 | | | V |
| $V_{IL}$ | Low-level input voltage | | | 0.8 | V |
| $I_{OH}$ | High-level output current | | | −3.2 | mA |
| $I_{OL}$ | Low-level output current | | | 16 | mA |
| $T_A$ | Operating free-air temperature range | 0 | | 70 | °C |

### electrical characteristics over recommended operating free-air temperature range (unless otherwise noted)

| PARAMETER | TEST CONDITIONS | | NW MIN | NW TYP[†] | NW MAX | UNIT |
|---|---|---|---|---|---|---|
| $V_{IK}$ | $V_{CC} = 4.75$, | $I_I = -18$ mA | | | −1.2 | V |
| $V_{OH}$ | $V_{CC} = 4.75$, | $I_{OH} = -3.2$ mA | 2.4 | 3.1 | | V |
| $V_{OL}$ | $V_{CC} = 4.75$, | $I_{OL} = 16$ mA | | | 0.5 | V |
| $I_{OZH}$ | $V_{CC} = 5.25$, | $V_O = 2.4$ V | | | 50 | μA |
| $I_{OZL}$ | $V_{CC} = 5.25$, | $V_O = 0.5$ V | | | −50 | μA |
| $I_I$ | $V_{CC} = 5.25$, | $V_I = 5.5$ V | | | 1 | mA |
| $I_{IH}$ | $V_{CC} = 5.25$, | $V_I = 2.7$ V | | | 25 | μA |
| $I_{IL}$ | $V_{CC} = 5.25$, | $V_I = 0.5$ V | | | −0.25 | mA |
| $I_{OS}$[‡] | $V_{CC} = 5.25$ | | −20 | | −100 | mA |
| $I_{CC}$ | $V_{CC} = 5.25$ | | | 130 | 175 | mA |

### switching characteristics over recommended ranges of $T_A$ and $V_{CC}$ (unless otherwise noted)

| PARAMETER | | TEST CONDITIONS | NW MIN | NW TYP[†] | NW MAX | UNIT |
|---|---|---|---|---|---|---|
| $t_{a(A)}$ | Access time from address | $C_L = 30$ pF | | 35 | 75 | ns |
| $t_{a(S)}$ | Access time from chip select (enable time) | See Note 3 | | 15 | 40 | ns |
| $t_{dis}$ | Disable time | $C_L = 5$ pF See Note 3 | | 15 | 40 | ns |

[†]All typical values are at $V_{CC} = 5$ V, $T_A = 25$°C.
[‡]Not more than one output should be shorted at a time, and duration of the short circuit should not exceed one second.
NOTE 3: Load circuits and voltage waveforms are shown in Section 1.

**TEXAS INSTRUMENTS**

**4**

**PROMs**

## logic symbol

TBP28L22
PROM 256 X 8

| | |
|---|---|
| A0 (1) | |
| A1 (2) | |
| A2 (3) | A ▽ (6) Q0 |
| A3 (4) | A ▽ (7) Q1 |
| A4 (5) | A ▽ (8) Q2 |
| | A $\frac{0}{255}$ A ▽ (9) Q3 |
| A5 (17) | A ▽ (11) Q4 |
| A6 (18) | A ▽ (12) Q5 |
| A7 (19) | A ▽ (13) Q6 |
| $\overline{G}2$ (16) | A ▽ (14) Q7 |
| $\overline{G}1$ (15) | & EN |

## pin assignment

TBP28L22
J OR N PACKAGE
(TOP VIEW)

| | | | |
|---|---|---|---|
| A0 | 1 | 20 | VCC |
| A1 | 2 | 19 | A7 |
| A2 | 3 | 18 | A6 |
| A3 | 4 | 17 | A5 |
| A4 | 5 | 16 | $\overline{G}2$ |
| Q0 | 6 | 15 | $\overline{G}1$ |
| Q1 | 7 | 14 | Q7 |
| Q2 | 8 | 13 | Q6 |
| Q3 | 9 | 12 | Q5 |
| GND | 10 | 11 | Q4 |

## recommended operating conditions

| | PARAMETER | MJ MIN | MJ NOM | MJ MAX | J OR N MIN | J OR N NOM | J OR N MAX | UNIT |
|---|---|---|---|---|---|---|---|---|
| $V_{CC}$ | Supply voltage | 4.5 | 5 | 5.5 | 4.75 | 5 | 5.25 | V |
| $V_{IH}$ | High-level input voltage | 2 | | | 2 | | | V |
| $V_{IL}$ | Low-level input voltage | | | 0.8 | | | 0.8 | V |
| $I_{OH}$ | High-level output current | | | −2 | | | −6.5 | mA |
| $I_{OL}$ | Low-level output current | | | 16 | | | 16 | mA |
| $T_A$ | Operating free-air temperature range | −55 | | 125 | 0 | | 70 | °C |

## electrical characteristics over recommended operating free-air temperature range (unless otherwise noted)

| PARAMETER | TEST CONDITIONS[†] | | MJ MIN | MJ TYP[‡] | MJ MAX | J OR N MIN | J OR N TYP[‡] | J OR N MAX | UNIT |
|---|---|---|---|---|---|---|---|---|---|
| $V_{IK}$ | $V_{CC}$ = MIN, | $I_I$ = −18 mA | | | −1.2 | | | −1.2 | V |
| $V_{OH}$ | $V_{CC}$ = MIN, | $I_{OH}$ = MAX | 2.4 | 3.1 | | 2.4 | 3.1 | | V |
| $V_{OL}$ | $V_{CC}$ = MIN, | $I_{OL}$ = 16 mA | | | 0.5 | | | 0.5 | V |
| $I_{OZH}$ | $V_{CC}$ = MAX, | $V_O$ = 2.4 V | | | 50 | | | 50 | µA |
| $I_{OZL}$ | $V_{CC}$ = MAX, | $V_O$ = 0.5 V | | | −50 | | | −50 | µA |
| $I_I$ | $V_{CC}$ = MAX, | $V_I$ = 5.5 V | | | 1 | | | 1 | mA |
| $I_{IH}$ | $V_{CC}$ = MAX, | $V_I$ = 2.7 V | | | 25 | | | 25 | µA |
| $I_{IL}$ | $V_{CC}$ = MAX, | $V_I$ = 0.5 V | | | −0.25 | | | −0.25 | mA |
| $I_{OS}$[§] | $V_{CC}$ = MAX | | −25 | | −100 | −30 | | −100 | mA |
| $I_{CC}$ | $V_{CC}$ = MAX | | | 75 | 100 | | 75 | 100 | mA |

## switching characteristics over recommended ranges of $T_A$ and $V_{CC}$ (unless otherwise noted)

| | PARAMETER | TEST CONDITIONS | MJ MIN | MJ TYP[‡] | MJ MAX | J OR N MIN | J OR N TYP[‡] | J OR N MAX | UNIT |
|---|---|---|---|---|---|---|---|---|---|
| $t_{aA}$) | Access time from address | $C_L$ = 30 pF See Note 3 | | 45 | 75 | | 45 | 70 | ns |
| $t_{a(S)}$ | Access time from chip select (enable time) | | | 20 | 40 | | 20 | 35 | ns |
| $t_{dis}$ | Disable time | $C_L$ = 5 pF See Note 3 | | 15 | 35 | | 15 | 30 | ns |

[†]For conditions shown as MIN or MAX, use appropriate value specified under recommended operating conditions.
[‡]All typical values are at $V_{CC}$ = 5 V, $T_A$ = 25 °C.
[§]Not more than one output should be shorted at a time, and duration of the short circuit should not exceed one second.
NOTE 3: Load circuits and voltage waveforms are shown in Section 1.

**TEXAS**
**INSTRUMENTS**

**4**

**PROMs**

## TBP28LA22
## 2048 BITS (256 WORDS BY 8 BITS)
## LOW-POWER PROGRAMMABLE READ-ONLY MEMORIES WITH OPEN-COLLECTOR OUTPUTS

### logic symbol

### pin assignment

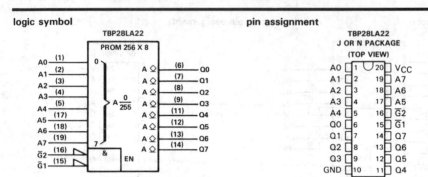

TBP28LA22
PROM 256 X 8

TBP28LA22
J OR N PACKAGE
(TOP VIEW)

### recommended operating conditions

| | PARAMETER | MJ | | | J OR N | | | UNIT |
|---|---|---|---|---|---|---|---|---|
| | | MIN | NOM | MAX | MIN | NOM | MAX | |
| $V_{CC}$ | Supply voltage | 4.5 | 5 | 5.5 | 4.75 | 5 | 5.25 | V |
| $V_{IH}$ | High-level input voltage | 2 | | | 2 | | | V |
| $V_{IL}$ | Low-level input voltage | | | 0.8 | | | 0.8 | V |
| $V_{OH}$ | High-level output voltage | | | 5.5 | | | 5.5 | V |
| $I_{OL}$ | Low-level output current | | | 16 | | | 16 | mA |
| $T_A$ | Operating free-air temperature range | −55 | | 125 | 0 | | 70 | °C |

### electrical characteristics over recommended operating free-air temperature range (unless otherwise noted)

| PARAMETER | TEST CONDITIONS[†] | | MJ | | | J OR N | | | UNIT |
|---|---|---|---|---|---|---|---|---|---|
| | | | MIN | TYP[‡] | MAX | MIN | TYP[‡] | MAX | |
| $V_{IK}$ | $V_{CC}$ = MIN, | $I_I$ = −18 mA | | | −1.2 | | | −1.2 | V |
| $I_{OH}$ | $V_{CC}$ = MIN, | $V_{OH}$ = 2.4 V | | | 0.05 | | | 0.05 | mA |
| | | $V_{OH}$ = 5.5 V | | | 0.1 | | | 0.1 | |
| $V_{OL}$ | $V_{CC}$ = MIN, | $I_{OL}$ = 16 mA | | | 0.5 | | | 0.5 | V |
| $I_I$ | $V_{CC}$ = MAX, | $V_I$ = 5.5 V | | | 1 | | | 1 | mA |
| $I_{IH}$ | $V_{CC}$ = MAX, | $V_I$ = 2.7 V | | | 25 | | | 25 | µA |
| $I_{IL}$ | $V_{CC}$ = MAX, | $V_I$ = 0.5 V | | | −0.25 | | | −0.25 | mA |
| $I_{CC}$ | $V_{CC}$ = MAX | | | 75 | 100 | | 75 | 100 | mA |

### switching characteristics over recommended ranges of $T_A$ and $V_{CC}$ (unless otherwise noted)

| | PARAMETER | TEST CONDITIONS | MJ | | | J OR N | | | UNIT |
|---|---|---|---|---|---|---|---|---|---|
| | | | MIN | TYP[‡] | MAX | MIN | TYP[‡] | MAX | |
| $t_{a(A)}$ | Access time from address | $C_L$ = 30 pF | | 40 | 80 | | 45 | 75 | ns |
| $t_{a(S)}$ | Access time from chip select (enable time) | $R_{L1}$ = 300 Ω | | 20 | 40 | | 20 | 35 | ns |
| $t_{PLH}$ | Propagation delay time low-to-high-level output from chip select | $R_{L2}$ = 600 Ω<br>See Note 3 | | 15 | 35 | | 15 | 30 | ns |

[†]For conditions shown as MIN or MAX, use appropriate value specified under recommended operating conditions.
[‡]All typical values are at $V_{CC}$ = 5 V, $T_A$ = 25°C.
NOTE 3: Load circuits and voltage waveforms are shown in Section 1.

TEXAS
INSTRUMENTS

4
PROMs

## logic symbol

## pin assignment

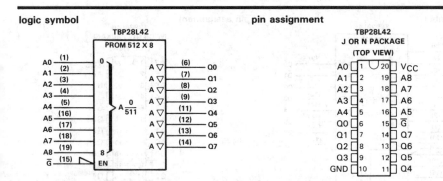

## recommended operating conditions

| PARAMETER | | MJ | | | J OR N | | | UNIT |
|---|---|---|---|---|---|---|---|---|
| | | MIN | NOM | MAX | MIN | NOM | MAX | |
| $V_{CC}$ | Supply voltage | 4.5 | 5 | 5.5 | 4.75 | 5 | 5.25 | V |
| $V_{IH}$ | High-level input voltage | 2 | | | 2 | | | V |
| $V_{IL}$ | Low-level input voltage | | | 0.8 | | | 0.8 | V |
| $I_{OH}$ | High-level output current | | | −1 | | | −1.6 | mA |
| $I_{OL}$ | Low-level output current | | | 8 | | | 8 | mA |
| $T_A$ | Operating free-air temperature range | −55 | | 125 | 0 | | 70 | °C |

## electrical characteristics over recommended operating free-air temperature range (unless otherwise noted)

| PARAMETER | TEST CONDITIONS[†] | | MJ | | | J OR N | | | UNIT |
|---|---|---|---|---|---|---|---|---|---|
| | | | MIN | TYP[‡] | MAX | MIN | TYP[‡] | MAX | |
| $V_{IK}$ | $V_{CC}$ = MIN, | $I_I$ = −18 mA | | | −1.2 | | | −1.2 | V |
| $V_{OH}$ | $V_{CC}$ = MIN, | $I_{OH}$ = MAX | 2.4 | 3.1 | | 2.4 | 3.1 | | V |
| $V_{OL}$ | $V_{CC}$ = MIN, | $I_{OL}$ = 8 mA | | | 0.5 | | | 0.5 | V |
| $I_{OZH}$ | $V_{CC}$ = MAX, | $V_O$ = 2.4 V | | | 50 | | | 50 | μA |
| $I_{OZL}$ | $V_{CC}$ = MAX, | $V_O$ = 0.5 V | | | −50 | | | −50 | μA |
| $I_I$ | $V_{CC}$ = MAX, | $V_I$ = 5.5 V | | | 1 | | | 1 | mA |
| $I_{IH}$ | $V_{CC}$ = MAX, | $V_I$ = 2.7 V | | | 25 | | | 25 | μA |
| $I_{IL}$ | $V_{CC}$ = MAX, | $V_I$ = 0.5 V | | | −0.25 | | | −0.25 | mA |
| $I_{OS}$[§] | $V_{CC}$ = MAX | | −10 | | −100 | −10 | | −100 | mA |
| $I_{CC}$ | $V_{CC}$ = MAX | | | 50 | 85 | | 50 | 85 | mA |

## switching characteristics over recommended ranges of $T_A$ and $V_{CC}$ (unless otherwise noted)

| PARAMETER | | TEST CONDITIONS | MJ | | | J OR N | | | UNIT |
|---|---|---|---|---|---|---|---|---|---|
| | | | MIN | TYP[‡] | MAX | MIN | TYP[‡] | MAX | |
| $t_{a(A)}$ | Access time from address | $C_L$ = 30 pF | | 55 | 110 | | 55 | 95 | ns |
| $t_{a(S)}$ | Access time from chip select (enable time) | See Note 3 | | 25 | 60 | | 25 | 60 | ns |
| $t_{dis}$ | Disable time | $C_L$ = 5 pF See Note 3 | | 25 | 50 | | 25 | 40 | ns |

[†]For conditions shown as MIN or MAX, use appropriate value specified under recommended operating conditions.
[‡]All typical values are at $V_{CC}$ = 5 V, $T_A$ = 25 °C.
[§]Not more than one output should be shorted at a time, and duration of the short circuit should not exceed one second.
NOTE 3: Load circuits and voltage waveforms are shown in Section 1.

**4**

**PROMs**

TEXAS
INSTRUMENTS

# TBP28L46
## 4096 BITS (512 WORDS BY 8 BITS)
## LOW-POWER PROGRAMMABLE READ-ONLY MEMORIES WITH 3-STATE OUTPUTS

## logic symbol

```
                    TBP28L46
                  PROM 512 X 8
      (8)     ┌──────────────┐
A0 ──────────┤0             │      (9)
A1 ──(7)─────┤           A ▽ ├──────── Q0
A2 ──(6)─────┤           A ▽ ├──(10)── Q1
A3 ──(5)─────┤           A ▽ ├──(11)── Q2
A4 ──(4)─────┤   A  0    A ▽ ├──(13)── Q3
A5 ──(3)─────┤     511   A ▽ ├──(14)── Q4
A6 ──(2)─────┤           A ▽ ├──(15)── Q5
A7 ──(1)─────┤           A ▽ ├──(16)── Q6
A8 ──(23)────┤8          A ▽ ├──(17)── Q7
G̅4 ──(21)────┤&             │
G3 ──(19)────┤              │
G2 ──(18)────┤    EN        │
G̅1 ──(20)────┤              │
             └──────────────┘
```

## pin assignment

TBP28L46
JW OR NW PACKAGE
(TOP VIEW)

```
        ┌───U───┐
A7  □ 1       24 □ VCC
A6  □ 2       23 □ A8
A5  □ 3       22 □ NC
A4  □ 4       21 □ G̅4
A3  □ 5       20 □ G̅1
A2  □ 6       19 □ G3
A1  □ 7       18 □ G2
A0  □ 8       17 □ Q7
Q0  □ 9       16 □ Q6
Q1  □ 10      15 □ Q5
Q2  □ 11      14 □ Q4
GND □ 12      13 □ Q3
        └───────┘
```

## recommended operating conditions

| PARAMETER | | MJW | | | JW OR NW | | | UNIT |
|---|---|---|---|---|---|---|---|---|
| | | MIN | NOM | MAX | MIN | NOM | MAX | |
| V_CC | Supply voltage | 4.5 | 5 | 5.5 | 4.75 | 5 | 5.25 | V |
| V_IH | High-level input voltage | 2 | | | 2 | | | V |
| V_IL | Low-level input voltage | | | 0.8 | | | 0.8 | V |
| I_OH | High-level output current | | | −1 | | | −1.6 | mA |
| I_OL | Low-level output current | | | 8 | | | 8 | mA |
| T_A | Operating free-air temperature range | −55 | | 125 | 0 | | 70 | °C |

## electrical characteristics over recommended operating free-air temperature range (unless otherwise noted)

| PARAMETER | TEST CONDITIONS[†] | | MJW | | | JW OR NW | | | UNIT |
|---|---|---|---|---|---|---|---|---|---|
| | | | MIN | TYP[‡] | MAX | MIN | TYP[‡] | MAX | |
| V_IK | V_CC = MIN, | I_I = −18 mA | | | −1.2 | | | −1.2 | V |
| V_OH | V_CC = MIN, | I_OH = MAX | 2.4 | 3.1 | | 2.4 | 3.1 | | V |
| V_OL | V_CC = MIN, | I_OL = 8 mA | | | 0.5 | | | 0.5 | V |
| I_OZH | V_CC = MAX, | V_O = 2.4 V | | | 50 | | | 50 | μA |
| I_OZL | V_CC = MAX, | V_O = 0.5 V | | | −50 | | | −50 | μA |
| I_I | V_CC = MAX, | V_I = 5.5 V | | | 1 | | | 1 | mA |
| I_IH | V_CC = MAX, | V_I = 2.7 V | | | 25 | | | 25 | μA |
| I_IL | V_CC = MAX, | V_I = 0.5 V | | | −0.25 | | | −0.25 | mA |
| I_OS[§] | V_CC = MAX | | −10 | | −100 | −10 | | −100 | mA |
| I_CC | V_CC = MAX | | | 50 | 85 | | 50 | 85 | mA |

## switching characteristics over recommended ranges of T_A and V_CC (unless otherwise noted)

| PARAMETER | | TEST CONDITIONS | MJW | | | JW OR NW | | | UNIT |
|---|---|---|---|---|---|---|---|---|---|
| | | | MIN | TYP[‡] | MAX | MIN | TYP[‡] | MAX | |
| t_a(A) | Access time from address | C_L = 30 pF | | 55 | 110 | | 55 | 95 | ns |
| t_a(S) | Access time from chip select (enable time) | See Note 3 | | 25 | 60 | | 25 | 60 | ns |
| t_dis | Disable time | C_L = 5 pF See Note 3 | | 25 | 50 | | 25 | 40 | ns |

[†]For conditions shown as MIN or MAX, use appropriate value specified under recommended operating conditions.
[‡]All typical values are at V_CC = 5 V, T_A = 25°C.
[§]Not more than one output should be shorted at a time, and duration of the short circuit should not exceed one second.
NOTE 3: Load circuits and voltage waveforms are shown in Section 1.

4

PROMs

TEXAS
INSTRUMENTS

## logic symbol

**TBP28L86A**

PROM 1024 X 8

| | |
|---|---|
| A0 (8) — 0 | A▽ (9) — Q0 |
| A1 (7) | A▽ (10) — Q1 |
| A2 (6) | A▽ (11) — Q2 |
| A3 (5) | A▽ (13) — Q3 |
| A4 (4) | A▽ (14) — Q4 |
| A5 (3) A $\frac{0}{1023}$ | A▽ (15) — Q5 |
| A6 (2) | A▽ (16) — Q6 |
| A7 (1) | A▽ (17) — Q7 |
| A8 (23) | |
| A9 (22) — 9 | |
| $\overline{G4}$ (21) — & | |
| G3 (19) — EN | |
| G2 (18) | |
| $\overline{G1}$ (20) | |

## pin assignment

**TBP28L86A**
**JW OR NW PACKAGE**
**(TOP VIEW)**

| | | | |
|---|---|---|---|
| A7 | 1 | 24 | V_CC |
| A6 | 2 | 23 | A8 |
| A5 | 3 | 22 | A9 |
| A4 | 4 | 21 | $\overline{G4}$ |
| A3 | 5 | 20 | $\overline{G1}$ |
| A2 | 6 | 19 | G3 |
| A1 | 7 | 18 | G2 |
| A0 | 8 | 17 | Q7 |
| Q0 | 9 | 16 | Q6 |
| Q1 | 10 | 15 | Q5 |
| Q2 | 11 | 14 | Q4 |
| GND | 12 | 13 | Q3 |

## recommended operating conditions

| PARAMETER | | MJW | | | JW OR NW | | | UNIT |
|---|---|---|---|---|---|---|---|---|
| | | MIN | NOM | MAX | MIN | NOM | MAX | |
| V_CC | Supply voltage | 4.5 | 5 | 5.5 | 4.75 | 5 | 5.25 | V |
| V_IH | High-level input voltage | 2 | | | 2 | | | V |
| V_IL | Low-level input voltage | | | 0.8 | | | 0.8 | V |
| I_OH | High-level output current | | | −1 | | | −1.6 | mA |
| I_OL | Low-level output current | | | 8 | | | 8 | mA |
| T_A | Operating free-air temperature range | −55 | | 125 | 0 | | 70 | °C |

## electrical characteristics over recommended operating free-air temperature range (unless otherwise noted)

| PARAMETER | TEST CONDITIONS[†] | | MJW | | | JW OR NW | | | UNIT |
|---|---|---|---|---|---|---|---|---|---|
| | | | MIN | TYP[‡] | MAX | MIN | TYP[‡] | MAX | |
| V_IK | V_CC = MIN, | I_I = −18 mA | | | −1.2 | | | −1.2 | V |
| V_OH | V_CC = MIN, | I_OH = MAX | 2.4 | 3.1 | | 2.4 | 3.1 | | V |
| V_OL | V_CC = MIN, | I_OL = 8 mA | | | 0.5 | | | 0.5 | V |
| I_OZH | V_CC = MAX, | V_O = 2.4 V | | | 50 | | | 50 | μA |
| I_OZL | V_CC = MAX, | V_O = 0.5 V | | | −50 | | | −50 | μA |
| I_I | V_CC = MAX, | V_I = 5.5 V | | | 1 | | | 1 | mA |
| I_IH | V_CC = MAX, | V_I = 2.7 V | | | 25 | | | 25 | μA |
| I_IL | V_CC = MAX, | V_I = 0.5 V | | | −0.25 | | | −0.25 | mA |
| I_OS[§] | V_CC = MAX | | −10 | | −100 | −10 | | −100 | mA |
| I_CC | V_CC = MAX | | | 55 | 95 | | 55 | 80 | mA |

## switching characteristics over recommended ranges of T_A and V_CC (unless otherwise noted)

| PARAMETER | | TEST CONDITIONS | MJW | | | JW OR NW | | | UNIT |
|---|---|---|---|---|---|---|---|---|---|
| | | | MIN | TYP[‡] | MAX | MIN | TYP[‡] | MAX | |
| t_a(A) | Access time from address | C_L = 30 pF | | 65 | 200 | | 65 | 110 | ns |
| t_a(S) | Access time from chip select (enable time) | See Note 3 | | 40 | 125 | | 40 | 80 | ns |
| t_dis | Disable time | C_L = 5 pF See Note 3 | | 25 | 100 | | 25 | 60 | ns |

[†]For conditions shown as MIN or MAX, use appropriate value specified under recommended operating conditions.
[‡]All typical values are at V_CC = 5 V, T_A = 25°C.
[§]Not more than one output should be shorted at a time, and duration of the short circuit should not exceed one second.
NOTE 3: Load circuits and voltage waveforms are shown in Section 1.

**TEXAS**
**INSTRUMENTS**

4

PROMs

# TBP28L166
# 16,384 BITS (2084 WORDS BY 8 BITS)
# LOW-POWER PROGRAMMABLE READ-ONLY MEMORIES WITH 3-STATE OUTPUTS

## logic symbol

## pin assignment

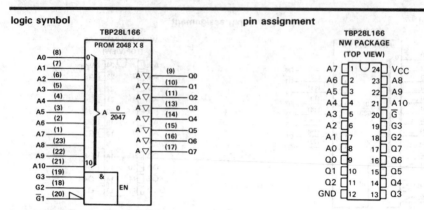

## recommended operating conditions

| PARAMETER | | NW | | | UNIT |
|---|---|---|---|---|---|
| | | MIN | NOM | MAX | |
| $V_{CC}$ | Supply voltage | 4.75 | 5 | 5.25 | V |
| $V_{IH}$ | High-level input voltage | 2 | | | V |
| $V_{IL}$ | Low-level input voltage | | | 0.8 | V |
| $I_{OH}$ | High-level output current | | | −1.6 | mA |
| $I_{OL}$ | Low-level output current | | | 8 | mA |
| $T_A$ | Operating free-air temperature range | 0 | | 70 | °C |

## electrical characteristics over recommended operating free-air temperature range (unless otherwise noted)

| PARAMETER | TEST CONDITIONS | | NW[†] | | | UNIT |
|---|---|---|---|---|---|---|
| | | | MIN | TYP[†] | MAX | |
| $V_{IK}$ | $V_{CC} = 4.75$, | $I_I = −18$ mA | | | −1.2 | V |
| $V_{OH}$ | $V_{CC} = 4.75$, | $I_{OH} = −1.6$ mA | 2.4 | 3.1 | | V |
| $V_{OL}$ | $V_{CC} = 4.75$, | $I_{OL} = 8$ mA | | | 0.5 | V |
| $I_{OZH}$ | $V_{CC} = 5.25$, | $V_O = 2.4$ V | | | 50 | $\mu$A |
| $I_{OZL}$ | $V_{CC} = 5.25$, | $V_O = 0.5$ V | | | −50 | $\mu$A |
| $I_I$ | $V_{CC} = 5.25$, | $V_I = 5.5$ V | | | 1 | mA |
| $I_{IH}$ | $V_{CC} = 5.25$, | $V_I = 2.7$ V | | | 25 | $\mu$A |
| $I_{IL}$ | $V_{CC} = 5.25$, | $V_I = 0.5$ V | | | −0.25 | mA |
| $I_{OS}$[‡] | $V_{CC} = 5.25$ | | −10 | | −100 | mA |
| $I_{CC}$ | $V_{CC} = 5.25$ | | | 75 | 110 | mA |

## switching characteristics over recommended ranges of $T_A$ and $V_{CC}$ (unless otherwise noted)

| PARAMETER | | TEST CONDITIONS | NW | | | UNIT |
|---|---|---|---|---|---|---|
| | | | MIN | TYP[†] | MAX | |
| $t_{a(A)}$ | Access time from address | $C_L = 30$ pF | | 80 | 125 | ns |
| $t_{a(S)}$ | Access time from chip select (enable time) | See Note 3 | | 40 | 65 | ns |
| $t_{dis}$ | Disable time | $C_L = 5$ pF See Note 3 | | 30 | 65 | ns |

[†]All typical values are at $V_{CC} = 5$ V, $T_A = 25$ °C.
[‡]Not more than one output should be shorted at a time, and duration of the short circuit should not exceed one second.
NOTE 3:  Load circuits and voltage waveforms are shown in Section 1.

4-32

**recommended operating conditions for programming (see Figure 1)**

| | | MIN | NOM | MAX | UNIT |
|---|---|---|---|---|---|
| Steady-state supply voltage | $V_{CC}$ | 4.75 | 5 | 5.25 | V |
| Input voltage | $V_{IH}$ | 3 | 4 | 5 | V |
| | $V_{IL}$ | 0 | 0 | 0.5 | |
| Voltage at all outputs except the one to be programmed | | 0 | 0 | 0.5 | V |
| Supply voltage level to program a bit | $V_{CC(pr)}$ | 5.75 | 6 | 6.25 | V |
| Select or enable level to program a bit | $V_{S(pr)}$ | 9.75 | 10 | 11 | V |
| Output level during interval $t_5$ | $V_{O(pr)}$ | 15.75 | 16 | 16.25 | V |
| Supply voltage during verification (see step 14) | Low | 4.4 | 4.5 | 4.6 | V |
| | High | 5.4 | 5.5 | 5.6 | |
| Time from $V_{CC}$ to settle and to verify need to program | $t_1$ | 0 | 5 | 10 | $\mu s$ |
| Time from $V_{CC}$ = 6 V until chip select (enable) is at 10 V | $t_2$ | 5 | 5 | 10 | $\mu s$ |
| Time from chip select (enable) high to start of program ramp | $t_3$ | 0.1 | 5 | 10 | $\mu s$ |
| Ramp time, output program pulse | $t_4$ | 10 | 15 | 20 | $\mu s$ |
| Duration of output program pulse | $t_5$ | 15 | 20 | 20 | $\mu s$ |
| Time from end of program pulse to chip select (enable) low | $t_6$ | 5 | 5 | 10 | $\mu s$ |
| Time from chip select (enable) $V_{CC}$ = 0 V | $t_7$ | 0.1 | 5 | 5 | $\mu s$ |
| Time for cooling between bits | $t_8$ | 30 | 50 | 100 | $\mu s$ |
| Time for cooling between words | $t_9$ | 30 | 50 | | $\mu s$ |
| Free-air temperature | $T_A$ | 20 | 25 | 30 | °C |

**step-by-step programming instruction (see Figure 1)**

1. Address the word to be programmed, apply 5 volts to $V_{CC}$ and active levels to all chip select (S and $\overline{S}$) or chip enable (E and $\overline{E}$) inputs.

2. Verify the status of a bit location by checking the output level.

3. Decreass $V_{CC}$ to 0 volts.

4. For bit locations that do not require programming, skip steps 5 through 11.

5. Increase $V_{CC}$ to $V_{CC(pr)}$ with a minimum current capability of 250 milliamperes.

6. Apply $V_{S(pr)}$ to all the $\overline{S}$, $\overline{E}$ or $\overline{G}$ inputs. $I_I \leq 25$ milliamperes. Active-high enables may be left high.

7. Connect all outputs, except the one to be programmed, to $V_{IL}$. Only one bit is to be programmed at a time.

8. Apply the output programming pulse for 20 microseconds. Minimum current capability of the programming supply should be 250 milliamperes.

9. After terminating the output pulse, disconnect all outputs from $V_{IL}$ conditions.

10. Reduce the voltage at $\overline{S}$, $\overline{E}$, or $\overline{G}$ inputs to $V_{II}$.

11. Decrease $V_{CC}$ to 0 volts.

12. Return to step 4 until all outputs in the word have been programmed.

13. Repeat steps 2 through 11 for each word in memory.

14. Verify programming of every word after all words have been programmed using $V_{CC}$ values of 4.5 and 5.5 volts.

**4**

**PROMs**

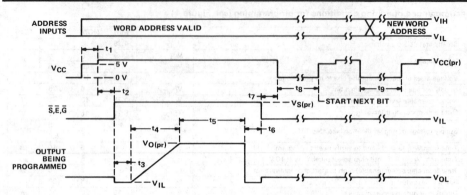

NOTE 4: Rise and fall times should be ≤ 1 μs.

**FIGURE 1. TIMING DIAGRAM AND VOLTAGE
WAVEFORMS FOR PROGRAMMING SEQUENCE**

- Fastest Schottky PROM Family

- High-Speed Access Times

- Allows Storage of Output Data

- Titanium-Tungsten (Ti-W) Fuse Links for Reliable Low-Voltage Programming

## description

The TBP34R4' is a series-3 IMPACT™ TTL programmable read-only memory (PROM) featuring high-speed access times and dependable titanium-tungsten fuse link program elements. It is organized as 1024 words by 4 bits, providing 4096 bits.

The output register receives data from the PROM array on the rising edge of RCLK. Data is programmed at any bit location with the standard series 3 programming algorithm. The program elements store a high logic level before any programming, and are permanently set to a low logic level after programming. After execution of the programming procedure, the output for that bit location cannot be reversed. The series 3 programming procedure should be referred to for further details. Additional circuits have been designed into these devices to improve testability and ensure high programmability.

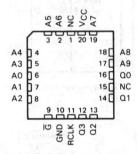

TBP34R41 . . . J OR N PACKAGE
(TOP VIEW)

| | |
|---|---|
| A6 1 | 18 V<sub>CC</sub> |

```
TBP34R41 . . . J OR N PACKAGE
        (TOP VIEW)

    A6  [ 1    18 ]  VCC
    A5  [ 2    17 ]  A7
    A4  [ 3    16 ]  A8
    A3  [ 4    15 ]  A9
    A0  [ 5    14 ]  Q0
    A1  [ 6    13 ]  Q1
    A2  [ 7    12 ]  Q2
     G  [ 8    11 ]  Q3
   GND  [ 9    10 ]  RCLK
```

TBP34R42 . . . FN OR FK PACKAGE
(TOP VIEW)

```
          A5 A6 NC VCC A7
           3  2  1 20 19
    A4  [ 4           18 ]  A8
    A3  [ 5           17 ]  A9
    A0  [ 6           16 ]  Q0
    A1  [ 7           15 ]  NC
    A2  [ 8           14 ]  Q1
           9 10 11 12 13
           G GND RCLK Q3 Q2
```

These PROMs are offered with a choice of setup times (dash numbers). These dash numbers are found in the recommended operating conditions table, and are included in the part numbers.

An MFK or MJ suffix designates full-temperature circuits that are characterized for operation over the full military temperature range of −55°C to 125°C. An FN or N suffix designates commercial-temperature circuits that are characterized for operation from 0°C to 70°C.

IMPACT is a trademark of Texas Instruments.

**4**

**PROMs**

**TEXAS INSTRUMENTS**

Copyright © 1986, Texas Instruments Incorporated

## TBP34R41, TBP34R42
## 4096-BIT (1024 WORDS BY 4 BITS) REGISTERED
## PROGRAMMABLE READ-ONLY MEMORY

### logic symbol†

### logic diagram (positive logic)

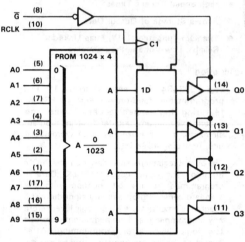

†This symbol is in accordance with ANSI/IEEE Std 91-1984 and
IEC Publication 617-12.

### TERMINAL FUNCTIONS

| TERMINALS | FUNCTION |
|---|---|
| A0 — A9 | Address inputs for data from PROM array |
| $\overline{G}$ | If $\overline{G}$ is high, Q0 thru Q3 are in high-impedance state. If $\overline{G}$ is low, Q0 thru Q3 are enabled. |
| RCLK | Low-to-high transition loads output register from PROM array. |
| Q0 — Q3 | Register outputs under control of $\overline{G}$ |

### absolute maximum ratings over operating free-air temperature range (unless otherwise noted)

Supply voltage, $V_{CC}$ (see Note 1) . . . . . . . . . . . . . . . . . . . . . . . . . . . . . . . . . . . . . . . . . . . . . . . . . 7 V
Input voltage, $V_I$ . . . . . . . . . . . . . . . . . . . . . . . . . . . . . . . . . . . . . . . . . . . . . . . . . . . . . . . . . . . . 5.5 V
Off-state output voltage, $V_{O(off)}$ . . . . . . . . . . . . . . . . . . . . . . . . . . . . . . . . . . . . . . . . . . . . . . . . 5.5 V
Operating free-air temperature range: Military-temperature-range circuits . . . . . . . −55 °C to 125 °C
Commercial-temperature-range circuits . . . . . . . . 0 °C to 70 °C
Storage temperature range . . . . . . . . . . . . . . . . . . . . . . . . . . . . . . . . . . . . . . . . . . . −65 °C to 150 °C

NOTE 1: All voltage values are with respect to network ground terminal. The supply voltage rating does not apply during programming.

4

PROMS

### TEXAS
### INSTRUMENTS

## recommended operating conditions

| | PARAMETER | | MILITARY | | | UNIT |
|---|---|---|---|---|---|---|
| | | | MIN | NOM | MAX | |
| $V_{CC}$ | Supply voltage | | 4.5 | 5 | 5.5 | V |
| $V_{IH}$ | High-level input voltage | | 2 | | | V |
| $V_{IL}$ | Low-level input voltage | | | | 0.8 | V |
| $I_{OH}$ | High-level output current | | | | −2 | mA |
| $I_{OL}$ | Low-level output current | | | | 16 | mA |
| $t_w$ | Pulse duration | CLK high | 12 | | | ns |
| | | CLK low | 16 | | | |
| $t_{su}$ | Setup time, address before RCLK | −28 Suffix | 28 | | | ns |
| $t_h$ | Hold time, address after RCLK | | 0 | | | ns |
| $T_A$ | Operating free-air temperature range | | −55 | | 125 | °C |

## electrical characteristics over recommended operating free-air temperature range (unless otherwise noted)

| PARAMETER | TEST CONDITIONS | | MILITARY | | | UNIT |
|---|---|---|---|---|---|---|
| | | | MIN | TYP[†] | MAX | |
| $V_{IK}$ | $V_{CC}$ = MIN, | $I_I$ = −18 mA | | | −1.2 | V |
| $V_{OH}$ | $V_{CC}$ = MIN, | $I_{OH}$ = −2 mA | 2.4 | 3.1 | | V |
| $V_{OL}$ | $V_{CC}$ = MIN, | $I_{OL}$ = 16 mA | | | 0.5 | V |
| $I_{OZH}$ | $V_{CC}$ = MAX, | $V_O$ = 2.4 V | | | 50 | $\mu$A |
| $I_{OZL}$ | $V_{CC}$ = MAX, | $V_O$ = 0.5 V | | | −50 | $\mu$A |
| $I_I$ | $V_{CC}$ = MAX, | $V_I$ = 5.5 V | | | 0.1 | mA |
| $I_{IH}$ | $V_{CC}$ = MAX, | $V_I$ = 2.7 V | | | 20 | $\mu$A |
| $I_{IL}$ | $V_{CC}$ = MAX, | $V_I$ = 0.5 V | | | −0.25 | mA |
| $I_O$[‡] | $V_{CC}$ = MAX, | $V_O$ = 2.25 V | −30 | | −112 | mA |
| $I_{CC}$ | $V_{CC}$ = MAX | | | 85 | 120 | mA |

## switching characteristics over recommended ranges of $T_A$ and $V_{CC}$ (unless otherwise noted)

| PARAMETER | FROM (INPUT) | TO (OUTPUT) | TEST CONDITIONS (See Note 2) | MILITARY −28 SUFFIX | | | UNIT |
|---|---|---|---|---|---|---|---|
| | | | | MIN | TYP[‡] | MAX | |
| $t_{pd}$ | RCLK | Any Q | $R_1$ = 300 Ω, | | 8 | 15 | ns |
| $t_{en}$ | $\overline{G}$ | Any Q | $R_2$ = 600 Ω, | | 8 | 15 | ns |
| $t_{dis}$ | $\overline{G}$ | Any Q | $C_L$ = 50 pF | | 6 | 12 | ns |

[†] All typical values are at $V_{CC}$ = 5 V, $T_A$ = 25°C.
[‡] The output conditions have been chosen to produce a current that closely approximates one half of the true short-circuit output current, $I_{OS}$.
NOTE 2: Load circuits and voltage waveforms are shown in Section 1.

**4**

**PROMs**

![Texas Instruments logo]
**TEXAS**
**INSTRUMENTS**

### recommended operating conditions

| PARAMETER | | | COMMERCIAL | | | UNIT |
|---|---|---|---|---|---|---|
| | | | MIN | NOM | MAX | |
| $V_{CC}$ | Supply voltage | | 4.5 | 5 | 5.5 | V |
| $V_{IH}$ | High-level input voltage | | 2 | | | V |
| $V_{IL}$ | Low-level input voltage | | | | 0.8 | V |
| $I_{OH}$ | High-level output current | | | | -3.2 | mA |
| $I_{OL}$ | Low-level output current | | | | 24 | mA |
| $t_w$ | Pulse duration | CLK high | 10 | | | ns |
| | | CLK low | 15 | | | |
| $t_{su}$ | Setup time, address before RCLK! | -25 Suffix | 25 | | | ns |
| $t_h$ | Hold time, address after RCLK | | | | | ns |
| $T_A$ | Operating free-air temperature range | | 0 | | 70 | °C |

### electrical characteristics over recommended operating free-air temperature range (unless otherwise noted)

| PARAMETER | TEST CONDITIONS | | COMMERCIAL | | | UNIT |
|---|---|---|---|---|---|---|
| | | | MIN | TYP[†] | MAX | |
| $V_{IK}$ | $V_{CC}$ = MIN, | $I_I$ = -18 mA | | | -1.2 | V |
| $V_{OH}$ | $V_{CC}$ = MIN, | $I_{OH}$ = -3.2 mA | 2.4 | 3.1 | | V |
| $V_{OL}$ | $V_{CC}$ = MIN, | $I_{OL}$ = 24 mA | | | 0.5 | V |
| $I_{OZH}$ | $V_{CC}$ = MAX, | $V_O$ = 2.4 V | | | 50 | μA |
| $I_{OZL}$ | $V_{CC}$ = MAX, | $V_O$ = 0.5 V | | | -50 | μA |
| $I_I$ | $V_{CC}$ = MAX, | $V_I$ = 5.5 V | | | 0.1 | mA |
| $I_{IH}$ | $V_{CC}$ = MAX, | $V_I$ = 2.7 V | | | 20 | μA |
| $I_{IL}$ | $V_{CC}$ = MAX, | $V_I$ = 0.5 V | | | -0.25 | mA |
| $I_O$ [‡] | $V_{CC}$ = MAX, | $V_O$ = 2.25 V | -30 | | -112 | mA |
| $I_{CC}$ | $V_{CC}$ = MAX | | | 85 | 120 | mA |

### switching characteristics over recommended ranges of $T_A$ and $V_{CC}$ (unless otherwise noted)

| PARAMETER | FROM (INPUT) | TO (OUTPUT) | TEST CONDITIONS (See Note 2) | COMMERCIAL -25 SUFFIX | | | UNIT |
|---|---|---|---|---|---|---|---|
| | | | | MIN | TYP[‡] | MAX | |
| $t_{pd}$ | RCLK | Any Q | $R_1$ = 300 Ω, | | 8 | 12 | ns |
| $t_{en}$ | $\overline{G}$ | Any Q | $R_2$ = 600 Ω, | | 8 | 12 | ns |
| $t_{dis}$ | $\overline{G}$ | Any Q | $C_L$ = 50 pF | | 6 | 10 | ns |

[†] All typical values are at $V_{CC}$ = 5 V, $T_A$ = 25°C.
[‡] The output conditions have been chosen to produce a current that closely approximates one half of the true short-circuit output current, $I_{OS}$.
NOTE 2: Load circuits and voltage waveforms are shown in Section 1.

**4**

**PROMS**

## recommended operating conditions for programming (see Figure 1)

| | | MIN | NOM | MAX | UNIT |
|---|---|---|---|---|---|
| $V_{CC}$ | Supply voltage during verification | 4.5 | 5 | 5.5 | V |
| $V_{IH}$ | High-level input voltage | 3 | 3 | 4 | V |
| $V_{IL}$ | Low-level input voltage | 0 | 0.2 | 0.4 | V |
| | Enable $\overline{G}$ voltage during verification | 0 | 0.2 | 0.4 | V |
| | Enable $\overline{G}$ inactive voltage during programming | 4.5 | 5 | 5.5 | V |
| $V_{CC(pr)}$ | Supply voltage program pulse amplitude | 12 | 12.5 | 13 | V |
| $t_{w1}$ | $V_{CC}$ program pulse duration, 1st attempt | 10 | 11 | 12 | $\mu$s |
| $t_{w2}$ | $V_{CC}$ program pulse duration, 2nd attempt | 20 | 22 | 25 | $\mu$s |
| $t_{w3}$ | $V_{CC}$ program pulse duration, 3rd attempt | 20 | 22 | 25 | $\mu$s |
| $t_{su}$ | Setup time, enable $\overline{G}$ low before $V_{CC(pr)}$[†] | 0.1 | 0.5 | 1 | $\mu$s |
| $t_h$ | Hold time, enable $\overline{G}$ low before $V_{CC(pr)}$[‡] | 0.1 | 0.5 | 1 | $\mu$s |
| $t_{r(VCC)}$ | Rise time, $V_{CC(pr)}$ (5 V to 12 V) | 0.3 | 0.4 | 0.5 | $\mu$s |
| $t_{f(VCC)}$ | Fall time, $V_{CC(pr)}$ (12 V to 5 V) | 0.05 | 0.1 | 0.2 | $\mu$s |
| $t_d$ | Delay time between successive $V_{CC(pr)}$ pulses | 10 | 20 | 30 | $\mu$s |
| $t_{cool}$ | Cooling time between words | 100 | 150 | 200 | $\mu$s |
| $T_A$ | Free-air temperature | 20 | 35 | 30 | °C |

[†] Measured from 1.5 V on enable pin to 5.5 V on $V_{CC(pr)}$.
[‡] Measured from 5.5 V on $V_{CC(pr)}$ to 1.5 V on enable pin.

## step-by-step programming instructions (see Figure 1)

1. Address the word to be programmed, apply 5 V to $V_{CC}$ and a low logic level to the $\overline{G}$ input.
2. Verify the selected bit location that requires programming. Note: The only bit positions that require programming are outputs to be at a high logic level.
3. For bit locations that do not require programming, go to step 2 for the next bit, or to step 1 for the next word.
4. Deselect PROM by applying 5 V to $\overline{G}$.
5. Connect a 4-mA current source (clamped to $V_{CC}$) to the output to be programmed.
6. Increase $V_{CC}$ to $V_{CC(pr)}$ for a pulse duration equal to $t_{wX}$ (where X is determined by the number of programming attempts, i.e., 1, 2, 3). Minimum current capability for the $V_{CC}$ power supply should be 400 mA.
7. Verify that the output has been programmed to a high logic level. If the output has been programmed correctly, go to the next bit. If not, repeat steps 2 through 7 and increment X (where X equals 1 on the first programming attempt). If the output has not been programmed by the third attempt, stop programming and go to a new device.
8. Verify programming of every word after all words have been programmed using $V_{CC}$ values of 4.5 volts and 5.5 volts.

TEXAS
INSTRUMENTS

4

PROMs

### series 3 programming sequence

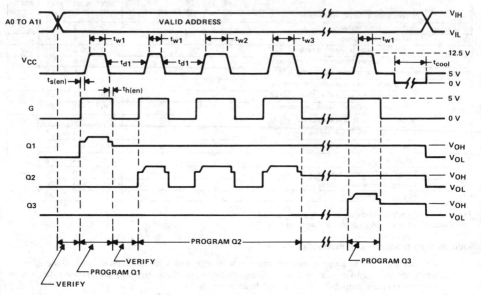

Illustrated above is the following sequence:

1. It is desired to program the selected address with 0111(Q0-Q3). Outputs Q1, Q2, and Q3 need programming.
2. Q1 is verified to be at a low logic level and then the programming sequence is executed. The output is then verified to be at a high logic level.
3. Q3 is an example of an output requiring three attempts to be programmed successfully.
4. Q3 is programmed to a high logic level.

### FIGURE 1. SERIES 3 PROGRAMMING SEQUENCE

**4**

**PROMs**

TEXAS
INSTRUMENTS

- Fastest Schottky PROM Family

- High-Speed Access Times

- Allows Storage of Output Data

- Titanium-Tungsten (Ti-W) Fuse Links for Reliable Low-Voltage Programming

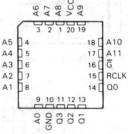

### description

The TBP34R16′ is a series-3 IMPACT™ TTL programmable read-only memory (PROM) featuring high-speed access times and dependable titanium-tungsten fuse link program elements. It is organized as 4096 words by 4 bits, providing 16,384 bits.

The output register receives data from the PROM array on the rising edge of RCLK. Data is programmed at any bit location with the standard series 3 programming algorithm. The program elements store a low logic level before any programming, and are permanently set to a high logic level after programming. After execution of the programming procedure, the output for that bit location cannot be reversed. The series 3 programming procedure should be referred to for further details. Additional circuits have been designed into these devices to improve testability and ensure high programmability.

These PROMs are offered with a choice of setup times (dash numbers). these dash numbers are found in the recommended operating conditions table, and are included in the part numbers.

An MFK or MJ suffix designates full-temperature circuits that are characterized for operation over the full military temperature range of −55 °C to 125 °C. An FN or N suffix designates commercial-temperature circuits that are characterized for operation from 0 °C to 70 °C.

IMPACT is a trademark of Texas Instruments.

4

PROMs

Copyright © 1985, Texas Instruments Incorporated

**TEXAS INSTRUMENTS**

## TBP34R162, TBP34R16X
## 16,384-BIT (4096 WORDS BY 4 BITS) REGISTERED
## PROGRAMMABLE READ-ONLY MEMORY

### logic symbol†

### logic diagram (positive logic)

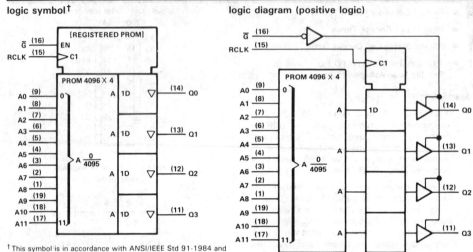

† This symbol is in accordance with ANSI/IEEE Std 91-1984 and IEC Publication 617-12.

### TERMINAL FUNCTIONS

| TERMINALS | FUNCTION |
|---|---|
| A0 — A11 | Address inputs for data from PROM array |
| $\overline{G}$ | If $\overline{G}$ is high, Q0 thru Q3 are in high-impedance state. |
| | If $\overline{G}$ is low, Q0 thru Q3 are enabled. |
| RCLK | Low-to-high transition loads output register from PROM array. |
| Q0 — Q3 | Register outputs under control of $\overline{G}$ |

### absolute maximum ratings over operating free-air temperature range (unless otherwise noted)

Supply voltage, $V_{CC}$ (see Note 1) . . . . . . . . . . . . . . . . . . . . . . . . . . . . . . . . . . . . . . . . . . . . . 7 V
Input voltage, $V_I$ . . . . . . . . . . . . . . . . . . . . . . . . . . . . . . . . . . . . . . . . . . . . . . . . . . . . . . . . . . . 5.5 V
Off-state output voltage, $V_{O(off)}$ . . . . . . . . . . . . . . . . . . . . . . . . . . . . . . . . . . . . . . . . . . . . . . . 5.5 V
Operating free-air temperature range: Military-temperature-range circuits . . . . . . . −55°C to 125°C
Commercial-temperature-range circuits . . . . . . . . 0°C to 70°C
Storage temperature range . . . . . . . . . . . . . . . . . . . . . . . . . . . . . . . . . . . . . . . . . . . . −65°C to 150°C

NOTE 1: All voltage values are with respect to network ground terminal. The supply voltage rating does not apply during programming.

**TEXAS INSTRUMENTS**

## recommended operating conditions

| PARAMETER | | MILITARY | | | UNIT |
|---|---|---|---|---|---|
| | | MIN | NOM | MAX | |
| $V_{CC}$ | Supply voltage | 4.5 | 5 | 5.5 | V |
| $V_{IH}$ | High-level input voltage | 2 | | | V |
| $V_{IL}$ | Low-level input voltage | | | 0.8 | V |
| $I_{OH}$ | High-level output current | | | −2 | mA |
| $I_{OL}$ | Low-level output current | | | 16 | mA |
| $t_w$ | Pulse duration, RCLK high or low | 12 | | | ns |
| $t_{su}$ | Setup time, address before RCLK | | | | ns |
| $t_h$ | Hold time, address after RCLK | | | | ns |
| $T_A$ | Operating free-air temperature range | −55 | | 125 | °C |

## electrical characteristics over recommended operating free-air temperature range (unless otherwise noted)

| PARAMETER | TEST CONDITIONS | | MILITARY | | | UNIT |
|---|---|---|---|---|---|---|
| | | | MIN | TYP[†] | MAX | |
| $V_{IK}$ | $V_{CC}$ = MIN, | $I_I$ = −18 mA | | | −1.2 | V |
| $V_{OH}$ | $V_{CC}$ = MIN, | $I_{OH}$ = −2 mA | 2.4 | 3.1 | | V |
| $V_{OL}$ | $V_{CC}$ = MIN, | $I_{OL}$ = 16 mA | | | 0.5 | V |
| $I_{OZH}$ | $V_{CC}$ = MAX, | $V_O$ = 2.4 V | | | 50 | $\mu$A |
| $I_{OZL}$ | $V_{CC}$ = MAX, | $V_O$ = 0.5 V | | | −50 | $\mu$A |
| $I_I$ | $V_{CC}$ = MAX, | $V_I$ = 5.5 V | | | 0.1 | mA |
| $I_{IH}$ | $V_{CC}$ = MAX, | $V_I$ = 2.7 V | | | 20 | $\mu$A |
| $I_{IL}$ | $V_{CC}$ = MAX, | $V_I$ = 0.5 V | | | −0.25 | mA |
| $I_O$ [‡] | $V_{CC}$ = MAX, | $V_O$ = 2.25 V | −30 | | −112 | mA |
| $I_{CC}$ | $V_{CC}$ = MAX | | | | | mA |

## switching characteristics over recommended ranges of $T_A$ and $V_{CC}$ (unless otherwise noted)

| PARAMETER | FROM (INPUT) | TO (OUTPUT) | TEST CONDITIONS (See Note 2) | MILITARY | | | UNIT |
|---|---|---|---|---|---|---|---|
| | | | | MIN | TYP[‡] | MAX | |
| $t_{pd}$ | CLK | Any Q | $R_1$ = 300 Ω, | | 8 | | ns |
| $t_{en}$ | $\overline{G}$ | Any Q | $R_2$ = 600 Ω, | | 8 | | ns |
| $t_{dis}$ | $\overline{G}$ | Any Q | $C_L$ = 50 pF | | 6 | | ns |

[†] All typical values are at $V_{CC}$ = 5 V, $T_A$ = 25 °C.
[‡] The output conditions have been chosen to produce a current that closely approximates one half of the true short-circuit output current, $I_{OS}$.
NOTE 2: Load circuits and voltage waveforms are shown in Section 1.

4

PROMs

TEXAS
INSTRUMENTS

## TBP34R162, TBP34R16X
## 16,384-BIT (4096 WORDS BY 4 BITS) REGISTERED
## PROGRAMMABLE READ-ONLY MEMORY

### recommended operating conditions

| | PARAMETER | | COMMERCIAL | | | UNIT |
|---|---|---|---|---|---|---|
| | | | MIN | NOM | MAX | |
| $V_{CC}$ | Supply voltage | | 4.5 | 5 | 5.5 | V |
| $V_{IH}$ | High-level input voltage | | 2 | | | V |
| $V_{IL}$ | Low-level input voltage | | | | 0.8 | V |
| $I_{OH}$ | High-level output current | | | | −3.2 | mA |
| $I_{OL}$ | Low-level output current | | | | 24 | mA |
| $t_w$ | Pulse duration, RCLK high or low | | 12 | | | ns |
| $t_{su}$ | Setup time, address before RCLK↑ | −30 Suffix | 30 | | | ns |
| $t_h$ | Hold time, address after RCLK | | | | | ns |
| $T_A$ | Operating free-air temperature range | | 0 | | 70 | °C |

### electrical characteristics over recommended operating free-air temperature range (unless otherwise noted)

| PARAMETER | TEST CONDITIONS | | COMMERCIAL | | | UNIT |
|---|---|---|---|---|---|---|
| | | | MIN | TYP[†] | MAX | |
| $V_{IK}$ | $V_{CC}$ = MIN, | $I_I$ = −18 mA | | | −1.2 | V |
| $V_{OH}$ | $V_{CC}$ = MIN, | $I_{OH}$ = −3.2 mA | 2.4 | 3.1 | | V |
| $V_{OL}$ | $V_{CC}$ = MIN, | $I_{OL}$ = 24 mA | | | 0.5 | V |
| $I_{OZH}$ | $V_{CC}$ = MAX, | $V_O$ = 2.4 V | | | 50 | µA |
| $I_{OZL}$ | $V_{CC}$ = MAX, | $V_O$ = 0.5 V | | | −50 | µA |
| $I_I$ | $V_{CC}$ = MAX, | $V_I$ = 5.5 V | | | 0.1 | mA |
| $I_{IH}$ | $V_{CC}$ = MAX, | $V_I$ = 2.7 V | | | 20 | µA |
| $I_{IL}$ | $V_{CC}$ = MAX, | $V_I$ = 0.5 V | | | −0.25 | mA |
| $I_O$ [‡] | $V_{CC}$ = MAX, | $V_O$ = 2.25 V | −30 | | −112 | mA |
| $I_{CC}$ | $V_{CC}$ = MAX | | | 120 | 160 | mA |

### switching characteristics over recommended ranges of $T_A$ and $V_{CC}$ (unless otherwise noted)

| PARAMETER | FROM (INPUT) | TO (OUTPUT) | TEST CONDITIONS (See Note 2) | COMMERCIAL | | | UNIT |
|---|---|---|---|---|---|---|---|
| | | | | -30 SUFFIX | | | |
| | | | | MIN | TYP[‡] | MAX | |
| $t_{pd}$ | CLK | Any Q | $R_1$ = 300 Ω, | | 8 | 12 | ns |
| $t_{en}$ | $\overline{G}$ | Any Q | $R_2$ = 600 Ω, | | 8 | 12 | ns |
| $t_{dis}$ | $\overline{G}$ | Any Q | $C_L$ = 50 pF | | 6 | 10 | ns |

[†] All typical values are at $V_{CC}$ = 5 V, $T_A$ = 15°C.
[‡] The output conditions have been chosen to produce a current that closely approximates one half of the true short-circuit output current, $I_{OS}$.
NOTE 2: Load circuits and voltage waveforms are shown in Section 1.

4

PROMS

TEXAS
INSTRUMENTS

## recommended operating conditions for programming (see Figure 1)

|  |  | MIN | NOM | MAX | UNIT |
|---|---|---|---|---|---|
| $V_{CC}$ | Supply voltage during verification | 4.5 | 5 | 5.5 | V |
| $V_{IH}$ | High-level input voltage | 3 | 3 | 4 | V5 |
| $V_{IL}$ | Low-level input voltage | 0 | 0.2 | 0.4 | V |
|  | Enable $\overline{G}$ voltage during verification | 0 | 0.2 | 0.4 | V |
|  | Enable $\overline{G}$ inactive voltage during programming | 4.5 | 5 | 5.5 | V |
| $V_{CC(pr)}$ | Supply voltage program pulse amplitude | 12 | 12.5 | 13 | V |
| $t_{w1}$ | $V_{CC}$ program pulse duration, 1st attempt | 10 | 11 | 12 | $\mu$s |
| $t_{w2}$ | $V_{CC}$ program pulse duration, 2nd attempt | 20 | 22 | 25 | $\mu$s |
| $t_{w3}$ | $V_{CC}$ program pulse duration, 3rd attempt | 20 | 22 | 25 | $\mu$s |
| $t_{su}$ | Setup time, enable $\overline{G}$ low before $V_{CC(pr)}$[†] | 0.1 | 0.5 | 1 | $\mu$s |
| $t_{h}$ | Hold time, enable $\overline{G}$ low before $V_{CC(pr)}$[‡] | 0.1 | 0.5 | 1 | $\mu$s |
| $t_{r(VCC)}$ | Rise time, $V_{CC(pr)}$ (5 V to 12 V) | 0.3 | 0.4 | 0.5 | $\mu$s |
| $t_{f(VCC)}$ | Fall time, $V_{CC(pr)}$ (12 V to 5 V) | 0.05 | 0.1 | 0.2 | $\mu$s |
| $t_{d}$ | Delay time between successive $V_{CC(pr)}$ pulses | 10 | 20 | 30 | $\mu$s |
| $t_{cool}$ | Cooling time between words | 100 | 150 | 200 | $\mu$s |
| $T_{A}$ | Free-air temperature | 20 | 35 | 30 | °C |

[†] Measured from 1.5 V on enable pin to 5.5 V on $V_{CC(pr)}$.
[‡] Measured from 5.5 V on $V_{CC(pr)}$ to 1.5 V on enable pin.

### step-by-step programming instructions (see Figure 1)

1. Address the word to be programmed, apply 5 V to $V_{CC}$ and a low logic level to the $\overline{G}$ input.
2. Verify the selected bit location that requires programming. Note: The only bit positions that require programming are outputs to be at a high logic level.
3. For bit locations that do not require programming, go to step 2 for the next bit, or to step 1 for the next word.
4. Deselect PROM by applying 5 V to $\overline{G}$.
5. Connect a 4-mA current source (clamped to $V_{CC}$) to the output to be programmed.
6. Increase $V_{CC}$ to $V_{CC(pr)}$ for a pulse duration equal to $t_{wX}$ (where X is determined by the number of programming attempts, i.e., 1, 2, 3). Minimum current capability for the $V_{CC}$ power supply should be 400 mA.
7. Verify that the output has been programmed to a high logic level. If the output has been programmed correctly, go to the next bit. If not, repeat steps 2 through 7 and increment X (where X equals 1 on the first programming attempt). If the output has not been programmed by the third attempt, stop programming and go to a new device.
8. Verify programming of every word after all words have been programmed using $V_{CC}$ values of 4.5 volts and 5.5 volts.

**4**

**PROMs**

TEXAS
INSTRUMENTS

### series 3 programming sequence

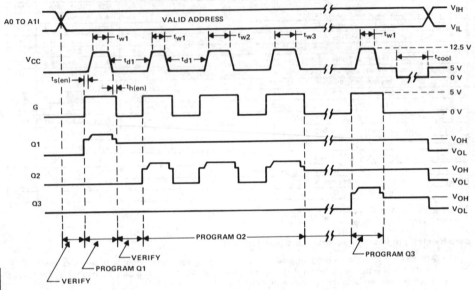

Illustrated above is the following sequence:

1. It is desired to program the selected address with 0111(Q0-Q3). Outputs Q1, Q2, and Q3 need programming.
2. Q1 is verified to be at a low logic level and then the programming sequence is executed. The output is then verified to be at a high logic level.
3. Q3 is an example of an output requiring three attempts to be programmed successfully.
4. Q3 is programmed to a high logic level.

### FIGURE 1. SERIES 3 PROGRAMMING SEQUENCE

TEXAS
INSTRUMENTS

**4**

**PROMS**

- Advanced Schottky IMPACT™ PROM Family

- High-Speed Access Times

- Low-Power, 3-State, and Open-Collector Options Available

- Titanium-Tungsten (Ti-W) Fuse Links for Reliable Low-Voltage Programming

- Applications Include:
  Microprogramming/Firmware Loaders
  Code Converters/Character Generators
  Translators/Emulators
  Address Mapping/Look-Up Tables

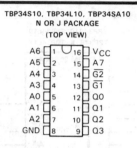

TBP34S10, TBP34L10, TBP34SA10
N OR J PACKAGE
(TOP VIEW)

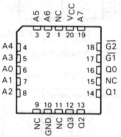

TBP34S1X, TBP34L1X, TBP34SA1X
FN OR FK PACKAGE
(TOP VIEW)

NC — No internal connection

## description

These Series-3 IMPACT™ TTL programmable read-only memories (PROMs) feature high-speed access times and dependable titanium-tungsten fuse link program elements. They are organized as 256 words by 4 bits each, providing a total of 1024 bits. The '34S1 has three-state outputs. The '34SA1 is the open-collector version and allows the device to be connected directly to data buses utilizing passive pull-up resistors. The low-power '34L1 is available for applications that require power conservation while maintaining bipolar speeds. It also has three-state outputs.

These PROMs are offered with a choice of address access times (dash numbers). These dash numbers are found in the switching characteristics table, and are included in the part numbers.

Data is programmed at any bit location with the standard Series 3 programming algorithm. The program elements store a low logic level before any programming, and are permanently set to a high logic level after programming. After execution of the programming procedure, the output for that bit location cannot be reversed. The Series 3 programming procedure should be referred to for further details. Additional circuitry has been designed into these devices to improve testability and insure high programmability.

An MJ or MFK suffix designates full-temperature circuits that are characterized for operation over the full military temperature range of −55°C to 125°C. An N or FN suffix designates commercial-temperature circuits that are characterized for operation from 0°C to 70°C.

IMPACT is a trademark of Texas Instruments.

Copyright © 1985, Texas Instruments Incorporated

### TEXAS
### INSTRUMENTS

4

PROMs

## TBP34S10, TBP34L10, TBP34SA10
## TBP34S1X, TBP34L1X, TBP34SA1X
## 1024-BIT (256 WORDS BY 4 BITS) PROGRAMMABLE READ-ONLY MEMORIES

### logic symbols†

TBP34S10, TBP34L10
TBP34S1X, TBP34L1X

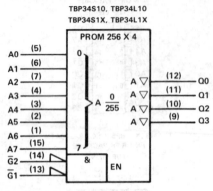

TBP34SA10
TBP34SA1X

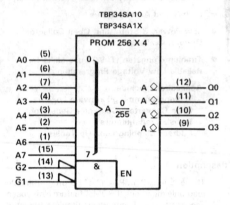

†These symbols are in accordance with ANSI/IEEE Std 91-1984
 and IEC Publication 617-12.
Pin numbers shown are for J and N packages.

### schematics of inputs and outputs

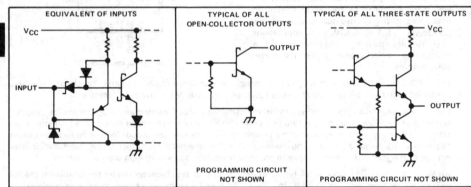

| EQUIVALENT OF INPUTS | TYPICAL OF ALL OPEN-COLLECTOR OUTPUTS | TYPICAL OF ALL THREE-STATE OUTPUTS |

PROGRAMMING CIRCUIT NOT SHOWN

PROGRAMMING CIRCUIT NOT SHOWN

### absolute maximum ratings over operating free-air temperature range (unless otherwise noted)

Supply voltage (see Note 1) . . . . . . . . . . . . . . . . . . . . . . . . . . . . . . . . . . . . . . . . . . 7 V
Input voltage . . . . . . . . . . . . . . . . . . . . . . . . . . . . . . . . . . . . . . . . . . . . . . . . . . . . . . 5.5 V
Off-state output voltage . . . . . . . . . . . . . . . . . . . . . . . . . . . . . . . . . . . . . . . . . . . . . 5.5 V
Operating free-air temperature range: Military-temperature-range circuits . . . . . . . −55°C to 125°C
                                        Commercial-temperature-range circuits . . . . . . . . 0°C to 70°C
Storage temperature range . . . . . . . . . . . . . . . . . . . . . . . . . . . . . . . . . . . . . . . . . . −65°C to 150°C

NOTE 1: Voltage values are with respect to network ground terminal. The supply voltage rating does not apply during programming.

## recommended operating conditions

| | | MILITARY | | | COMMERCIAL | | | UNIT |
|---|---|---|---|---|---|---|---|---|
| | | MIN | NOM | MAX | MIN | NOM | MAX | |
| $V_{CC}$ | Supply voltage | 4.5 | 5 | 5.5 | 4.5 | 5 | 5.5 | V |
| $V_{IH}$ | High-level input voltage | 2 | | | 2 | | | V |
| $V_{IL}$ | Low-level input voltage | | | 0.8 | | | 0.8 | V |
| $I_{OH}$ | High-level output current | | | $-2$ | | | $-3.2$ | mA |
| $I_{OL}$ | Low-level output current | | | 16 | | | 24 | mA |
| $T_A$ | Operating free-air temperature range | $-55$ | | 125 | 0 | | 70 | °C |

## electrical characteristics over recommended operating free-air temperature range (unless otherwise noted)

| PARAMETER | TEST CONDITIONS[†] | | MILITARY | | | COMMERCIAL | | | UNIT |
|---|---|---|---|---|---|---|---|---|---|
| | | | MIN | TYP[‡] | MAX | MIN | TYP[‡] | MAX | |
| $V_{IK}$ | $V_{CC}$ = MIN, | $I_I = -18$ mA | | | $-1.2$ | | | $-1.2$ | V |
| $V_{OH}$ | $V_{CC}$ = MIN, | $I_{OH}$ = MAX | 2.4 | 3.1 | | 2.4 | 3.1 | | V |
| $V_{OL}$ | $V_{CC}$ = MIN, | $I_{OL}$ = MAX | | | 0.5 | | | 0.5 | V |
| $I_{OZH}$ | $V_{CC}$ = MAX, | $V_O$ = 2.4 V | | | 50 | | | 50 | $\mu$A |
| $I_{OZL}$ | $V_{CC}$ = MAX, | $V_O$ = 0.5 V | | | $-50$ | | | $-50$ | $\mu$A |
| $I_I$ | $V_{CC}$ = MAX, | $V_I$ = 5.5 V | | | 0.1 | | | 0.1 | mA |
| $I_{IH}$ | $V_{CC}$ = MAX, | $V_I$ = 2.7 V | | | 20 | | | 20 | $\mu$A |
| $I_{IL}$ | $V_{CC}$ = MAX, | $V_I$ = 0.5 V | | | $-0.25$ | | | $-0.25$ | mA |
| $I_O$ [§] | $V_{CC}$ = MAX, | $V_O$ = 2.25 V | $-30$ | | $-112$ | $-30$ | | $-112$ | mA |
| $I_{CC}$ | $V_{CC}$ = MAX | | | 55 | 95 | | 55 | 95 | mA |

[†]For conditions shown as MIN or MAX, use appropriate value specified under recommended operating conditions.
[‡]All typical values are at $V_{CC}$ = 5 V, $T_A$ = 25°C.
[§]The output conditions have been chosen to produce a current that closely approximates one half of the true short-circuit output current, $I_{OS}$.

## switching characteristics over recommended ranges of $T_A$ and $V_{CC}$ (unless otherwise noted)

| TYPE | | TEST CONDITIONS | $t_{a(A)}$ ACCESS TIME FROM ADDRESS | | | $t_{en}$ ENABLE TIME | | | $t_{dis}$ DISABLE TIME | | | UNIT |
|---|---|---|---|---|---|---|---|---|---|---|---|---|
| | | | MIN | TYP[‡] | MAX | MIN | TYP[‡] | MAX | MIN | TYP[†] | MAX | |
| TBP34S10-30 | Military | $C_L$ = 50 pF, R1 = 300 $\Omega$, R2 = 600 $\Omega$, See Note 2 | | 15 | 30 | | 8 | 15 | | 5 | 12 | ns |
| TBP34S1X-30 | Military | | | | | | | | | | | |
| TBP34S10-25 | Commercial | | | 15 | 25 | | 8 | 12 | | 5 | 10 | ns |
| TBP34S1X-25 | Commercial | | | | | | | | | | | |
| TBP34S10-18 | Commercial | | | 15 | 18 | | 8 | 12 | | 5 | 10 | ns |
| TBP34S1X-18 | Commercial | | | | | | | | | | | |

[‡]All typical values are at $V_{CC}$ = 5 V, $T_A$ = 25°C.
NOTE 2: Load circuits and voltage waveforms are shown in Section 1.

**4**

**PROMs**

## TBP34L10, TBP34L1X
## 1024-BIT (256 WORDS BY 4 BITS)
## LOW-POWER PROGRAMMABLE READ-ONLY MEMORY WITH 3-STATE OUTPUTS

### recommended operating conditions

| | | MILITARY | | | COMMERCIAL | | | UNIT |
|---|---|---|---|---|---|---|---|---|
| | | MIN | NOM | MAX | MIN | NOM | MAX | |
| $V_{CC}$ | Supply voltage | 4.5 | 5 | 5.5 | 4.5 | 5 | 5.5 | V |
| $V_{IH}$ | High-level input voltage | 2 | | | 2 | | | V |
| $V_{IL}$ | Low-level input voltage | | | 0.8 | | | 0.8 | V |
| $I_{OH}$ | High-level output current | | | −1.6 | | | −3.2 | mA |
| $I_{OL}$ | Low-level output current | | | 16 | | | 24 | mA |
| $T_A$ | Operating free-air temperature range | −55 | | 125 | 0 | | 70 | °C |

### electrical characteristics over recommended operating free-air temperature range (unless otherwise noted)

| PARAMETER‡ | TEST CONDITIONS† | | MILITARY | | | COMMERCIAL | | | UNIT |
|---|---|---|---|---|---|---|---|---|---|
| | | | MIN | TYP‡ | MAX | MIN | TYP‡ | MAX | |
| $V_{IK}$ | $V_{CC}$ = MIN, | $I_I$ = −18 mA | | | −1.2 | | | −1.2 | V |
| $V_{OH}$ | $V_{CC}$ = MIN, | $I_{OH}$ = MAX | 2.4 | 3.1 | | 2.4 | 3.1 | | V |
| $V_{OL}$ | $V_{CC}$ = MIN, | $I_{OL}$ = MAX | | | 0.5 | | | 0.5 | V |
| $I_{OZH}$ | $V_{CC}$ = MAX, | $V_O$ = 2.4 V | | | 50 | | | 50 | $\mu$A |
| $I_{OZL}$ | $V_{CC}$ = MAX, | $V_O$ = 0.5 V | | | −50 | | | −50 | $\mu$A |
| $I_I$ | $V_{CC}$ = MAX, | $V_I$ = 5.5 V | | | 0.1 | | | 0.1 | mA |
| $I_{IH}$ | $V_{CC}$ = MAX, | $V_I$ = 2.7 V | | | 20 | | | 20 | $\mu$A |
| $I_{IL}$ | $V_{CC}$ = MAX, | $V_I$ = 0.5 V | | | −0.25 | | | −0.25 | mA |
| $I_O$ § | $V_{CC}$ = MAX, | $V_O$ = 2.25 V | −30 | | −112 | −30 | | −112 | mA |
| $I_{CC}$ | $V_{CC}$ = MAX | | | 30 | 50 | | 30 | 50 | mA |

†For conditions shown as MIN or MAX, use appropriate value specified under recommended operating conditions.
‡All typical values are at $V_{CC}$ = 5 V, $T_A$ = 25 °C.
§The output conditions have been chosen to produce a current that closely approximates one half of the true short-circuit output current, $I_{OS}$.

### switching characteristics over recommended ranges of $T_A$ and $V_{CC}$ (unless otherwise noted)

| TYPE | | TEST CONDITIONS | $t_{a(A)}$ ACCESS TIME FROM ADDRESS | | | $t_{en}$ ENABLE TIME | | | $t_{dis}$ DISABLE TIME | | | UNIT |
|---|---|---|---|---|---|---|---|---|---|---|---|---|
| | | | MIN | TYP‡ | MAX | MIN | TYP‡ | MAX | MIN | TYP‡ | MAX | |
| TBP34L10-40 | Military | | | 20 | 40 | | 8 | 18 | | 5 | 12 | ns |
| TBP34L1X-40 | | | | | | | | | | | | |
| TBP34L10-25 | Commercial | $C_L$ = 50 pF, | | 20 | 25 | | 8 | 15 | | 5 | 10 | ns |
| TBP34L1X-25 | | R1 = 300 Ω, | | | | | | | | | | |
| TBP34L10-27 | Commercial | R2 = 600 Ω | | 20 | 27 | | 8 | 15 | | 5 | 10 | ns |
| TBP34L1X-27 | | See Note 2 | | | | | | | | | | |
| TBP34L10-35 | Commercial | | | 20 | 35 | | 8 | 15 | | 5 | 10 | ns |
| TBP34L1X-35 | | | | | | | | | | | | |

‡All typical values are at $V_{CC}$ = 5 V, $T_A$ = 25 °C.
NOTE 2: Load circuits and voltage waveforms are shown in Section 1.

4

PROMs

y

TEXAS
INSTRUMENTS

## recommended operating conditions

| | | MILITARY | | | COMMERCIAL | | | UNIT |
|---|---|---|---|---|---|---|---|---|
| | | MIN | NOM | MAX | MIN | NOM | MAX | |
| $V_{CC}$ | Supply voltage | 4.5 | 5 | 5.5 | 4.5 | 5 | 5.5 | V |
| $V_{IH}$ | High-level input voltage | 2 | | | 2 | | | V |
| $V_{IL}$ | Low-level input voltage | | | 0.8 | | | 0.8 | V |
| $V_{OH}$ | High-level output voltage | | | 5.5 | | | 5.5 | V |
| $I_{OL}$ | Low-level output current | | | 16 | | | 24 | mA |
| $T_A$ | Operating free-air temperature range | −55 | | 125 | 0 | | 70 | °C |

## electrical characteristics over recommended operating free-air temperature range (unless otherwise noted)

| PARAMETER | TEST CONDITIONS[†] | | MILITARY | | | COMMERCIAL | | | UNIT |
|---|---|---|---|---|---|---|---|---|---|
| | | | MIN | TYP[‡] | MAX | MIN | TYP[‡] | MAX | |
| $V_{IK}$ | $V_{CC}$ = MIN, | $I_I$ = −18 mA | | | −1.2 | | | −1.2 | V |
| $I_{OH}$ | $V_{CC}$ = MIN, | $V_{OH}$ = 2.4 V | | | 0.05 | | | 0.05 | mA |
| | | $V_{OH}$ = 5.5 V | | | 0.1 | | | 0.1 | |
| $V_{OL}$ | $V_{CC}$ = MIN, | $I_{OL}$ = MAX | | | 0.5 | | | 0.5 | V |
| $I_I$ | $V_{CC}$ = MAX, | $V_I$ = 5.5 V | | | 0.1 | | | 0.1 | mA |
| $I_{IH}$ | $V_{CC}$ = MAX, | $V_I$ = 2.7 V | | | 20 | | | 20 | μA |
| $I_{IL}$ | $V_{CC}$ = MAX, | $V_I$ = 0.5 V | | | −0.25 | | | −0.25 | mA |
| $I_{CC}$ | $V_{CC}$ = MAX | | | 55 | 95 | | 55 | 95 | mA |

[†]For conditions shown as MIN or MAX, use appropriate value specified under recommended operating conditions.
[‡]All typical values are at $V_{CC}$ = 5 V, $T_A$ = 25 °C.

## switching characteristics over recommended ranges of $T_A$ and $V_{CC}$ (unless otherwise noted)

| TYPE | | TEST CONDITIONS | $t_{a(A)}$ ACCESS TIME FROM ADDRESS | | | $t_{en}$ ENABLE TIME | | | $t_{dis}$ DISABLE TIME | | | UNIT |
|---|---|---|---|---|---|---|---|---|---|---|---|---|
| | | | MIN | TYP[‡] | MAX | MIN | TYP[‡] | MAX | MIN | TYP[‡] | MAX | |
| TBP34SA10-30 | Military | $C_L$ = 50 pF, R1 = 300 Ω, R2 = 600 Ω, See Note 2 | | 15 | 30 | | 8 | 15 | | 8 | 12 | ns |
| TBP34SA1X-30 | | | | | | | | | | | | |
| TBP34SA10-25 | Commercial | | | 15 | 25 | | 8 | 12 | | 8 | 10 | ns |
| TBP34SA1X-25 | | | | | | | | | | | | |

[‡]All typical values are at $V_{CC}$ = 5 V, $T_A$ = 25 °C.
NOTE 2: Load circuits and voltage waveforms are shown in Section 1.

**4**

**PROMs**

**TEXAS INSTRUMENTS**

## recommended operating conditions for programming (see Figure 1)

| | | | MIN | NOM | MAX | UNIT |
|---|---|---|---|---|---|---|
| Supply voltage during verification | | $V_{CC}$ | 4.5 | 5 | 5.5 | V |
| Input voltage | | $V_{IH}$ | 3 | 4 | 5 | V |
| | | $V_{IL}$ | 0 | 0.2 | 0.5 | |
| Enable voltage during verification | | $\overline{G}1, \overline{G}2$ | 0 | 0.2 | 0.4 | V |
| Enable inactive voltage during programming | | $\overline{G}1, \overline{G}2$ | 4.5 | 5 | 5.5 | V |
| $V_{CC}$ program pulse amplitude | | $V_{CC(pr)}$ | 12 | 12.5 | 13 | V |
| $V_{CC}$ program pulse duration | 1st attempt | $t_{w1}$ | 10 | 11 | 12 | |
| | 2nd attempt | $t_{w2}$ | 20 | 22 | 25 | $\mu$s |
| | 3rd attempt | $t_{w3}$ | 20 | 22 | 25 | |
| Enable set-up time[†] before $V_{CC(pr)}$ | | $t_{su(en)}$ | 0.1 | 0.5 | 1 | $\mu$s |
| Enable hold time[‡] after $V_{CC(pr)}$ | | $t_{h(en)}$ | 0.1 | 0.5 | 1 | $\mu$s |
| Rise time of $V_{CC(pr)}$[§] | | $t_r(V_{CC})$ | 0.3 | 0.4 | 0.5 | $\mu$s |
| Fall time of $V_{CC(pr)}$[¶] | | $t_f(V_{CC})$ | 0.05 | 0.1 | 0.2 | $\mu$s |
| Delay time between successive $V_{CC(pr)}$ pulses | | $t_{d1}$ | 10 | 20 | 30 | $\mu$s |
| Delay time between successive $V_{CC(pr)}$ pulses | | $t_{d2}$ | 10 | 20 | 30 | $\mu$s |
| Cooling time between words | | $t_{cool}$ | 100 | 150 | 200 | $\mu$s |
| Free-air temperature | | $T_A$ | 20 | 25 | 30 | °C |

[†]Measured from 1.5 V on enable pin to 5.5 V on $V_{CC(pr)}$
[‡]Measured from 5.5 V on $V_{CC(pr)}$ to 1.5 V on enable pin
[§]Measured from 5 V to 12 V
[¶]Measured from 12 V to 5 V

### step-by-step programming instructions (see Figure 1)

1. Address the word to be programmed, apply 5 volts to $V_{CC}$ and active levels to all enable inputs ($\overline{G}1, \overline{G}2$).

2. Verify the selected bit location that requires programming. Note: The only bit positions that require programming are outputs needing a high logic level.

3. For bit locations that do not require programming, go to step 2 for the next bit, or to step 1 for next word.

4. Deselect PROM by applying 5 volts to $\overline{G}1$ or $\overline{G}2$.

5. Connect a 4-mA current source (clamped to $V_{CC}$) to the output that is to be programmed.

6. Increase $V_{CC}$ to $V_{CC(pr)}$ for a pulse duration equal to $t_{wX}$ (where X is determined by the number of programming attempts, i.e., 1,2,3). Minimum current capability for the $V_{CC}$ power supply should be 400 mA.

7. Verify that the output has been programmed to a high logic level. If the output has been programmed correctly, go to the next bit. If not, repeat step 2 through step 7 and increment X (where X is equal to 1 on the first programming attempt). If the output has not been programmed by the third attempt, stop programming and go to a new device.

8. Verify programming of every word after all words have been programmed using $V_{CC}$ values of 4.5 volts and 5.5 volts.

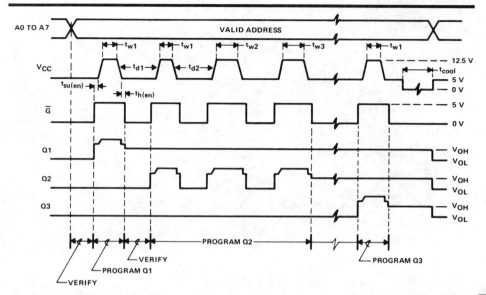

Illustrated above is the following sequence:

1) It is desired to program the selected address with 0111 (Q0-Q3). Only outputs Q1, Q2 and Q3 need programming.
2) Q1 is verified to be at a low logic level and then the programming sequence is executed. The output is then verified to be at a high logic level.
3) Q2 is an example of an output requiring three attempts to be programmed successfully.
4) Q3 is programmed to a high logic level.

**FIGURE 1. SERIES 3 PROGRAMMING SEQUENCE**

**4**

**PROMs**

- Advanced Schottky IMPACT™ PROM Family

- 1024 Words By 4-Bits

- High-Speed Access Times

- Low-Power, 3-State, and Open-Collector Options Available

- Titanium-Tungsten (Ti-W) Fuse Links for Reliable Low-Voltage Programming

- Applications Include:
  Microprogramming/Firmware Loaders
  Code Converters/Character Generators
  Translators/Emulators
  Address Mapping/Look-Up Tables

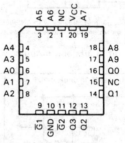

TBP34S41, TBP34L41, TBP34SA41
J OR N PACKAGE
(TOP VIEW)

| | | |
|---|---|---|
| A6 | 1 | 18 VCC |
| A5 | 2 | 17 A7 |
| A4 | 3 | 16 A8 |
| A3 | 4 | 15 A9 |
| A0 | 5 | 14 Q0 |
| A1 | 6 | 13 Q1 |
| A2 | 7 | 12 Q2 |
| $\overline{G}$1 | 8 | 11 Q3 |
| GND | 9 | 10 $\overline{G}$2 |

TBP34S42, TBP34L42, TBP34SA42
FK OR FN PACKAGE
(TOP VIEW)

NC — No internal connection

## description

These Series-3 IMPACT™ TTL programmable read-only memories (PROMs) feature high-speed access times and dependable titanium-tungsten fuse link program elements. They are organized as 1024 words by 4 bits each, providing a total of 4096 bits. The '34S4 has three-state outputs. The '34SA4 is the open-collector version and allows the device to be connected directly to data buses utilizing passive pull-up resistors. The low-power '34L4 is available for applications that require power conservation while maintaining bipolar speeds. It also has three-state outputs.

These PROMs are offered with a choice of address access times (dash numbers). These dash numbers are found in the switching characteristics table, and are included in the part numbers.

Data is programmed at any bit location with the standard Series 3 programming algorithm. The program elements store a low logic level before any programming, and are permanently set to a high logic level after programming. After execution of the programming procedure, the output for that bit location cannot be reversed. The Series 3 programming procedure should be referred to for further details. Additional circuitry has been designed into these devices to improve testability and ensure high programmability.

An MJ or MFK suffix designates full-temperature circuits that are characterized for operation over the full military temperature range of −55 °C to 125 °C. An N or FN suffix designates commercial-temperature circuits that are characterized for operation from 0 °C to 70 °C.

PROMs

4

IMPACT is a trademark of Texas Instruments.

Copyright © 1986, Texas Instruments Incorporated

**TEXAS INSTRUMENTS**

## TBP34S41, TBP34L41, TBP34SA41
## TBP34S42, TBP34L42, TBP34SA42
## 4096-BIT PROGRAMMABLE READ-ONLY MEMORIES

### logic symbols†

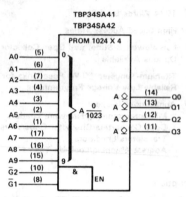

TBP34S41, TBP34L41
TBP34S42, TBP34L42

TBP34SA41
TBP34SA42

†These symbols are in accordance with ANSI/IEEE Std 91-1984 and IEC Publication 617-12.
Pin numbers shown are for J and N packages.

### schematics of inputs and outputs

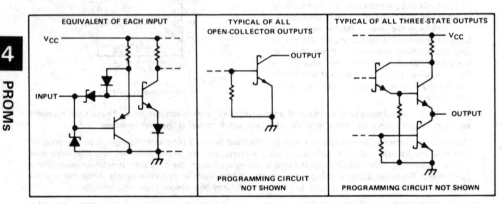

| EQUIVALENT OF EACH INPUT | TYPICAL OF ALL OPEN-COLLECTOR OUTPUTS | TYPICAL OF ALL THREE-STATE OUTPUTS |

PROGRAMMING CIRCUIT NOT SHOWN

PROGRAMMING CIRCUIT NOT SHOWN

### absolute maximum ratings over operating free-air temperature range (unless otherwise noted)

Supply voltage (see Note 1) ................................................. 7 V
Input voltage ............................................................. 5.5 V
Off-state output voltage ................................................... 5.5 V
Operating free-air temperature range: Military-temperature-range circuits ....... −55°C to 125°C
Commercial-temperature-range circuits ........ 0°C to 70°C
Storage temperature range ........................................ −65°C to 150°C

NOTE 1: Voltage values are with respect to network ground terminal. The supply voltage rating does not apply during programming.

## recommended operating conditions

| | PARAMETER | MILITARY | | | COMMERCIAL | | | UNIT |
|---|---|---|---|---|---|---|---|---|
| | | MIN | NOM | MAX | MIN | NOM | MAX | |
| $V_{CC}$ | Supply voltage | 4.5 | 5 | 5.5 | 4.5 | 5 | 5.5 | V |
| $V_{IH}$ | High-level input voltage | 2 | | | 2 | | | V |
| $V_{IL}$ | Low-level input voltage | | | 0.8 | | | 0.8 | V |
| $I_{OH}$ | High-level output current | | | −2 | | | −3.2 | mA |
| $I_{OL}$ | Low-level output current | | | 16 | | | 24 | mA |
| $T_A$ | Operating free-air temperature range | −55 | | 125 | 0 | | 70 | °C |

## electrical characteristics over recommended operating free-air temperature range (unless otherwise noted)

| PARAMETER | TEST CONDITIONS[†] | | MILITARY | | | COMMERCIAL | | | UNIT |
|---|---|---|---|---|---|---|---|---|---|
| | | | MIN | TYP[‡] | MAX | MIN | TYP[‡] | MAX | |
| $V_{IK}$ | $V_{CC}$ = MIN, | $I_I$ = −18 mA | | | −1.2 | | | −1.2 | V |
| $V_{OH}$ | $V_{CC}$ = MIN, | $I_{OH}$ = MAX | 2.4 | 3.1 | | 2.4 | 3.1 | | V |
| $V_{OL}$ | $V_{CC}$ = MIN, | $I_{OL}$ = MAX | | | 0.5 | | | 0.5 | V |
| $I_{OZH}$ | $V_{CC}$ = MAX, | $V_O$ = 2.4 V | | | 50 | | | 50 | µA |
| $I_{OZL}$ | $V_{CC}$ = MAX, | $V_O$ = 0.5 V | | | −50 | | | −50 | µA |
| $I_I$ | $V_{CC}$ = MAX, | $V_I$ = 5.5 V | | | 0.1 | | | 0.1 | mA |
| $I_{IH}$ | $V_{CC}$ = MAX, | $V_I$ = 2.7 V | | | 20 | | | 20 | µA |
| $I_{IL}$ | $V_{CC}$ = MAX, | $V_I$ = 0.5 V | | | −0.25 | | | −0.25 | mA |
| $I_O$ [§] | $V_{CC}$ = MAX, | $V_O$ = 2.25 V | −30 | | −112 | −30 | | −112 | mA |
| $I_{CC}$ | $V_{CC}$ = MAX | | | 75 | 110 | | 75 | 110 | mA |

[†] For conditions shown as MIN or MAX, use the appropriate value specified under recommended operating conditions.
[‡] All typical values are at $V_{CC}$ = 5 V, $T_A$ = 25°C.
[§] The output conditions have been chosen to produce a current that closely approximates one half of the true short-circuit output current, $I_{OS}$.

## switching characteristics over recommended ranges of $T_A$ and $V_{CC}$ (unless otherwise noted)

| TYPE | | TEST CONDITIONS | $t_{a(A)}$ ACCESS TIME FROM ADDRESS | | | $t_{en}$ ENABLE TIME | | | $t_{dis}$ DISABLE TIME | | | UNIT |
|---|---|---|---|---|---|---|---|---|---|---|---|---|
| | | | MIN | TYP[‡] | MAX | MIN | TYP[‡] | MAX | MIN | TYP[†] | MAX | |
| TBP34S41-30 | Military | $C_L$ = 50 pF, | | 14 | 30 | | 8 | 20 | | 6 | 15 | ns |
| TBP34S42-30 | | R1 = 300 Ω, | | | | | | | | | | |
| TBP34S41-25 | Commercial | R2 = 800 Ω, | | 14 | 25 | | 8 | 15 | | 6 | 12 | ns |
| TBP34S42-25 | | See Note 2 | | | | | | | | | | |

[‡] All typical values are at $V_{CC}$ = 5 V, $T_A$ = 25°C.
NOTE 2: Load circuits and voltage waveforms are shown in Section 1.

**4**

**PROMs**

**TEXAS INSTRUMENTS**

## recommended operating conditions

| | PARAMETER | MILITARY | | | COMMERCIAL | | | UNIT |
|---|---|---|---|---|---|---|---|---|
| | | MIN | NOM | MAX | MIN | NOM | MAX | |
| $V_{CC}$ | Supply voltage | 4.5 | 5 | 5.5 | 4.5 | 5 | 5.5 | V |
| $V_{IH}$ | High-level input voltage | 2 | | | 2 | | | V |
| $V_{IL}$ | Low-level input voltage | | | 0.8 | | | 0.8 | V |
| $I_{OH}$ | High-level output current | | | $-1.6$ | | | $-3.2$ | mA |
| $I_{OL}$ | Low-level output current | | | 16 | | | 24 | mA |
| $T_A$ | Operating free-air temperature range | $-55$ | | 125 | 0 | | 70 | °C |

## electrical characteristics over recommended operating free-air temperature range (unless otherwise noted)

| PARAMETER | TEST CONDITIONS[†] | | MILITARY | | | COMMERCIAL | | | UNIT |
|---|---|---|---|---|---|---|---|---|---|
| | | | MIN | TYP[‡] | MAX | MIN | TYP[‡] | MAX | |
| $V_{IK}$ | $V_{CC}$ = MIN, | $I_I = -18$ mA | | | $-1.2$ | | | $-1.2$ | V |
| $V_{OH}$ | $V_{CC}$ = MIN, | $I_{OH}$ = MAX | 2.4 | 3.1 | | 2.4 | 3.1 | | V |
| $V_{OL}$ | $V_{CC}$ = MIN, | $I_{OL}$ = MAX | | | 0.5 | | | 0.5 | V |
| $I_{OZH}$ | $V_{CC}$ = MAX, | $V_O$ = 2.4 V | | | 50 | | | 50 | $\mu$A |
| $I_{OZL}$ | $V_{CC}$ = MAX, | $V_O$ = 0.5 V | | | $-50$ | | | $-50$ | $\mu$A |
| $I_I$ | $V_{CC}$ = MAX, | $V_I$ = 5.5 V | | | 0.1 | | | 0.1 | mA |
| $I_{IH}$ | $V_{CC}$ = MAX, | $V_I$ = 2.7 V | | | 20 | | | 20 | $\mu$A |
| $I_{IL}$ | $V_{CC}$ = MAX, | $V_I$ = 0.5 V | | | $-0.25$ | | | $-0.25$ | mA |
| $I_O$ [§] | $V_{CC}$ = MAX, | $V_O$ = 2.25 V | $-30$ | | $-112$ | $-30$ | | $-112$ | mA |
| $I_{CC}$ | $V_{CC}$ = MAX | | | 30 | | | 30 | | mA |

[†] For conditions shown as MIN or MAX, use the appropriate value specified under recommended operating conditions.
[‡] All typical values are at $V_{CC}$ = 5 V, $T_A$ = 25°C.
[§] The output conditions have been chosen to produce a current that closely approximates one half of the true short-circuit output current, $I_{OS}$.

## switching characteristics over recommended ranges of $T_A$ and $V_{CC}$ (unless otherwise noted)

| TYPE | | TEST CONDITIONS | $t_{a(A)}$ ACCESS TIME FROM ADDRESS | | | $t_{en}$ ENABLE TIME | | | $t_{dis}$ DISABLE TIME | | | UNIT |
|---|---|---|---|---|---|---|---|---|---|---|---|---|
| | | | MIN | TYP[‡] | MAX | MIN | TYP[‡] | MAX | MIN | TYP[‡] | MAX | |
| TBP34L41-_ _ | Military | $C_L$ = 50 pF, | | 15 | | | 12 | | | 10 | | ns |
| TBP34L42-_ _ | | R1 = 300 Ω, | | | | | | | | | | |
| TBP34L41-_ _ | Commercial | R2 = 600 Ω, | | 15 | | | 12 | | | 10 | | ns |
| TBP34L42-_ _ | | See Note 2 | | | | | | | | | | |

[‡] All typical values are at $V_{CC}$ = 5 V, $T_A$ = 25°C.
NOTE 2: Load circuits and voltage waveforms are shown in Section 1.

**4**

**PROMS**

**TEXAS**
**INSTRUMENTS**

## recommended operating conditions

| PARAMETER | | MILITARY | | | COMMERCIAL | | | UNIT |
|---|---|---|---|---|---|---|---|---|
| | | MIN | NOM | MAX | MIN | NOM | MAX | |
| $V_{CC}$ | Supply voltage | 4.5 | 5 | 5.5 | 4.5 | 5 | 5.5 | V |
| $V_{IH}$ | High-level input voltage | 2 | | | 2 | | | V |
| $V_{IL}$ | Low-level input voltage | | | 0.8 | | | 0.8 | V |
| $V_{OH}$ | High-level output voltage | | | 5.5 | | | 5.5 | V |
| $I_{OL}$ | Low-level output current | | | 16 | | | 24 | mA |
| $T_A$ | Operating free-air temperature range | $-55$ | | 125 | 0 | | 70 | °C |

## electrical characteristics over recommended operating free-air temperature range (unless otherwise noted)

| PARAMETER | TEST CONDITIONS[†] | | MILITARY | | | COMMERCIAL | | | UNIT |
|---|---|---|---|---|---|---|---|---|---|
| | | | MIN | TYP[‡] | MAX | MIN | TYP[‡] | MAX | |
| $V_{IK}$ | $V_{CC}$ = MIN, | $I_I = -18$ mA | | | $-1.2$ | | | $-1.2$ | V |
| $I_{OH}$ | $V_{CC}$ = MIN, | $V_{OH} = 2.4$ V | | | 0.05 | | | 0.05 | mA |
| | | $V_{OH} = 5.5$ V | | | 0.1 | | | 0.1 | |
| $V_{OL}$ | $V_{CC}$ = MIN, | $I_{OL}$ = MAX | | | 0.5 | | | 0.5 | V |
| $I_I$ | $V_{CC}$ = MAX, | $V_I = 5.5$ V | | | 0.1 | | | 0.1 | mA |
| $I_{IH}$ | $V_{CC}$ = MAX, | $V_I = 2.7$ V | | | 20 | | | 20 | µA |
| $I_{IL}$ | $V_{CC}$ = MAX, | $V_I = 0.5$ V | | | $-0.25$ | | | $-0.25$ | mA |
| $I_{CC}$ | $V_{CC}$ = MAX | | | | | | | | mA |

[†]For conditions shown as MIN or MAX, use the appropriate value specified under recommended operating conditions.
[‡]All typical values are at $V_{CC}$ = 5 V, $T_A$ = 25°C.

## switching characteristics over recommended ranges of $T_A$ and $V_{CC}$ (unless otherwise noted)

| TYPE | | TEST CONDITIONS | $t_{a(A)}$ ACCESS TIME FROM ADDRESS | | | $t_{en}$ ENABLE TIME | | | $t_{dis}$ DISABLE TIME | | | UNIT |
|---|---|---|---|---|---|---|---|---|---|---|---|---|
| | | | MIN | TYP[‡] | MAX | MIN | TYP[‡] | MAX | MIN | TYP[‡] | MAX | |
| TBP34SA41-_ _ | Military | $C_L$ = 50 pF, | | 14 | | | 10 | | | 8 | | ns |
| TBP34SA42-_ _ | | R1 = 300 Ω, | | | | | | | | | | |
| TBP34SA41-_ _ | Commercial | R2 = 600 Ω, | | 14 | | | 10 | | | 8 | | ns |
| TBP34SA42-_ _ | | See Note 2 | | | | | | | | | | |

[‡]All typical values are at $V_{CC}$ = 5 V, $T_A$ = 25°C.
NOTE 2: Load circuits and voltage waveforms are shown in Section 1.

**4**

**PROMs**

**TEXAS
INSTRUMENTS**

**recommended operating conditions for programming (see Figure 1)**

| | | | MIN | NOM | MAX | UNIT |
|---|---|---|---|---|---|---|
| Supply voltage during verification | | $V_{CC}$ | 4.5 | 5 | 5.5 | V |
| Input voltage | | $V_{IH}$ | 3 | 4 | 5 | V |
| | | $V_{IL}$ | 0 | 0.2 | 0.5 | |
| Enable voltage during verification | | $\overline{G}1, \overline{G}2$ | 0 | 0.2 | 0.4 | V |
| Enable inactive voltage during programming | | $\overline{G}1, \overline{G}2$ | 4.5 | 5 | 5.5 | V |
| $V_{CC}$ program pulse amplitude | | $V_{CC(pr)}$ | 12 | 12.5 | 13 | V |
| $V_{CC}$ program pulse duration | 1st attempt | $t_{w1}$ | 10 | 11 | 12 | |
| | 2nd attempt | $t_{w2}$ | 20 | 22 | 25 | $\mu$s |
| | 3rd attempt | $t_{w3}$ | 20 | 22 | 25 | |
| Enable set-up time[†] before $V_{CC(pr)}$ | | $t_{su(en)}$ | 0.1 | 0.5 | 1 | $\mu$s |
| Enable hold time[‡] after $V_{CC(pr)}$ | | $t_{h(en)}$ | 0.1 | 0.5 | 1 | $\mu$s |
| Rise time of $V_{CC(pr)}$[§] | | $t_r(V_{CC})$ | 0.3 | 0.4 | 0.5 | $\mu$s |
| Fall time of $V_{CC(pr)}$[¶] | | $t_f(V_{CC})$ | 0.05 | 0.1 | 0.2 | $\mu$s |
| Delay time between successive $V_{CC(pr)}$ pulses | | $t_d$ | 10 | 20 | 30 | $\mu$s |
| Cooling time between words | | $t_{cool}$ | 100 | 150 | 200 | $\mu$s |
| Free-air temperature | | $T_A$ | 20 | 25 | 30 | °C |

[†] Measured from 1.5 V on enable pin to 5.5 V on $V_{CC(pr)}$
[‡] Measured from 5.5 V on $V_{CC(pr)}$ to 1.5 V on enable pin
[§] Measured from 5 V to 12 V
[¶] Measured from 12 V to 5 V

**step-by-step programming instructions (see Figure 1)**

1. Address the word to be programmed, apply 5 volts to $V_{CC}$ and a low-logic-level voltage to each enable input ($\overline{G}1$ and $\overline{G}2$).

2. Verify the selected bit location that requires programming. Note: The only bit positions that require programming are outputs needing a high logic level.

3. For bit locations that do not require programming, go to step 2 for the next bit, or to step 1 for next word.

4. Deselect PROM by applying 5 volts to $\overline{G}1$ or $\overline{G}2$.

5. Connect a 4-mA current source (clamped to $V_{CC}$) to the output that is to be programmed.

6. Increase $V_{CC}$ to $V_{CC(pr)}$ for a pulse duration equal to $t_w X$ (where X is determined by the number of programming attempts, i.e., 1,2,3). Minimum current capability for the $V_{CC}$ power supply should be 400 mA.

7. Verify that the output has been programmed to a high logic level. If the output has been programmed correctly, go to the next bit. If not, repeat step 2 through step 7 and increment X (where X is equal to 1 on the first programming attempt). If the output has not been programmed by the third attempt, stop programming and go to a new device.

8. Verify programming of every word after all words have been programmed using $V_{CC}$ values of 4.5 volts and 5.5 volts.

TEXAS
INSTRUMENTS

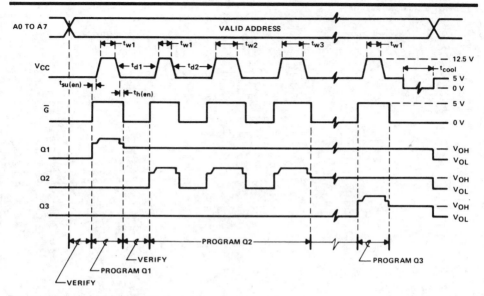

Illustrated above is the following sequence:

1) It is desired to program the selected address with 0111 (Q0-Q3). Only outputs Q1, Q2 and Q3 need programming.
2) Q1 is verified to be at a low logic level and then the programming sequence is executed. The output is then verified to be at a high logic level.
3) Q2 is an example of an output requiring three attempts to be programmed successfully.
4) Q3 is programmed to a high logic level.

### FIGURE 1. SERIES 3 PROGRAMMING SEQUENCE

**4**

**PROMs**

**4**

**PROMs**

**TBP34S162, TBP34L162, TBP34SA162**
**TBP34S16X, TBP34L16X, TBP34SA16X**
**16,384-BIT (4096 WORDS BY 4 BITS) PROGRAMMABLE READ-ONLY MEMORIES**

D2909, AUGUST 1984—REVISED MAY 1986

- **Fastest Schottky PROM Family**

- **High-Speed Access Times**

- **Low-Power, 3-State, and Open-Collector Options Available**

- **Titanium-Tungsten (Ti-W) Fuse Links for Reliable Low-Voltage Programming**

- **Applications Include:**
  Microprogramming/Firmware Loaders
  Code Converters/Character Generators
  Translators/Emulators
  Address Mapping/Look-Up Tables

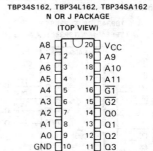

TBP34S162, TBP34L162, TBP34SA162
N OR J PACKAGE
(TOP VIEW)

### description

These Series-3 IMPACT™ TTL programmable read-only memories (PROMs) feature high-speed access times and dependable titanium-tungsten fuse link program elements. They are organized as 4096 words by 4 bits each, providing a total of 16,384 bits. The '34S16 has three-state outputs. The '34SA16 is the open-collector version and allows the device to be connected directly to data buses utilizing passive pull-up resistors. The low-power '34L16 is available for applications that require power conservation while maintaining bipolar speeds. It also has three-state outputs.

These PROMs are offered with a choice of address times (dash numbers). These dash numbers are found on the switching characteristics table, and are included in the part numbers.

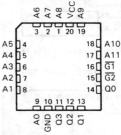

TBP34S16X, TBP34L16X, TBP34SA16X
FN OR FK PACKAGE
(TOP VIEW)

NC—No internal connection

Data is programmed at any bit location with the standard Series 3 programming algorithm. The program elements store a logic level low before any programming, and are permanently set to a logic level high after programming. After execution of the programming procedure, the output for that bit location cannot be reversed. The Series 3 programming procedure should be referred to for further details. Additional circuitry has been designed into these devices to improve testability and insure high programmability.

An MJ or MFK suffix designates full-temperature circuits that are characterized for operation over the full military temperature range of $-55\,^\circ$C to $125\,^\circ$C. An N or FN suffix designates commercial-temperature circuits that are characterized for operation from $0\,^\circ$C to $70\,^\circ$C.

IMPACT is a trademark of Texas Instruments

**TEXAS INSTRUMENTS**

4

**PROMs**

## TBP34S162, TBP34L162, TBP34SA162
## TBP34S16X, TBP34L16X, TBP34SA16X
## 16,384-BIT (4096 WORDS BY 4 BITS) PROGRAMMABLE READ-ONLY MEMORIES

### logic symbols[†]

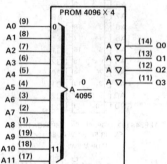

TBP34S162, TBP34S16X
TBP34L162, TBP34L16X

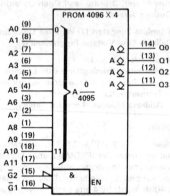

TBP34SA162, TBP34SA16X

[†]These symbols are in accordance with ANSI/IEEE Std 91-1984 and IEC Publication 617-12.

### schematics of inputs and outputs

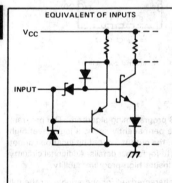

EQUIVALENT OF INPUTS

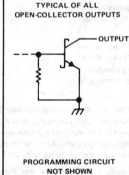

TYPICAL OF ALL
OPEN-COLLECTOR OUTPUTS

PROGRAMMING CIRCUIT
NOT SHOWN

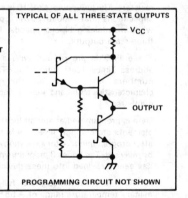

TYPICAL OF ALL THREE-STATE OUTPUTS

PROGRAMMING CIRCUIT NOT SHOWN

### absolute maximum ratings over operating free-air temperature range (unless otherwise noted)

Supply voltage (see Note 1) ............................................. 7 V
Input voltage .......................................................... 5.5 V
Off-state output voltage ............................................... 5.5 V
Operating free-air temperature range: Military-temperature-range circuits ....... −55°C to 125°C
Commercial-temperature-range circuits ........ 0°C to 70°C
Storage temperature range ........................................ −65°C to 150°C

NOTE 1: Voltage values are with respect to network ground terminal. The supply voltage rating does not apply during programming.

TEXAS
INSTRUMENTS

### recommended operating conditions

| PARAMETER | | MILITARY | | | COMMERCIAL | | | UNIT |
|---|---|---|---|---|---|---|---|---|
| | | MIN | NOM | MAX | MIN | NOM | MAX | |
| $V_{CC}$ | Supply voltage | 4.5 | 5 | 5.5 | 4.5 | 5 | 5.5 | V |
| $V_{IH}$ | High-level input voltage | 2 | | | 2 | | | V |
| $V_{IL}$ | Low-level input voltage | | | 0.8 | | | 0.8 | V |
| $I_{OH}$ | High-level output current | | | $-2$ | | | $-3.2$ | mA |
| $I_{OL}$ | Low-level output current | | | 16 | | | 24 | mA |
| $T_A$ | Operating free-air temperature range | $-55$ | | 125 | 0 | | 70 | °C |

### electrical characteristics over recommended operating free-air temperature range (unless otherwise noted)

| PARAMETER | TEST CONDITIONS[†] | | MILITARY | | | COMMERCIAL | | | UNIT |
|---|---|---|---|---|---|---|---|---|---|
| | | | MIN | TYP[‡] | MAX | MIN | TYP[‡] | MAX | |
| $V_{IK}$ | $V_{CC}$ = MIN, | $I_I = -18$ mA | | | $-1.2$ | | | $-1.2$ | V |
| $V_{OH}$ | $V_{CC}$ = MIN, | $I_{OH}$ = MAX | 2.4 | 3.1 | | 2.4 | 3.1 | | V |
| $V_{OL}$ | $V_{CC}$ = MIN, | $I_{OL}$ = MAX | | | 0.5 | | | 0.5 | V |
| $I_{OZH}$ | $V_{CC}$ = MAX, | $V_O = 2.4$ V | | | 50 | | | 50 | $\mu$A |
| $I_{OZL}$ | $V_{CC}$ = MAX, | $V_O = 0.5$ V | | | $-50$ | | | $-50$ | $\mu$A |
| $I_I$ | $V_{CC}$ = MAX, | $V_I = 5.5$ V | | | 0.1 | | | 0.1 | mA |
| $I_{IH}$ | $V_{CC}$ = MAX, | $V_I = 2.7$ V | | | 20 | | | 20 | $\mu$A |
| $I_{IL}$ | $V_{CC}$ = MAX, | $V_I = 0.5$ V | | | $-0.25$ | | | $-0.25$ | mA |
| $I_O$ [§] | $V_{CC}$ = MAX, | $V_O = 2.25$ V | $-30$ | | $-112$ | $-30$ | | $-112$ | mA |
| $I_{CC}$ | $V_{CC}$ = MAX | | | 95 | 155 | | 95 | 155 | mA |

[†]For conditions shown as MIN or MAX, use appropriate value specified under recommended operating conditions.
[‡]All typical values are at $V_{CC} = 5$ V, $T_A = 25$°C.
[§]The output conditions have been chosen to produce a current that closely approximates one half of the true short-circuit output current, $I_{OS}$.

### switching characteristics over recommended ranges of $T_A$ and $V_{CC}$ (unless otherwise noted)

| TYPE | | TEST CONDITIONS | $t_{a(A)}$ ACCESS TIME FROM ADDRESS | | | $t_{en}$ ENABLE TIME | | | $t_{dis}$ DISABLE TIME | | | UNIT |
|---|---|---|---|---|---|---|---|---|---|---|---|---|
| | | | MIN | TYP[‡] | MAX | MIN | TYP[‡] | MAX | MIN | TYP[‡] | MAX | |
| TBP34S162-45 | Military | | | 16 | 45 | | 6 | 15 | | 5 | 12 | ns |
| TBP34S16X-45 | | | | | | | | | | | | |
| TBP34S162-45 | Commercial | $C_L = 50$ pF, | | 16 | 45 | | 6 | 12 | | 5 | 10 | ns |
| TBP34S16X-45 | | R1 = 300 $\Omega$, | | | | | | | | | | |
| TBP34S162-35 | Commercial | R2 = 300 $\Omega$, | | 16 | 35 | | 6 | 12 | | 5 | 10 | ns |
| TBP34S16X-35 | | See Note 2 | | | | | | | | | | |
| TBP34S162-25 | Commercial | | | 16 | 25 | | 6 | 12 | | 5 | 10 | ns |
| TBP34S16X-25 | | | | | | | | | | | | |

[‡]All typical values are at $V_{CC} = 5$ V, $T_A = 25$°C.
NOTE 2: Load circuits and voltage waveforms as shown in Section 1.

**4**

**PROMs**

TEXAS
INSTRUMENTS

## TBP34L162, TBP34L16X
## 16,384-BIT (4096 WORDS BY 4 BITS)
## LOW-POWER PROGRAMMABLE READ-ONLY MEMORY WITH 3-STATE OUTPUTS

### recommended operating conditions

| | PARAMETER | MILITARY | | | COMMERCIAL | | | UNIT |
|---|---|---|---|---|---|---|---|---|
| | | MIN | NOM | MAX | MIN | NOM | MAX | |
| $V_{CC}$ | Supply voltage | 4.5 | 5 | 5.5 | 4.5 | 5 | 5.5 | V |
| $V_{IH}$ | High-level input voltage | 2 | | | 2 | | | V |
| $V_{IL}$ | Low-level input voltage | | | 0.8 | | | 0.8 | V |
| $I_{OH}$ | High-level output current | | | -1.6 | | | -3.2 | mA |
| $I_{OL}$ | Low-level output current | | | 16 | | | 24 | mA |
| $T_A$ | Operating free-air temperature range | -55 | | 125 | 0 | | 70 | °C |

### electrical characteristics over recommended operating free-air temperature range (unless otherwise noted)

| PARAMETER | TEST CONDITIONS[†] | | MILITARY | | | COMMERCIAL | | | UNIT |
|---|---|---|---|---|---|---|---|---|---|
| | | | MIN | TYP[‡] | MAX | MIN | TYP[‡] | MAX | |
| $V_{IK}$ | $V_{CC}$ = MIN, | $I_I$ = -18 mA | | | -1.2 | | | -1.2 | V |
| $V_{OH}$ | $V_{CC}$ = MIN, | $I_{OH}$ = MAX | 2.4 | 3.1 | | 2.4 | 3.1 | | V |
| $V_{OL}$ | $V_{CC}$ = MIN, | $I_{OL}$ = MAX | | | 0.5 | | | 0.5 | V |
| $I_{OZH}$ | $V_{CC}$ = MAX, | $V_O$ = 2.4 V | | | 50 | | | 50 | μA |
| $I_{OZL}$ | $V_{CC}$ = MAX, | $V_O$ = 0.5 V | | | -50 | | | -50 | μA |
| $I_I$ | $V_{CC}$ = MAX, | $V_I$ = 5.5 V | | | 0.1 | | | 0.1 | mA |
| $I_{IH}$ | $V_{CC}$ = MAX, | $V_I$ = 2.7 V | | | 20 | | | 20 | μA |
| $I_{IL}$ | $V_{CC}$ = MAX, | $V_I$ = 0.5 V | | | -0.25 | | | -0.25 | mA |
| $I_O$ [§] | $V_{CC}$ = MAX, | $V_O$ = 2.25 V | -30 | | -112 | -30 | | -112 | mA |
| $I_{CC}$ | $V_{CC}$ = MAX | | | 65 | 100 | | 65 | 100 | mA |

[†]For conditions shown as MIN or MAX, use appropriate value specified under recommended operating conditions.
[‡]All typical values are at $V_{CC}$ = 5 V, $T_A$ = 25 °C.
[§]The output conditions have been chosen to produce a current that closely approximates one half of the true short-circuit output current, $I_{OS}$.

### switching characteristics over recommended ranges of $T_A$ and $V_{CC}$ (unless otherwise noted)

| TYPE | | TEST CONDITIONS | $t_{a(A)}$ ACCESS TIME FROM ADDRESS | | | $t_{en}$ ENABLE TIME | | | $t_{dis}$ DISABLE TIME | | | UNIT |
|---|---|---|---|---|---|---|---|---|---|---|---|---|
| | | | MIN | TYP[‡] | MAX | MIN | TYP[‡] | MAX | MIN | TYP[‡] | MAX | |
| TBP34L162-40 | Military | | | 20 | 40 | | 10 | 20 | | 5 | 15 | ns |
| TBP34L16X-40 | | | | | | | | | | | | |
| TBP34L162-30 | Commercial | $C_L$ = 50 pF, | | 20 | 30 | | 10 | 15 | | 5 | 10 | ns |
| TBP34L16X-30 | | R1 = 300 Ω, | | | | | | | | | | |
| TBP34L162-35 | Commercial | R2 = 600 Ω, | | 20 | 35 | | 10 | 15 | | 5 | 10 | ns |
| TBP34L16X-35 | | See Note 2 | | | | | | | | | | |
| TBP34L162-50 | Commercial | | | 20 | 50 | | 10 | 15 | | 5 | 10 | ns |
| TBP34L16X-50 | | | | | | | | | | | | |

[‡]All typical values are at $V_{CC}$ = 5 V, $T_A$ = 25 °C.
NOTE 2: Load circuits and voltage waveforms as shown in Section 1.

Texas
Instruments

**4**

**PROMS**

## recommended operating conditions

| | PARAMETER | MILITARY | | | COMMERCIAL | | | UNIT |
|---|---|---|---|---|---|---|---|---|
| | | MIN | NOM | MAX | MIN | NOM | MAX | |
| $V_{CC}$ | Supply voltage | 4.5 | 5 | 5.5 | 4.5 | 5 | 5.5 | V |
| $V_{IH}$ | High-level input voltage | 2 | | | 2 | | | V |
| $V_{IL}$ | Low-level input voltage | | | 0.8 | | | 0.8 | V |
| $V_{OH}$ | High-level output voltage | | | 5.5 | | | 5.5 | V |
| $I_{OL}$ | Low-level output current | | | 16 | | | 24 | mA |
| $T_A$ | Operating free-air temperature range | $-55$ | | 125 | 0 | | 70 | °C |

## electrical characteristics over recommended operating free-air temperature range (unless otherwise noted)

| PARAMETER | TEST CONDITIONS[†] | | MILITARY | | COMMERCIAL | | UNIT |
|---|---|---|---|---|---|---|---|
| | | | MIN | TYP[‡] MAX | MIN | TYP[‡] MAX | |
| $V_{IK}$ | $V_{CC}$ = MIN, | $I_I = -18$ mA | | $-1.2$ | | $-1.2$ | V |
| $I_{OH}$ | $V_{CC}$ = MIN, | $V_{OH}$ = 2.4 V | | 0.05 | | 0.05 | mA |
| | | $V_{OH}$ = 5.5 V | | 0.1 | | 0.1 | |
| $V_{OL}$ | $V_{CC}$ = MIN, | $I_{OL}$ = MAX | | 0.5 | | 0.5 | V |
| $I_I$ | $V_{CC}$ = MAX, | $V_I$ = 5.5 V | | 0.1 | | 0.1 | mA |
| $I_{IH}$ | $V_{CC}$ = MAX, | $V_I$ = 2.7 V | | 20 | | 20 | $\mu$A |
| $I_{IL}$ | $V_{CC}$ = MAX, | $V_I$ = 0.5 V | | $-0.25$ | | $-0.25$ | mA |
| $I_{CC}$ | $V_{CC}$ = MAX | | | 95  155 | | 95  155 | mA |

[†]For conditions shown as MIN or MAX, use appropriate value specified under recommended operating conditions.
[‡]All typical values are at $V_{CC}$ = 5 V, $T_A$ = 25 °C.

## switching characteristics over recommended ranges of $T_A$ and $V_{CC}$ (unless otherwise noted)

| TYPE | | TEST CONDITIONS | $t_{a(A)}$ ACCESS TIME FROM ADDRESS | | | $t_{en}$ ENABLE TIME | | | $t_{dis}$ DISABLE TIME | | | UNIT |
|---|---|---|---|---|---|---|---|---|---|---|---|---|
| | | | MIN | TYP[‡] | MAX | MIN | TYP[‡] | MAX | MIN | TYP[‡] | MAX | |
| TBP34SA162-40 | Military | $C_L$ = 50 pF, | | 22 | 40 | | 6 | 15 | | 8 | 20 | ns |
| TBP34SA16X-40 | | R1 = 300 $\Omega$, | | | | | | | | | | |
| TBP34SA162-35 | Commercial | R2 = 600 $\Omega$, | | 22 | 35 | | 6 | 12 | | 8 | 15 | ns |
| TBP34SA16X-35 | | See Note 2 | | | | | | | | | | |

[‡]All typical values are at $V_{CC}$ = 5 V, $T_A$ = 25 °C.
NOTE 2: Load circuits and voltage waveforms as shown in Section 1.

**4**

**PROMs**

TEXAS
INSTRUMENTS

### recommended operating conditions for programming (see Figure 1)

| | | | MIN | NOM | MAX | UNIT |
|---|---|---|---|---|---|---|
| Supply voltage during verification | | $V_{CC}$ | 4.5 | 5 | 5.5 | V |
| Input voltage | | $V_{IH}$ | 3 | 4 | 5 | V |
| | | $V_{IL}$ | 0 | 0.2 | 0.5 | |
| Enable voltage during verification | | G1, G2 | 0 | 0.2 | 0.4 | V |
| Enable inactive voltage during programming | | G1, G2 | 4.5 | 5 | 5.5 | V |
| $V_{CC}$ program pulse amplitude | | $V_{CC(pr)}$ | 12 | 12.5 | 13 | V |
| $V_{CC}$ program pulse duration | 1st attempt | $t_{w1}$ | 10 | 11 | 12 | |
| | 2nd attempt | $t_{w2}$ | 20 | 22 | 25 | $\mu$s |
| | 3rd attempt | $t_{w3}$ | 20 | 22 | 25 | |
| Enable set-up time‡ before $V_{CC(pr)}$ | | $t_{su(en)}$ | 0.1 | 0.5 | 1 | $\mu$s |
| Enable hold time‡ after $V_{CC(pr)}$ | | $t_{h(en)}$ | 0.1 | 0.5 | 1 | $\mu$s |
| Rise time of $V_{CC(pr)}$§ | | $t_r(V_{CC})$ | 0.3 | 0.4 | 0.5 | $\mu$s |
| Fall time of $V_{CC(pr)}$¶ | | $t_f(V_{CC})$ | 0.05 | 0.1 | 0.2 | $\mu$s |
| Delay time between successive $V_{CC(pr)}$ pulses | | $t_{d1}$ | 10 | 20 | 30 | $\mu$s |
| Delay time between successive $V_{CC(pr)}$ pulses | | $t_{d2}$ | 10 | 20 | 30 | $\mu$s |
| Cooling time between words | | $t_{cool}$ | 100 | 150 | 200 | $\mu$s |
| Free-air temperature | | $T_A$ | 20 | 25 | 30 | °C |

†Measured from 1.5 V on enable pin to 5.5 V on $V_{CC(pr)}$
‡Measured from 5.5 V on $V_{CC(pr)}$ to 1.5 V on enable pin
§Measured from 5 V to 12 V
¶Measured from 12 V to 5 V

### step-by-step programming instructions (see Figure 1)

1. Address the word to be programmed, apply 5 volts to $V_{CC}$ and active levels to all enable inputs ($\overline{G1}$, $\overline{G2}$).

2. Verify the selected bit location that requires programming. Note: The only bit positions that require programming are outputs needing a high logic level.

3. For bit locations that do not require programming, go to step 2 for the next bit, or to step 1 for next word.

4. Deselect PROM by applying 5 volts to $\overline{G1}$ or $\overline{G2}$.

5. Connect a 4-mA current source (clamped to $V_{CC}$) to the output that is to be programmed.

6. Increase $V_{CC}$ to $V_{CC(pr)}$ for a pulse duration equal to $t_{wX}$ (where X is determined by the number of programming attempts, i.e., 1,2,3). Minimum current capability for the $V_{CC}$ power supply should be 400 mA.

7. Verify that the output has been programmed to a high logic level. If the output has been programmed correctly, go to the next bit. If not, repeat step 2 through step 7 and increment X (where X is equal to 1 on the first programming attempt). If the output has not been programmed by the third attempt, stop programming and go to a new device.

8. Verify programming of every word after all words have been programmed using $V_{CC}$ values of 4.5 volts and 5.5 volts.

**TEXAS INSTRUMENTS**

**4**

**PROMs**

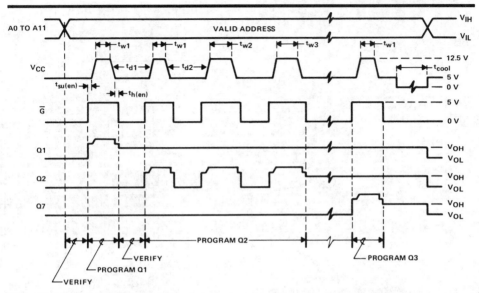

Illustrated above is the following sequence:

1) It is desired to program the selected address with 0111 (Q0-Q3). Only outputs Q1, Q2 and Q3 need programming.
2) Q1 is verified to be at a low logic level and then the programming sequence is executed. The output is then verified to be at a high logic level.
3) Q2 is an example of an output requiring three attempts to be programmed successfully.
4) Q3 is programmed to a high logic level.

**FIGURE 1. SERIES 3 PROGRAMMING SEQUENCE**

4

PROMs

FIGURE 3 SERIES 3 PROGRAMMING SEQUENCE

- **Fastest Schottky PROM Family**
- **High-Speed Access Times**
- **Allows Storage of Output Data**
- **Applications Include:**
  **Microprogram Control Store with**
  **Built-In System Diagnostic Testing**
  **Serial Character Generator**
  **Parallel In/Serial Out Memory**

## description

The TBP34SR16′ is a series-3 IMPACT™ TTL programmable read-only memory (PROM) featuring high-speed access times and dependable titanium-tungsten fuse link program elements. It is organized as 4096 words by 4 bits each, providing 16,384 bits.

The TBP34SR16′ features a 4-bit shadow register that allows diagnostic observation and control without introducing intermediate illegal states. It is loaded on the rising edge of SRCLK from either the output register or the serial data input (SDI). In addition, it can be loaded with parallel data from the outputs. The output register receives data from either the PROM array or the shadow register as determined by the mode control input. The output register is loaded on the rising edge of ORCLK. The mode-dependent function table should be referred to for further details.

During diagnostics, data loaded into the output register from the PROM array can be parallel-loaded into the shadow register and serially shifted out through the SDO output. This allows observation of the system without introducing intermediate illegal states. Similarly, diagnostic data can be serially loaded into the shadow register and parallel-loaded into the output register. This allows control and test scanning to be imposed on the system.

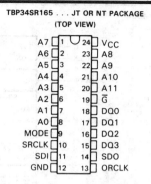

TBP34SR165 . . . JT OR NT PACKAGE
(TOP VIEW)

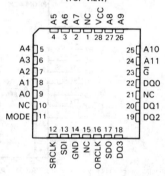

TBP34SR16X . . . FN OR FK PACKAGE
(TOP VIEW)

NC – No internal connection

Data is programmed at any bit location with the standard series 3 programming algorithm. The program elements store a high logic level before any programming, and are permanently set to a low logic level after programming. After execution of the programming procedure, the output for that bit location cannot be reversed. The series 3 programming procedure should be referred to for further details. Additional circuits have been designed into these devices to improve testability and ensure high programmability.

An MFK or MJT suffix designates circuits that are characterized for operation over the full military temperature range of −55 °C to 125 °C. An FN or NT suffix designates commercial-temperature circuits that are characterized for operation from 0 °C to 70 °C.

IMPACT is a trademark of Texas Instruments

Copyright © 1985, Texas Instruments Incorporated

**TEXAS INSTRUMENTS**

4

PROMs

## logic symbol†

† This symbol is in accordance with ANSI/IEEE Std 91-1984 and
IEC Publication 617-12.
Pin numbers shown are for JT and NT packages.

**TEXAS**
**INSTRUMENTS**

**logic diagram (positive logic)**

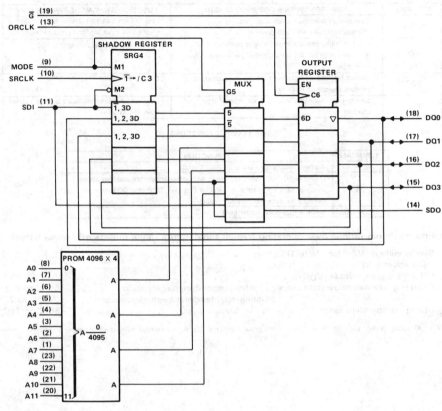

Pin numbers shown are for JT and NT packages.

## TBP34SR165, TBP34SR16X
## 16,384-BIT (4096 WORDS BY 4 BITS)
## SHADOW-REGISTERED PROGRAMMABLE READ-ONLY MEMORY

### MODE-DEPENDENT TERMINAL FUNCTIONS

| TERMINAL | FUNCTION WHEN MODE INPUT IS HIGH | FUNCTION WHEN MODE INPUT IS LOW |
|---|---|---|
| SRCLK | Low-to-high transition loads data into shadow register under SDI control. | Low-to-high transition shifts data present on the SDI input into the shadow register. |
| SDI | If SDI is high, shadow register does nothing. If SDI is low, data may be clocked into shadow register from output bus. | Serial input to shadow register LSB |
| SDO | Output for data directly from SDI for cascading other shadow-registered PROMs | Output for shadow register MSB |
| RCLK | Low-to-high transition loads output register from shadow register. | Low-to-high transition loads output register from PROM array. |

### OTHER TERMINAL FUNCTIONS

| TERMINALS | FUNCTION |
|---|---|
| A0 — A11 | Address inputs for data from PROM array |
| $\overline{G}$ | If $\overline{G}$ is high, DQ0 thru DQ3 are in high-impedance state and can accept external data for shadow register. If $\overline{G}$ is low, DQ0 thru DQ3 are outputs for data from output register. |
| DQ0—DQ3 | Input/output ports under control of $\overline{G}$ |

## absolute maximum ratings over operating free-air temperature range (unless otherwise noted)

Supply voltage, $V_{CC}$ (see Note 1) . . . . . . . . . . . . . . . . . . . . . . . . . . . . . . . . . . . . . . . . . . . . . 7 V
Input voltage, $V_I$ . . . . . . . . . . . . . . . . . . . . . . . . . . . . . . . . . . . . . . . . . . . . . . . . . . . . . . . . 5.5 V
Off-state output voltage, $V_{O(off)}$ . . . . . . . . . . . . . . . . . . . . . . . . . . . . . . . . . . . . . . . . . . . . . 5.5 V
Operating free-air temperature range: Military-temperature-range circuits . . . . . . . −55°C to 125°C
                                        Commercial-temperature-range circuits . . . . . . . . 0°C to 70°C
Storage temperature range . . . . . . . . . . . . . . . . . . . . . . . . . . . . . . . . . . . . . . . . . −65°C to 150°C

NOTE 1: All voltage values are with respect to network ground terminal. The supply voltage rating does not apply during programming.

TEXAS
INSTRUMENTS

**4**

**PROMS**

**TBP34SR165, TBP34SR16X**
**16,384-BIT (4096 WORDS BY 4 BITS)**
**SHADOW-REGISTERED PROGRAMMABLE READ-ONLY MEMORY**

## recommended operating conditions

| | PARAMETER | | MILITARY | | | UNIT |
|---|---|---|---|---|---|---|
| | | | MIN | NOM | MAX | |
| $V_{CC}$ | Supply voltage | | 4.5 | 5 | 5.5 | V |
| $V_{IH}$ | High-level input voltage | | 2 | | | V |
| $V_{IL}$ | Low-level input voltage | | | | 0.8 | V |
| $I_{OH}$ | High-level input current | | | | −2 | mA |
| $I_{OL}$ | Low-level input current | | | | 16 | mA |
| $f_{clock}$ | Clock frequency, SRCLK (MODE = L)[†] | | | | | MHz |
| $f_{clock}$ | Clock frequency, ORCLK[‡] | | | | | MHz |
| $t_w$ | Pulse duration | SRCLK high | | | | ns |
| | | SRCLK low | | | | |
| | | ORCLK high | | | | |
| | | ORCLK low | | | | |
| $t_{su}$ | Setup time | DQ3 thru DQ0 before SRCLK↑ ($\overline{G}$ and MODE = H, SDI = L) | | | | ns |
| | | SDI and MODE before SRCLK↑ | | | | |
| | | Address before ORCLK↑ (MODE = L) | | | | |
| | | MODE before ORCLK↑ | | | | |
| | | SRCLK↑ before ORCLK↑ ($\overline{G}$ and MODE = H, SDI = L) | | | | |
| $t_h$ | Hold time | DQ3 − DQ0 after SRCLK↑ ($\overline{G}$ and MODE = H, SDI = L) | | | | ns |
| | | SDI and MODE after SRCLK↑ or ORCLK↑ | | | | |
| | | Address after ORCLK↑ (MODE = L) | | | | |
| | | MODE after ORCLK↑ | | | | |
| $T_A$ | Operating free-air temperature range | | −55 | | 125 | °C |

[†] Maximum diagnostic clock frequency = $\dfrac{1}{t_{wSRCLK(high)} + t_{wSRCLK(low)}}$

[‡] Maximum output register clock frequency = $\dfrac{1}{t_{su}, \text{Address before ORCLK}\uparrow}$

4

PROMs

TEXAS
INSTRUMENTS

**electrical characteristics over recommended operating free-air temperature range (unless otherwise noted)**

| PARAMETER | TEST CONDITIONS† | | MILITARY | | | UNIT |
|---|---|---|---|---|---|---|
| | | | MIN | TYP† | MAX | |
| $V_{IK}$ | $V_{CC} = 4.5$ V, | $I_I = -18$ mA | | | -1.2 | V |
| $V_{OH}$ | $V_{CC} = 4.5$ V, | $I_{OH} = -2$ mA | 2.4 | 3.1 | | V |
| $V_{OL}$ | $V_{CC} = 4.5$ V, | $I_{OL} = 16$ mA | | | 0.5 | V |
| $I_{OZH}$ | $V_{CC} = 5.5$ V, | $V_O = 2.4$ V | | | 50 | $\mu$A |
| $I_{OZL}$ | $V_{CC} = 5.5$ V, | $V_O = 0.5$ V | | | -100 | $\mu$A |
| $I_I$ | $V_{CC} = 5.5$ V, | $V_I = 5.5$ V | | | 0.1 | mA |
| $I_{IH}$ | $V_{CC} = 5.5$ V, | $V_I = 2.7$ V | | | 20 | $\mu$A |
| $I_{IL}$ | $V_{CC} = 5.5$ V, | $V_I = 0.5$ V | | | -0.25 | mA |
| $I_O$‡ | $V_{CC} = 5.5$ V, | $V_O = 2.25$ V | -30 | | -112 | mA |
| $I_{CC}$ | $V_{CC} = 5.5$ V, | See Note 2 | | 120 | | mA |

**switching characteristics over recommended ranges of $T_A$ and $V_{CC}$ (unless otherwise noted)**

| PARAMETER | FROM (INPUT) | TO (OUTPUT) | TEST CONDITION (See Note 3) | MILITARY | | | UNIT |
|---|---|---|---|---|---|---|---|
| | | | | MIN | TYP† | MAX | |
| $f_{max}$§ | SRCLK (MODE = L) | | | | | | MHz |
| $f_{max}$¶ | ORCLK | | | | | | MHz |
| $t_{pd}$ | ORCLK | DQ0 – DQ3 | $C_L = 50$ pF, | | | | |
| $t_{pd}$ | SRCLK (MODE = L) | SDO | $R1 = 300$ Ω, | | | | |
| $t_{pd}$ | SDI (MODE = H) | SDO | $R2 = 600$ Ω | | | | ns |
| $t_{pd}$ | MODE (SDI = L) | | | | | | |
| $t_{en}$ | $\overline{G}$ | DQ0 – DQ3 | | | | | |
| $t_{dis}$ | $\overline{G}$ | DQ0 – DQ3 | | | | | |

† All typical values are at $V_{CC} = 5$ V, $T_A = 25$°C.
‡ The output conditions have been chosen to produce a current that closely approximates one half of the true short-circuit output current, $I_{OS}$.

§ Maximum diagnostic clock frequency = $\dfrac{1}{t_{wSRCLK(high)} + t_{wSRCLK(low)}}$

¶ Maximum output register clock frequency = $\dfrac{1}{t_{su}, \text{Address before ORCLK}\uparrow}$

NOTES: 2. $I_{CC}$ is measured with all outputs open and with all inputs at TTL levels.
3. Load circuits and voltage waveforms are shown in Section 1.

**TEXAS INSTRUMENTS**

## recommended operating conditions

| PARAMETER | | COMMERCIAL | | | UNIT |
|---|---|---|---|---|---|
| | | MIN | NOM | MAX | |
| $V_{CC}$ | Supply voltage | 4.5 | 5 | 5.5 | V |
| $V_{IH}$ | High-level input voltage | 2 | | | V |
| $V_{IL}$ | Low-level input voltage | | | 0.8 | V |
| $I_{OH}$ | High-level input current | | | −3.2 | mA |
| $I_{OL}$ | Low-level input current | | | 24 | mA |
| $f_{clock}$ | Clock frequency, SRCLK (MODE = L)[†] | 0 | | 40 | MHz |
| $f_{clock}$ | Clock frequency, ORCLK[‡] | 0 | | 30 | MHz |
| $t_w$ | Pulse duration | SRCLK high | 12 | | | ns |
| | | SRCLK low | 12 | | | |
| | | ORCLK high | 12 | | | |
| | | ORCLK low | 12 | | | |
| $t_{su}$ | Setup time | DQ3 thru DQ0 before SRCLK↑ ($\overline{G}$ and MODE = H, SDI = L) | 20 | | | ns |
| | | SDI and MODE before SRCLK↑ | 20 | | | |
| | | Address before ORCLK↑ (MODE = L) | 30 | | | |
| | | MODE before ORCLK↑ | 20 | | | |
| | | SRCLK↑ before ORCLK↑ ($\overline{G}$ and MODE = H, SDI = L) | 20 | | | |
| $t_h$ | Hold time | DQ3 − DQ0 after SRCLK↑ ($\overline{G}$ and MODE = H, SDI = L) | 0 | | | ns |
| | | SDI and MODE after SRCLK↑ or ORCLK↑ | 0 | | | |
| | | Address after ORCLK↑ (MODE = L) | 0 | | | |
| | | MODE after ORCLK↑ | 0 | | | |
| $T_A$ | Operating free-air temperature range | | 0 | | 70 | °C |

[†] Maximum diagnostic clock frequency = $\dfrac{1}{t_{wSRCLK(high)} + t_{wSRCLK(low)}}$

[‡] Maximum output register clock frequency = $\dfrac{1}{t_{su}, \text{Address before ORCLK↑}}$

**4**

**PROMs**

**TEXAS
INSTRUMENTS**

**electrical characteristics over recommended operating free-air temperature range (unless otherwise noted)**

| PARAMETER | TEST CONDITIONS[†] | | COMMERCIAL | | | UNIT |
|---|---|---|---|---|---|---|
| | | | MIN | TYP[†] | MAX | |
| $V_{IK}$ | $V_{CC} = 4.5$ V, | $I_I = -18$ mA | | | -1.2 | V |
| $V_{OH}$ | $V_{CC} = 4.5$ V, | $I_{OH} = -3.2$ mA | 2.4 | 3.1 | | V |
| $V_{OL}$ | $V_{CC} = 4.5$ V, | $I_{OL} = 24$ mA | | | 0.5 | V |
| $I_{OZH}$ | $V_{CC} = 5.5$ V, | $V_O = 2.4$ V | | | 50 | $\mu$A |
| $I_{OZL}$ | $V_{CC} = 5.5$ V, | $V_O = 0.5$ V | | | -100 | $\mu$A |
| $I_I$ | $V_{CC} = 5.5$ V, | $V_I = 5.5$ V | | | 0.1 | mA |
| $I_{IH}$ | $V_{CC} = 5.5$ V, | $V_I = 2.7$ V | | | 20 | $\mu$A |
| $I_{IL}$ | $V_{CC} = 5.5$ V, | $V_I = 0.5$ V | | | -0.25 | mA |
| $I_O$[‡] | $V_{CC} = 5.5$ V, | $V_O = 2.25$ V | -30 | | -112 | mA |
| $I_{CC}$ | $V_{CC} = 5.5$ V, | See Note 2 | | 130 | 195 | mA |

**switching characteristics over recommended ranges of $T_A$ and $V_{CC}$ (unless otherwise noted)**

| PARAMETER | FROM (INPUT) | TO (OUTPUT) | TEST CONDITION (See Note 3) | COMMERCIAL | | | UNIT |
|---|---|---|---|---|---|---|---|
| | | | | MIN | TYP[†] | MAX | |
| $f_{max}$[§] | SRCLK (MODE = L) | | | 40 | | | MHz |
| $f_{max}$[¶] | ORCLK | | | 30 | | | MHz |
| $t_{pd}$ | ORCLK | DQ0 — DQ3 | $C_L = 50$ pF, R1 = 300 $\Omega$, R2 = 600 $\Omega$ | | 8 | 15 | ns |
| $t_{pd}$ | SRCLK (MODE = L) | SDO | | | 8 | 15 | |
| $t_{pd}$ | SDI (MODE = H) | SDO | | | 8 | 15 | |
| $t_{pd}$ | MODE (SDI = L) | | | | 8 | 15 | |
| $t_{en}$ | $\overline{G}$ | DQ0 — DQ3 | | | 7 | 12 | |
| $t_{dis}$ | $\overline{G}$ | DQ0 — DQ3 | | | 6 | 10 | |

[†] All typical values are at $V_{CC} = 5$ V, $T_A = 25°C$.

[‡] The output conditions have been chosen to produce a current that closely approximates one half of the true short-circuit output current, $I_{OS}$.

[§] Maximum diagnostic clock frequency $= \dfrac{1}{t_{wSRCLK(high)} + t_{wSRCLK(low)}}$

[¶] Maximum output register clock frequency $= \dfrac{1}{t_{su}, \text{Address before ORCLK↑}}$

NOTES: 2. $I_{CC}$ is measured with all outputs open and with all inputs at TTL levels.
3. Load circuits and voltage waveforms are shown in Section 1.

TEXAS
INSTRUMENTS

### recommended operating conditions for programming (see Figure 1)

| | | MIN | NOM | MAX | UNIT |
|---|---|---|---|---|---|
| $V_{CC}$ | Supply voltage during verification | 4.5 | 5 | 5.5 | V |
| $V_{IH}$ | High-level input voltage | 3 | 4 | 5 | V |
| $V_{IL}$ | Low-level input voltage | 0 | 0.2 | 0.4 | V |
| | Enable $\overline{G}$ voltage during verification | 0 | 0.2 | 0.4 | V |
| | Enable $\overline{G}$ inactive voltage during programming | 4.5 | 5 | 5.5 | V |
| $V_{CC(pr)}$ | Supply voltage program pulse amplitude | 12 | 12.5 | 13 | V |
| $t_{w1}$ | $V_{CC}$ program pulse duration, 1st attempt | 10 | 11 | 12 | $\mu$s |
| $t_{w2}$ | $V_{CC}$ program pulse duration, 2nd attempt | 20 | 22 | 25 | $\mu$s |
| $t_{w3}$ | $V_{CC}$ program pulse duration, 3rd attempt | 20 | 22 | 25 | $\mu$s |
| $t_{su}$ | Setup time, enable $\overline{G}$ low before $V_{CC(pr)}$ [†] | 0.1 | 0.5 | 1 | $\mu$s |
| $t_h$ | Hold time, enable $\overline{G}$ low after $V_{CC(pr)}$ [‡] | 0.1 | 0.5 | 1 | $\mu$s |
| $t_{r(VCC)}$ | Rise time, $V_{CC(pr)}$ (5 V to 12 V) | 0.3 | 0.4 | 0.5 | $\mu$s |
| $t_{f(VCC)}$ | Fall time, $V_{CC(pr)}$ (12 V to 5 V) | 0.05 | 0.1 | 0.2 | $\mu$s |
| $t_d$ | Delay time between successive $V_{CC(pr)}$ pulses | 10 | 20 | 30 | $\mu$s |
| $t_{cool}$ | Cooling time between words | 100 | 150 | 200 | $\mu$s |
| $T_A$ | Free-air temperature | 20 | 25 | 30 | °C |

[†]Measured from 1.5 V on enable pin to 5.5 V on $V_{CC(pr)}$.

[‡]Measured from 5.5 V on $V_{CC(pr)}$ to 1.5 V on enable pin.

### step-by-step programming instructions (see Figure 1)

1. Address the word to be programmed, apply 5 V to $V_{CC}$ and a low logic level to the G input.
2. Verify the selected bit location that requires programming. Note: The only bit positions that require programming are outputs to be at a high logic level.
3. For bit locations that do not require programming, go to step 2 for the next bit, or to step 1 for the next word.
4. Deselect PROM by applying 5 V to G.
5. Connect a 4-mA current source (clamped to $V_{CC}$) to the output to be programmed.
6. Increase $V_{CC}$ to $V_{CC(pr)}$ for a pulse duration equal to $t_{wX}$ (where X is determined by the number of programming attempts, i.e., 1, 2, 3). Minimum current capability for the $V_{CC}$ power supply should be 400 mA.
7. Verify that the output has been programmed to a high logic level. If the output has been programmed correctly, go to the next bit. If not, repeat steps 2 through 7 and increment X (where X equals 1 on the first programming attempt). If the output has not been programmed by the third attempt, stop programming and go to a new device.
8. Verify programming of every word after all words have been programmed using $V_{CC}$ values of 4.5 volts and 5.5 volts.

**4**

**PROMs**

![Texas Instruments logo]
**TEXAS**
**INSTRUMENTS**

### series 3 programming sequence

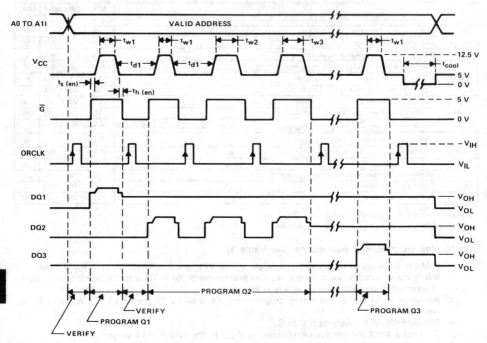

Illustrated above is the following sequence:

1) It is desired to program the selected address with 0111 (Q0-Q3). Only outputs DQ1, DQ2, and DQ3 need programming.
2) Q1 is verified to be at a high logic level and then the programming sequence is executed. The output is then verified to be at a low logic level.
3) DQ2 is an example of an output requiring three attempts to be programmed successfully.
4) DQ3 is programmed to a low logic level.

**FIGURE 1. SERIES 3 PROGRAMMING SEQUENCE**

**TEXAS INSTRUMENTS**

- Advanced Schottky IMPACT™ PROM Family
- High-Speed Access Times
- Low-Power, Open-Collector, and 3-State Options Available
- Titanium-Tungsten (Ti-W) Fuse Links for Reliable Low-Voltage Programming
- P-N-P Inputs for Reduced Loading on System Buffers/Drivers
- Applications Include:
  Microprogramming/Firmware Loaders
  Code Converters/Character Generators
  Translators/Emulators
  Address Mapping/Look-Up Tables
- Package Options Include 16-Pin DIP, and 20-Pin Chip-Carrier

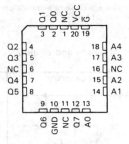

TBP38L030, TBP38S030, TBP38SA030 . . . J OR N PACKAGE
(TOP VIEW)

TBP38L03X, TBP38S03X, TBP38SA03X . . . FK OR FN PACKAGE
(TOP VIEW)

NC — No internal connection

## description

These Series-3 IMPACT™ TTL programmable read-only memories (PROMs) feature high-speed access times and dependable titanium-tungsten fuse link program elements. They are organized as 32 words by 8 bits each, providing a total of 256 bits. The TBP38S03' has three-state outputs. The TBP38SA03' is the open-collector version and allows the device to be connected directly to data buses utilizing passive pull-up resistors. The low-power TBP38L03' is available for applications that require power conservation while maintaining bipolar speeds.

These PROMs are offered with a choice of address access times (dash numbers). These dash numbers are found in the switching characteristics table, and are included in the part numbers.

Data is programmed at any bit location with the standard Series 3 programming algorithm. The program elements store a low logic level before any programming, and are permanently set to a high logic level after programming. After execution of the programming procedure, the output for that bit location cannot be reversed. The Series 3 programming procedure should be referred to for further details. Additional circuitry has been designed into these devices to improve testability and ensure high programmability.

An MJ or MFK suffix designates full-temperature circuits that are characterized for operation over the full military temperature range of −55°C to 125°C. An N or FN suffix designates commercial temperature circuits that are characterized for operation from 0°C to 70°C.

IMPACT is a trademark of Texas Instruments

TEXAS
INSTRUMENTS

4

PROMs

## TBP38S030, TBP38L030, TBP38SA030
## TBP38S03X, TBP38L03X, TBP38SA03X
## 256-BIT (32 WORDS BY 8 BITS) PROGRAMMABLE READ-ONLY MEMORIES

### logic symbols[†]

TBP38S030, TBP38L030

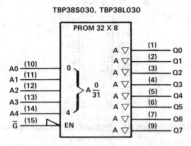

TBP38SA030

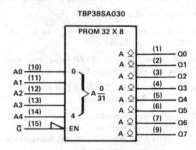

[†]These symbols are in accordance with ANSI/IEEE Std 91-1984
and IEC Publication 617-12.
Pin numbers shown are for J and N packages.

### schematics of inputs and outputs

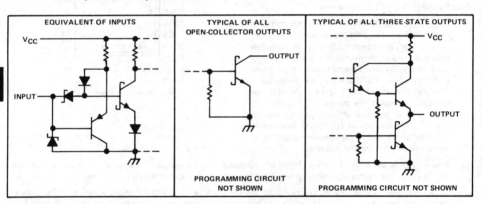

### absolute maximum ratings over operating free-air temperature range (unless otherwise noted)

Supply voltage (see Note 1) . . . . . . . . . . . . . . . . . . . . . . . . . . . . . . . . . . . . . . . . . . . 7 V
Input voltage . . . . . . . . . . . . . . . . . . . . . . . . . . . . . . . . . . . . . . . . . . . . . . . . . . . . . 5.5 V
Off-state output voltage . . . . . . . . . . . . . . . . . . . . . . . . . . . . . . . . . . . . . . . . . . . . . . 5.5 V
Operating free-air temperature range: Military-temperature-range circuits . . . . . . . −55°C to 125°C
                                  Commercial-temperature-range circuits . . . . . . . 0°C to 70°C
Storage temperature range . . . . . . . . . . . . . . . . . . . . . . . . . . . . . . . . . . . . . −65°C to 150°C

NOTE 1: Voltage values are with respect to network ground terminal. The supply voltage rating does not apply during programming.

TEXAS
INSTRUMENTS

## recommended operating conditions

| | PARAMETER | MILITARY | | | COMMERCIAL | | | UNIT |
|---|---|---|---|---|---|---|---|---|
| | | MIN | NOM | MAX | MIN | NOM | MAX | |
| $V_{CC}$ | Supply voltage | 4.5 | 5 | 5.5 | 4.5 | 5 | 5.5 | V |
| $V_{IH}$ | High-level input voltage | 2 | | | 2 | | | V |
| $V_{IL}$ | Low-level input voltage | | | 0.8 | | | 0.8 | V |
| $I_{OH}$ | High-level output current | | | $-2$ | | | $-3.2$ | mA |
| $I_{OL}$ | Low-level output current | | | 16 | | | 24 | mA |
| $T_A$ | Operating free-air temperature range | $-55$ | | 125 | 0 | | 70 | °C |

## electrical characteristics over recommended operating free-air temperature range (unless otherwise noted)

| PARAMETER | TEST CONDITIONS[†] | | MILITARY | | | COMMERCIAL | | | UNIT |
|---|---|---|---|---|---|---|---|---|---|
| | | | MIN | TYP[‡] | MAX | MIN | TYP[‡] | MAX | |
| $V_{IK}$ | $V_{CC}$ = MIN, | $I_I = -18$ mA | | | $-1.2$ | | | $-1.2$ | V |
| $V_{OH}$ | $V_{CC}$ = MIN, | $I_{OH}$ = MAX | 2.4 | 3.1 | | 2.4 | 3.1 | | V |
| $V_{OL}$ | $V_{CC}$ = MIN, | $I_{OL}$ = MAX | | | 0.5 | | | 0.5 | V |
| $I_{OZH}$ | $V_{CC}$ = MAX, | $V_O$ = 2.4 V | | | 50 | | | 50 | $\mu$A |
| $I_{OZL}$ | $V_{CC}$ = MAX, | $V_O$ = 0.5 V | | | $-50$ | | | $-50$ | $\mu$A |
| $I_I$ | $V_{CC}$ = MAX, | $V_I$ = 5.5 V | | | 0.1 | | | 0.1 | mA |
| $I_{IH}$ | $V_{CC}$ = MAX, | $V_I$ = 2.7 V | | | 20 | | | 20 | $\mu$A |
| $I_{IL}$ | $V_{CC}$ = MAX, | $V_I$ = 0.5 V | | | $-0.25$ | | | $-0.25$ | mA |
| $I_O$ [§] | $V_{CC}$ = MAX, | $V_O$ = 2.25 V | $-30$ | | $-112$ | $-30$ | | $-112$ | mA |
| $I_{CC}$ | $V_{CC}$ = MAX | | | 80 | 125 | | 80 | 125 | mA |

[†]For conditions shown as MIN or MAX, use appropriate value specified under recommended operating conditions.
[‡]All typical values are at $V_{CC}$ = 5 V, $T_A$ = 25°C.
[§]The output conditions have been chosen to produce a current that closely approximates one half of the true short-circuit output current, $I_{OS}$.

## switching characteristics over recommended ranges of $T_A$ and $V_{CC}$ (unless otherwise noted)

| TYPE | | TEST CONDITIONS | $t_{a(A)}$ ACCESS TIME FROM ADDRESS | | | $t_{en}$ ENABLE TIME | | | $t_{dis}$ DISABLE TIME | | | UNIT |
|---|---|---|---|---|---|---|---|---|---|---|---|---|
| | | | MIN | TYP[‡] | MAX | MIN | TYP[‡] | MAX | MIN | TYP[‡] | MAX | |
| TBP38S030-20 | Military | | | 10 | 20 | | 5 | 12 | | 5 | 12 | ns |
| TBP38S03X-20 | | | | | | | | | | | | |
| TBP38S030-30 | Military | $C_L$ = 50 pF, | | 10 | 30 | | 5 | 15 | | 3 | 10 | ns |
| TBP38S03X-30 | | R1 = 300 Ω, | | | | | | | | | | |
| TBP38S030-15 | Commercial | R2 = 600 Ω, | | 10 | 15 | | 5 | 10 | | 5 | 10 | ns |
| TBP38S03X-15 | | See Note 2 | | | | | | | | | | |
| TBP38S030-25 | Commercial | | | 10 | 25 | | 5 | 12 | | 3 | 8 | ns |
| TBP38S03X-25 | | | | | | | | | | | | |

[‡]All typical values are at $V_{CC}$ = 5 V, $T_A$ = 25°C.
NOTE 2: Load circuits and voltage waveforms are shown in Section 1.

**4**

**PROMs**

Texas
Instruments

**TBP38L030, TBP38L03X**
**256-BIT (32 WORDS BY 8 BITS)**
**LOW-POWER PROGRAMMABLE READ-ONLY MEMORY WITH 3-STATE OUTPUTS**

**PRODUCT**
**PREVIEW**

## recommended operating conditions

| PARAMETER | | MILITARY | | | COMMERCIAL | | | UNIT |
|---|---|---|---|---|---|---|---|---|
| | | MIN | NOM | MAX | MIN | NOM | MAX | |
| $V_{CC}$ | Supply voltage | 4.5 | 5 | 5.5 | 4.5 | 5 | 5.5 | V |
| $V_{IH}$ | High-level input voltage | 2 | | | 2 | | | V |
| $V_{IL}$ | Low-level input voltage | | | 0.8 | | | 0.8 | V |
| $I_{OH}$ | High-level output current | | | −1.6 | | | −1.6 | mA |
| $I_{OL}$ | Low-level output current | | | 16 | | | 16 | mA |
| $T_A$ | Operating free-air temperature range | −55 | | 125 | 0 | | 70 | °C |

## electrical characteristics over recommended operating free-air temperature range (unless otherwise noted)

| PARAMETER | TEST CONDITIONS[†] | | MILITARY | | | COMMERCIAL | | | UNIT |
|---|---|---|---|---|---|---|---|---|---|
| | | | MIN | TYP[‡] | MAX | MIN | TYP[‡] | MAX | |
| $V_{IK}$ | $V_{CC}$ = MIN, | $I_I$ = −18 mA | | | −1.2 | | | −1.2 | V |
| $V_{OH}$ | $V_{CC}$ = MIN, | $I_{OH}$ = −1.6 mA | 2.4 | 3.1 | | 2.4 | 3.1 | | V |
| $V_{OL}$ | $V_{CC}$ = MIN, | $I_{OL}$ = 16 mA | | | 0.5 | | | 0.5 | V |
| $I_{OZH}$ | $V_{CC}$ = MAX, | $V_O$ = 2.4 V | | | 50 | | | 50 | $\mu$A |
| $I_{OZL}$ | $V_{CC}$ = MAX, | $V_O$ = 0.5 V | | | −50 | | | −50 | $\mu$A |
| $I_I$ | $V_{CC}$ = MAX, | $V_I$ = 5.5 V | | | 0.1 | | | 0.1 | mA |
| $I_{IH}$ | $V_{CC}$ = MAX, | $V_I$ = 2.7 V | | | 20 | | | 20 | $\mu$A |
| $I_{IL}$ | $V_{CC}$ = MAX, | $V_I$ = 0.5 V | | | −0.25 | | | −0.25 | mA |
| $I_O$ [§] | $V_{CC}$ = MAX, | $V_O$ = 2.25 V | −30 | | −112 | −30 | | −112 | mA |
| $I_{CC}$ | $V_{CC}$ = MAX | | | 45 | | | 45 | | mA |

[†]For conditions shown as MIN or MAX, use appropriate value specified under recommended operating conditions.
[‡]All typical values are at $V_{CC}$ = 5 V, $T_A$ = 25°C.
[§]The output conditions have been chosen to produce a current that closely approximates one half of the true short-circuit output current, $I_{OS}$.

## switching characteristics over recommended ranges of $T_A$ and $V_{CC}$ (unless otherwise noted)

| TYPE | | TEST CONDITIONS | $t_{a(A)}$ ACCESS TIME FROM ADDRESS | | | $t_{en}$ ENABLE TIME | | | $t_{dis}$ DISABLE TIME | | | UNIT |
|---|---|---|---|---|---|---|---|---|---|---|---|---|
| | | | MIN | TYP[‡] | MAX | MIN | TYP[‡] | MAX | MIN | TYP[‡] | MAX | |
| TBP38L030- _ _ | Military | $C_L$ = 50 pF, | | 20 | | | 15 | | | 12 | | ns |
| TBP38L03X- _ _ | | R1 = 300 Ω, | | | | | | | | | | |
| TBP38L030- _ _ | Commercial | R2 = 600 Ω, | | 20 | | | 15 | | | 12 | | ns |
| TBP38L03X- _ _ | | See Note 2 | | | | | | | | | | |

[‡]All typical values are at $V_{CC}$ = 5 V, $T_A$ = 25°C.
NOTE 2: Load circuits and voltage waveforms are shown in Section 1.

**4**

**PROMS**

4-84

**TEXAS**
**INSTRUMENTS**

recommended operating conditions

| PARAMETER | | MILITARY | | | COMMERCIAL | | | UNIT |
|---|---|---|---|---|---|---|---|---|
| | | MIN | NOM | MAX | MIN | NOM | MAX | |
| $V_{CC}$ | Supply voltage | 4.5 | 5 | 5.5 | 4.5 | 5 | 5.5 | V |
| $V_{IH}$ | High-level input voltage | 2 | | | 2 | | | V |
| $V_{IL}$ | Low-level input voltage | | | 0.8 | | | 0.8 | V |
| $V_{OH}$ | High-level output voltage | | | 5.5 | | | 5.5 | V |
| $I_{OL}$ | Low-level output current | | | 16 | | | 24 | mA |
| $T_A$ | Operating free-air temperature range | -55 | | 125 | 0 | | 70 | °C |

electrical characteristics over recommended operating free-air temperature range (unless otherwise noted)

| PARAMETER | TEST CONDITIONS[†] | | MILITARY | | | COMMERCIAL | | | UNIT |
|---|---|---|---|---|---|---|---|---|---|
| | | | MIN | TYP[‡] | MAX | MIN | TYP[‡] | MAX | |
| $V_{IK}$ | $V_{CC}$ = MIN, | $I_I$ = -18 mA | | | -1.2 | | | -1.2 | V |
| $I_{OH}$ | $V_{CC}$ = MIN | $V_{OH}$ = 2.4 V | | | 0.05 | | | 0.05 | mA |
| | | $V_{OH}$ = 5.5 V | | | 0.1 | | | 0.1 | |
| $V_{OL}$ | $V_{CC}$ = MIN, | $I_{OL}$ = MAX | | | 0.5 | | | 0.5 | V |
| $I_I$ | $V_{CC}$ = MAX, | $V_I$ = 5.5 V | | | 0.1 | | | 0.1 | mA |
| $I_{IH}$ | $V_{CC}$ = MAX, | $V_I$ = 2.7 V | | | 20 | | | 20 | $\mu$A |
| $I_{IL}$ | $V_{CC}$ = MAX, | $V_I$ = 0.5 V | | | -0.25 | | | -0.25 | mA |
| $I_{CC}$ | $V_{CC}$ = MAX | | | 80 | 125 | | 80 | 125 | mA |

[†]For conditions shown as MIN or MAX, use appropriate value specified under recommended operating conditions.
[‡]All typical values are at $V_{CC}$ = 5 V, $T_A$ = 25°C.

switching characteristics over recommended ranges of $T_A$ and $V_{CC}$ (unless otherwise noted)

| TYPE | | TEST CONDITIONS | $t_{a(A)}$ ACCESS TIME FROM ADDRESS | | | $t_{en}$ ENABLE TIME | | | $t_{dis}$ DISABLE TIME | | | UNIT |
|---|---|---|---|---|---|---|---|---|---|---|---|---|
| | | | MIN | TYP[‡] | MAX | MIN | TYP[‡] | MAX | MIN | TYP[‡] | MAX | |
| TBP38SA030-30 | Military | $C_L$ = 50 pF, R1 = 300 Ω, R2 = 600 Ω, See Note 2 | | 15 | 30 | | 10 | 20 | | 9 | 18 | ns |
| TBP38SA03X-30 | | | | | | | | | | | | |
| TBP38SA030-25 | Commercial | | | 15 | 25 | | 10 | 15 | | 9 | 14 | ns |
| TBP38SA03X-25 | | | | | | | | | | | | |

[‡]All typical values are at $V_{CC}$ = 5 V, $T_A$ = 25°C.
NOTE 2: Load circuits and voltage waveforms are shown in Section 1.

**4**

**PROMs**

TEXAS
INSTRUMENTS

## TBP38S030, TBP38L030, TBP38SA030
## TBP38S03X, TBP38L03X, TBP38SA03X
## 256-BIT (32 WORDS BY 8 BITS) PROGRAMMABLE READ-ONLY MEMORIES

### recommended operating conditions for programming (see Figure 1)

| | | | MIN | NOM | MAX | UNIT |
|---|---|---|---|---|---|---|
| Supply voltage during verification | | $V_{CC}$ | 4.5 | 5 | 5.5 | V |
| Input voltage | | $V_{IH}$ | 3 | 4 | 5 | V |
| | | $V_{IL}$ | 0 | 0.2 | 0.5 | |
| Enable voltage during verification | | $\overline{G}$ | 0 | 0.2 | 0.4 | V |
| Enable inactive voltage during programming | | $\overline{G}$ | 4.5 | 5 | 5.5 | V |
| $V_{CC}$ program pulse amplitude | | $V_{CC(pr)}$ | 12 | 12.5 | 13 | V |
| $V_{CC}$ program pulse duration | 1st attempt | $t_{w1}$ | 10 | 11 | 12 | |
| | 2nd attempt | $t_{w2}$ | 20 | 22 | 25 | $\mu$s |
| | 3rd attempt | $t_{w3}$ | 20 | 22 | 25 | |
| Enable set-up time[†] before $V_{CC(pr)}$ | | $t_{su(en)}$ | 0.1 | 0.5 | 1 | $\mu$s |
| Enable hold time[‡] after $V_{CC(pr)}$ | | $t_{h(en)}$ | 0.1 | 0.5 | 1 | $\mu$s |
| Rise time of $V_{CC(pr)}$[§] | | $t_r(V_{CC})$ | 0.3 | 0.4 | 0.5 | $\mu$s |
| Fall time of $V_{CC(pr)}$[¶] | | $t_f(V_{CC})$ | 0.05 | 0.1 | 0.2 | $\mu$s |
| Delay time between successive $V_{CC(pr)}$ pulses | | $t_{d1}$ | 10 | 20 | 30 | $\mu$s |
| Hold time between successive $V_{CC(pr)}$ pulses | | $t_{d2}$ | 10 | 20 | 30 | $\mu$s |
| Cooling time between words | | $t_{cool}$ | 100 | 150 | 200 | $\mu$s |
| Free-air temperature | | $T_A$ | 20 | 25 | 30 | °C |

[†]Measured from 1.5 V on enable pin to 5.5 V on $V_{CC(pr)}$
[‡]Measured from 5.5 V on $V_{CC(pr)}$ to 1.5 V on enable pin
[§]Measured from 5 V to 12 V
[¶]Measured from 12 V to 5 V

### step-by-step programming instructions (see Figure 1)

1.  Address the word to be programmed, apply 5 volts to $V_{CC}$ and a low-logic-level voltage to the enable $\overline{G}$ input.

2.  Verify the selected bit location that requires programming. Note: The only bit positions that require programming áre outputs needing a high logic level.

3.  For bit locations that do not require programming, go to step 2 for the next bit, or to step 1 for next word.

4.  Deselect PROM by applying 5 volts to $\overline{G}$.

5.  Connect a 4-mA current source (clamped to $V_{CC}$) to the output that is to be programmed.

6.  Increase $V_{CC}$ to $V_{CC(pr)}$ for a pulse duration equal to $t_{wX}$ (where X is determined by the number of programming attempts, i.e., 1,2,3). Minimum current capability for the $V_{CC}$ power supply should be 400 mA.

7.  Verify that the output has been programmed to a high logic level. If the output has been programmed correctly, go to the next bit. If not, repeat step 2 through step 7 and increment X (where X is equal to 1 on the first programming attempt). If the output has not been programmed by the third attempt, stop programming and go to a new device.

8.  Verify programming of every word after all words have been programmed using $V_{CC}$ values of 4.5 volts and 5.5 volts.

TEXAS
INSTRUMENTS

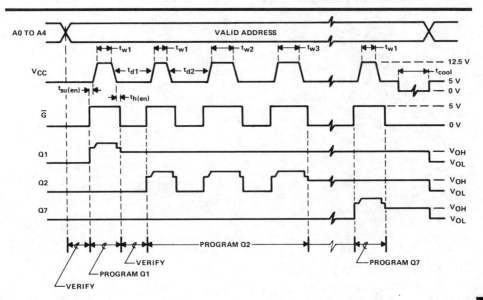

Illustrated above is the following sequence:

1) It is desired to program the selected address with 01100001 (Q0-Q7). Only outputs Q1, Q2, and Q7 need programming.
2) Q1 is verified to be at a low logic level and then the programming sequence is executed. The output is then verified to be at a high logic level.
3) Q2 is an example of an output requiring three atttempts to be programmed successfully.
4) Q7 is programmed to a high logic level.

### FIGURE 1. SERIES 3 PROGRAMMING SEQUENCE

4

PROMs

TEXAS
INSTRUMENTS

- **Fastest Schottky PROM Family**

- **High-Speed Access Times**

- **Low-Power, 3-State, and Open-Collector Options Available**

- **Titanium-Tungsten (Ti-W) Fuse Links for Reliable Low-Voltage Programming**

- **Applications Include:**
  **Microprogramming/Firmware Loaders**
  **Code Converters/Character Generators**
  **Translators/Emulators**
  **Address Mapping/Look-Up Tables**

- **Package Options Include 300-Mil or 600-Mil 24-Pin DIP, and 28-Pin Chip-Carrier Packages**

TBP38L85, TBP38S85, TBP38SA85 . . . NT OR JT PACKAGE
TBP38L86, TBP38S86, TBP38SA86 . . . NW OR JW PACKAGE
(TOP VIEW)

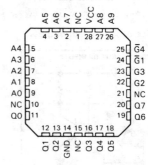

TBP38L8X, TBP38S8X, TBP38SA8X . . . FN OR FK PACKAGE
(TOP VIEW)

NC − No internal connection

## description

These Series-3 monolithic TTL programmable read-only memories (PROMs) feature high-speed access times and dependable titanium-tungsten fuse link program elements. They are organized as 1024 words by 8 bits each, providing a total of 8,192 bits. The '38S8 has three-state outputs. The '38SA8 is the open-collector version and allows the device to be connected directly to data buses utilizing passive pull-up resistors. The low-power '38L8 is available for applications that require power conservation while maintaining bipolar speeds. It also has three-state outputs.

Data is programmed at any bit location with the standard Series 3 programming algorithm. The program elements store a logic level low before any programming, and are permanently set to a logic level high after programming. After execution of the programming procedure, the output for that bit location cannot be reversed. The Series 3 programming procedure should be referred to for further details. Additional circuitry has been designed into these devices to improve testability and insure high programmability.

Copyright © 1984, Texas Instruments Incorporated

**TEXAS INSTRUMENTS**

4

PROMs

## TBP38S8, TBP38L8, TBP38SA8
## 8,192-BIT (1024 WORDS BY 8 BITS)
## PROGRAMMABLE READ-ONLY MEMORIES

### logic symbols

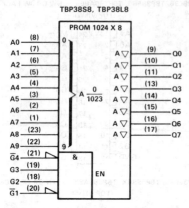

TBP38S8, TBP38L8

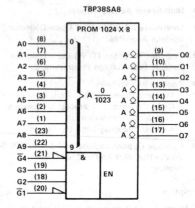

TBP38SA8

Pin numbers shown are for JT, JW, NT, or NW packages.

### schematics of inputs and outputs

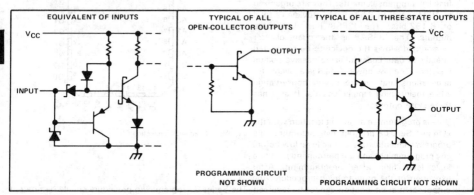

### absolute maximum ratings over operating free-air temperature range (unless otherwise noted)

Supply voltage (see Note 1) . . . . . . . . . . . . . . . . . . . . . . . . . . . . . . . . . . . . . . . . . . . . . 7 V
Input voltage . . . . . . . . . . . . . . . . . . . . . . . . . . . . . . . . . . . . . . . . . . . . . . . . . . . . . . . . . . 5.5 V
Off-state output voltage . . . . . . . . . . . . . . . . . . . . . . . . . . . . . . . . . . . . . . . . . . . . . . . . . 5.5 V
Operating free-air temperature range: Military-temperature-range circuits . . . . . . . −55°C to 125°C
　　　　　　　　　　　　　　　　　 Commercial-temperature-range circuits . . . . . . . . 0°C to 70°C
Storage temperature range . . . . . . . . . . . . . . . . . . . . . . . . . . . . . . . . . . . . . . . . . . −65°C to 150°C

NOTE 1: Voltage values are with respect to network ground terminal. The supply voltage rating does not apply during programming.

TEXAS
INSTRUMENTS

## TBP38L165, TBP38L166, TBP38L16X
## 16,384-BIT (2048 WORDS BY 8 BITS) LOW-POWER
## PROGRAMMABLE READ-ONLY MEMORY WITH 3-STATE OUTPUTS

D2909, JANUARY 1985—REVISED JULY 1985

- Advanced Schottky IMPACT™ PROM Family

- High-Speed Access Times

- Low-Power, 3-State Outputs

- Functional Equivalent to Signetics N82S191A or N82S191B

- Titanium-Tungsten (Ti-W) Fuse Links for Reliable Low-Voltage Programming

- Applications Include:
  Microprogramming/Firmware Loaders
  Code Converters/Character Generators
  Translators/Emulators
  Address Mapping/Look-Up Tables

- Package Options Include 300-Mil or 600-Mil 24-Pin DIP, and 28-Pin Chip-Carrier Packages

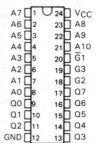

TBP38L165 . . . JT OR NT PACKAGE
TBP38L166 . . . JW OR NW PACKAGE
(TOP VIEW)

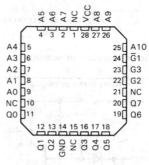

TBP38L16X . . . FK OR FN PACKAGE
(TOP VIEW)

NC—No internal connection

## description

These Series-3 IMPACT™ TTL programmable read-only memories (PROMs) feature high-speed access times and dependable titanium-tungsten fuse link program elements. They are organized as 2048 words by 8 bits each, providing a total of 16,384 bits.

The TBP38L16′ is available for applications that require power conservation while maintaining bipolar speeds. It also has three-state outputs.

These PROMs are offered with a choice of address access times (dash numbers). These dash numbers are found in the switching characteristics table, and are included in the part numbers.

Data is programmed at any bit location with the standard Series 3 programming algorithm. The program elements store a low logic level before any programming, and are permanently set to a high logic level after programming. After execution of the programming procedure, the output for that bit location cannot be reversed. The Series 3 programming procedure should be referred to for further details. Additional circuitry has been designed into these devices to improve testability and insure high programmability.

An MFK, MJT, or MJW suffix designates full temperature circuits that are characterized for operation over the full military temperature range of −55 °C to 125 °C. An FN, NT, or NW suffix designates commercial-temperature circuits that are characterized for operation from 0 °C to 70 °C.

IMPACT is a trademark of Texas Instruments Incorporated

TEXAS INSTRUMENTS

**PROMs** 4

## TBP38L165, TBP38L166, TBP38L16X
## 16,384-BIT (2048 WORDS BY 8 BITS) LOW-POWER
## PROGRAMMABLE READ-ONLY MEMORY WITH 3-STATE OUTPUTS

### logic symbol†

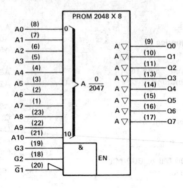

Pin numbers shown are for JT, JW, NT, or NW packages.

†This symbol is in accordance with ANSI/IEEE Std 91-1984 and
IEC Publication 617-12.

### schematics of inputs and outputs

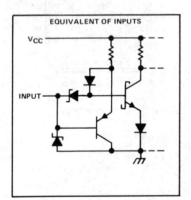

EQUIVALENT OF INPUTS

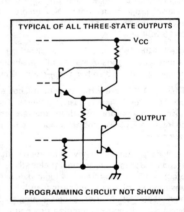

TYPICAL OF ALL THREE-STATE OUTPUTS

PROGRAMMING CIRCUIT NOT SHOWN

### absolute maximum ratings over operating free-air temperature range (unless otherwise noted)

Supply voltage (see Note 1) ............................................................. 7 V
Input voltage ........................................................................... 5.5 V
Off-state output voltage ................................................................ 5.5 V
Operating free-air temperature range: Military-temperature-range circuits ........ −55°C to 125°C
　　　　　　　　　　　　　　　　　　　 Commercial-temperature-range circuits ........ 0°C to 70°C
Storage temperature range ..................................................... −65°C to 150°C

NOTE 1: Voltage values are with respect to network ground terminal. The supply voltage rating does not apply during programming.

TEXAS
INSTRUMENTS

### recommended operating conditions

| PARAMETER | | COMMERCIAL | | | UNIT |
|---|---|---|---|---|---|
| | | MIN | NOM | MAX | |
| $V_{CC}$ | Supply voltage | 4.5 | 5 | 5.5 | V |
| $V_{IH}$ | High-level input voltage | 2 | | | V |
| $V_{IL}$ | Low-level input voltage | | | 0.8 | V |
| $I_{OH}$ | High-level output current | | | −3.2 | mA |
| $I_{OL}$ | Low-level output current | | | 24 | mA |
| $T_A$ | Operating free-air temperature range | 0 | | 70 | °C |

### electrical characteristics over recommended operating free-air temperature range (unless otherwise noted)

| PARAMETER | TEST CONDITIONS[†] | | COMMERCIAL | | | UNIT |
|---|---|---|---|---|---|---|
| | | | MIN | TYP[‡] | MAX | |
| $V_{IK}$ | $V_{CC}$ = MIN, | $I_I$ = −18 mA | | | −1.2 | V |
| $V_{OH}$ | $V_{CC}$ = MIN, | $I_{OH}$ = −3.2 mA | 2.4 | 3.1 | | V |
| $V_{OL}$ | $V_{CC}$ = MIN, | $I_{OL}$ = 24 mA | | | 0.5 | V |
| $I_{OZH}$ | $V_{CC}$ = MAX, | $V_O$ = 2.4 V | | | 50 | μA |
| $I_{OZL}$ | $V_{CC}$ = MAX, | $V_O$ = 0.5 V | | | −50 | μA |
| $I_I$ | $V_{CC}$ = MAX, | $V_I$ = 5.5 V | | | 0.1 | mA |
| $I_{IH}$ | $V_{CC}$ = MAX, | $V_I$ = 2.7 V | | | 20 | μA |
| $I_{IL}$ | $V_{CC}$ = MAX, | $V_I$ = 0.5 V | | | −0.25 | mA |
| $I_O$ [§] | $V_{CC}$ = MAX, | $V_O$ = 2.25 V | −30 | | −112 | mA |
| $I_{CC}$ | $V_{CC}$ = MAX | | | 65 | 100 | mA |

[†]For conditions shown as MIN or MAX, use appropriate value specified under recommended operating conditions.
[§]The output conditions have been chosen to produce a current that closely approximates one half of the true short-circuit output current, $I_{OS}$.

### switching characteristics over recommended ranges of $T_A$ and $V_{CC}$ (unless otherwise noted)

| TYPE | | TEST CONDITIONS | $t_{a(A)}$ ACCESS TIME FROM ADDRESS | | | $t_{en}$ ENABLE TIME | | | $t_{dis}$ DISABLE TIME | | | UNIT |
|---|---|---|---|---|---|---|---|---|---|---|---|---|
| | | | MIN | TYP[†] | MAX | MIN | TYP[†] | MAX | MIN | TYP[†] | MAX | |
| TBP38L165-35 | | | | | | | | | | | | |
| TBP38L166-35 | Commercial | $C_L$ = 50 pF, | | 25 | 35 | | 10 | 20 | | 5 | 15 | ns |
| TBP38L16X-35 | | R1 = 300 Ω, | | | | | | | | | | |
| TBP38L165-45 | | R2 = 600 Ω, | | | | | | | | | | |
| TBP38L166-45 | Commercial | See Note 2 | | 25 | 45 | | 10 | 25 | | 5 | 20 | ns |
| TBP38L16X-45 | | | | | | | | | | | | |

[‡]All typical values are at $V_{CC}$ = 5 V, $T_A$ = 25 °C.
NOTE 2: Load circuits and voltage waveforms are shown in Section 1.

**4**

**PROMs**

**TEXAS INSTRUMENTS**

TBP38L165, TBP38L166, TBP38L16X
16,384-BIT (2048 WORDS BY 8-BITS) LOW-POWER
PROGRAMMABLE READ-ONLY MEMORY WITH 3-STATE OUTPUTS

PRODUCT
PREVIEW

## recommended operating conditions

| PARAMETER | | MILITARY | | | UNIT |
|---|---|---|---|---|---|
| | | MIN | NOM | MAX | |
| $V_{CC}$ | Supply voltage | 4.5 | 5 | 5.5 | V |
| $V_{IH}$ | High-level input voltage | 2 | | | V |
| $V_{IL}$ | Low-level input voltage | | | 0.8 | V |
| $I_{OH}$ | High-level output current | | | -1.6 | mA |
| $I_{OL}$ | Low-level output current | | | 16 | mA |
| $T_A$ | Operating free-air temperature range | -55 | | 125 | °C |

## electrical characteristics over recommended operating free-air temperature range (unless otherwise noted)

| PARAMETER | TEST CONDITIONS[†] | | MILITARY | | | UNIT |
|---|---|---|---|---|---|---|
| | | | MIN | TYP[‡] | MAX | |
| $V_{IK}$ | $V_{CC}$ = MIN, | $I_I$ = -18 mA | | | -1.2 | V |
| $V_{OH}$ | $V_{CC}$ = MIN, | $I_{OH}$ = -1.6 mA | 2.4 | 3.1 | | V |
| $V_{OL}$ | $V_{CC}$ = MIN, | $I_{OL}$ = 16 mA | | | 0.5 | V |
| $I_{OZH}$ | $V_{CC}$ = MAX, | $V_O$ = 2.4 V | | | 50 | µA |
| $I_{OZL}$ | $V_{CC}$ = MAX, | $V_O$ = 0.5 V | | | -50 | µA |
| $I_I$ | $V_{CC}$ = MAX, | $V_I$ = 5.5 V | | | 0.1 | mA |
| $I_{IH}$ | $V_{CC}$ = MAX, | $V_I$ = 2.7 V | | | 20 | µA |
| $I_{IL}$ | $V_{CC}$ = MAX, | $V_I$ = 0.5 V | | | -0.25 | mA |
| $I_O$ [§] | $V_{CC}$ = MAX, | $V_O$ = 2.25 V | -30 | | -112 | mA |
| $I_{CC}$ | $V_{CC}$ = MAX | | | 65 | 100 | mA |

[†]For conditions shown as MIN or MAX, use appropriate value specified under recommended operating conditions.
[§]The output conditions have been chosen to produce a current that closely approximates one half of the true short-circuit output current, $I_{OS}$.

## switching characteristics over recommended ranges of $T_A$ and $V_{CC}$ (unless otherwise noted)

| TYPE | | TEST CONDITIONS | $t_{a(A)}$ ACCESS TIME FROM ADDRESS | | | $t_{en}$ ENABLE TIME | | | $t_{dis}$ DISABLE TIME | | | UNIT |
|---|---|---|---|---|---|---|---|---|---|---|---|---|
| | | | MIN | TYP[†] | MAX | MIN | TYP[†] | MAX | MIN | TYP[†] | MAX | |
| TBP38L165-__ TBP38L166-__ TBP38L16X-__ | Military | $C_L$ = 50 pF, See Note 2 | | 25 | | | 10 | | | 5 | | ns |
| TBP38L165-__ TBP38L166-__ TBP38L16X-__ | Military | | | 25 | | | 10 | | | 5 | | ns |

[‡]All typical values are at $V_{CC}$ = 5 V, $T_A$ = 25°C.
NOTE 2: Load circuits and voltage waveforms are shown in Section 1.

Additional information on these products can be obtained from the factory as it becomes available.

TEXAS
INSTRUMENTS

4 PROMs

**recommended operating conditions for programming (see Figure 1)**

| | | | MIN | NOM | MAX | UNIT |
|---|---|---|---|---|---|---|
| Supply voltage during verification | | $V_{CC}$ | 4.5 | 5 | 5.5 | V |
| Input voltage | | $V_{IH}$ | 3 | 4 | 5 | V |
| | | $V_{IL}$ | 0 | 0.2 | 0.5 | |
| Enable voltage during verification | | G1 | 0 | 0.2 | 0.4 | V |
| | | G2, G3 | 3 | 4 | 5 | |
| Enable inactive voltage during programming | | G1 | 4.5 | 5 | 5.5 | V |
| | | G2, G3 | 0 | 0.2 | 0.4 | |
| $V_{CC}$ program pulse amplitude | | $V_{CC(pr)}$ | 12 | 12.5 | 13 | V |
| $V_{CC}$ program pulse duration | 1st attempt | $t_{w1}$ | 10 | 11 | 12 | |
| | 2nd attempt | $t_{w2}$ | 20 | 22 | 25 | $\mu s$ |
| | 3rd attempt | $t_{w3}$ | 20 | 22 | 25 | |
| Enable set-up time[†] before $V_{CC(pr)}$ | | $t_{su(en)}$ | 0.1 | 0.5 | 1 | $\mu s$ |
| Enable hold time[‡] after $V_{CC(pr)}$ | | $t_{h(en)}$ | 0.1 | 0.5 | 1 | $\mu s$ |
| Rise time of $V_{CC(pr)}$[§] | | $t_{r(VCC)}$ | 0.3 | 0.4 | 0.5 | $\mu s$ |
| Fall time of $V_{CC(pr)}$[¶] | | $t_{f(VCC)}$ | 0.05 | 0.1 | 0.2 | $\mu s$ |
| Delay time between successive $V_{CC(pr)}$ pulses | | $t_{d1}$ | 10 | 20 | 30 | $\mu s$ |
| Delay time between successive $V_{CC(pr)}$ pulses | | $t_{d2}$ | 10 | 20 | 30 | $\mu s$ |
| Cooling time between words | | $t_{cool}$ | 100 | 150 | 200 | $\mu s$ |
| Free-air temperature | | $T_A$ | 20 | 25 | 30 | °C |

[†]Measured from 1.5 V on enable pin to 5.5 V on $V_{CC(pr)}$
[‡]Measured from 5.5 V on $V_{CC(pr)}$ to 1.5 V on enable pin
[§]Measured from 5 V to 12 V
[¶]Measured from 12 V to 5 V

### step-by-step programming instructions (see Figure 1)

1. Address the word to be programmed, apply 5 volts to $V_{CC}$ and active levels to all enable inputs ($\overline{G}1$, G2, G3).

2. Verify the selected bit location that requires programming. Note: The only bit positions that require programming are outputs needing a high logic level.

3. For bit locations that do not require programming, go to step 2 for the next bit, or to step 1 for next word.

4. Deselect PROM by applying 5 volts to $\overline{G}1$, or 0 volts to G2 or G3.

5. Connect a 4-mA current source (clamped to $V_{CC}$) to the output that is to be programmed.

6. Increase $V_{CC}$ to $V_{CC(pr)}$ for a pulse duration equal to $t_{wX}$ (where X is determined by the number of programming attempts, i.e., 1,2,3). Minimum current capability for the $V_{CC}$ power supply should be 400 mA.

7. Verify that the output has been programmed to a high logic level. If the output has been programmed correctly, go to the next bit. If not, repeat step 2 through step 7 and increment X (where X is equal to 1 on the first programming attempt). If the output has not been programmed by the third attempt, stop programming and go to a new device.

8. Verify programming of every word after all words have been programmed using $V_{CC}$ values of 4.5 volts and 5.5 volts.

TEXAS
INSTRUMENTS

# TBP38L165, TBP38L166, TBP38L16X
## 16,384-BIT (2048 WORDS BY 8 BITS) LOW-POWER
## PROGRAMMABLE READ-ONLY MEMORY WITH 3-STATE OUTPUTS

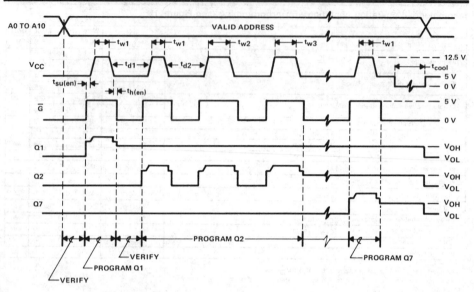

Illustrated above is the following sequence:

1) It is desired to program the selected address with 01100001 (Q0-Q7). Only outputs Q1, Q2 and Q7 need programming.
2) Q1 is verified to be at a low logic level and then the programming sequence is executed. The output is then verified to be at a high logic level.
3) Q2 is an example of an output requiring three attempts to be programmed successfully.
4) Q7 is programmed to a high logic level.

## FIGURE 1. SERIES 3 PROGRAMMING SEQUENCE

TEXAS
INSTRUMENTS

- Fastest Schottky PROM Family

- High-Speed Access Times

- Allows Storage of Output Data

- Titanium-Tungsten (Ti-W) Fuse Links for Reliable Low-Voltage Programming

- Choice of 16 Programmable Initialize Words

### description

The TBP38R16' is a series-3 monolithic TTL programmable read-only memory (PROM) featuring high-speed access times and dependable titanium-tungsten fuse link program elements. It is organized as 2048 words by 8 bits, providing 16,384 bits.

The output register receives data from the PROM array on the rising edge of CLK. The TBP38R16' also contains 16 programmable initialization words. Initialization words allow the outputs to quickly be set to a predetermined value for start up or time-out sequencing. These words are read by taking the INIT pin low and pulsing the clock (CLK) input line. When INIT is low, inputs A0-A3 select the desired initialization word independently of A4-A10. By programming all sixteen words the same, initialization can be achieved by taking INIT low independently of A0-A3.

These PROMs are offered with a choice of setup times (dash numbers). These dash numbers are found in the recommended operating conditions table, and are included in the part numbers.

Data is programmed at any bit location with the standard series 3 programming algorithm. The program elements store a high logic level before any programming, and are permanently set to a low logic level after programming. After execution of the programming procedure, the output for that bit location cannot be reversed.

The series 3 programming procedure should be referred to for further details. Additional circuits have been designed into these devices to improve testability and ensure high programmability.

An MFK or MJT suffix designates circuits that are characterized for operation over the full military temperature range of −55 °C to 125 °C. An FN or NT suffix designates commercial-temperature circuits that are characterized for operation from 0 °C to 70 °C.

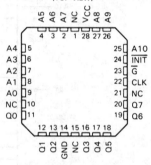

TBP38R165 . . . NT OR JT PACKAGE
(TOP VIEW)

TBP38R167 . . . FN OR FK PACKAGE
(TOP VIEW)

NC – No internal connection

**PROMs**

**4**

TEXAS
INSTRUMENTS

Copyright © 1985, Texas Instruments Incorporated

# TBP38R165, TBP38R167
## 16,384-BIT (2048 WORDS BY 8 BITS) REGISTERED PROGRAMMABLE READ-ONLY MEMORIES

## logic symbol†

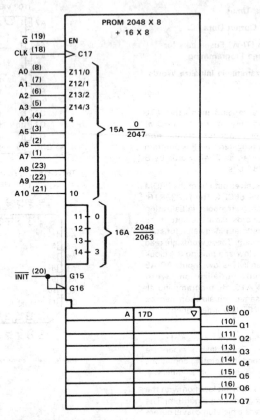

† This symbol is in accordance with ANSI/IEEE Std 91-1984 and
IEC Publication 617-12.

### TERMINAL FUNCTIONS

| TERMINALS | FUNCTION |
|---|---|
| A0-A10 | Address inputs for data from PROM array |
| $\overline{\text{INIT}}$ | If $\overline{\text{INIT}}$ is high, any one of 2048 8-bit words can be addressed. If $\overline{\text{INIT}}$ is low, any one of 16 8-bit initialization words can be addressed using A0 thru A3. |
| $\overline{\text{G}}$ | If $\overline{\text{G}}$ is high, Q0 thru Q7 are in the high-impedance state. If $\overline{\text{G}}$ is low, Q0 thru Q7 are enabled. |
| CLK | Low-to-high transition loads output register from PROM array. |
| Q0-Q7 | Register outputs under control of $\overline{\text{G}}$ |

TEXAS
INSTRUMENTS

**logic diagram (positive logic)**

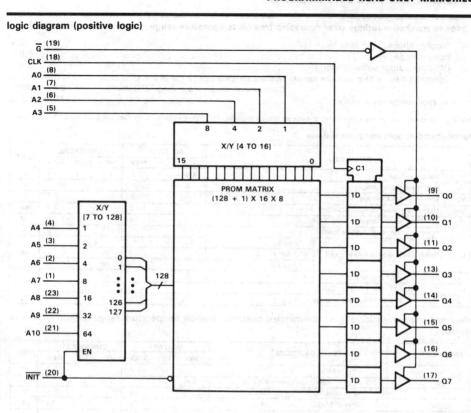

**PROMs**

4

TEXAS
INSTRUMENTS

## absolute maximum ratings over operating free-air temperature range (unless otherwise noted)

Supply voltage, $V_{CC}$ (see Note 1) . . . . . . . . . . . . . . . . . . . . . . . . . . . . . . . . . . . . . . . . . . . . . . . . 7 V
Input voltage, $V_I$ . . . . . . . . . . . . . . . . . . . . . . . . . . . . . . . . . . . . . . . . . . . . . . . . . . . . . . . . . . . . . 5.5 V
Off-state output voltage, $V_{O(off)}$ . . . . . . . . . . . . . . . . . . . . . . . . . . . . . . . . . . . . . . . . . . . . . . . . 5.5 V
Operating free-air temperature range: Military-temperature-range circuits . . . . . . . −55 °C to 125 °C
Commercial-temperature range circuits . . . . . . . . 0 °C to 70 °C
Storage temperature range . . . . . . . . . . . . . . . . . . . . . . . . . . . . . . . . . . . . . . . . . . . . . . −65 °C to 150 °C

NOTE 1: All voltage values are with respect to network ground terminal. The supply voltage rating does not apply during programming.

## recommended operating conditions

| PARAMETER | | MILITARY | | | COMMERCIAL | | | UNIT |
|---|---|---|---|---|---|---|---|---|
| | | MIN | NOM | MAX | MIN | NOM | MAX | |
| $V_{CC}$ | Supply voltage | 4.5 | 5 | 5.5 | 4.5 | 5 | 5.5 | V |
| $V_{IH}$ | High-level input voltage | 2 | | | 2 | | | V |
| $V_{IL}$ | Low-level input voltage | | | 0.8 | | | 0.8 | V |
| $I_{OH}$ | High-level output current (standard output) | | | −2 | | | −3.2 | mA |
| $I_{OL}$ | Low-level output current | | | 16 | | | 24 | mA |
| $t_w$ | Pulse duration, CLK (high or low) | 15 | | | 12 | | | ns |
| $t_{su}$ | Setup time, address before CLK↑ | -25 suffix | 25 | | | | | | ns |
| | | -20 suffix | | | | 20 | | | |
| | | -18 suffix | | | | 18 | | | |
| $t_{su}$ | Setup time INIT before CLK↑ | 40 | | | 35 | | | ns |
| $t_h$ | Hold time INIT, address after CLK↑ | 0 | | | 0 | | | ns |
| $T_A$ | Operating free-air temperature range | −55 | | 125 | 0 | | 70 | °C |

## electrical characteristics over recommended operating free-air temperature range (unless otherwise noted)

| PARAMETER | TEST CONDITIONS† | MILITARY | | | COMMERCIAL | | | UNIT |
|---|---|---|---|---|---|---|---|---|
| | | MIN | TYP‡ | MAX | MIN | TYP‡ | MAX | |
| $V_{IK}$ | $V_{CC}$ = MIN, $I_I$ = −18 mA | | | −1.2 | | | 1.2 | V |
| $V_{OH}$ | $V_{CC}$ = MIN, $I_{OH}$ = MAX | 2.4 | 3.1 | | 2.4 | 3.1 | | V |
| $V_{OL}$ | $V_{CC}$ = MIN, $I_{OL}$ = MAX | | | 0.5 | | | 0.5 | V |
| $I_{OZH}$ | $V_{CC}$ = MAX, $V_O$ = 2.4 V | | | 50 | | | 50 | μA |
| $I_{OZL}$ | $V_{CC}$ = MAX, $V_O$ = 0.5 V | | | −50 | | | −50 | μA |
| $I_I$ | $V_{CC}$ = MAX, $V_I$ = 5.5 V | | | 0.1 | | | 0.1 | mA |
| $I_{IH}$ | $V_{CC}$ = MAX, $V_I$ = 2.7 V | | | 20 | | | 20 | μA |
| $I_{IL}$ | $V_{CC}$ = MAX, $V_I$ = 0.5 V | | | −0.25 | | | −0.25 | mA |
| $I_O$§ | $V_{CC}$ = MAX, $V_O$ = 2.25 V | −30 | | −112 | −30 | | −112 | mA |
| $I_{CC}$ | $V_{CC}$ = MAX | | 125 | 185 | | 125 | 185 | mA |

## switching characteristics over recommended ranges of $T_A$ and $V_{CC}$ (unless otherwise noted)

| PARAMETER | FROM (INPUT) | TO (OUTPUT) | TEST CONDITIONS (See Note 2) | MILITARY -25 SUFFIX | | | COMMERCIAL | | | | | | UNIT |
|---|---|---|---|---|---|---|---|---|---|---|---|---|---|
| | | | | | | | -18 SUFFIX | | | -20 SUFFIX | | | |
| | | | | MIN | TYP‡ | MAX | MIN | TYP‡ | MAX | MIN | TYP‡ | MAX | |
| $t_{pd}$ | CLK | Any Q | $R_1$ = 300 Ω, | | 8 | 18 | | 8 | 12 | | 8 | 15 | ns |
| $t_{en}$ | $\overline{G}$ | Any Q | $R_2$ = 600 Ω, | | 8 | 15 | | 8 | 12 | | 8 | 12 | ns |
| $t_{dis}$ | $\overline{G}$ | Any Q | $C_L$ = 50 pF | | 6 | 12 | | 6 | 10 | | 6 | 10 | ns |

† For conditions shown as MIN or MAX, use appropriate value specified under recommended operating conditions.
‡ All typical values are at $V_{CC}$ = 5 V, $T_A$ = 15 °C.
§ The output conditions have been chosen to produce a current that closely approximates one half of the true short-circuit output current, $I_{OS}$.
NOTE 2: Load circuits and voltage waveforms are shown in Section 1.

**TEXAS**
**INSTRUMENTS**

## recommended operating conditions for programming (see Figure 1)

| | | | MIN | NOM | MAX | UNIT |
|---|---|---|---|---|---|---|
| Supply voltage during verification | | $V_{CC}$ | 4.25 | 5 | 5.75 | V |
| Input voltage | | $V_{IH}$ | 3 | 4 | 5 | V |
| | | $V_{IL}$ | 0 | 0.2 | 0.5 | |
| Enable voltage during verification | | $\overline{G1}$ | 0 | 0.2 | 0.4 | V |
| | | G2, G3 | 3 | 4 | 5 | |
| Enable inactive voltage during programming | | $\overline{G1}$ | 4.25 | 5 | 5.75 | V |
| | | G2, G3 | 0 | 0.2 | 0.4 | |
| $V_{CC}$ program pulse amplitude | | $V_{CC(pr)}$ | 11 | 11.5 | 12 | V |
| $V_{CC}$ program pulse duration | 1st attempt | $t_{w1}$ | 10 | 11 | 12 | |
| | 2nd attempt | $t_{w2}$ | 20 | 22 | 25 | V |
| | 3rd attempt | $t_{w3}$ | 20 | 22 | 25 | |
| Enable setup time† before $V_{CC(pr)}$ | | $t_{su(en)}$ | 0.1 | 0.5 | 1 | $\mu$S |
| Enable hold time‡ after $V_{CC(pr)}$ | | $t_{h(en)}$ | 0.1 | 0.5 | 1 | $\mu$S |
| Rise time of $V_{CC(pr)}$§ | | $t_{r(VCC)}$ | 0.3 | 0.4 | 0.5 | $\mu$S |
| Fall time of $V_{CC(pr)}$¶ | | $t_{f(VCC)}$ | 0.05 | 0.1 | 0.2 | $\mu$S |
| Delay time between successive $V_{CC(pr)}$ pulses | | $t_{d1}$ | 10 | 20 | 30 | $\mu$S |
| Delay time between successive $V_{CC(pr)}$ pulses | | $t_{d2}$ | 10 | 20 | 30 | $\mu$S |
| Cooling time between words | | $t_{cool}$ | 100 | 150 | 200 | $\mu$S |
| Free-air temperature | | $T_A$ | 20 | 25 | 30 | °C |

† Measured from 1.5 V on enable pin to 5.5 V on $V_{CC(pr)}$
‡ Measured from 5.5 V on $V_{CC(pr)}$ to 1.5 V on enable pin
§ Measured from 5 V to 12 V
¶ Measured from 12 V to 5 V

## step-by-step programming instructions (see Figure 1)

1. Address the word to be programmed, apply 5 volts to $V_{CC}$, apply $V_{IL(pr)}$ to the enable input $\overline{G}$ and $V_{IH}$ to the $\overline{INIT}$ input. During initialization word programming apply $V_{IL}$ to the $\overline{INIT}$ input.
2. Verify the selected bit location that requires programming. Note: The only bit positions that require programming are outputs to be a low logic level.
3. For bit locations that do not require programming, go to step 2 for the next bit, or to step 1 for the next word.
4. Deselect PRCM by applying $V_{IH(pr)}$ to $\overline{G}$.
5. Connect a 4-mA current source (clamped to $V_{CC}$) to the output that is to be programmed.
6. Increase $V_{CC}$ to $V_{CC(pr)}$ for a pulse duration equal to $t_{wX}$ (where X is determined by the number of programming attempts, i.e., 1, 2, 3). Minimum current capability for the $V_{CC}$ power supply should be 500 mA.
7. Verify that the output has been programmed to a low logic level. If the output has been programmed correctly, go to the next bit. If not, repeat step 2 through step 7 and increment X (where X is equal to 1 on the first programming attempt). If the output has not been programmed by the third attempt, stop programming and go to a new device. Note: Data must be clocked into the output register to verify programming.
8. Verify programming of every word after all words have been programmed using $V_{CC}$ values of 4.5 volts and 5.5 volts.

4

PROMs

**TEXAS
INSTRUMENTS**

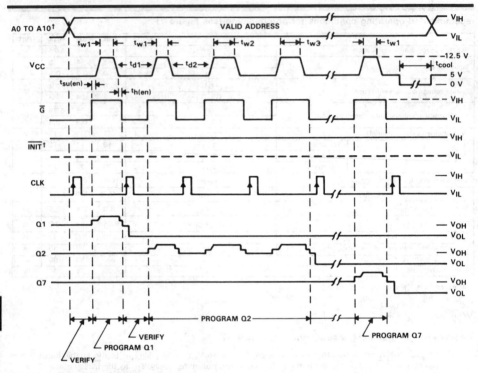

Illustrated above is the following sequence:

1. It is desired to program the selected address with 01100001 (Q0-Q7). Only outputs Q1, Q2, and Q7 need programming.
2. Q1 is verified to be at a high logic level and then the programming sequence is executed. The output is then verified to be at a low logic level.
3. Q2 is an example of an output requiring three attempts to be programmed successfully.
4. Q7 is programmed to a low logic level.

†During initialization word programming $V_{IL}$ is applied to the $\overline{INIT}$ input and address lines A0-A3 are used independently of A4-A10.

### FIGURE 1. SERIES 3 PROGRAMMING SEQUENCE

TEXAS
INSTRUMENTS

# TBP38S165, TBP38S166, TBP38S16X
## 16,384-BIT (2048 WORDS BY 8 BITS) STANDARD
## PROGRAMMABLE READ-ONLY MEMORY WITH 3-STATE OUTPUTS

D2909, JANUARY 1985–REVISED JULY 1985

- Advanced Schottky IMPACT™ PROM Family

- High-Speed Access Times

- 3-State Outputs

- Titanium-Tungsten (Ti-W) Fuse Links for Reliable Low-Voltage Programming

- Applications Include:
  Microprogramming/Firmware Loaders
  Code Converters/Character Generators
  Translators/Emulators
  Address Mapping/Look-Up Tables

- Package Options Include 300-Mil or 600-Mil 24-Pin DIP, and 28-Pin Chip-Carrier Packages

TBP38S165 . . . NT OR JT PACKAGE
TBP38L166 . . . NW OR JW PACKAGE
(TOP VIEW)

TBP38S16X . . . FN OR FK PACKAGE
(TOP VIEW)

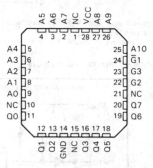

NC – No internal connection

## description

These Series-3 IMPACT™ TTL programmable read-only memories (PROMs) feature high-speed access times and dependable titanium-tungsten fuse link program elements. They are organized as 2048 words by 8 bits each, providing a total of 16,384 bits. The TBP38S16' has three-state outputs.

These PROMs are offered with a choice of Address Access times (dash numbers). These dash numbers are found in the switching characteristics table and are included in the part numbers.

Data is programmed at any bit location with the standard Series 3 programming algorithm. The program elements store a low logic level before any programming, and are permanently set to a high logic level after programming. After execution of the programming procedure, the output for that bit location cannot be reversed. The Series 3 programming procedure should be referred to for further details. Additional circuitry has been designed into these devices to improve testability and insure high programmability.

An MFK, MJT, or MJW suffix designates full-temperature circuits that are characterized for operation over the full military temperature range of −55 °C to 125 °C. An FN, NT, or NW suffix designates commercial-temperature circuits that are characterized for operation from 0 °C to 70 °C.

IMPACT is a trademark of Texas Instruments.

PROMs

4

## TBP38S165, TBP38S166, TBP38S16X
## 16,384-BIT (2048 WORDS BY 8 BITS) STANDARD
## PROGRAMMABLE READ-ONLY MEMORY WITH 3-STATE OUTPUTS

### logic symbol†

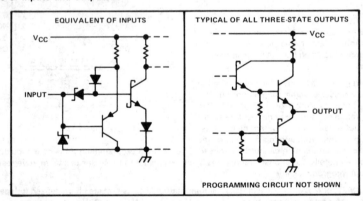

TBP38S165, TBP38S166
TBP38S16X

†This symbol is in accordance with ANSI/IEEE Std 91-1984 and
IEC Publication 617-12.
Pin numbers shown are for JT, JW, NT, or NW packages.

### schematics of inputs and outputs

| EQUIVALENT OF INPUTS | TYPICAL OF ALL THREE-STATE OUTPUTS |
|---|---|
| INPUT | OUTPUT |
| | PROGRAMMING CIRCUIT NOT SHOWN |

### absolute maximum ratings over operating free-air temperature range (unless otherwise noted)

Supply voltage (see Note 1) . . . . . . . . . . . . . . . . . . . . . . . . . . . . . . . . . . . . . . . . . 7 V
Input voltage . . . . . . . . . . . . . . . . . . . . . . . . . . . . . . . . . . . . . . . . . . . . . . . . . . 5.5 V
Off-state output voltage . . . . . . . . . . . . . . . . . . . . . . . . . . . . . . . . . . . . . . . . . . . 5.5 V
Operating free-air temperature range: Military-temperature-range circuits . . . . . . . −55°C to 125°C
Commercial-temperature-range circuits . . . . . . . 0°C to 70°C
Storage temperature range . . . . . . . . . . . . . . . . . . . . . . . . . . . . . . . . . . . . −65°C to 150°C

NOTE 1: Voltage values are with respect to network ground terminal. The supply voltage rating does not apply during programming.

TEXAS
INSTRUMENTS

4

PROMS

### recommended operating conditions for programming (see Figure 1)

| | | | MIN | NOM | MAX | UNIT |
|---|---|---|---|---|---|---|
| Supply voltage during verification | | $V_{CC}$ | 4.5 | 5 | 5.5 | V |
| Input voltage | | $V_{IH}$ | 3 | 4 | 5 | V |
| | | $V_{IL}$ | 0 | 0.2 | 0.5 | |
| Enable voltage during verification | | $\overline{G}1$ | 0 | 0.2 | 0.4 | V |
| | | G2, G3 | 3 | 4 | 5 | |
| Enable inactive voltage during programming | | $\overline{G}1$ | 4.5 | 5 | 5.5 | V |
| | | G2, G3 | 0 | 0.2 | 0.4 | |
| $V_{CC}$ program pulse amplitude | | $V_{CC(pr)}$ | 12 | 12.5 | 13 | V |
| $V_{CC}$ program pulse duration | 1st attempt | $t_{w1}$ | 10 | 11 | 12 | |
| | 2nd attempt | $t_{w2}$ | 20 | 22 | 25 | $\mu$s |
| | 3rd attempt | $t_{w3}$ | 20 | 22 | 25 | |
| Enable set-up time[†] before $V_{CC(pr)}$ | | $t_{su(en)}$ | 0.1 | 0.5 | 1 | $\mu$s |
| Enable hold time[‡] after $V_{CC(pr)}$ | | $t_{h(en)}$ | 0.1 | 0.5 | 1 | $\mu$s |
| Rise time of $V_{CC(pr)}$[§] | | $t_r(V_{CC})$ | 0.3 | 0.4 | 0.5 | $\mu$s |
| Fall time of $V_{CC(pr)}$[¶] | | $t_f(V_{CC})$ | 0.05 | 0.1 | 0.2 | $\mu$s |
| Delay time between successive $V_{CC(pr)}$ pulses | | $t_{d1}$ | 10 | 20 | 30 | $\mu$s |
| Delay time between successive $V_{CC(pr)}$ pulses | | $t_{d2}$ | 10 | 20 | 30 | $\mu$s |
| Cooling time between words | | $t_{cool}$ | 100 | 150 | 200 | $\mu$s |
| Free-air temperature | | $T_A$ | 20 | 25 | 30 | °C |

[†]Measured from 1.5 V on enable pin to 5.5 V on $V_{CC(pr)}$
[‡]Measured from 5.5 V on $V_{CC(pr)}$ to 1.5 V on enable pin
[§]Measured from 5 V to 12 V
[¶]Measured from 12 V to 5 V

### step-by-step programming instructions (see Figure 1)

1.  Address the word to be programmed, apply 5 volts to $V_{CC}$ and active levels to all enable inputs ($\overline{G}1$, G2, G3).

2.  Verify the selected bit location that requires programming. Note: The only bit positions that require programming are outputs needing a high logic level.

3.  For bit locations that do not require programming, go to step 2 for the next bit, or to step 1 for next word.

4.  Deselect PROM by applying 5 volts to $\overline{G}1$, or 0 volts to G2 or G3.

5.  Connect a 4-mA current source (clamped to $V_{CC}$) to the output that is to be programmed.

6.  Increase $V_{CC}$ to $V_{CC(pr)}$ for a pulse duration equal to $t_{wX}$ (where X is determined by the number of programming attempts, i.e., 1,2,3). Minimum current capability for the $V_{CC}$ power supply should be 400 mA.

7.  Verify that the output has been programmed to a high logic level. If the output has been programmed correctly, go to the next bit. If not, repeat step 2 through step 7 and increment X (where X is equal to 1 on the first programming attempt). If the output has not been programmed by the third attempt, stop programming and go to a new device.

8.  Verify programming of every word after all words have been programmed using $V_{CC}$ values of 4.5 volts and 5.5 volts.

4

PROMs

TEXAS
INSTRUMENTS

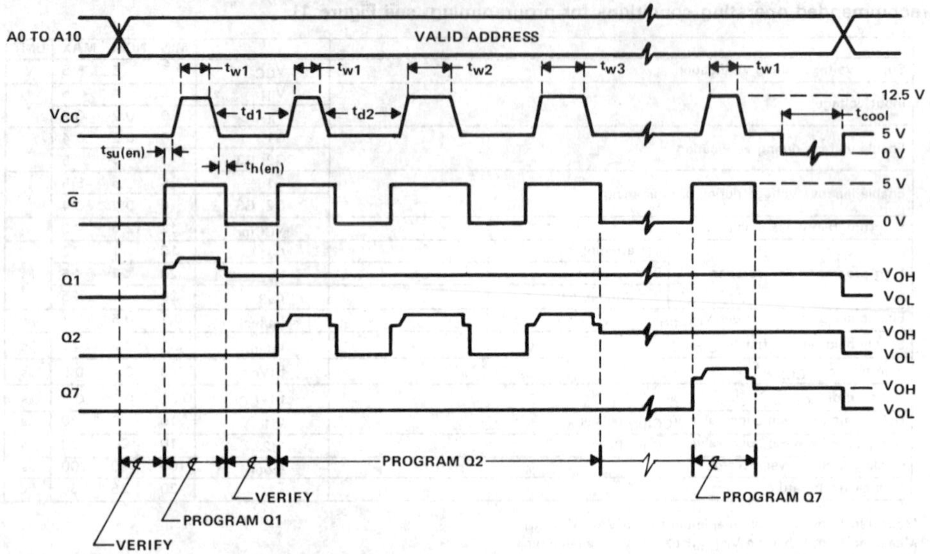

Illustrated above is the following sequence:

1) It is desired to program the selected address with 01100001 (Q0-Q7). Only outputs Q1, Q2 and Q7 need programming.
2) Q1 is verified to be at a low logic level and then the programming sequence is executed. The output is then verified to be at a high logic level.
3) Q2 is an example of an output requiring three attempts to be programmed successfully.
4) Q7 is programmed to a high logic level.

### FIGURE 1. SERIES 3 PROGRAMMING SEQUENCE

**4**

**PROMS**

TEXAS
INSTRUMENTS

## recommended operating conditions

| PARAMETER | | MILITARY | | | COMMERCIAL | | | UNIT |
|---|---|---|---|---|---|---|---|---|
| | | MIN | NOM | MAX | MIN | NOM | MAX | |
| $V_{CC}$ | Supply voltage | 4.5 | 5 | 5.5 | 4.5 | 5 | 5.5 | V |
| $V_{IH}$ | High-level input voltage | 2 | | | 2 | | | V |
| $V_{IL}$ | Low-level input voltage | | | 0.8 | | | 0.8 | V |
| $I_{OH}$ | High-level output current | | | −2 | | | −3.2 | mA |
| $I_{OL}$ | Low-level output current | | | 16 | | | 24 | mA |
| $T_A$ | Operating free-air temperature range | −55 | | 125 | 0 | | 70 | °C |

## electrical characteristics over recommended operating free-air temperature range (unless otherwise noted)

| PARAMETER | TEST CONDITIONS[†] | | MILITARY | | | COMMERCIAL | | | UNIT |
|---|---|---|---|---|---|---|---|---|---|
| | | | MIN | TYP[‡] | MAX | MIN | TYP[‡] | MAX | |
| $V_{IK}$ | $V_{CC}$ = MIN, | $I_I$ = −18 mA | | | −1.2 | | | −1.2 | V |
| $V_{OH}$ | $V_{CC}$ = MIN, | $I_{OH}$ = MAX | 2.4 | 3.1 | | 2.4 | 3.1 | | V |
| $V_{OL}$ | $V_{CC}$ = MIN, | $I_{OL}$ = MAX | | | 0.5 | | | 0.5 | V |
| $I_{OZH}$ | $V_{CC}$ = MAX, | $V_O$ = 2.4 V | | | 50 | | | 50 | μA |
| $I_{OZL}$ | $V_{CC}$ = MAX, | $V_O$ = 0.5 V | | | −50 | | | −50 | μA |
| $I_I$ | $V_{CC}$ = MAX, | $V_I$ = 5.5 V | | | 0.1 | | | 0.1 | mA |
| $I_{IH}$ | $V_{CC}$ = MAX, | $V_I$ = 2.7 V | | | 20 | | | 20 | μA |
| $I_{IL}$ | $V_{CC}$ = MAX, | $V_I$ = 0.5 V | | | −0.25 | | | −0.25 | mA |
| $I_O$ [§] | $V_{CC}$ = MAX, | $V_O$ = 2.25 V | −30 | | −112 | −30 | | −112 | mA |
| $I_{CC}$ | $V_{CC}$ = MAX | | | 120 | 175 | | 120 | 175 | mA |

[†]For conditions shown as MIN or MAX, use appropriate value specified under recommended operating conditions.
[§]The output conditions have been chosen to produce a current that closely approximates one half of the true short-circuit output current, $I_{OS}$.

## switching characteristics over recommended ranges of $T_A$ and $V_{CC}$ (unless otherwise noted)

| TYPE | | TEST CONDITIONS | $t_{a(A)}$ ACCESS TIME FROM ADDRESS | | | $t_{en}$ ENABLE TIME | | | $t_{dis}$ DISABLE TIME | | | UNIT |
|---|---|---|---|---|---|---|---|---|---|---|---|---|
| | | | MIN | TYP[‡] | MAX | MIN | TYP[‡] | MAX | MIN | TYP[‡] | MAX | |
| TBP38S165-30 | | | | | | | | | | | | |
| TBP38S166-30 | Military | | | 18 | 30 | | 8 | 20 | | 6 | 15 | ns |
| TBP38S16X-30 | | $C_L$ = 50 pF, | | | | | | | | | | |
| TBP38S165-35 | | R1 = 300 Ω, | | | | | | | | | | |
| TBP38S166-35 | Commercial | R2 = 600 Ω, | | 18 | 35 | | 8 | 15 | | 6 | 12 | ns |
| TBP38S16X-35 | | See Note 2 | | | | | | | | | | |
| TBP38S165-25 | | | | | | | | | | | | |
| TBP38S166-25 | Commercial | | | 18 | 25 | | 8 | 15 | | 6 | 12 | ns |
| TBP38S16X-25 | | | | | | | | | | | | |

[‡]All typical values are at $V_{CC}$ = 5 V, $T_A$ = 25°C.
NOTE 2:  Load circuits and voltage waveforms are shown in Section 1.

**4**

**PROMs**

## TBP38SA165, TBP38SA166, TBP38SA16X
## 16,384-BIT (2048 WORDS BY 8 BITS) STANDARD
## PROGRAMMABLE READ-ONLY MEMORY WITH OPEN-COLLECTOR OUTPUTS

JANUARY 1985 – REVISED NOVEMBER 1985

- Fastest Schottky PROM Family

- High-Speed Access Times

- Open-Collector Outputs

- Titanium-Tungsten (Ti-W) Fuse Links for Reliable Low-Voltage Programming

- Applications Include:
  Microprogramming/Firmware Loaders
  Code Converters/Character Generators
  Translators/Emulators
  Address Mapping/Look-Up Tables

- Package Options Include 300-Mil or 600-Mil 24-Pin DIP, and 28-Pin Chip-Carrier Packages

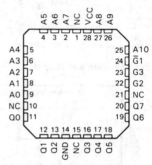

TBP38SA165 . . . JT OR NT PACKAGE
TBP38SA166 . . . JW OR NW PACKAGE
(TOP VIEW)

| | |
|---|---|
| A7 [1 | 24] $V_{CC}$ |
| A6 [2 | 23] A8 |
| A5 [3 | 22] A9 |
| A4 [4 | 21] A10 |
| A3 [5 | 20] $\overline{G1}$ |
| A2 [6 | 19] G3 |
| A1 [7 | 18] G2 |
| A0 [8 | 17] Q7 |
| Q0 [9 | 16] Q6 |
| Q1 [10 | 15] Q5 |
| Q2 [11 | 14] Q4 |
| GND [12 | 13] Q3 |

TBP38SA16X . . . FK OR FN PACKAGE
(TOP VIEW)

NC – No internal connection

## description

These Series-3 monolithic TTL programmable read-only memories (PROMs) feature high-speed access times and dependable titanium-tungsten fuse link program elements. They are organized as 2048 words by 8 bits each, providing a total of 16,384 bits. The TBP38SA16' has open-collector outputs and allows the device to be connected directly to data buses utilizing passive pull-up resistors.

These PROMs are offered with a choice of Address Access times (dash numbers). These dash numbers are found on the switching characteristics table, and are included in the part numbers.

Data is programmed at any bit location with the standard Series 3 programming algorithm. The program elements store a logic level low before any programming, and are permanently set to a logic level high after programming. After execution of the programming procedure, the output for that bit location cannot be reversed. The Series 3 programming procedure should be referred to for further details. Additional circuitry has been designed into these devices to improve testability and insure high programmability.

An MJT or MJW suffix designates full temperature circuits and are characterized for operation over the full military temperature range of −55 °C to 125 °C. An NT or NW suffix designates commercial-temperature circuits and are characterized for operation from 0 °C to 70 °C.

4

PROMs

TEXAS
INSTRUMENTS

## TBP38SA165, TBP38SA166, TBP38SA16X
## 16,384-BIT (2048 WORDS BY 8 BITS) STANDARD
## PROGRAMMABLE READ-ONLY MEMORY WITH OPEN-COLLECTOR OUTPUTS

### logic symbol†

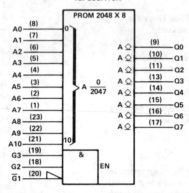

TBP38SA165, TBP38SA166
TBP38SA16X

PROM 2048 X 8

| | (8) | |
|A0| | 0 |
|A1| (7) | |
|A2| (6) | |
|A3| (5) | |
|A4| (4) | |
|A5| (3) | |
|A6| (2) | |
|A7| (1) | |
|A8| (23) | |
|A9| (22) | |
|A10| (21) | 10 |

A  0 / 2047

| | (9) | Q0 |
| A | (10) | Q1 |
| A | (11) | Q2 |
| A | (13) | Q3 |
| A | (14) | Q4 |
| A | (15) | Q5 |
| A | (16) | Q6 |
| A | (17) | Q7 |

|G3| (19) | & |
|G2| (18) | |
|G̅1| (20) | EN |

†This symbol is in accordance with ANSI/IEEE Std 91-1984 and
   IEC Publication 617-12.
Pin numbers shown are for JT, JW, NT, or NW packages.

### schematics of inputs and outputs

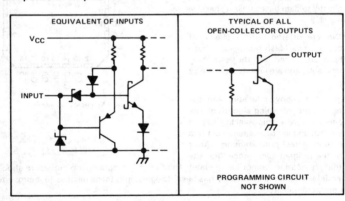

| EQUIVALENT OF INPUTS | TYPICAL OF ALL OPEN-COLLECTOR OUTPUTS |
|---|---|
| V_CC / INPUT | OUTPUT / PROGRAMMING CIRCUIT NOT SHOWN |

### absolute maximum ratings over operating free-air temperature range (unless otherwise noted)

Supply voltage (see Note 1) ............................................................. 7 V
Input voltage ........................................................................ 5.5 V
Off-state output voltage ............................................................. 5.5 V
Operating free-air temperature range: Military-temperature-range circuits ....... −55°C to 125°C
                                      Commercial-temperature-range circuits ........ 0°C to 70°C
Storage temperature range ...................................................... −65°C to 150°C

NOTE 1: Voltage values are with respect to network ground terminal. The supply voltage rating does not apply during programming.

TEXAS
INSTRUMENTS

## recommended operating conditions

| | PARAMETER | MILITARY | | | COMMERCIAL | | | UNIT |
|---|---|---|---|---|---|---|---|---|
| | | MIN | NOM | MAX | MIN | NOM | MAX | |
| $V_{CC}$ | Supply voltage | 4.5 | 5 | 5.5 | 4.5 | 5 | 5.5 | V |
| $V_{IH}$ | High-level input voltage | 2 | | | 2 | | | V |
| $V_{IL}$ | Low-level input voltage | | | 0.8 | | | 0.8 | V |
| $V_{OH}$ | High-level output voltage | | | 5.5 | | | 5.5 | V |
| $I_{OL}$ | Low-level output current | | | 16 | | | 24 | mA |
| $T_A$ | Operating free-air temperature range | −55 | | 125 | 0 | | 70 | °C |

## electrical characteristics over recommended operating free-air temperature range (unless otherwise noted)

| PARAMETER | TEST CONDITIONS[†] | | MILITARY | | | COMMERCIAL | | | UNIT |
|---|---|---|---|---|---|---|---|---|---|
| | | | MIN | TYP[‡] | MAX | MIN | TYP[‡] | MAX | |
| $V_{IK}$ | $V_{CC}$ = MIN, | $I_I$ = −18 mA | | | −1.2 | | | −1.2 | V |
| $I_{OH}$ | $V_{CC}$ = MIN, | $V_{OH}$ = 2.4 V | | | 0.05 | | | 0.05 | mA |
| | | $V_{OH}$ = 5.5 V | | | 0.1 | | | 0.1 | |
| $V_{OL}$ | $V_{CC}$ = MIN, | $I_{OL}$ = MAX | | | 0.5 | | | 0.5 | V |
| $I_I$ | $V_{CC}$ = MAX, | $V_I$ = 5.5 V | | | 0.1 | | | 0.1 | mA |
| $I_{IH}$ | $V_{CC}$ = MAX, | $V_I$ = 2.7 V | | | 20 | | | 20 | μA |
| $I_{IL}$ | $V_{CC}$ = MAX, | $V_I$ = 0.5 V | | | −0.25 | | | −0.25 | mA |
| $I_{CC}$ | $V_{CC}$ = MAX | | 120 | | 175 | 120 | | 175 | mA |

[†]For conditions shown as MIN or MAX, use appropriate value specified under recommended operating conditions.
[‡]All typical values are at $V_{CC}$ = 5 V, $T_A$ = 25°C.

## switching characteristics over recommended ranges of $T_A$ and $V_{CC}$ (unless otherwise noted)

| TYPE | | TEST CONDITIONS | $t_{a(A)}$ ACCESS TIME FROM ADDRESS | | | $t_{a(S)}$ ACCESS TIME FROM ENABLE | | | $t_{dis}$ DISABLE TIME | | | UNIT |
|---|---|---|---|---|---|---|---|---|---|---|---|---|
| | | | MIN | TYP[‡] | MAX | MIN | TYP[‡] | MAX | MIN | TYP[‡] | MAX | |
| TBP38SA165-40 | Military | $C_L$ = 50 pF R1 = 300 Ω, R2 = 600 Ω, See Note 2 | | 22 | 40 | | 7 | 20 | | 12 | 25 | ns |
| TBP38SA166-40 | | | | | | | | | | | | |
| TBP38SA16X-40 | | | | | | | | | | | | |
| TBP38SA165-35 | Commercial | | | 22 | 35 | | 7 | 15 | | 12 | 20 | ns |
| TBP38SA166-35 | | | | | | | | | | | | |
| TBP38SA16X-35 | | | | | | | | | | | | |

[‡]All typical values are at $V_{CC}$ = 5 V, $T_A$ = 25°C.
NOTE 2: Load circuits and voltage waveforms are shown in Section 1.

4

PROMs

TEXAS
INSTRUMENTS

### recommended operating conditions for programming (see Figure 1)

|  |  |  | MIN | NOM | MAX | UNIT |
|---|---|---|---|---|---|---|
| Supply voltage during verification |  | $V_{CC}$ | 4.5 | 5 | 5.5 | V |
| Input voltage |  | $V_{IH}$ | 3 | 4 | 5 | V |
|  |  | $V_{IL}$ | 0 | 0.2 | 0.5 | |
| Enable voltage during verification |  | $\overline{G}1$ | 0 | 0.2 | 0.4 | V |
|  |  | G2, G3 | 3 | 4 | 5 | |
| Enable inactive voltage during programming |  | $\overline{G}1$ | 4.5 | 5 | 5.5 | V |
|  |  | G2, G3 | 0 | 0.2 | 0.4 | |
| $V_{CC}$ program pulse amplitude |  | $V_{CC(pr)}$ | 12 | 12.5 | 13 | V |
| $V_{CC}$ program pulse duration | 1st attempt | $t_{w1}$ | 10 | 11 | 12 | |
|  | 2nd attempt | $t_{w2}$ | 20 | 22 | 25 | $\mu$s |
|  | 3rd attempt | $t_{w3}$ | 20 | 22 | 25 | |
| Enable set-up time† before $V_{CC(pr)}$ |  | $t_{su(en)}$ | 0.1 | 0.5 | 1 | $\mu$s |
| Enable hold time‡ after $V_{CC(pr)}$ |  | $t_{h(en)}$ | 0.1 | 0.5 | 1 | $\mu$s |
| Rise time of $V_{CC(pr)}$§ |  | $t_r(V_{CC})$ | 0.3 | 0.4 | 0.5 | $\mu$s |
| Fall time of $V_{CC(pr)}$¶ |  | $t_f(V_{CC})$ | 0.05 | 0.1 | 0.2 | $\mu$s |
| Delay time between successive $V_{CC(pr)}$ pulses |  | $t_{d1}$ | 10 | 20 | 30 | $\mu$s |
| Delay time between successive $V_{CC(pr)}$ pulses |  | $t_{d2}$ | 10 | 20 | 30 | $\mu$s |
| Cooling time between words |  | $t_{cool}$ | 100 | 150 | 200 | $\mu$s |
| Free-air temperature |  | $T_A$ | 20 | 25 | 30 | °C |

†Measured from 1.5 V on enable pin to 5.5 V on $V_{CC(pr)}$
‡Measured from 5.5 V on $V_{CC(pr)}$ to 1.5 V on enable pin
§Measured from 5 V to 12 V
¶Measured from 12 V to 5 V

### step-by-step programming instructions (see Figure 1)

1. Address the word to be programmed, apply 5 volts to $V_{CC}$ and active levels to all enable inputs ($\overline{G}1$, G2, G3).

2. Verify the selected bit location that requires programming. Note: The only bit positions that require programming are outputs needing a high logic level.

3. For bit locations that do not require programming, go to step 2 for the next bit, or to step 1 for next word.

4. Deselect PROM by applying 5 volts to $\overline{G}1$, or 0 volts to G2 or G3.

5. Connect a 4-mA current source (clamped to $V_{CC}$) to the output that is to be programmed.

6. Increase $V_{CC}$ to $V_{CC(pr)}$ for a pulse duration equal to $t_{wX}$ (where X is determined by the number of programming attempts, i.e., 1,2,3). Minimum current capability for the $V_{CC}$ power supply should be 400 mA.

7. Verify that the output has been programmed to a high logic level. If the output has been programmed correctly, go to the next bit. If not, repeat step 2 through step 7 and increment X (where X is equal to 1 on the first programming attempt). If the output has not been programmed by the third attempt, stop programming and go to a new device.

8. Verify programming of every word after all words have been programmed using $V_{CC}$ values of 4.5 volts and 5.5 volts.

TEXAS
INSTRUMENTS

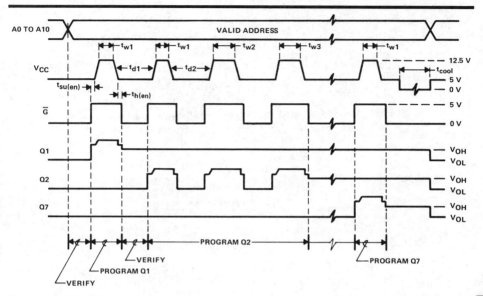

Illustrated above is the following sequence:

1) It is desired to program the selected address with 01100001 (Q0-Q7). Only outputs Q1, Q2 and Q7 need programming.
2) Q1 is verified to be at a low logic level and then the programming sequence is executed. The output is then verified to be at a high logic level.
3) Q2 is an example of an output requiring three attempts to be programmed successfully.
4) Q7 is programmed to a high logic level.

**FIGURE 1. SERIES 3 PROGRAMMING SEQUENCE**

PROMs

# TBP38S22, TBP38L22, TBP38SA22
# TBP38S2X, TBP38L2X, TBP38SA2X
## 2,048-BIT (256 WORDS BY 8 BITS) PROGRAMMABLE READ-ONLY MEMORIES

D2909, DECEMBER 1984—REVISED APRIL 1986

- Advanced Schottky IMPACT™ PROM Family

- High-Speed Access Times

- Low-Power, Open-Collector, and 3-State Options Available

- Titanium-Tungsten (Ti-W) Fuse Links for Reliable Low-Voltage Programming

- P-N-P Inputs for Reduced Loading on System Buffers/Drivers

- Applications Include:
  Microprogramming/Firmware Loaders
  Code Converters/Character Generators
  Translators/Emulators
  Address Mapping/Look-Up Tables

- Package Options Include 20-Pin DIP, and 20-Pin Chip-Carrier

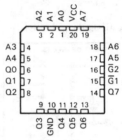

TBP38S22, TBP38L22, TBP38SA22 . . . J OR N PACKAGE
(TOP VIEW)

| | | |
|---|---|---|
| A0 | 1 | $V_{CC}$ 20 |
| A1 | 2 | A7 19 |
| A2 | 3 | A6 18 |
| A3 | 4 | A5 17 |
| A4 | 5 | $\overline{G2}$ 16 |
| Q0 | 6 | $\overline{G1}$ 15 |
| Q1 | 7 | Q7 14 |
| Q2 | 8 | Q6 13 |
| Q3 | 9 | Q5 12 |
| GND | 10 | Q4 11 |

TBP38S2X, TBP38L2X, TBP38SA2X . . . FK OR FN PACKAGE
(TOP VIEW)

NC—No internal connection

## description

These Series-3 IMPACT™ TTL programmable read-only memories (PROMs) feature high-speed access times and dependable titanium-tungsten fuse link program elements. They are organized as 256 words by 8 bits each, providing a total of 2,048 bits. The '38S22 has three-state outputs. The '38SA22 is the open-collector version and allows the device to be connected directly to data buses utilizing passive pull-up resistors. The low-power '38L22 is available for applications that require power conservation while maintaining bipolar speeds.

These PROMs are offered with a choice of address access times (dash numbers). These dash numbers are found in the switching characteristics table, and are included in the part numbers.

Data is programmed at any bit location with the standard Series 3 programming algorithm. The program elements store a low logic level before any programming, and are permanently set to a high logic level after programming. After execution of the programming procedure, the output for that bit location cannot be reversed. The Series 3 programming procedure should be referred to for further details. Additional circuitry has been designed into these devices to improve testability and ensure high programmability.

An MFK or MJ suffix designates full-temperature circuits that are characterized for operation over the full military temperature range of −55°C to 125°C. An FN or N suffix designates commercial-temperature circuits that are characterized for operation from 0°C to 70°C.

PROMs

4

---

IMPACT is a trademark of Texas Instruments.

**TEXAS INSTRUMENTS**

## logic symbols[†]

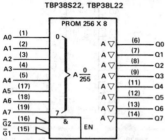

**TBP38S22, TBP38L22**

**TBP38SA22**

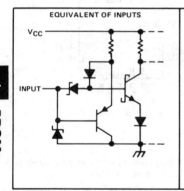 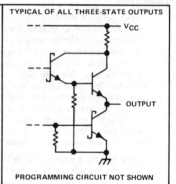

[†] These symbols are in accordance with ANSI/IEEE Std 91-1984 and IEC Publication 617-12.

## schematics of inputs and outputs

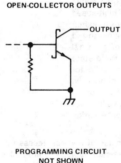

| EQUIVALENT OF INPUTS | TYPICAL OF ALL OPEN-COLLECTOR OUTPUTS | TYPICAL OF ALL THREE-STATE OUTPUTS |
|---|---|---|
| | PROGRAMMING CIRCUIT NOT SHOWN | PROGRAMMING CIRCUIT NOT SHOWN |

## absolute maximum ratings over operating free-air temperature range (unless otherwise noted)

Supply voltage (see Note 1) . . . . . . . . . . . . . . . . . . . . . . . . . . . . . . . . . . . . . . . . . . . . . . . . 7 V
Input voltage . . . . . . . . . . . . . . . . . . . . . . . . . . . . . . . . . . . . . . . . . . . . . . . . . . . . . . . . . . . 5.5 V
Off-state output voltage . . . . . . . . . . . . . . . . . . . . . . . . . . . . . . . . . . . . . . . . . . . . . . . . . . . 5.5 V
Operating free-air temperature range: Military-temperature-range circuits . . . . . . . −55°C to 125°C
　　　　　　　　　　　　　　　　　　 Commercial-temperature-range circuits . . . . . . . . 0°C to 70°C
Storage temperature range . . . . . . . . . . . . . . . . . . . . . . . . . . . . . . . . . . . . . . . . . −65°C to 150°C

NOTE 1: Voltage values are with respect to network ground terminal. The supply voltage rating does not apply during programming.

**TEXAS**
**INSTRUMENTS**

4
PROMs

## recommended operating conditions

| | PARAMETER | COMMERCIAL | | | UNIT |
|---|---|---|---|---|---|
| | | MIN | NOM | MAX | |
| $V_{CC}$ | Supply voltage | 4.5 | 5 | 5.5 | V |
| $V_{IH}$ | High-level input voltage | 2 | | | V |
| $V_{IL}$ | Low-level input voltage | | | 0.8 | V |
| $I_{OH}$ | High-level output current | | | −3.2 | mA |
| $I_{OL}$ | Low-level output current | | | 24 | mA |
| $T_A$ | Operating free-air temperature range | 0 | | 70 | °C |

## electrical characteristics over recommended operating free-air temperature range (unless otherwise noted)

| PARAMETER | TEST CONDITIONS† | | COMMERCIAL | | | UNIT |
|---|---|---|---|---|---|---|
| | | | MIN | TYP‡ | MAX | |
| $V_{IK}$ | $V_{CC}$ = MIN, | $I_I$ = −18 mA | | | −1.2 | V |
| $V_{OH}$ | $V_{CC}$ = MIN, | $I_{OH}$ = −3.2 mA | 2.4 | 3.1 | | V |
| $V_{OL}$ | $V_{CC}$ = MIN, | $I_{OL}$ = 24 mA | | | 0.5 | V |
| $I_{OZH}$ | $V_{CC}$ = MAX, | $V_O$ = 2.4 V | | | 50 | $\mu$A |
| $I_{OZL}$ | $V_{CC}$ = MAX, | $V_O$ = 0.5 V | | | −50 | $\mu$A |
| $I_I$ | $V_{CC}$ = MAX, | $V_I$ = 5.5 V | | | 0.1 | mA |
| $I_{IH}$ | $V_{CC}$ = MAX, | $V_I$ = 2.7 V | | | 20 | $\mu$A |
| $I_{IL}$ | $V_{CC}$ = MAX, | $V_I$ = 0.5 V | | | −0.25 | mA |
| $I_O$§ | $V_{CC}$ = MAX, | $V_O$ = 2.25 V | −30 | | −112 | mA |
| $I_{CC}$ | $V_{CC}$ = MAX | | | 80 | 125 | mA |

†For conditions shown as MIN or MAX, use appropriate value specified under recommended operating conditions.
‡All typical values are at $V_{CC}$ = 5 V, $T_A$ = 25°C.
§The output conditions have been chosen to produce a current that closely approximates one half of the true short-circuit output current, $I_{OS}$.

## switching characteristics over recommended ranges of $T_A$ and $V_{CC}$ (unless otherwise noted)

| TYPE | | TEST CONDITIONS | $t_{a(A)}$ ACCESS TIME FROM ADDRESS | | | $t_{en}$ ENABLE TIME | | | $t_{dis}$ DISABLE TIME | | | UNIT |
|---|---|---|---|---|---|---|---|---|---|---|---|---|
| | | | MIN | TYP‡ | MAX | MIN | TYP‡ | MAX | MIN | TYP‡ | MAX | |
| TBP38S22-18 | Commercial | $C_L$ = 50 pF, R1 = 300 Ω, R2 = 600 Ω, See Note 2 | | 14 | 18 | | 9 | 13 | | 5 | 10 | ns |
| TBP38S2X-18 | | | | | | | | | | | | |
| TBP38S22-25 | | | | 16 | 25 | | 9 | 15 | | 5 | 10 | ns |
| TBP38S2X-25 | | | | | | | | | | | | |

‡All typical values are at $V_{CC}$ = 5 V, $T_A$ = 25°C.
NOTE 2: Load circuits and voltage waveforms are shown in Section 1.

**TEXAS INSTRUMENTS**

4

PROMs

## TBP38S22, TBP38S2X
## 2,048-BIT (256 WORDS BY 8 BITS)
## STANDARD PROGRAMMABLE READ-ONLY MEMORY WITH 3-STATE OUTPUTS

### recommended operating conditions

| PARAMETER | | MILITARY | | | UNIT |
|---|---|---|---|---|---|
| | | MIN | NOM | MAX | |
| $V_{CC}$ | Supply voltage | 4.5 | 5 | 5.5 | V |
| $V_{IH}$ | High-level input voltage | 2 | | | V |
| $V_{IL}$ | Low-level input voltage | | | 0.8 | V |
| $I_{OH}$ | High-level output current | | | −2 | mA |
| $I_{OL}$ | Low-level output current | | | 16 | mA |
| $T_A$ | Operating free-air temperature range | −55 | | 125 | °C |

### electrical characteristics over recommended operating free-air temperature range (unless otherwise noted)

| PARAMETER | TEST CONDITIONS[†] | | MILITARY | | | UNIT |
|---|---|---|---|---|---|---|
| | | | MIN | TYP[‡] | MAX | |
| $V_{IK}$ | $V_{CC}$ = MIN, | $I_I$ = −18 mA | | | −1.2 | V |
| $V_{OH}$ | $V_{CC}$ = MIN, | $I_{OH}$ = −2 mA | 2.4 | 3.1 | | V |
| $V_{OL}$ | $V_{CC}$ = MIN, | $I_{OL}$ = 16 mA | | | 0.5 | V |
| $I_{OZH}$ | $V_{CC}$ = MAX, | $V_O$ = 2.4 V | | | 50 | μA |
| $I_{OZL}$ | $V_{CC}$ = MAX, | $V_O$ = 0.5 V | | | −50 | μA |
| $I_I$ | $V_{CC}$ = MAX, | $V_I$ = 5.5 V | | | 0.1 | mA |
| $I_{IH}$ | $V_{CC}$ = MAX, | $V_I$ = 2.7 V | | | 20 | μA |
| $I_{IL}$ | $V_{CC}$ = MAX, | $V_I$ = 0.5 V | | | −0.25 | mA |
| $I_O$ [§] | $V_{CC}$ = MAX, | $V_O$ = 2.25 V | −30 | | −112 | mA |
| $I_{CC}$ | $V_{CC}$ = MAX | | | 80 | 125 | mA |

[†]For conditions shown as MIN or MAX, use appropriate value specified under recommended operating conditions.
[‡]All typical values are at $V_{CC}$ = 5 V, $T_A$ = 25°C.
[§]The output conditions have been chosen to produce a current that closely approximates one half of the true short-circuit output current, $I_{OS}$.

### switching characteristics over recommended ranges of $T_A$ and $V_{CC}$ (unless otherwise noted)

| TYPE | | TEST CONDITIONS | $t_{a(A)}$ ACCESS TIME FROM ADDRESS | | | $t_{en}$ ENABLE TIME | | | $t_{dis}$ DISABLE TIME | | | UNIT |
|---|---|---|---|---|---|---|---|---|---|---|---|---|
| | | | MIN | TYP[‡] | MAX | MIN | TYP[‡] | MAX | MIN | TYP[‡] | MAX | |
| TBP38S22-_ _ | Military | $C_L$ = 50 pF, R1 = 300 Ω, R2 = 600 Ω, See Note 2 | | 14 | | | 9 | | | 5 | | ns |
| TBP38S2X-_ _ | | | | | | | | | | | | |
| TBP38S22-_ _ | | | | 16 | | | 9 | | | 5 | | ns |
| TBP38S2X-_ _ | | | | | | | | | | | | |

[‡]All typical values are at $V_{CC}$ = 5 V, $T_A$ = 25°C.
NOTE 2: Load circuits and voltage waveforms are shown in Section 1.

4

PROMS

TEXAS
INSTRUMENTS

### recommended operating conditions

| PARAMETER | | MILITARY | | | COMMERCIAL | | | UNIT |
|---|---|---|---|---|---|---|---|---|
| | | MIN | NOM | MAX | MIN | NOM | MAX | |
| $V_{CC}$ | Supply voltage | 4.5 | 5 | 5.5 | 4.5 | 5 | 5.5 | V |
| $V_{IH}$ | High-level input voltage | 2 | | | 2 | | | V |
| $V_{IL}$ | Low-level input voltage | | | 0.8 | | | 0.8 | V |
| $I_{OH}$ | High-level output current | | | $-1.6$ | | | $-3.2$ | mA |
| $I_{OL}$ | Low-level output current | | | 16 | | | 24 | mA |
| $T_A$ | Operating free-air temperature range | $-55$ | | 125 | 0 | | 70 | °C |

### electrical characteristics over recommended operating free-air temperature range (unless otherwise noted)

| PARAMETER | TEST CONDITIONS[†] | | MILITARY | | | COMMERCIAL | | | UNIT |
|---|---|---|---|---|---|---|---|---|---|
| | | | MIN | TYP[‡] | MAX | MIN | TYP[‡] | MAX | |
| $V_{IK}$ | $V_{CC} = $ MIN, | $I_I = -18$ mA | | | $-1.2$ | | | $-1.2$ | V |
| $V_{OH}$ | $V_{CC} = $ MIN, | $I_{OH} = $ MAX | 2.4 | 3.1 | | 2.4 | 3.1 | | V |
| $V_{OL}$ | $V_{CC} = $ MIN, | $I_{OL} = $ MAX | | | 0.5 | | | 0.5 | V |
| $I_{OZH}$ | $V_{CC} = $ MAX, | $V_O = 2.4$ V | | | 50 | | | 50 | $\mu$A |
| $I_{OZL}$ | $V_{CC} = $ MAX, | $V_O = 0.5$ V | | | $-50$ | | | $-50$ | $\mu$A |
| $I_I$ | $V_{CC} = $ MAX, | $V_I = 5.5$ V | | | 0.1 | | | 0.1 | mA |
| $I_{IH}$ | $V_{CC} = $ MAX, | $V_I = 2.7$ V | | | 20 | | | 20 | $\mu$A |
| $I_{IL}$ | $V_{CC} = $ MAX, | $V_I = 0.5$ V | | | $-0.25$ | | | $-0.25$ | mA |
| $I_O$ [§] | $V_{CC} = $ MAX, | $V_O = 2.25$ V | $-30$ | | $-112$ | $-30$ | | $-112$ | mA |
| $I_{CC}$ | $V_{CC} = $ MAX | | | 45 | 70 | | 45 | 70 | mA |

[†]For conditions shown as MIN or MAX, use appropriate value specified under recommended operating conditions.
[‡]All typical values are at $V_{CC} = 5$ V, $T_A = 25$ °C.
[§]The output conditions have been chosen to produce a current that closely approximates one half of the true short-circuit output current, $I_{OS}$.

### switching characteristics over recommended ranges of $T_A$ and $V_{CC}$ (unless otherwise noted)

| TYPE | | TEST CONDITIONS | $t_{a(A)}$ ACCESS TIME FROM ADDRESS | | | $t_{en}$ ENABLE TIME | | | $t_{dis}$ DISABLE TIME | | | UNIT |
|---|---|---|---|---|---|---|---|---|---|---|---|---|
| | | | MIN | TYP | MAX | MIN | TYP | MAX | MIN | TYP | MAX | |
| TBP38L22-40 | Military | $C_L = 50$ pF, R1 $= 300$ Ω, R2 $= 600$ Ω, See Note 2 | | 20 | 40 | | 10 | 25 | | 7 | 20 | ns |
| TBP38L2X-40 | | | | | | | | | | | | |
| TBP38L22-35 | Commercial | | | 20 | 35 | | 10 | 20 | | 7 | 15 | ns |
| TBP38L2X-35 | | | | | | | | | | | | |
| TBP38L22-45 | Commercial | | | 20 | 45 | | 10 | 20 | | 7 | 15 | ns |
| TBP38L2X-45 | | | | | | | | | | | | |

NOTE 2: Load circuits and voltage waveforms are shown in Section 1.

**4**

**PROMs**

TEXAS
INSTRUMENTS

## recommended operating conditions

| PARAMETER | | MILITARY | | | COMMERCIAL | | | UNIT |
|---|---|---|---|---|---|---|---|---|
| | | MIN | NOM | MAX | MIN | NOM | MAX | |
| $V_{CC}$ | Supply voltage | 4.5 | 5 | 5.5 | 4.5 | 5 | 5.5 | V |
| $V_{IH}$ | High-level input voltage | 2 | | | 2 | | | V |
| $V_{IL}$ | Low-level input voltage | | | 0.8 | | | 0.8 | V |
| $V_{OH}$ | High-level output voltage | | | 5.5 | | | 5.5 | V |
| $I_{OL}$ | Low-level output current | | | 16 | | | 24 | mA |
| $T_A$ | Operating free-air temperature range | -55 | | 125 | 0 | | 70 | °C |

## electrical characteristics over recommended operating free-air temperature range (unless otherwise noted)

| PARAMETER | TEST CONDITIONS[†] | | MILITARY | | | COMMERCIAL | | | UNIT |
|---|---|---|---|---|---|---|---|---|---|
| | | | MIN | TYP[‡] | MAX | MIN | TYP[‡] | MAX | |
| $V_{IK}$ | $V_{CC}$ = MIN, | $I_I$ = -18 mA | | | -1.2 | | | -1.2 | V |
| $I_{OH}$ | $V_{CC}$ = MIN, | $V_{OH}$ = 2.4 V | | | 0.05 | | | 0.05 | mA |
| | | $V_{OH}$ = 5.5 V | | | 0.1 | | | 0.1 | |
| $V_{OL}$ | $V_{CC}$ = MIN, | $I_{OL}$ = MAX | | | 0.5 | | | 0.5 | V |
| $I_I$ | $V_{CC}$ = MAX, | $V_I$ = 5.5 V | | | 0.1 | | | 0.1 | mA |
| $I_{IH}$ | $V_{CC}$ = MAX, | $V_I$ = 2.7 V | | | 20 | | | 20 | $\mu$A |
| $I_{IL}$ | $V_{CC}$ = MAX, | $V_I$ = 0.5 V | | | -0.25 | | | -0.25 | mA |
| $I_{CC}$ | $V_{CC}$ = MAX | | | 80 | 125 | | 80 | 125 | mA |

[†]For conditions shown as MIN or MAX, use appropriate value specified under recommended operating conditions.
[‡]All typical values are at $V_{CC}$ = 5 V, $T_A$ = 25°C.

## switching characteristics over recommended ranges of $T_A$ and $V_{CC}$ (unless otherwise noted)

| TYPE | | TEST CONDITIONS | $t_{a(A)}$ ACCESS TIME FROM ADDRESS | | | $t_{en}$ ENABLE TIME | | | $t_{dis}$ DISABLE TIME | | | UNIT |
|---|---|---|---|---|---|---|---|---|---|---|---|---|
| | | | MIN | TYP[‡] | MAX | MIN | TYP[‡] | MAX | MIN | TYP[‡] | MAX | |
| TBP38SA22-35 | Military | $C_L$ = 50 pF, R1 = 300 Ω, R2 = 600 Ω, See Note 2 | | 19 | 35 | | 8 | 17 | | 8 | 17 | ns |
| TBP38SA22-30 | Commercial | | | 19 | 30 | | 8 | 15 | | 8 | 15 | ns |

[‡]All typical values are at $V_{CC}$ = 5 V, $T_A$ = 25°C.
NOTE 2: Load circuits and voltage waveforms are shown in Section 1.

**4**

**PROMS**

TEXAS
INSTRUMENTS

### recommended operating conditions for programming (see Figure 1)

| | | | MIN | NOM | MAX | UNIT |
|---|---|---|---|---|---|---|
| Supply voltage during verification | | $V_{CC}$ | 4.5 | 5 | 5.5 | V |
| Input voltage | | $V_{IH}$ | 3 | 4 | 5 | V |
| | | $V_{IL}$ | 0 | 0.2 | 0.5 | |
| Enable voltage during verification | | $\overline{G}1, \overline{G}2$ | 0 | 0.2 | 0.4 | V |
| Enable inactive voltage during programming | | $\overline{G}1, \overline{G}2$ | 4.5 | 5 | 5.5 | V |
| $V_{CC}$ program pulse amplitude | | $V_{CC(pr)}$ | 12 | 12.5 | 13 | V |
| $V_{CC}$ program pulse duration | 1st attempt | $t_{w1}$ | 10 | 11 | 12 | |
| | 2nd attempt | $t_{w2}$ | 20 | 22 | 25 | $\mu$s |
| | 3rd attempt | $t_{w3}$ | 20 | 22 | 25 | |
| Enable set-up time† before $V_{CC(pr)}$ | | $t_{su(en)}$ | 0.1 | 0.5 | 1 | $\mu$s |
| Enable hold time‡ after $V_{CC(pr)}$ | | $t_{h(en)}$ | 0.1 | 0.5 | 1 | $\mu$s |
| Rise time of $V_{CC(pr)}$§ | | $t_r(V_{CC})$ | 0.3 | 0.4 | 0.5 | $\mu$s |
| Fall time of $V_{CC(pr)}$¶ | | $t_f(V_{CC})$ | 0.05 | 0.1 | 0.2 | $\mu$s |
| Delay time between successive $V_{CC(pr)}$ pulses | | $t_{d1}$ | 10 | 20 | 30 | $\mu$s |
| Hold time between successive $V_{CC(pr)}$ pulses | | $t_{d2}$ | 10 | 20 | 30 | $\mu$s |
| Cooling time between words | | $t_{cool}$ | 100 | 150 | 200 | $\mu$s |
| Free-air temperature | | $T_A$ | 20 | 25 | 30 | °C |

†Measured from 1.5 V on enable pin to 5.5 V on $V_{CC(pr)}$
‡Measured from 5.5 V on $V_{CC(pr)}$ to 1.5 V on enable pin
§Measured from 5 V to 12 V
¶Measured from 12 V to 5 V

### step-by-step programming instructions (see Figure 1)

1.  Address the word to be programmed, apply 5 volts to $V_{CC}$ and a low-logic-level voltage to the enable inputs $\overline{G}1$ and $\overline{G}2$.

2.  Verify the selected bit location that requires programming. Note: The only bit positions that require programming are outputs needing a high logic level.

3.  For bit locations that do not require programming, go to step 2 for the next bit, or to step 1 for next word.

4.  Deselect PROM by applying 5 volts to $\overline{G}1$ or $\overline{G}2$.

5.  Connect a 4-mA current source (clamped to $V_{CC}$) to the output that is to be programmed.

6.  Increase $V_{CC}$ to $V_{CC(pr)}$ for a pulse duration equal to $t_{wX}$ (where X is determined by the number of programming attempts, i.e., 1,2,3). Minimum current capability for the $V_{CC}$ power supply should be 400 mA.

7.  Verify that the output has been programmed to a high logic level. If the output has been programmed correctly, go to the next bit. If not, repeat step 2 through step 7 and increment X (where X is equal to 1 on the first programming attempt). If the output has not been programmed by the third attempt, stop programming and go to a new device.

8.  Verify programming of every word after all words have been programmed using $V_{CC}$ values of 4.5 volts and 5.5 volts.

4

PROMs

## TBP38S22, TBP38L22, TBP38SA22
## TBP38S2X, TBP38L2X, TBP38SA2X
## 2,048-BIT (256 WORDS BY 8 BITS) PROGRAMMABLE READ-ONLY MEMORIES

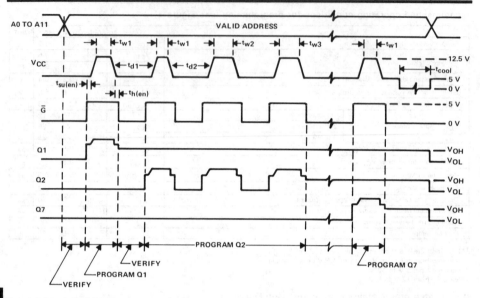

Illustrated above is the following sequence:

1) It is desired to program the selected address with 01100001 (Q0-Q7). Only outputs Q1, Q2 and Q7 need programming.
2) Q1 is verified to be at a low logic level and then the programming sequence is executed. The output is then verified to be at a high logic level.
3) Q2 is an example of an output requiring three attempts to be programmed successfully.
4) Q7 is programmed to a high logic level.

### FIGURE 1. SERIES 3 PROGRAMMING SEQUENCE

**TEXAS INSTRUMENTS**

5

**RAMs**

D1416, DECEMBER 1972–REVISED FEBRUARY 1984

- For Application as a "Scratch Pad" Memory with Nondestructive Read-Out

- Fully Decoded Memory Organized as 16 Words of Four Bits Each

- Fast Access Time . . . 33 ns Typical

- Diode-Clamped, Buffered Inputs

- Open-Collector Outputs Provide Wire-AND Capability

- Typical Power Dissipation . . . 375 mW

- Compatible with Most TTL Circuits

**SN7489 . . . J OR N PACKAGE**
**(TOP VIEW)**

```
        A0  [ 1   U  16 ]  VCC
        ME  [ 2      15 ]  A1
        WE  [ 3      14 ]  A2
        D1  [ 4      13 ]  A3
        Q̄1  [ 5      12 ]  D4
        D2  [ 6      11 ]  Q̄4
        Q̄2  [ 7      10 ]  D3
       GND  [ 8       9 ]  Q̄3
```

## description

This 64-bit active-element memory is a monolithic, high-speed, transistor-transistor logic (TTL) array of 64 flip-flop memory cells organized in a matrix to provide 16 words of four bits each. Each of the 16 words is addressed in straight binary with full on-chip decoding.

The buffered memory inputs consist of four address lines, four data inputs, a write enable, and a memory enable for controlling the entry and access of data. The memory has open-collector outputs which may be wired-AND connected to permit expansion up to 4704 words of N-bit length without additional output buffering. Access time is typically 33 nanoseconds; power dissipation is typically 375 milliwatts.

**logic symbol**

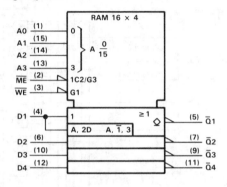

### FUNCTION TABLE

| ME | WE | OPERATION | CONDITION OF OUTPUTS |
|----|----|-----------|----------------------|
| L | L | Write | Complement of Data Inputs |
| L | H | Read | Complement of Selected Word |
| H | L | Inhibit Storage | Complement of Data Inputs |
| H | H | Do Nothing | High |

## write operation

Information present at the data inputs is written into the memory by addressing the desired word and holding both the memory enable and write enable low. Since the internal output of the data input gate is common to the input of the sense amplifier, the sense output will assume the opposite state of the information at the data inputs when the write enable is low.

## read operation

The complement of the information which has been written into the memory is nondestructively read out at the four sense outputs. This is accomplished by holding the memory enable low, the write enable high, and selecting the desired address.

**TEXAS INSTRUMENTS**

**5**

**RAMs**

**logic diagram**

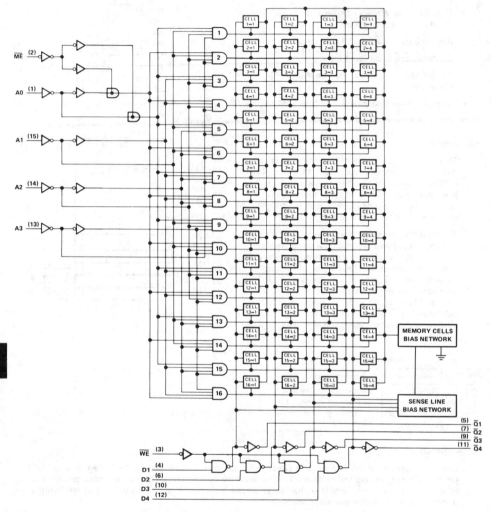

**TEXAS INSTRUMENTS**

## schematics of inputs and outputs

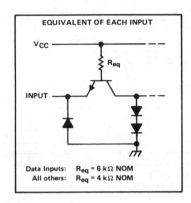

EQUIVALENT OF EACH INPUT

$V_{CC}$

$R_{eq}$

INPUT

Data Inputs:  $R_{eq}$ = 6 kΩ NOM
All others:   $R_{eq}$ = 4 kΩ NOM

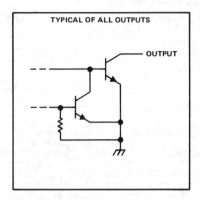

TYPICAL OF ALL OUTPUTS

OUTPUT

## absolute maximum ratings over operating free-air temperature range (unless otherwise noted)

Supply voltage, $V_{CC}$ (see Note 1) . . . . . . . . . . . . . . . . . . . . . . . . . . . . . . . . . . . . . . . . 7 V
Input voltage (see Note 1) . . . . . . . . . . . . . . . . . . . . . . . . . . . . . . . . . . . . . . . . . . . . . . . 5.5 V
High-level output voltage, $V_{OH}$ (see Notes 1 and 2) . . . . . . . . . . . . . . . . . . . . . . . . . . . . 5.5 V
Operating free-air temperature range . . . . . . . . . . . . . . . . . . . . . . . . . . . . . . . . . . . . . 0°C to 70°C
Storage temperature range . . . . . . . . . . . . . . . . . . . . . . . . . . . . . . . . . . . . . . . −65°C to 150°C

NOTES: 1. Voltage values are with respect to network ground terminal.
2. This is the maximum voltage that should be applied to any output when it is in the off state.

## recommended operating conditions

| | MIN | NOM | MAX | UNIT |
|---|---|---|---|---|
| Supply voltage, $V_{CC}$ | 4.75 | 5 | 5.25 | V |
| Width of write-enable pulse, $t_w$ | 40 | | | ns |
| Setup time, data input with respect to write enable, $t_{su}$ (see Figure 1) | 40 | | | ns |
| Hold time, data input with respect to write enable, $t_h$ (see Figure 1) | 5 | | | ns |
| Select input setup time with respect to write enable, $t_{su}$ | 0 | | | ns |
| Select input hold time after writing, $t_h$ (see Figure 1) | 5 | | | ns |
| Operating free-air temperature, $T_A$ | 0 | | 70 | °C |

5

RAMs

**electrical characteristics over recommended operating free-air temperature range (unless otherwise noted)**

| | PARAMETER | TEST CONDITIONS† | | MIN | TYP‡ | MAX | UNIT |
|---|---|---|---|---|---|---|---|
| $V_{IH}$ | High-level input voltage | | | 2 | | | V |
| $V_{IL}$ | Low-level input voltage | | | | | 0.8 | V |
| $V_{IK}$ | Input clamp voltage | $V_{CC}$ = MIN, | $I_I$ = −12 mA | | | −1.5 | V |
| $I_{OH}$ | High-level output current | $V_{CC}$ = MIN, $V_{IL}$ = 0.8 V, | $V_{IH}$ = 2 V, $V_{OH}$ = 5.5 V | | | 20 | $\mu$A |
| $V_{OL}$ | Low-level output voltage | $V_{CC}$ = MIN, $V_{IH}$ = 2 V, $V_{IL}$ = 0.8 V | $I_{OL}$ = 12 mA | | | 0.4 | V |
| | | | $I_{OL}$ = 16 mA | | | 0.45 | |
| $I_I$ | Input current at maximum input voltage | $V_{CC}$ = MAX, | $V_I$ = 5.5 V | | | 1 | mA |
| $I_{IH}$ | High-level input current | $V_{CC}$ = MAX, | $V_I$ = 2.4 V | | | 40 | $\mu$A |
| $I_{IL}$ | Low-level input current | $V_{CC}$ = MAX, | $V_I$ = 0.4 V | | | −1.6 | mA |
| $I_{CC}$ | Supply current | $V_{CC}$ = MAX, | See Note 3 | | 75 | 105 | mA |
| $C_o$ | Off-state output capacitance | $V_{CC}$ = 5 V, f = 1 MHz | $V_O$ = 2.4 V, | | 6.5 | | pF |

†For conditions shown as MIN or MAX, use the appropriate value specified under recommended operating conditions.
‡All typical values are at $V_{CC}$ = 5 V, $T_A$ = 25°C.
NOTE 3: $I_{CC}$ is measured with the memory enable grounded, all other inputs at 4.5 V, and all outputs open.

**switching characteristics, $V_{CC}$ = 5 V, $T_A$ = 25°C**

| | PARAMETER | | TEST CONDITIONS | MIN | TYP | MAX | UNIT |
|---|---|---|---|---|---|---|---|
| $t_{PLH}$ | Propagation delay time, low-to-high-level output from memory enable | | | | 26 | 50 | ns |
| $t_{PHL}$ | Propagation delay time, high-to-low-level output from memory enable | | $C_L$ = 30 pF, $R_{L1}$ = 300 Ω, $R_{L2}$ = 600 Ω, See Figure 1 | | 33 | 50 | |
| $t_{PLH}$ | Propagation delay time, low-to-high-level output from any address input | | | | 30 | 60 | ns |
| $t_{PHL}$ | Propagation delay time, high-to-low-level output from any address input | | | | 35 | 60 | |
| $t_{SR}$ | Sense recovery time after writing | Output initially high | | | 39 | 70 | ns |
| | | Output initially low | | | 48 | 70 | |

**TEXAS INSTRUMENTS**

## PARAMETER MEASUREMENT INFORMATION

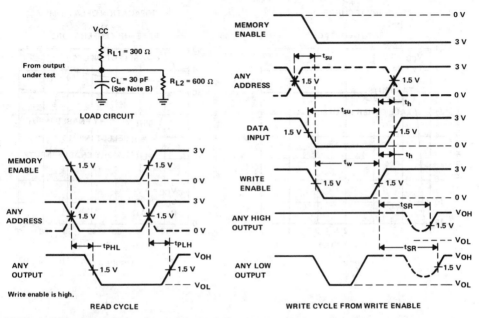

NOTES: A. The input pulse generators have the following characteristics: $t_r \leq 10$ ns, $t_f \leq 10$ ns, PRR = 1 MHz, $Z_{out} \approx 50\ \Omega$.
B. $C_L$ includes probe and jig capacitance.

FIGURE 1—SWITCHING CHARACTERISTICS

5

RAMs

TEXAS
INSTRUMENTS

# SN7489
## 64-BIT RANDOM-ACCESS READ/WRITE MEMORY

### TYPICAL CHARACTERISTICS

INPUT CURRENT
vs
INPUT VOLTAGE

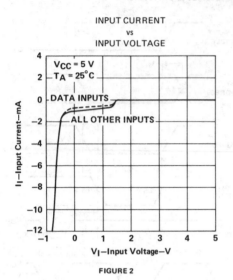

FIGURE 2

PROPAGATION DELAY TIME
vs
FREE-AIR TEMPERATURE

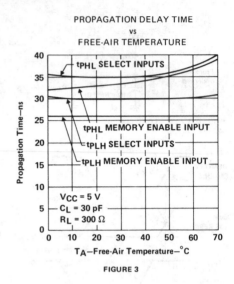

FIGURE 3

5

RAMs

5-8

TEXAS
INSTRUMENTS

## SN54184, SN74184 BCD-TO-BINARY CONVERTERS
## SN54185A, SN74185A BINARY-TO-BCD CONVERTERS

SN54184, SN54185A . . . J OR W PACKAGE
SN74184, SN74185A . . . J OR N PACKAGE
(TOP VIEW)

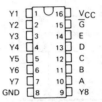

### description

These monolithic converters are derived from the custom MSI 256-bit read-only memories SN5488 and SN7488. Emitter connections are made to provide direct read-out of converted codes at outputs Y8 through Y1 as shown in the function tables. These converters demonstrate the versatility of a read-only memory in that an unlimited number of reference tables or conversion tables may be built into a system using economical, customized read-only memories. Both of these converters comprehend that the least significant bits (LSB) of the binary and BCD codes are logically equal, and in each case the LSB bypasses the converter as illustrated in the typical applications. This means that a 6-bit converter is produced in each case. Both devices are cascadable to N bits.

**TABLE I**
**SN54184, SN74184**
**PACKAGE COUNT AND DELAY TIMES**
**FOR BCD-TO-BINARY CONVERSION**

| INPUT | PACKAGES | TOTAL DELAY TIMES (ns) | |
|---|---|---|---|
| (DECADES) | REQUIRED | TYP | MAX |
| 2 | 2 | 56 | 80 |
| 3 | 6 | 140 | 200 |
| 4 | 11 | 196 | 280 |
| 5 | 19 | 280 | 400 |
| 6 | 28 | 364 | 520 |

An overriding enable input is provided on each converter which, when taken high, inhibits the function, causing all outputs to go high. For this reason, and to minimize power consumption, unused outputs Y7 and Y8 of the '185A and all "don't care" conditions of the '184 are programmed high. The outputs are of the open-collector type.

The SN54184 and SN54185A are characterized for operation over the full military temperature range of −55°C to 125°C; the SN74184 and SN74185A are characterized for operation from 0°C to 70°C.

### SN54184 and SN74184 BCD-to-binary converters

The 6-bit BCD-to-binary function of the SN54184 and SN74184 is analogous to the algorithm:

  a. Shift BCD number right one bit and examine each decade. Subtract three from each 4-bit decade containing a binary value greater than seven.

  b. Shift right, examine, and correct after each shift until the least significant decade contains a number smaller than eight and all other converted decades contain zeros.

In addition to BCD-to-binary conversion, the SN54184 and SN74184 are programmed to generate BCD 9's complement or BCD 10's complement. Again, in each case, one bit of the complement code is logically equal to one of the BCD bits; therefore, these complements can be produced on three lines. As outputs Y6, Y7, and Y8 are not required in the BCD-to-binary conversion, they are utilized to provide these complement codes as specified in the function table (following page, right) when the devices are connected as shown above the function table.

5 RAMs

## SN54184 and SN74184 BCD-to-binary converters (continued)

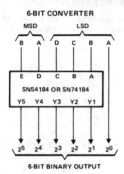

**6-BIT CONVERTER** — SN54184 OR SN74184
MSD B A / LSD D C B A → inputs E D C B A → outputs Y5 Y4 Y3 Y2 Y1 → $2^5$ $2^4$ $2^3$ $2^2$ $2^1$ $2^0$

**6-BIT BINARY OUTPUT**

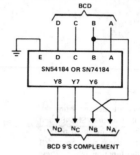

**BCD 9'S COMPLEMENT CONVERTER** — SN54184 OR SN74184
BCD D C B A → inputs E D C B A → outputs Y8 Y7 Y6 → $N_D$ $N_C$ $N_B$ $N_A$

**BCD 9'S COMPLEMENT**

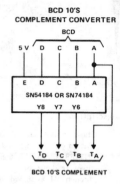

**BCD 10'S COMPLEMENT CONVERTER** — SN54184 OR SN74184
5 V / BCD D C B A → inputs E D C B A → outputs Y8 Y7 Y6 → $T_D$ $T_C$ $T_B$ $T_A$

**BCD 10'S COMPLEMENT**

### FUNCTION TABLE
### BCD-TO-BINARY CONVERTER

| BCD WORDS | INPUTS (See Note A) | | | | | | OUTPUTS (See Note B) | | | | |
|---|---|---|---|---|---|---|---|---|---|---|---|
| | E | D | C | B | A | Ḡ | Y5 | Y4 | Y3 | Y2 | Y1 |
| 0-1 | L | L | L | L | L | L | L | L | L | L | L |
| 2-3 | L | L | L | L | H | L | L | L | L | L | H |
| 4-5 | L | L | L | H | L | L | L | L | L | H | L |
| 6-7 | L | L | L | H | H | L | L | L | L | H | H |
| 8-9 | L | L | H | L | L | L | L | L | H | L | L |
| 10-11 | L | H | L | L | L | L | L | L | H | L | H |
| 12-13 | L | H | L | L | H | L | L | L | H | H | L |
| 14-15 | L | H | L | H | L | L | L | L | H | H | H |
| 16-17 | L | H | L | H | H | L | L | H | L | L | L |
| 18-19 | L | H | H | L | L | L | L | H | L | L | H |
| 20-21 | H | L | L | L | L | L | L | H | L | H | L |
| 22-23 | H | L | L | L | H | L | L | H | L | H | H |
| 24-25 | H | L | L | H | L | L | L | H | H | L | L |
| 26-27 | H | L | L | H | H | L | L | H | H | L | H |
| 28-29 | H | L | H | L | L | L | L | H | H | H | L |
| 30-31 | H | H | L | L | L | L | L | H | H | H | H |
| 32-33 | H | H | L | L | H | L | H | L | L | L | L |
| 34-35 | H | H | L | H | L | L | H | L | L | L | H |
| 36-37 | H | H | L | H | H | L | H | L | L | H | L |
| 38-39 | H | H | H | L | L | L | H | L | L | H | H |
| ANY | X | X | X | X | X | H | H | H | H | H | H |

### FUNCTION TABLE
### BCD 9'S OR BCD 10'S COMPLEMENT CONVERTER

| BCD WORD | INPUTS (See Note C) | | | | | | OUTPUTS (See Note D) | | |
|---|---|---|---|---|---|---|---|---|---|
| | E† | D | C | B | A | Ḡ | Y8 | Y7 | Y6 |
| 0 | L | L | L | L | L | L | H | L | H |
| 1 | L | L | L | L | H | L | H | L | L |
| 2 | L | L | L | H | L | L | L | H | H |
| 3 | L | L | L | H | H | L | L | H | L |
| 4 | L | L | H | L | L | L | L | L | H |
| 5 | L | L | H | L | H | L | L | L | L |
| 6 | L | L | H | H | L | L | L | H | H |
| 7 | L | L | H | H | H | L | L | H | L |
| 8 | L | H | L | L | L | L | L | L | H |
| 9 | L | H | L | L | H | L | L | L | L |
| 0 | H | L | L | L | L | L | L | L | L |
| 1 | H | L | L | L | H | L | H | L | H |
| 2 | H | L | L | H | L | L | H | L | L |
| 3 | H | L | L | H | H | L | L | H | H |
| 4 | H | L | H | L | L | L | L | H | L |
| 5 | H | L | H | L | H | L | L | L | H |
| 6 | H | L | H | H | L | L | L | L | L |
| 7 | H | L | H | H | H | L | L | H | H |
| 8 | H | H | L | L | L | L | L | H | L |
| 9 | H | H | L | L | H | L | L | L | H |
| ANY | X | X | X | X | X | H | H | H | H |

H = high level, L = low level, X = irrelevant

NOTES: A. Input conditions other than those shown produce highs at outputs Y1 through Y5.
B. Outputs Y6, Y7, and Y8 are not used for BCD-to-binary conversion.

H = high level, L = low level, X = irrelevant

NOTES: C. Input conditions other than those shown produce highs at outputs Y6, Y7, and Y8.
D. Outputs Y1 through Y5 are not used for BCD 9's or BCD 10's complement conversion.

†When these devices are used as complement converters, input E is used as a mode control. With this input low, the BCD 9's complement is generated; when it is high, the BCD 10's complement is generated.

**TEXAS INSTRUMENTS**

## SN54185A and SN74185A binary-to-BCD converters

The function performed by these 6-bit binary-to-BCD converters is analogous to the algorithm:

    a. Examine the three most significant bits. If the sum is greater than four, add three and shift left one bit.

    b. Examine each BCD decade. If the sum is greater than four, add three and shift left one bit.

    c. Repeat step b until the least-significant binary bit is in the least-significant BCD location.

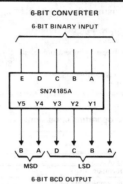

6-BIT CONVERTER

6-BIT BINARY INPUT

SN74185A

6-BIT BCD OUTPUT

**TABLE II**

**SN54185A, SN74185A**

**PACKAGE COUNT AND DELAY TIMES**

**FOR BINARY-TO-BCD CONVERSION**

| INPUT (BITS) | PACKAGES REQUIRED | TOTAL DELAY TIME (ns) | |
|---|---|---|---|
| | | TYP | MAX |
| 4 to 6 | 1 | 25 | 40 |
| 7 or 8 | 3 | 50 | 80 |
| 9 | 4 | 75 | 120 |
| 10 | 6 | 100 | 160 |
| 11 | 7 | 125 | 200 |
| 12 | 8 | 125 | 200 |
| 13 | 10 | 150 | 240 |
| 14 | 12 | 175 | 280 |
| 15 | 14 | 175 | 280 |
| 16 | 16 | 200 | 320 |
| 17 | 19 | 225 | 360 |
| 18 | 21 | 225 | 360 |
| 19 | 24 | 250 | 400 |
| 20 | 27 | 275 | 440 |

**FUNCTION TABLE**

| BINARY WORDS | INPUTS | | | | | | OUTPUTS | | | | | | | |
|---|---|---|---|---|---|---|---|---|---|---|---|---|---|---|
| | BINARY SELECT | | | | | ENABLE | | | | | | | | |
| | E | D | C | B | A | Ḡ | Y8 | Y7 | Y6 | Y5 | Y4 | Y3 | Y2 | Y1 |
| 0-1 | L | L | L | L | L | L | H | H | L | L | L | L | L | L |
| 2-3 | L | L | L | L | H | L | H | H | L | L | L | L | L | H |
| 4-5 | L | L | L | H | L | L | H | H | L | L | L | L | H | L |
| 6-7 | L | L | L | H | H | L | H | H | L | L | L | L | H | H |
| 8-9 | L | L | H | L | L | L | H | H | L | L | L | H | L | L |
| 10-11 | L | L | H | L | H | L | H | H | L | L | L | H | L | H |
| 12-13 | L | L | H | H | L | L | H | H | L | L | L | H | H | L |
| 14-15 | L | L | H | H | H | L | H | H | L | L | H | L | H | L |
| 16-17 | L | H | L | L | L | L | H | H | L | L | L | L | L | L |
| 18-19 | L | H | L | L | H | L | H | H | L | L | H | H | L | L |
| 20-21 | L | H | L | H | L | L | H | H | L | H | L | L | L | L |
| 22-23 | L | H | L | H | H | L | H | H | L | L | H | L | L | H |
| 24-25 | L | H | H | L | L | L | H | H | L | H | L | L | H | L |
| 26-27 | L | H | H | L | H | L | H | H | L | H | L | L | H | H |
| 28-29 | L | H | H | H | L | L | H | H | L | H | L | H | L | L |
| 30-31 | L | H | H | H | H | L | H | H | L | H | H | L | L | L |
| 32-33 | H | L | L | L | L | L | H | H | L | H | H | L | L | H |
| 34-35 | H | L | L | L | H | L | H | H | L | H | H | L | H | L |
| 36-37 | H | L | L | H | L | L | H | H | L | H | H | L | H | H |
| 38-39 | H | L | L | H | H | L | H | H | L | H | H | H | L | L |
| 40-41 | H | L | H | L | L | L | H | H | H | L | L | L | L | L |
| 42-43 | H | L | H | L | H | L | H | H | H | L | L | L | L | H |
| 44-45 | H | L | H | H | L | L | H | H | H | L | L | L | H | L |
| 46-47 | H | L | H | H | H | L | H | H | H | L | L | L | H | H |
| 48-49 | H | H | L | L | L | L | H | H | H | L | L | H | L | L |
| 50-51 | H | H | L | L | H | L | H | H | H | L | H | L | L | L |
| 52-53 | H | H | L | H | L | L | H | H | H | L | H | L | H | L |
| 54-55 | H | H | L | H | H | L | H | H | H | L | H | L | H | L |
| 56-57 | H | H | H | L | L | L | H | H | H | L | H | L | H | H |
| 58-59 | H | H | H | L | H | L | H | H | H | L | H | H | L | L |
| 60-61 | H | H | H | H | L | L | H | H | H | H | L | L | L | L |
| 62-63 | H | H | H | H | H | L | H | H | H | H | L | L | L | H |
| ALL | X | X | X | X | X | H | H | H | H | H | H | H | H | H |

H = high level, L = low level, X = irrelevant

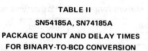

**5**

**RAMs**

TEXAS INSTRUMENTS

**absolute maximum ratings over operating free-air temperature range (unless otherwise noted)**

Supply voltage, $V_{CC}$ (see Note 1) . . . . . . . . . . . . . . . . . . . . . . . . . . . 7 V
Input voltage . . . . . . . . . . . . . . . . . . . . . . . . . . . . . . . . . . . . . . 5.5 V
Operating free-air temperature range: SN54184, SN54185A . . . . . . . . . . . . . $-55°$C to $125°$C
　　　　　　　　　　　　　　　　　　SN74184, SN74185A . . . . . . . . . . . . . $0°$C to $70°$C
Storage temperature range . . . . . . . . . . . . . . . . . . . . . . . . . . . . $-65°$C to $150°$C

NOTE 1: Voltage values are with respect to network ground terminal.

**recommended operating conditions**

|  | SN54184, SN54185A | | | SN74184, SN74185A | | | UNIT |
|---|---|---|---|---|---|---|---|
|  | MIN | NOM | MAX | MIN | NOM | MAX |  |
| Supply voltage, $V_{CC}$ | 4.5 | 5 | 5.5 | 4.75 | 5 | 5.25 | V |
| Low-level output current, $I_{OL}$ |  |  | 12 |  |  | 12 | mA |
| Operating free-air temperature, $T_A$ | $-55$ |  | 125 | 0 |  | 70 | $°$C |

**electrical characteristics over recommended operating free-air temperature range (unless otherwise noted)**

| PARAMETER | | TEST CONDITIONS[†] | | MIN | TYP[‡] | MAX | UNIT |
|---|---|---|---|---|---|---|---|
| $V_{IH}$ | High-level input voltage | | | 2 | | | V |
| $V_{IL}$ | Low-level input voltage | | | | | 0.8 | V |
| $V_{IK}$ | Input clamp voltage | $V_{CC}$ = MIN, | $I_I$ = $-12$ mA | | | $-1.5$ | V |
| $I_{OH}$ | High-level output current | $V_{CC}$ = MIN, $V_{IH}$ = 2 V, $V_{IL}$ = 0.8 V, $V_{OH}$ = 5.5 V | | | | 100 | $\mu$A |
| $V_{OL}$ | Low-level output voltage | $V_{CC}$ = MIN, $V_{IH}$ = 2 V, $V_{IL}$ = 0.8 V, $I_{OL}$ = 12 mA | | | | 0.4 | V |
| $I_I$ | Input current at maximum input voltage | $V_{CC}$ = MAX, | $V_I$ = 5.5 V | | | 1 | mA |
| $I_{IH}$ | High-level input current | $V_{CC}$ = MAX, | $V_I$ = 2.4 V | | | 40 | $\mu$A |
| $I_{IL}$ | Low-level input current | $V_{CC}$ = MAX, | $V_I$ = 0.4 V | | | $-1$ | mA |
| $I_{CCH}$ | Supply current, all outputs high | $V_{CC}$ = MAX | | | 50 | | mA |
| $I_{CCL}$ | Supply current, all programmed outputs low | | | | 62 | 99 | |

[†]For conditions shown as MIN or MAX, use the appropriate value specified under recommended operating conditions for the applicable type.
[‡]All typical values are at $V_{CC}$ = 5 V, $T_A$ = 25$°$C.

**switching characteristics, $V_{CC}$ = 5 V, $T_A$ = 25$°$C**

| PARAMETER | | TEST CONDITIONS | MIN | TYP | MAX | UNIT |
|---|---|---|---|---|---|---|
| $t_{PLH}$ | Propagation delay time, low-to-high-level output from enable $\overline{G}$ | $C_L$ = 30 pF, | | 19 | 30 | ns |
| $t_{PHL}$ | Propagation delay time, high-to-low-level output from enable $\overline{G}$ | $R_{L1}$ = 300 $\Omega$, | | 22 | 35 | ns |
| $t_{PLH}$ | Propagation delay time, low-to-high-level output from binary select | $R_{L2}$ = 600 $\Omega$, | | 27 | 40 | ns |
| $t_{PHL}$ | Propagation delay time, high-to-low-level output from binary select | See Figure 1 and Note 2 | | 23 | 40 | ns |

TEXAS
INSTRUMENTS

schematics of inputs and outputs

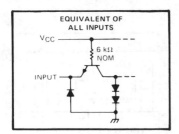

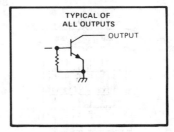

## PARAMETER MEASUREMENT INFORMATION

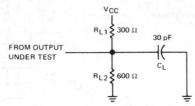

$C_L$ includes probe and jig capacitance.

**LOAD CIRCUIT**
**FIGURE 1**

NOTE 2: See General Information Section for load circuits and voltage waveforms.

# TYPICAL APPLICATION DATA
## SN54184, SN74184

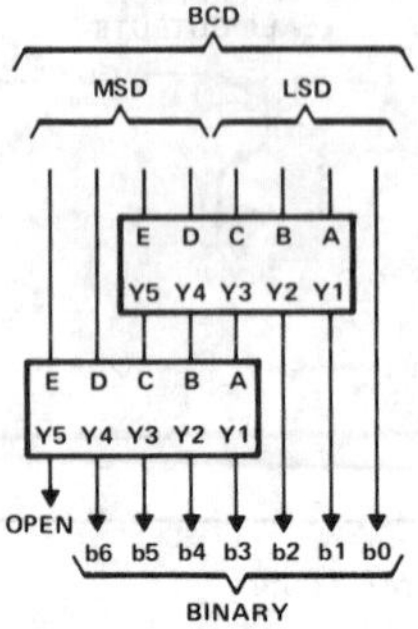

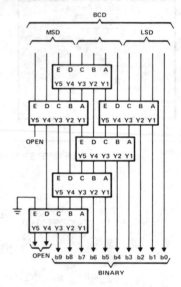

FIGURE 2—BCD-TO-BINARY CONVERTER
FOR TWO BCD DECADES

MSD—most significant decade
LSD—least significant decade
Each rectangle represents an SN54184 or SN74184

FIGURE 3—BCD-TO-BINARY CONVERTER
FOR THREE BCD DECADES

TEXAS
INSTRUMENTS

## TYPICAL APPLICATION DATA
### SN54184, SN74184

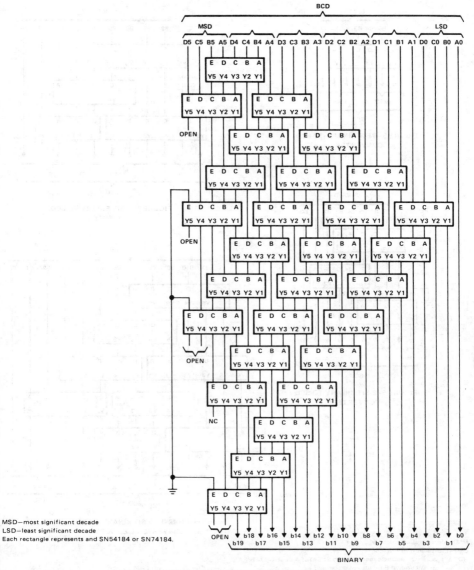

MSD—most significant decade
LSD—least significant decade
Each rectangle represents and SN54184 or SN74184.

FIGURE 4—BCD-TO-BINARY CONVERTER FOR SIX BCD DECADES

TEXAS
INSTRUMENTS

5

RAMs

### TYPICAL APPLICATION DATA
### SN54185A, SN74185A

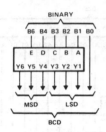

FIGURE 5—6-BIT BINARY-TO-BCD
CONVERTER

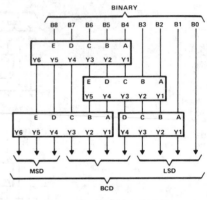

FIGURE 7—9-BIT BINARY-TO-BCD
CONVERTER

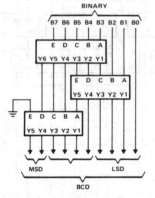

FIGURE 6—8-BIT BINARY-TO-BCD
CONVERTER

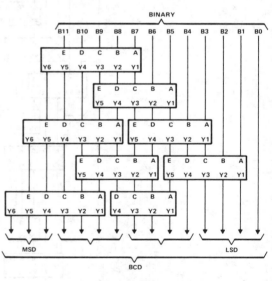

FIGURE 8—12-BIT BINARY-TO-BCD
CONVERTER (SEE NOTE B)

MSD—Most significant decade
LSD—Least significant decade
NOTES: A. Each rectangle represents an SN54185A or an SN74185A.
       B. All unused E inputs are grounded.

5

RAMs

TEXAS
INSTRUMENTS

## TYPICAL APPLICATION DATA
### SN54185A, SN74185A

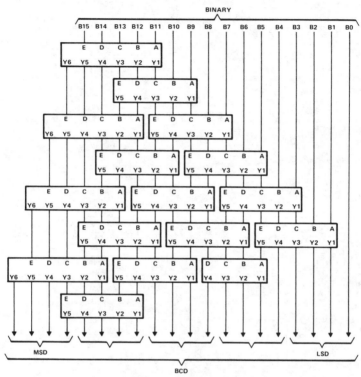

FIGURE 9—16 BIT BINARY-TO-BCD
CONVERTER (SEE NOTE B)

MSD—most significant decade
LSD—least significant decade

NOTES:   A.  Each rectangle represents an SN54185A or SN74185A.
   B.  All unused E inputs are grounded.

TEXAS
INSTRUMENTS

**5**

**RAMs**

**SN54LS189A, SN54LS219A, SN54LS289A, SN54LS319A**
**SN74LS189A, SN74LS219A, SN74LS289A, SN74LS319A**
**64-BIT RANDOM-ACCESS MEMORIES**

D2417, SEPTEMBER 1980 — REVISED FEBRUARY 1985

- **Organized as 16 Words of Four Bits Each**
- **Choice of Buffered 3-State or Open-Collector outputs**
- **Choice of Noninverted or Inverted Outputs**
- **Typical Access Time . . . 50 ns**

### description

These monolithic TTL memories feature Schottky clamping for high performance and a fast chip-select access time to enhance decoding at the system level. A three-state output version and an open-collector-output version are offered for both of the logic choices. A three-state output offers the convenience of an open-collector output with the speed of a totem-pole output; it can be bus-connected to other similar outputs, yet it retains the fast rise time characteristic of the TTL totem-pole output. An open-collector output offers the capability of direct interface with a data line having a passive pull-up.

SN54LS189A, SN54LS289A . . . J PACKAGE
SN74LS189A, SN74LS289A . . . J OR N PACKAGE
(TOP VIEW)

```
        ___
A0  [ 1  U  16 ] VCC
 S  [ 2     15 ] A1
R/W [ 3     14 ] A2
D1  [ 4     13 ] A3
Q̄1  [ 5     12 ] D4
D2  [ 6     11 ] Q̄4
Q̄2  [ 7     10 ] D3
GND [ 8      9 ] Q̄3
```

SN54LS219A, SN54LS319A . . . J PACKAGE
SN74LS219A, SN74LS319A . . . J OR N PACKAGE
(TOP VIEW)

```
        ___
A0  [ 1  U  16 ] VCC
 S  [ 2     15 ] A1
R/W [ 3     14 ] A2
D1  [ 4     13 ] A3
Q1  [ 5     12 ] D4
D2  [ 6     11 ] Q4
Q2  [ 7     10 ] D3
GND [ 8      9 ] Q3
```

### write cycle

Information to be stored in the memory is written into the selected address location when the chip-select ($\overline{S}$) and the write-enable (R/$\overline{W}$) inputs are low. While the write-enable input is low, the memory outputs are off (three-state = Hi-Z, open-collector = high). When a number of outputs are bus-connected, this off state neither loads nor drives the data bus; however, it permits the bus line to be driven by other active outputs or a passive pull-up.

### read cycle

Information stored in the memory (see function table for input/output phase relationship) is available at the outputs when the write-enable input is high and the chip-select input is low. When the chip-select input is high, the outputs will be off.

**5**

**RAMs**

**FUNCTION TABLE**

| FUNCTION | INPUTS | | OUTPUTS | | | |
|---|---|---|---|---|---|---|
| | CHIP SELECT | WRITE ENABLE | 'LS189A | 'LS289A | 'LS219A | 'LS319A |
| Write | L | L | Z | Off | Z | Off |
| Read | L | H | Complement of Data Entered | Complement of Data Entered | Data Entered | Data Entered |
| Inhibit | H | X | Z | Off | Z | Off |

H = high level, L = low level, X = irrelevant, Z = high impedance

**TEXAS INSTRUMENTS**

## SN54LS189A, SN54LS219A, SN54LS289A, SN54LS319A
## SN74LS189A, SN74LS219A, SN74LS289A, SN74LS319A
## 64-BIT RANDOM-ACCESS MEMORIES

### logic symbols

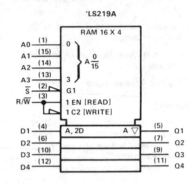

'LS189A

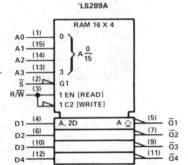

'LS289A

'LS219A

'LS319A

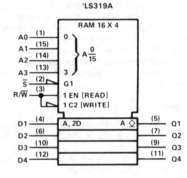

### schematics of inputs and outputs

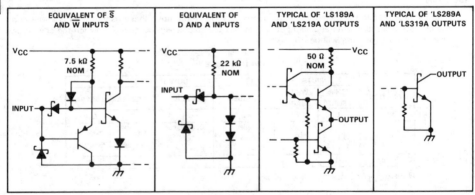

| EQUIVALENT OF $\overline{S}$ AND $\overline{W}$ INPUTS | EQUIVALENT OF D AND A INPUTS | TYPICAL OF 'LS189A AND 'LS219A OUTPUTS | TYPICAL OF 'LS289A AND 'LS319A OUTPUTS |

TEXAS
INSTRUMENTS

**absolute maximum ratings over operating free-air temperature range (unless otherwise noted)**

| | |
|---|---|
| Supply voltage, $V_{CC}$ (see Note 1) | 7 V |
| Input voltage | 7 V |
| Off-state output voltage: 'LS189A, 'LS219A | 5.5 V |
|         'LS289A, 'LS319A | 7 V |
| Operating free-air temperature range: SN54LS' Circuits | $-55\,°C$ to $125\,°C$ |
|       SN74LS' Circuits | $0\,°C$ to $70\,°C$ |
| Storage temperature range | $-65\,°C$ to $150\,°C$ |

NOTE 1: Voltage values are with respect to network ground terminal.

**recommended operating conditions**

| | | SN54LS189A, SN54LS219A | | | SN74LS189A, SN74LS219A | | | UNIT |
|---|---|---|---|---|---|---|---|---|
| | | MIN | NOM | MAX | MIN | NOM | MAX | |
| Supply voltage, $V_{CC}$ | | 4.5 | 5 | 5.5 | 4.75 | 5 | 5.25 | V |
| High-level output current, $I_{OH}$ | | | | $-1$ | | | $-2.6$ | mA |
| Low-level output current, $I_{OL}$ | | | | 12 | | | 24 | mA |
| Width of write pulse (write enable low), $t_{w(wr)}$ | | 100 | | | 70 | | | |
| Setup time | Address before write pulse, $t_{su(ad)}$ | 0↓ | | | 0↓ | | | ns |
| | Data before end of write pulse, $t_{su(da)}$ | 100↑ | | | 60↑ | | | |
| | Chip-select before end of write pulse, $t_{su(S)}$ | 100↑ | | | 60↑ | | | |
| Hold time | Address after write pulse, $t_{h(ad)}$ | 0↑ | | | 0↑ | | | ns |
| | Data after write pulse, $t_{h(da)}$ | 0↑ | | | 0↑ | | | |
| | Chip-select after write pulse, $t_{h(S)}$ | 0↑ | | | 0↑ | | | |
| Operating free-air temperature, $T_A$ | | $-55$ | | 125 | 0 | | 70 | °C |

↑↓The arrow indicates the transition of the write-enable input used for reference: ↑ for the low-to-high transition, ↓ for the high-to-low transition.

TEXAS
INSTRUMENTS

5

RAMs

**electrical characteristics over recommended operating free-air temperature range (unless otherwise noted)**

| PARAMETER | | TEST CONDITIONS[†] | | SN54LS189A SN54LS219A MIN | SN54LS189A SN54LS219A TYP[‡] | SN54LS189A SN54LS219A MAX | SN74LS189A SN74LS219A MIN | SN74LS189A SN74LS219A TYP[‡] | SN74LS189A SN74LS219A MAX | UNIT |
|---|---|---|---|---|---|---|---|---|---|---|
| $V_{IH}$ | High-level input voltage | | | 2 | | | 2 | | | V |
| $V_{IL}$ | Low-level input voltage | | | | | 0.7 | | | 0.8 | V |
| $V_{IK}$ | Input clamp voltage | $V_{CC} = MIN$, | $I_I = -18$ mA | | | $-1.5$ | | | $-1.5$ | V |
| $V_{OH}$ | High-level output voltage | $V_{CC} = MIN$, $V_{IL} = V_{IL}max$, | $V_{IH} = 2$ V, $I_{OH} = MAX$ | 2.4 | 3.1 | | 2.4 | 3.1 | | V |
| $V_{OL}$ | Low-level output voltage | $V_{CC} = MIN$, $V_{IH} = 2$ V, | $I_{OL} = 12$ mA | | 0.25 | 0.4 | | 0.25 | 0.4 | V |
| | | $V_{IL} = V_{IL}max$ | $I_{OL} = 24$ mA | | | | | 0.35 | 0.5 | |
| $I_{OZH}$ | Off-state output current high-level voltage applied | $V_{CC} = MAX$, $V_{IH} = 2$ V, $V_{IL} = V_{IL}max$, $V_O = 2.7$ V | | | | 20 | | | 20 | $\mu$A |
| $I_{OZL}$ | Off-state output current, low-level voltage applied | $V_{CC} = MAX$, $V_{IH} = 2$ V, $V_{IL} = V_{IL}max$, $V_O = 0.4$ V | | | | $-20$ | | | $-20$ | $\mu$A |
| $I_I$ | Input current at maximum input voltage | $V_{CC} = MAX$, $V_I = 7$ V | | | | 100 | | | 100 | $\mu$A |
| $I_{IH}$ | High-level input current | $V_{CC} = MAX$, $V_I = 2.7$ V | | | | 20 | | | 20 | $\mu$A |
| $I_{IL}$ | Low-level input current | $V_{CC} = MAX$, $V_I = 0.4$ V | | | | $-0.4$ | | | $-0.4$ | mA |
| $I_{OS}$ | Short-circuit output current[§] | $V_{CC} = MAX$ | | $-30$ | | $-130$ | $-30$ | | $-130$ | mA |
| $I_{CC}$ | Supply current | $V_{CC} = MAX$, See Note 2 | | | 35 | 60 | | 35 | 60 | mA |

[†]For conditions shown as MIN or MAX, use the appropriate value specified under recommended operating conditions.
[‡]All typical values are at $V_{CC} = 5$ V, $T_A = 25°C$.
[§]Not more than one output should be shorted at a time and duration of the short circuit should not exceed one second.
NOTE 2: $I_{CC}$ is measured with the write-enable and chip-select inputs grounded, all other inputs at 4.5 V, and all outputs open.

**switching characteristics over recommended operating ranges of $T_A$ and $V_{CC}$ (unless otherwise noted)**

| PARAMETER | | TEST CONDITIONS | SN54LS189A SN54LS219A MIN | SN54LS189A SN54LS219A TYP[‡] | SN54LS189A SN54LS219A MAX | SN74LS189A SN74LS219A MIN | SN74LS189A SN74LS219A TYP[‡] | SN74LS189A SN74LS219A MAX | UNIT |
|---|---|---|---|---|---|---|---|---|---|
| $t_{a(ad)}$ | Access time from address | $C_L = 45$ pF, See Note 3 | | 50 | 90 | | 50 | 80 | ns |
| $t_{a(S)}$ | Access time from chip select (enable time) | | | 35 | 70 | | 35 | 60 | ns |
| $t_{SR}$ | Sense recovery time | | | 55 | 100 | | 55 | 90 | ns |
| $t_{PXZ}$ | Disable time from high or low level from $\overline{S}$ | $C_L = 5$ pF, See Note 3 | | 30 | 60 | | 30 | 50 | ns |
| | from $R/\overline{W}$ | | | 40 | 70 | | 40 | 60 | |

[‡]All typical values are at $V_{CC} = 5$ V, $T_A = 25°$.
NOTE 3: Load circuits and voltage waveforms are shown in Section 1.

**5**

**RAMs**

TEXAS
INSTRUMENTS

## recommended operating conditions

| | | SN54LS289A, SN54LS319A | | | SN74LS289A, SN74LS319A | | | UNIT |
|---|---|---|---|---|---|---|---|---|
| | | MIN | NOM | MAX | MIN | NOM | MAX | |
| Supply voltage, $V_{CC}$ | | 4.5 | 5 | 5.5 | 4.75 | 5 | 5.25 | V |
| High-level output voltage, $V_{OH}$ | | | | 5.5 | | | 5.5 | V |
| Low-level output current, $I_{OL}$ | | | | 12 | | | 24 | mA |
| Width of write pulse (write enable low), $t_{w(wr)}$ | | 100 | | | 70 | | | ns |
| Setup time | Address before write pulse, $t_{su(ad)}$ | 0↑ | | | 0↑ | | | ns |
| | Data before end of write pulse, $t_{su(da)}$ | 100↑ | | | 60↑ | | | |
| | Chip-select before end of write pulse, $t_{su(S)}$ | 100↑ | | | 60↑ | | | |
| Hold time | Address after write pulse, $t_{h(ad)}$ | 0↑ | | | 0↑ | | | ns |
| | Data after write pulse, $t_{h(da)}$ | 0↑ | | | 0↑ | | | |
| | Chip-select after write pulse, $t_{h(S)}$ | 0↑ | | | 0↑ | | | |
| Operating free-air temperature, $T_A$ | | −55 | | 125 | 0 | | 70 | °C |

↑↓The arrow indicates the transition of the write-enable input used for reference: ↑ for the low-to-high transition, ↓ for the high-to-low transition.

## electrical characteristics over recommended operating free-air temperature range (unless otherwise noted)

| PARAMETER | | TEST CONDITIONS[†] | SN54LS289A SN54LS319A | | | SN74LS289A SN74LS319A | | | UNIT |
|---|---|---|---|---|---|---|---|---|---|
| | | | MIN | TYP[‡] | MAX | MIN | TYP[‡] | MAX | |
| $V_{IH}$ | High-level input voltage | | 2 | | | 2 | | | V |
| $V_{IL}$ | Low-level input voltage | | | | 0.7 | | | 0.8 | V |
| $V_{IK}$ | Input clamp voltage | $V_{CC}$ = MIN, $I_I$ = −18 mA | | | −1.5 | | | −1.5 | V |
| $I_{OH}$ | High-level output current | $V_{CC}$ = MIN, $V_{IH}$ = 2 V, $V_O$ = 2.4 V | | | 20 | | | 20 | μA |
| | | $V_{IL}$ = $V_{IL}$max, $V_O$ = 5.5 V | | | 100 | | | 100 | |
| $V_{OL}$ | Low-level output voltage | $V_{CC}$ = MIN, $V_{IH}$ = 2 V, $I_{OL}$ = 12 mA | 0.25 | 0.4 | | 0.25 | 0.4 | | V |
| | | $V_{IL}$ = $V_{IL}$max, $I_{OL}$ = 24 mA | | | | 0.35 | 0.5 | | |
| $I_I$ | Input current at maximum input voltage | $V_{CC}$ = MAX, $V_I$ = 7 V | | | 100 | | | 100 | μA |
| $I_{IH}$ | High-level input current | $V_{CC}$ = MAX, $V_I$ = 2.7 V | | | 20 | | | 20 | μA |
| $I_{IL}$ | Low-level input current | $V_{CC}$ = MAX, $V_I$ = 0.4 V | | | −0.4 | | | −0.4 | mA |
| $I_{CC}$ | Supply current | $V_{CC}$ = MAX, See Note 2 | | 35 | 60 | | 35 | 60 | mA |

[†]For conditions shown as MIN or MAX, use the appropriate value specified under recommended operating conditions.
[‡]All typical values are at $V_{CC}$ = 5 V, $T_A$ = 25°C.
[§]Not more than one output should be shorted at a time and duration of the short circuit should not exceed one second.
NOTE 2: $I_{CC}$ is measured with the write-enable and chip-select inputs grounded, all other inputs at 4.5 V, and all outputs open.

## switching characteristics over recommended operating ranges of $T_A$ and $V_{CC}$ (unless otherwise noted)

| PARAMETER | | | TEST CONDITIONS | SN54LS289A SN54LS319A | | | SN74LS289A SN74LS319A | | | UNIT |
|---|---|---|---|---|---|---|---|---|---|---|
| | | | | MIN | TYP[‡] | MAX | MIN | TYP[‡] | MAX | |
| $t_{a(ad)}$ | Access time from address | | | | 50 | 90 | | 50 | 80 | ns |
| $t_{a(S)}$ | Access time from chip select (enable time) | | $C_L$ = 45 pF, $R_L$ = 667Ω, See Note 3 | | 35 | 70 | | 35 | 60 | ns |
| $t_{SR}$ | Sense recovery time | | | | 55 | 100 | | 55 | 90 | ns |
| $t_{PLH}$ | Propagation delay time, low-to-high-level output (disable time) | from $\overline{S}$ | | | 30 | 60 | | 30 | 50 | ns |
| | | from R/$\overline{W}$ | | | 40 | 70 | | 40 | 60 | |

[‡]All typical values are at $V_{CC}$ = 5 V, $T_A$ = 25°.
NOTE 3: Load circuits and voltage waveforms are shown in Section 1.

**5**
**RAMs**

**TEXAS INSTRUMENTS**

## STATIC RANDOM-ACCESS MEMORIES

- Fully Decoded RAMs Organized as 16 Words of Four Bits Each

- Schottky-Clamped for High Speed:
  Read Cycle Time . . . 25 ns Typical
  Write Cycle Time . . . 25 ns Typical

- Choice of Three-State or Open-Collector Outputs

- Compatible with Most TTL and $I^2L$ Circuits

- Chip-Select Input Simplifies External Decoding

**SN54S189B, SN54S289B . . . J OR W PACKAGE**
**SN74S189B, SN74S289B . . . J OR N PACKAGE**
**(TOP VIEW)**

```
        ___
A0  [ 1  U 16 ] VCC
 S  [ 2    15 ] A1
 W  [ 3    14 ] A2
D1  [ 4    13 ] A3
Q1  [ 5    12 ] D4
D2  [ 6    11 ] Q4
Q2  [ 7    10 ] D3
GND [ 8     9 ] Q3
```

### description

These 64-bit active-element memories are monolithic Schottky-clamped transistor-transistor logic (TTL) arrays organized as 16 words of four bits each. They are fully decoded and feature a chip-select input to simplify decoding required to achieve expanded system organization. The memories feature p-n-p input transistors that reduce the low-level input current requirement to a maximum of $-0.25$ milliamperes, only one-eighth that of a Series 54S/74S standard load factor. The chip-select circuitry is implemented with minimal delay times to compensate for added system decoding.

### write cycle

The information applied at the data input is written into the selected location when the chip-select input and the write-enable input are low. While the write-enable input is low, the 'S189B output is in the high-impedance state and the 'S289B output is off. When a number of outputs are bus-connected, this high-impedance or off state will neither load nor drive the bus line, but it will allow the bus line to be driven by another active output or a passive pull-up.

### read cycle

The stored information (complement of information applied at the data input during the write cycle) is available at the output when the write-enable input is high and the chip-select input is low. When the chip-select input is high, the 'S189B output will be in the high-impedance state and the 'S289B output will be off.

### FUNCTION TABLE

| FUNCTION | INPUTS | | 'S189B OUTPUT | 'S289B OUTPUT |
|---|---|---|---|---|
| | CHIP SELECT | WRITE ENABLE | | |
| Write | L | L | High Impedance | Off |
| Read | L | H | Complement of Data Entered | Complement of Data Entered |
| Inhibit | H | X | High Impedance | Off |

H = high level, L = low level, X = irrelevant

**TEXAS**
**INSTRUMENTS**

**5**

**RAMs**

### logic symbols

### functional block diagram

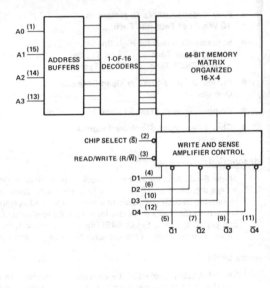

### schematics of inputs and outputs

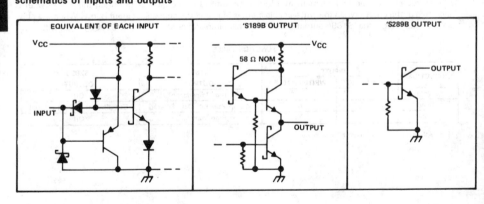

**TEXAS INSTRUMENTS**

## absolute maximum ratings over operating free-air temperature range (unless otherwise noted)

Supply voltage, $V_{CC}$ (see Note 1) . . . . . . . . . . . . . . . . . . . . . . . . . . . . . . . . . . . . . . . . . . . . . 7 V
Input voltage . . . . . . . . . . . . . . . . . . . . . . . . . . . . . . . . . . . . . . . . . . . . . . . . . . . . . . . . . . . . . 5.5 V
Off-State output voltage . . . . . . . . . . . . . . . . . . . . . . . . . . . . . . . . . . . . . . . . . . . . . . . . . . . . 5.5 V
Operating free-air temperature range: SN54S' Circuits . . . . . . . . . . . . . . . . . . . . −55 °C to 125 °C
 SN74S' Circuits . . . . . . . . . . . . . . . . . . . . . . . . 0 °C to 70 °C
Storage temperature range . . . . . . . . . . . . . . . . . . . . . . . . . . . . . . . . . . . . . . . . . −65 °C to 150 °C

NOTE 1: Voltage values are with respect to network ground terminal.

## recommended operating conditions

| | | SN54S' | | | SN74S' | | | UNIT |
|---|---|---|---|---|---|---|---|---|
| | | MIN | NOM | MAX | MIN | NOM | MAX | |
| Supply voltage, $V_{CC}$ | | 4.5 | 5 | 5.5 | 4.75 | 5 | 5.25 | V |
| High-level output voltage, $V_{OH}$ | 'S289B | | | 5.5 | | | 5.5 | V |
| High-level output current, $I_{OH}$ | 'S189B | | | −2 | | | −6.5 | mA |
| Low-level output current, $I_{OL}$ | | | | 16 | | | 16 | mA |
| Width of write pulse (write enable low), $t_{w(wr)}$ | | 25 | | | 25 | | | ns |
| Setup time | Address before write pulse, $t_{su(da)}$ | 0↓ | | | 0↓ | | | ns |
| | Data before end of write pulse, $t_{su(da)}$ | 25↑ | | | 25↑ | | | |
| | Chip-select before end of write pulse, $t_{su(S)}$ | 25↑ | | | 25↑ | | | |
| Hold time | Address after write pulse, $t_{h(ad)}$ | 3↑ | | | 0↑ | | | ns |
| | Data after write pulse, $t_{h(da)}$ | 0↑ | | | 0↑ | | | |
| | Chip-select after write pulse, $t_{h(\overline{S})}$ | 0↑ | | | 0↑ | | | |
| Operating free-air temperature, $T_A$ | | −55 | | 125 | 0 | | 70 | °C |

↑↓The arrow indicates the transition of the write-enable input used for reference: ↑ for the low-to-high transition, ↓ for the high-to-low transition.

## electrical characteristics over recommended operating free-air temperature range (unless otherwise noted)

| PARAMETER | | TEST CONDITIONS† | 'S189B MIN | 'S189B TYP‡ | 'S189B MAX | 'S289B MIN | 'S289B TYP‡ | 'S289B MAX | UNIT |
|---|---|---|---|---|---|---|---|---|---|
| $V_{IH}$ | High-level input voltage | | 2 | | | 2 | | | V |
| $V_{IL}$ | Low-level input voltage | | | | 0.8 | | | 0.8 | V |
| $V_{IK}$ | Input clamp voltage | $V_{CC}$ = MIN, $I_I$ = −18 mA | | | −1.2 | | | −1.2 | V |
| $V_{OH}$ | High-level output voltage | $V_{CC}$ = MIN, $V_{IH}$ = 2 V, SN54S'<br>$V_{IL}$ = 0.8 V, $I_{OH}$ = MAX SN74S' | 2.4<br>2.4 | 3.4<br>3.2 | | | | | V |
| $I_{OH}$ | High-level output current | $V_{CC}$ = MIN, $V_{IH}$ = 2 V, $V_O$ = 2.4 V<br>$V_{IL}$ = 0.8 V, $V_O$ = 5.5 V | | | | | | 40<br>100 | µA |
| $V_{OL}$ | Low-level output voltage | $V_{CC}$ = MIN, $V_{IH}$ = 2 V,<br>$V_{IL}$ = 0.8 V, $I_{OL}$ = 16 mA | | 0.35 | 0.5 | | 0.35 | 0.5 | V |
| $I_{OZH}$ | Off-state output current, high-level voltage applied | $V_{CC}$ = MAX, $V_{IH}$ = 2 V,<br>$V_{IL}$ = 0.8 V, $V_{OH}$ = 2.4 V | | | 50 | | | | µA |
| $I_{OZL}$ | Off-state output current, low-level voltage applied | $V_{CC}$ = MAX, $V_{IH}$ = 2 V,<br>$V_{IL}$ = 0.8 V, $V_{OL}$ = 0.4 V | | | −50 | | | | µA |
| $I_I$ | Input current at maximum input voltage | $V_{CC}$ = MAX, $V_I$ = 5.5 V | | | 1 | | | 1 | mA |
| $I_{IH}$ | High-level input current | $V_{CC}$ = MAX, $V_I$ = 2.7 V | | | 25 | | | 25 | µA |
| $I_{IL}$ | Low-level input current | $V_{CC}$ = MAX, $V_I$ = 0.5 V | | | −250 | | | −250 | µA |
| $I_{OS}$ | Short-circuit output current§ | $V_{CC}$ = MAX | −30 | | −100 | | | | mA |
| $I_{CC}$ | Supply current | $V_{CC}$ = MAX, See Note 2 | | 75 | 110 | | 75 | 105 | mA |

NOTE 2: $I_{CC}$ is measured with the read/write and chip-select inputs grounded. All other inputs at 4.5 V, and the outputs open.

## 'S189B switching characteristics over recommended operating ranges of $T_A$ and $V_{CC}$ (unless otherwise noted)

| PARAMETER | | TEST CONDITIONS | SN54S189B MIN | SN54S189B TYP‡ | SN54S189B MAX | SN74S189B MIN | SN74S189B TYP‡ | SN74S189B MAX | UNIT |
|---|---|---|---|---|---|---|---|---|---|
| $t_{a(ad)}$ | Access time from address | | | 25 | 50 | | 25 | 35 | ns |
| $t_{a(S)}$ | Access time from chip select (enable time) | $C_L$ = 30 pF,<br>See Note 3 | | 18 | 25 | | 18 | 22 | ns |
| $t_{SR}$ | Sense recovery time | | | 22 | 40 | | 22 | 35 | ns |
| $t_{PXZ}$ | Disable time from high or low level — From S̄ | $C_L$ = 5 pF,<br>See Note 3 | | 12 | 25 | | 12 | 17 | ns |
| | From W̄ | | | 12 | 30 | | 12 | 25 | |

## 'S289B switching characteristics over recommended operating ranges of $T_A$ and $V_{CC}$ (unless otherwise noted)

| PARAMETER | | TEST CONDITIONS | SN54S289B MIN | SN54S289B TYP‡ | SN54S289B MAX | SN74S289B MIN | SN74S289B TYP‡ | SN74S289B MAX | UNIT |
|---|---|---|---|---|---|---|---|---|---|
| $t_{a(ad)}$ | Access time from address | | | 25 | 50 | | 25 | 35 | ns |
| $t_{a(S)}$ | Access time from chip-select (enable time) | $C_L$ = 30 pF,<br>$R_{L1}$ = 300 Ω,<br>$R_{L2}$ = 600 Ω,<br>See Note 3 | | 18 | 25 | | 18 | 22 | ns |
| $t_{SR}$ | Sense recovery time | | | 22 | 40 | | 22 | 35 | ns |
| $t_{PLH}$ | Propagation delay time, low-to-high-level output (disable time) — From S̄ | | | 12 | 25 | | 12 | 17 | ns |
| | From W̄ | | | 12 | 30 | | 12 | 25 | |

†For conditions shown as MIN or MAX use the appropriate value specified under recommended operating conditions.

‡All typical values are at $V_{CC}$ = 5 V, $T_A$ = 25°.

§Duration of the short circuit should not exceed one second.

NOTE 3: Load circuits and voltage waveforms are shown in Section 1.

TEXAS
INSTRUMENTS

## STATIC RANDOM-ACCESS MEMORIES

- Static Fully Decoded RAM's Organized as 256 Words of One Bit Each

- Schottky-Clamped for High Performance

- Choice of Three-State or Open-Collector Outputs

- Compatible with Most TTL and $I^2L$ Circuits

- Chip-Select Input Simplify External Decoding

- Typical Performance:
  Read Access Time . . . 42 ns
  Power dissipation . . . 500 mW

SN74S201, SN74S301 . . . J OR N PACKAGE
(TOP VIEW)

| | | |
|---|---|---|
| A0 | 1 | 16 | $V_{CC}$ |
| A1 | 2 | 15 | A2 |
| $\overline{S}1$ | 3 | 14 | A7 |
| $\overline{S}2$ | 4 | 13 | D |
| $\overline{S}3$ | 5 | 12 | R/$\overline{W}$ |
| $\overline{Q}$ | 6 | 11 | A6 |
| A3 | 7 | 10 | A5 |
| GND | 8 | 9 | A4 |

## description

These 256-bit active-element memories are monolithic transistor-transistor logic (TTL) arrays organized as 256 words of one bit. They are fully decoded and have three chip-select inputs to simplify decoding required to achive expanded system organizations.

## write cycle

The information applied at the data input is written into the selected location when the chip-select inputs and the write-enable input are low. While the write-enable input is low, the 'S201 outputs are in the high-impedance state and the 'S301 outputs are off. When a number of outputs are bus-connected, this high-impedance or off state will neither load nor drive the bus line, but it will allow the bus line to be driven by another active output or a passive pull-up.

## read cycle

The stored information (complement of information applied at the data input during the write cycle) is available at the output when the write-enable input is high and the three chip-select inputs is low. When any one of the chip-select inputs are high, the 'S201 outputs will be in the high-impedance state and the 'S301 outputs will be off.

### FUNCTION TABLE

| FUNCTION | INPUTS | | 'S201 OUTPUT ($\overline{Q}$) | 'S301 OUTPUT ($\overline{Q}$) |
|---|---|---|---|---|
| | CHIP SELECT $\overline{S}$ | WRITE ENABLE R/$\overline{W}$ | | |
| Write | L | L | High Impedance | Off |
| Read | L | H | Complement of Data Entered | Complement of Data Entered |
| Inhibit | H | X | High Impedance | Off |

H ≡ high level, L ≡ low level, X ≡ irrelevant
For chip-select: L ≡ all $\overline{S}i$ inputs low, H ≡ one or more $\overline{S}i$ inputs high

5

RAMs

TEXAS
INSTRUMENTS

# SN74S201, SN74S301
## 256-BIT HIGH-PERFORMANCE RANDOM-ACCESS MEMORIES

## logic symbols

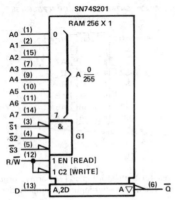

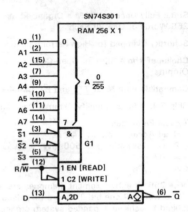

## schematics of inputs and outputs

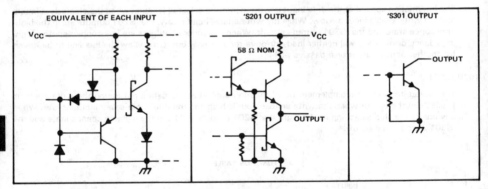

## absolute maximum ratings over operating free-air temperature range (unless otherwise noted)

Supply voltage, $V_{CC}$ (see Note 1) . . . . . . . . . . . . . . . . . . . . . . . . . . . . . . . . . . . . . . . . . . . . . . . 7 V
Input voltage . . . . . . . . . . . . . . . . . . . . . . . . . . . . . . . . . . . . . . . . . . . . . . . . . . . . . . . . . . . . . . . 5.5 V
Off-State output voltage . . . . . . . . . . . . . . . . . . . . . . . . . . . . . . . . . . . . . . . . . . . . . . . . . . . . . . 5.5 V
Operating free-air temperature range . . . . . . . . . . . . . . . . . . . . . . . . . . . . . . . . . . . . . . . . 0°C to 70°C
Storage temperature range . . . . . . . . . . . . . . . . . . . . . . . . . . . . . . . . . . . . . . . . . . . . . −65°C to 150°C

**TEXAS**
**INSTRUMENTS**

## recommended operating conditions

| | | SN74S201 | | | SN74S301 | | | UNIT |
|---|---|---|---|---|---|---|---|---|
| | | MIN | NOM | MAX | MIN | NOM | MAX | |
| Supply voltage, $V_{CC}$(see Note 1) | | 4.75 | 5 | 5.25 | 4.75 | 5 | 5.25 | V |
| High-level output voltage, $V_{OH}$ | | | | | | | 5.5 | V |
| High-level output current, $I_{OH}$ | | | | −10.3 | | | | mA |
| Low-level output current, $I_{OL}$ | | | | 16 | | | 16 | mA |
| Width of write pulse (write enable low), $t_{w(wr)}$ | | 65 | | | 65 | | | ns |
| Setup time | Address before write pulse, $t_{su(ad)}$ | 0↓ | | | 0↓ | | | ns |
| | Data before end of write pulse, $t_{su(da)}$ | 65↑ | | | 65↑ | | | |
| | Chip-select before end of write pulse, $t_{su(\overline{S})}$ | 65↑ | | | 65↑ | | | |
| Hold time | Address after write pulse, $t_{h(ad)}$ | 0↑ | | | 0↑ | | | ns |
| | Data after write pulse, $t_{h(da)}$ | 0↑ | | | 0↑ | | | |
| | Chip-select after write pulse, $t_{h(\overline{S})}$ | 0↑ | | | 0↑ | | | |
| Operating free-air temperature, $T_A$ | | 0 | | 70 | 0 | | 70 | °C |

↑↓The arrow indicates the transition of the write-enable input used for reference: ↑ for the low-to-high transition, ↓ for the high-to-low transition.
NOTE 1: Voltage values are with respect to network ground terminal.

## electrical characteristics over recommended operating free-air temperature range (unless otherwise noted)

| | PARAMETER | TEST CONDITIONS[†] | 'S201 | | | 'S301 | | | UNIT |
|---|---|---|---|---|---|---|---|---|---|
| | | | MIN | TYP[‡] | MAX | MIN | TYP[‡] | MAX | |
| $V_{IH}$ | High-level input voltage | | 2 | | | 2 | | | V |
| $V_{IL}$ | Low-level input voltage | | | | 0.8 | | | 0.8 | V |
| $V_{IK}$ | Input clamp voltage | $V_{CC}$ = MIN, $I_I$ = −18 mA | | | −1.2 | | | −1.2 | V |
| $V_{OH}$ | High-level output voltage | $V_{CC}$ = MIN, $V_{IH}$ = 2 V, $V_{IL}$ = 0.8 V, $I_{OH}$ = MAX | 2.4 | | | | | | V |
| $V_{OL}$ | Low-level output voltage | $V_{CC}$ = MIN, $V_{IH}$ = 2 V, $I_{OL}$ = 16 mA | | | 0.45 | | | 0.45 | V |
| $I_{OH}$ | High-level output current | $V_{CC}$ = MIN, $V_{IH}$ = 2 V, $V_{IL}$ = 0.8 V, $V_O$ = 2.4 V | | | | | | 40 | µA |
| | | $V_O$ = 5.5 V | | | | | | 100 | |
| $I_{OZH}$ | Off-state output current, high-level voltage applied | $V_{CC}$ = MAX, $V_{IH}$ = 2 V, $V_{IL}$ = 0.8 V, $V_{OH}$ = 2.4 V | | | 40 | | | | µA |
| $I_{OZL}$ | Off-state output current, low-level voltage applied | $V_{CC}$ = MAX, $V_{IH}$ = 2 V, $V_{IL}$ = 0.8 V, $V_{OL}$ = 0.5 V | | | −40 | | | | µA |
| $I_I$ | Input current at maximum input voltage | $V_{CC}$ = MAX, $V_I$ = 5.5 V | | | 1 | | | 1 | mA |
| $I_{IH}$ | High-level input current | $V_{CC}$ = MAX, $V_I$ = 2.7 V | | | 25 | | | 25 | µA |
| $I_{IL}$ | Low-level input current | $V_{CC}$ = MAX, $V_I$ = 0.5 V | | | −250 | | | −250 | µA |
| $I_{OS}$ | Short-circuit output current [§] | $V_{CC}$ = MAX | −30 | | −100 | | | | mA |
| $I_{CC}$ | Supply current | $V_{CC}$ = MAX, See Note 2 | | 100 | 140 | | 100 | 140 | mA |

[†]For conditions shown as MIN or MAX use the appropriate value specified under recommended operating conditions.
[‡]All typical values are at $V_{CC}$ = 5 V, $T_A$ = 25 °C.
[§]Duration of the short circuit should not exceed one second.
NOTE 2: $I_{CC}$ is measured with all chip-select inputs grounded, all other inputs at 4.5 V, and the output open.

**5**

**RAMs**

### 'S201 switching characteristics over recommended operating ranges of $T_A$ and $V_{CC}$ (unless otherwise noted)

| PARAMETER | | TEST CONDITIONS | MIN | TYP[‡] | MAX | UNIT |
|---|---|---|---|---|---|---|
| $t_{a(ad)}$ Access time from address | | $C_L$ = 30 pF, See Note 3 | | 42 | 65 | ns |
| $t_{a(S)}$ Access time from chip select (select time) | | | | 13 | 30 | ns |
| $t_{SR}$ Sense recovery time | | | | 20 | 40 | ns |
| $t_{PXZ}$ Disable time from high or low level | From $\overline{S}$ | $C_L$ = 5 pF, See Note 3 | | 9 | 20 | ns |
| | From R/$\overline{W}$ | | | | | |

### 'S301 switching characteristics over recommended operating ranges of $T_A$ and $V_{CC}$ (unless otherwise noted)

| PARAMETER | | TEST CONDITIONS | MIN | TYP[‡] | MAX | UNIT |
|---|---|---|---|---|---|---|
| $t_{a(ad)}$ Access time from address | | $C_L$ = 30 pF, $R_{L1}$ = 300 Ω, $R_{L2}$ = 600 Ω, See Note 3 | | 42 | 65 | ns |
| $t_{a(S)}$ Access time from chip enable (enable time) | | | | 13 | 30 | ns |
| $t_{SR}$ Sense recovery time | | | | 20 | 40 | ns |
| $t_{PLH}$ Propagation delay time, low-to-high-level output (disable time) | From $\overline{S}$ | | | 8 | 20 | ns |
| | From R/$\overline{W}$ | | | 15 | 35 | |

[‡]All typical values are at $V_{CC}$ = 5 V, $T_A$ = 25°.
NOTE 3: Load circuits and voltage waveforms are shown in Section 1.

TEXAS
INSTRUMENTS

MAY 1972 — REVISED DECEMBER 1983

- **Fast Multiplication of Two Binary Numbers**
  **8-Bit Product in 40 ns Typical**

- **Expandable for N-Bit-by-n-Bit Applications:**
  **16-Bit Product in 70 ns Typical**
  **32-Bit Product in 103 ns Typical**

- **Fully Compatible with Most TTL Circuits**

- **Diode-Clamped Inputs Simplify System Design**

## description

These high-speed TTL circuits are designed to be used in high-performance parallel multiplication applications. When connected as shown in Figure A, these circuits perform the positive-logic multiplication of two 4-bit binary words. The eight-bit binary product is generated with typically only 40 nanoseconds delay.

This basic four-by-four multiplier can be utilized as a fundamental building block for implementing larger multipliers. For example, the four-by-four building blocks can be connected as shown in Figure B to generate submultiple partial products. These results can then be summed in a Wallace tree, and, as illustrated, will produce a 16-bit product for the two eight-bit words typically in 70 nanoseconds. SN54H183/SN74H183 carry-save adders and SN54S181/SN74S181 arithmetic logic units with the SN54S182/SN74S182 look-ahead generator are used to achieve this high performance. The scheme is expandable for implementing N × M bit multipliers.

The SN54284 and SN54285 are characterized for operation over the full military temperature range of −55°C to 125°C; the SN74284 and SN74285 are characterized for operation from 0°C to 70°C.

```
SN54284 . . . J OR W PACKAGE
SN74284 . . . J OR N PACKAGE
          (TOP VIEW)

      2C  [ 1  U 16 ]  VCC
      2B  [ 2    15 ]  2D
      2A  [ 3    14 ]  GA
      1D  [ 4    13 ]  GB
      1A  [ 5    12 ]  Y4
      1B  [ 6    11 ]  Y5
      1C  [ 7    10 ]  Y6
     GND  [ 8     9 ]  Y7
```

```
SN54285 . . . J OR W PACKAGE
SN74285 . . . J OR N PACKAGE
          (TOP VIEW)

      2C  [ 1  U 16 ]  VCC
      2B  [ 2    15 ]  2D
      2A  [ 3    14 ]  GA
      1D  [ 4    13 ]  GB
      1A  [ 5    12 ]  Y0
      1B  [ 6    11 ]  Y1
      1C  [ 7    10 ]  Y2
     GND  [ 8     9 ]  Y3
```

## logic symbols

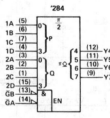

'284

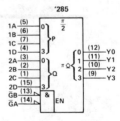

'285

Pin numbers shown are for J and N packages.

**TEXAS INSTRUMENTS**

5

RAMs

**schematics**

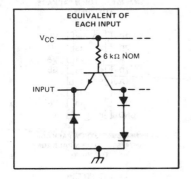

EQUIVALENT OF
EACH INPUT

$V_{CC}$

6 kΩ NOM

INPUT

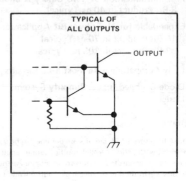

TYPICAL OF
ALL OUTPUTS

OUTPUT

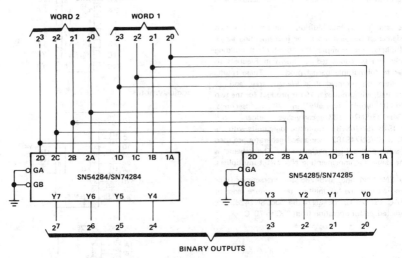

BINARY INPUTS

WORD 2

$2^3$ $2^2$ $2^1$ $2^0$

WORD 1

$2^3$ $2^2$ $2^1$ $2^0$

| 2D | 2C | 2B | 2A | | 1D | 1C | 1B | 1A |

GA
GB

SN54284/SN74284

Y7  Y6  Y5  Y4

$2^7$ $2^6$ $2^5$ $2^4$

| 2D | 2C | 2B | 2A | | 1D | 1C | 1B | 1A |

GA
GB

SN54285/SN74285

Y3  Y2  Y1  Y0

$2^3$ $2^2$ $2^1$ $2^0$

BINARY OUTPUTS

FIGURE A—4 X 4 MULTIPLIER

5

RAMs

TEXAS
INSTRUMENTS

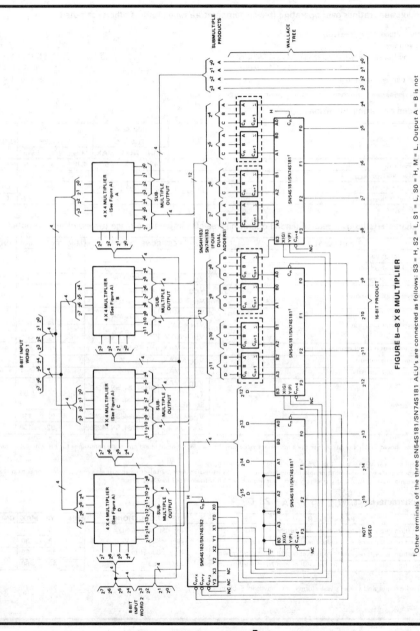

FIGURE B–8 X 8 MULTIPLIER

†Other terminals of the three SN54S181/SN74S181 ALU's are connected as follows: S3 = H, S2 = L, S1 = L, S0 = H, M = L. Output A = B is not used for this application.

## SN54284, SN54285, SN74284, SN74285
## 4-BIT BY 4-BIT PARALLEL BINARY MULTIPLIERS

### absolute maximum ratings over operating free-air temperature range (unless otherwise noted)

Supply voltage, $V_{CC}$ (see Note 1) . . . . . . . . . . . . . . . . . . . . . . . . . . . . . . . . 7 V
Input voltage . . . . . . . . . . . . . . . . . . . . . . . . . . . . . . . . . . . . . . . . . . . 5.5 V
Operating free-air temperature range: SN54' Circuits . . . . . . . . . . . . . . . . . . $-55°C$ to $125°C$
SN74' Circuits . . . . . . . . . . . . . . . . . . . . . $0°C$ to $70°C$
Storage temperature range . . . . . . . . . . . . . . . . . . . . . . . . . . . . . $-65°C$ to $150°C$

NOTE 1: Voltage values are with respect to network ground terminal.

### recommended operating conditions

| | SN54284 SN54285 | | | SN74284 SN74285 | | | UNIT |
|---|---|---|---|---|---|---|---|
| | MIN | NOM | MAX | MIN | NOM | MAX | |
| Supply voltage, $V_{CC}$ | 4.5 | 5 | 5.5 | 4.75 | 5 | 5.25 | V |
| High-level output voltage, $V_{OH}$ | | | 5.5 | | | 5.5 | V |
| Low-level output current, $I_{OL}$ | | | 16 | | | 16 | mA |
| Operating free-air temperature, $T_A$ | $-55$ | | 125 | 0 | | 70 | °C |

### electrical characteristics over recommended operating free-air temperature range (unless otherwise noted)

| PARAMETER | | TEST CONDITIONS[†] | | MIN | TYP[‡] | MAX | UNIT |
|---|---|---|---|---|---|---|---|
| $V_{IH}$ | High-level input voltage | | | 2 | | | V |
| $V_{IL}$ | Low-level input voltage | | | | | 0.8 | V |
| $V_I$ | Input clamp voltage | $V_{CC}$ = MIN, $I_I$ = $-12$ mA | | | | $-1.5$ | V |
| $I_{OH}$ | High-level output current | $V_{CC}$ = MIN, $V_{IH}$ = 2 V, $V_{IL}$ = 0.8 V, $V_{OH}$ = 5.5 V | | | | 40 | $\mu$A |
| $V_{OL}$ | Low-level output voltage | $V_{CC}$ = MIN, $V_{IH}$ = 2 V, $V_{IL}$ = 0.8 V | $I_{OL}$ = 12 mA | | | 0.4 | V |
| | | | $I_{OL}$ = 16 mA | | | 0.45 | |
| $I_I$ | Input current at maximum input voltage | $V_{CC}$ = MAX, $V_I$ = 5.5 V | | | | 1 | mA |
| $I_{IH}$ | High-level input current | $V_{CC}$ = MAX, $V_I$ = 2.4 V | | | | 40 | $\mu$A |
| $I_{IL}$ | Low-level input current | $V_{CC}$ = MAX, $V_I$ = 0.4 V | | | | $-1$ | mA |
| $I_{CC}$ | Supply current | $V_{CC}$ = MAX, $T_A$ = 125°C, See Note 2 | SN54284, SN54285 N package only | | | 99 | mA |
| | | $V_{CC}$ = MAX, See Note 2 | SN54284, SN54285 | | 92 | 110 | |
| | | | SN74284, SN74285 | | 92 | 130 | |

[†]For conditions shown as MIN or MAX, use the appropriate value specified under recommended operating conditions for the applicable device type.
[‡]All typical values are at $V_{CC}$ = 5 V, $T_A$ = 25°C.
NOTE 2: With outputs open and both enable inputs grounded, $I_{CC}$ is measured first by selecting an output product which contains three or more high-level bits, then by selecting an output product which contains four low-level bits.

### switching characteristics, $V_{CC}$ = 5 V, $T_A$ = 25°C

| PARAMETER | | TEST CONDITIONS | MIN | TYP | MAX | UNIT |
|---|---|---|---|---|---|---|
| $t_{PLH}$ | Propagation delay time, low-to-high-level output from enable | $C_L$ = 30 pF to GND, $R_{L1}$ = 300 $\Omega$ to $V_{CC}$, $R_{L2}$ = 600 $\Omega$ to GND, See Note 3 | | 20 | 30 | ns |
| $t_{PHL}$ | Propagation delay time, high-to-low-level output from enable | | | 20 | 30 | |
| $t_{PLH}$ | Propagation delay time, low-to-high-level output from word inputs | | | 40 | 60 | ns |
| $t_{PHL}$ | Propagation delay time, high-to-low-level output from word inputs | | | 40 | 60 | |

NOTE 3: Load circuits and voltage waveforms are shown in Section 1.

TEXAS
INSTRUMENTS

**5**

**RAMS**

D2534, JUNE 1979—REVISED FEBRUARY 1984

## SN54S484A, SN74S484A, BCD-TO-BINARY CONVERTERS
## SN54S485A, SN74S485A BINARY-TO-BCD CONVERTERS

- **Significant Savings in Package Count Compared with SN54184, SN54185A, SN74184, or SN74185A (Over Half in Many Applications)**

- **Three-State Outputs**

### description

These monolithic converters are derived from the TBP28L22 factory-programmed read-only memories. Both of these converters comprehend that the least-significant bits (LSB) of the binary and BCD are logically equal, and in each case, the LSB bypasses the converter as shown in the typical applications. This means that a nine-bit converter is produced in each case. The devices are cascadable to N bits.

The three-state outputs offer the convenience of open-collector outputs with the speed of totem-pole outputs: they can be bus-connected to other similar outputs yet they retain the fast rise-time characteristic of totem-pole outputs. A high logic level at either enable ($\overline{G}$) input causes the outputs to be in high-impedance state.

In many applications these converters can, by including 3 more bits than the SN54184/SN74184 or SN54185A/SN74185A, reduce power consumption significantly and package count by more than half as shown in the tables below.

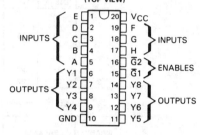

SN54S484A, SN54S485A . . . J PACKAGE
SN54S484A, SN54S485A . . . J OR N PACKAGE
(TOP VIEW)

### logic symbols

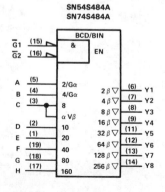

SN54S484A
SN74S484A

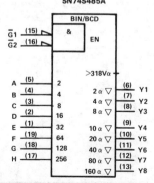

SN54S485A
SN74S485A

TEXAS
INSTRUMENTS

5
RAMs

**SN54S484A/SN74S484A vs SN54184/SN74184**

| DECADES | PACKAGE COUNT | | MAXIMUM SUPPLY CURRENT (A) | | TYPICAL ACCESS TIME @ $T_A$ = 25°C (ns) | |
|---|---|---|---|---|---|---|
| | 'S484A | '184 | 'S484A | '184 | 'S484A | '184 |
| 3 | 3 | 6 | 0.41 | 0.59 | 117 | 135 |
| 4 | 5 | 11 | 0.72 | 1.09 | 180 | 189 |
| 5 | 8 | 18 | 1.18 | 1.78 | 270 | 270 |
| 6 | 12 | 27 | 1.75 | 2.67 | 342 | 351 |
| 7 | 16 | 38 | 2.37 | 3.76 | 405 | 405 |
| 8 | 21 | 49 | 3.14 | 4.85 | 495 | 485 |
| 9 | 27 | 62 | 4.02 | 6.14 | 567 | 540 |

**SN54S485A/SN74S485A vs SN54185A/SN74185A**

| BINARY BITS | PACKAGE COUNT | | MAXIMUM SUPPLY CURRENT (A) | | TYPICAL ACCESS TIME @ $T_A$ = 25°C (ns) | |
|---|---|---|---|---|---|---|
| | 'S485A | '185A | '485A | '185A | 'S485A | '185A |
| 8 | 2 | 3 | 0.25 | 0.30 | 72 | 81 |
| 16 | 8 | 16 | 1.12 | 1.58 | 252 | 216 |
| 24 | 19 | 40 | 2.67 | 3.96 | 459 | 351 |
| 32 | 33 | 74 | 4.78 | 5.45 | 612 | 486 |

TEXAS
INSTRUMENTS

## SN54S484A, SN74S484A
## BCD-TO-BINARY CONVERTER
## FUNCTION TABLE

| INPUTS | | | | | | | | OUTPUTS | | | | | | | |
|---|---|---|---|---|---|---|---|---|---|---|---|---|---|---|---|
| H | G | F | E | D | C | B | A | Y8 | Y7 | Y6 | Y5 | Y4 | Y3 | Y2 | Y1 |
| 160 | 80 | 40 | 20 | 10 | 8 | 4 | 2 | 256 | 128 | 64 | 32 | 16 | 8 | 4 | 2 |
| L | L | L | L | L | L | L | L | L | L | L | L | L | L | L | L |
| L | L | L | L | L | L | L | H | L | L | L | L | L | L | L | H |
| L | L | L | L | L | L | H | L | L | L | L | L | L | L | H | L |
| L | L | L | L | L | L | H | H | L | L | L | L | L | L | H | H |
| L | L | L | L | L | H | L | L | L | L | L | L | L | H | L | L |
| L | L | L | L | L | H | L | H | Invalid BCD code (All outputs are high) | | | | | | | |
| L | L | L | L | L | H | H | L | Invalid BCD code (All outputs are high) | | | | | | | |
| L | L | L | L | L | H | H | H | Invalid BCD code (All outputs are high) | | | | | | | |
| L | L | L | L | H | L | L | L | L | L | L | L | L | H | L | H |
| L | L | L | L | H | L | L | H | L | L | L | L | L | H | H | L |
| L | L | L | L | H | L | H | L | L | L | L | L | L | H | H | H |
| H | H | H | H | L | L | H | L | H | L | L | H | H | L | L | L |
| H | H | H | H | L | L | H | H | H | L | L | H | H | L | L | H |
| H | H | H | H | L | H | L | L | H | L | L | H | H | L | H | L |
| H | H | H | H | L | H | L | H | Invalid BCD code (All outputs are high) | | | | | | | |
| H | H | H | H | L | H | H | L | Invalid BCD code (All outputs are high) | | | | | | | |
| H | H | H | H | L | H | H | H | Invalid BCD code (All outputs are high) | | | | | | | |
| H | H | H | H | H | L | L | L | H | L | L | H | H | L | H | H |
| H | H | H | H | H | L | L | H | H | L | L | H | H | H | L | L |
| H | H | H | H | H | L | H | L | H | L | L | H | H | H | L | H |
| H | H | H | H | H | L | H | H | H | L | L | H | H | H | H | L |
| H | H | H | H | H | H | L | L | H | L | L | H | H | H | H | H |
| H | H | H | H | H | H | L | H | Invalid BCD code (All outputs are high) | | | | | | | |
| H | H | H | H | H | H | H | L | Invalid BCD code (All outputs are high) | | | | | | | |
| H | H | H | H | H | H | H | H | Invalid BCD code (All outputs are high) | | | | | | | |
| X | X | X | X | X | H | X | H | H | H | H | H | H | H | H | H |
| X | X | X | X | X | H | H | X | H | H | H | H | H | H | H | H |

H = high level    L = low level    X = irrelevant

## SN54S485A, SN74S485A
## BINARY-TO-BCD CONVERTER
## FUNCTION TABLE

| INPUTS | | | | | | | | OUTPUTS | | | | | | | |
|---|---|---|---|---|---|---|---|---|---|---|---|---|---|---|---|
| H | G | F | E | D | C | B | A | Y8 | Y7 | Y6 | Y5 | Y4 | Y3 | Y2 | Y1 |
| 256 | 128 | 64 | 32 | 16 | 8 | 4 | 2 | 160 | 80 | 40 | 20 | 10 | 8 | 4 | 2 |
| L | L | L | L | L | L | L | L | L | L | L | L | L | L | L | L |
| L | L | L | L | L | L | L | H | L | L | L | L | L | L | L | H |
| L | L | L | L | L | L | H | L | L | L | L | L | L | L | H | L |
| L | L | L | L | L | L | H | H | L | L | L | L | L | L | H | H |
| L | L | L | L | L | H | L | L | L | L | L | L | L | H | L | L |
| L | L | L | L | L | H | L | H | L | L | L | L | H | L | L | L |
| L | L | L | L | L | H | H | L | L | L | L | L | H | L | L | H |
| L | L | L | L | L | H | H | H | L | L | L | L | H | L | H | L |
| L | L | L | L | H | L | L | L | L | L | L | L | H | L | H | H |
| L | L | L | L | H | L | L | H | L | L | L | L | H | H | L | L |
| L | L | L | L | H | L | H | L | L | L | L | H | L | L | L | L |
| H | L | L | H | L | L | L | L | H | H | H | L | L | H | L | L |
| H | L | L | H | L | L | L | H | H | H | H | L | L | H | L | H |
| H | L | L | H | L | L | H | L | H | H | H | L | L | H | H | L |
| H | L | L | H | L | L | H | H | H | H | H | L | L | H | H | H |
| H | L | L | H | L | H | L | L | H | H | H | L | H | L | H | H |
| H | L | L | H | L | H | L | H | H | H | H | L | H | H | L | L |
| H | L | L | H | L | H | H | L | H | H | H | H | L | L | L | L |
| H | L | L | H | L | H | H | H | H | H | H | H | L | L | L | H |
| H | L | L | H | H | L | L | L | H | H | H | H | L | L | H | L |
| H | L | L | H | H | L | L | H | H | H | H | H | L | L | H | H |
| H | L | L | H | H | L | H | L | H | H | H | H | L | H | L | L |
| H | L | L | H | H | L | H | H | H | H | H | H | H | L | L | L |
| H | L | L | H | H | H | L | L | H | H | H | H | H | L | L | H |
| H | L | L | H | H | H | L | H | H | H | H | H | H | L | H | L |
| H | L | L | H | H | H | H | L | H | H | H | H | H | L | H | H |
| H | L | L | H | H | H | H | H | H | H | H | H | H | H | L | L |
| H | L | H | L | L | L | L | L | H | H | H | H | H | H | H | H |
| thru | | | | | | | | | | | | | | | |
| H | H | H | H | H | H | H | H | | | | | | | | |

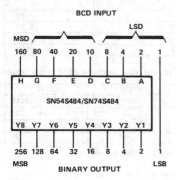

**BCD INPUT**

MSD 160 80 40 20 10 — LSD 8 4 2 1

H G F E D C B A — SN54S484/SN74S484 — Y8 Y7 Y6 Y5 Y4 Y3 Y2 Y1

256 128 64 32 16 8 4 2 — 1

MSB — **BINARY OUTPUT** — LSB

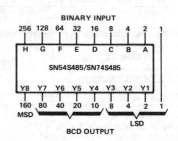

**BINARY INPUT**

256 128 64 32 16 8 4 2 1

H G F E D C B A — SN54S485/SN74S485 — Y8 Y7 Y6 Y5 Y4 Y3 Y2 Y1

160 80 40 20 10 — 8 4 2 1

MSD — **BCD OUTPUT** — LSD

5 RAMs

## SN54S484A, SN54S485A, SN74S484A, SN74S485A
## BCD-TO-BINARY AND BINARY-TO-BCD CONVERTERS

### absolute maximum ratings over operating free-air temperature (unless otherwise noted)

Supply voltage, $V_{CC}$ (see Note 1) ........................................... 7 V
Input voltage ...................................................... 5.5 V
Off-state output voltage ............................................. 5.5 V
Operating free-air temperature range: SN54S484A, SN54S485A ............. −55 °C to 125 °C
SN74S484A, SN74S485A ................ 0 °C to 70 °C
Storage temperature range ....................................... −65 °C to 150 °C

### recommended operating conditions

|  | SN54S' | | | SN74S' | | | UNIT |
|---|---|---|---|---|---|---|---|
|  | MIN | NOM | MAX | MIN | NOM | MAX |  |
| Supply voltage, $V_{CC}$ | 4.5 | 5 | 5.5 | 4.75 | 5 | 5.25 | V |
| High-level output current, $I_{OH}$ |  |  | −2 |  |  | −6.5 | mA |
| Low-level output current, $I_{OL}$ |  |  | 16 |  |  | 16 | mA |
| Operating free-air temperature | −55 |  | 125 | 0 |  | 70 | °C |

### electrical characteristics over recommended operating free-air temperature range (unless otherwise noted)

| PARAMETER | | TEST CONDITIONS[†] | | | MIN | TYP[‡] | MAX | UNIT |
|---|---|---|---|---|---|---|---|---|
| $V_{IH}$ | High-level input voltage | | | | 2 | | | V |
| $V_{IL}$ | Low-level input voltage | | | | | | 0.8 | V |
| $V_{IK}$ | Input clamp voltage | $V_{CC}$ = MIN, | $I_I$ = −18 mA | | | | −1.2 | V |
| $V_{OH}$ | High-level output voltage | $V_{VV}$ = MIN, | $V_{IH}$ = 2 V, | $V_{IL}$ = 0.8 V, | 2.4 | 3.1 | | V |
| | | $I_{OH}$ = MAX | | | | | | |
| $V_{OL}$ | Low-level output voltage | $V_{CC}$ = MIN, | $V_{IH}$ = 2 V, | $V_{IL}$ = 0.8 V | | | 0.5 | V |
| | | $I_{OL}$ = MAX | | | | | | |
| $I_{OZH}$ | Off-state output current, high-level voltage applied | $V_{CC}$ = MAX, | $V_{IH}$ = 2 V, | $V_O$ = 2.4 V | | | 50 | μA |
| $I_{OZL}$ | Off-state output current, low-level voltage applied | $V_{CC}$ = MAX, | $V_{IH}$ = 2 V, | $V_O$ = 0.5 V | | | −50 | μA |
| $I_I$ | Input current at maximum input voltage | $V_{CC}$ = MAX, | $V_I$ = 5.5 V | | | | 1 | mA |
| $I_{IH}$ | High-level input current | $V_{CC}$ = MAX, | $V_I$ = 2.7 V | | | | 25 | μA |
| $I_{IL}$ | Low-level input current | $V_{CC}$ = MAX, | $V_I$ = 0.5 V | | | | −0.25 | mA |
| $I_{OS}$ | Short-circuit output current[§] | $V_{CC}$ = MAX, | | | −30 | | −100 | mA |
| $I_{CC}$ | Supply current | $V_{CC}$ = MAX, | See Note 2 | | | 75 | 100 | mA |

### switching characteristics over recommended ranges of $T_A$ and $V_{CC}$ (unless otherwise noted)

| PARAMETER | | TEST CONDITIONS | SN54S' | | | SN74S' | | | UNIT |
|---|---|---|---|---|---|---|---|---|---|
| | | | MIN | TYP[‡] | MAX | MIN | TYP[‡] | MAX | |
| $t_{a(A)}$ | Access time from address | $C_L$ = 30 pF, See Note 3 | | 45 | 75 | | 45 | 70 | ns |
| $t_{a(S)}$ | Access time from chip select | | | 20 | 40 | | 20 | 35 | ns |
| $t_{PXZ}$ | Output disable time | $C_L$ = 5 pF, See Note 3 | | 15 | 35 | | 15 | 30 | ns |

[†] For conditions shown as MIN or MAX, use the appropriate value specified under recommended operating condtions.

[‡] All typical values are at $V_{CC}$ = 5 V, $T_A$ = 25°.

[§] Not more than one output should be shorted at a time and duration of the short-circuit should not exceed one second.

NOTES: 1. Voltage values are with respect to network ground terminal.
2. With outputs open and enable (G) inputs grounded, $I_{CC}$ is measured first by selecting a word that contains the maximum number of high-level outputs, then by selecting a word that contains the maximum number of low-level inputs.
3. Load circuits and voltage waveforms are shown in Section 1.

**TEXAS INSTRUMENTS**

**5**

**RAMS**

**schematics of inputs and outputs**

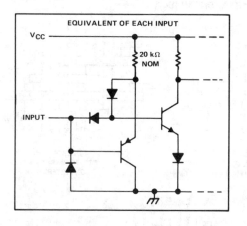

EQUIVALENT OF EACH INPUT

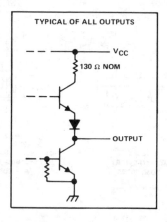

TYPICAL OF ALL OUTPUTS

## TYPICAL APPLICATION DATA

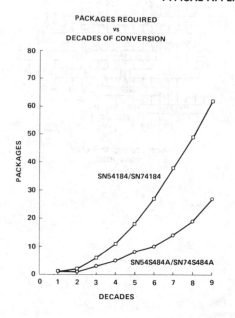

PACKAGES REQUIRED
vs
DECADES OF CONVERSION

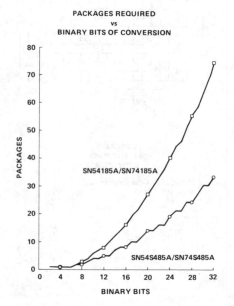

PACKAGES REQUIRED
vs
BINARY BITS OF CONVERSION

5

RAMs

## TYPICAL APPLICATION DATA
### SN54S484A, SN74S484A

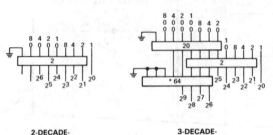

**2-DECADE-
BCD-TO-BINARY
CONVERTER**

**3-DECADE-
BCD-TO-BINARY
CONVERTER**

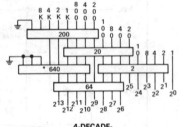

**4-DECADE-
BCD-TO-BINARY
CONVERTER**

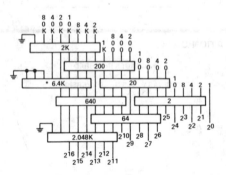

**5-DECADE-
BCD-TO-BINARY
CONVERTER**

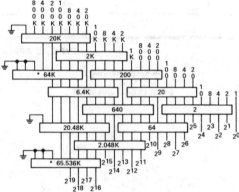

**6-DECADE-BCD-TO-BINARY
CONVERTER**

*SN54184A/SN74184A can be used.
$K = 10^3$, $M = 10^6$

TEXAS
INSTRUMENTS

## TYPICAL APPLICATION DATA
### SN54S484A, SN74S484A

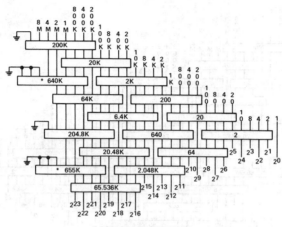

**7-DECADE-BCD-TO-BINARY
CONVERTER**

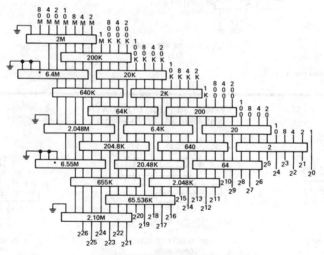

**8-DECADE-BCD-TO-BINARY
CONVERTER**

*SN54184A/SN74184A can be used.
$K = 10^3$, $M = 10^6$

5

RAMs

## SN54S484A, SN54S485A, SN74S484A, SN74S485A
## BCD-TO-BINARY AND BINARY-TO-BCD CONVERTERS

### TYPICAL APPLICATION DATA
### SN54S484A, SN74S484A

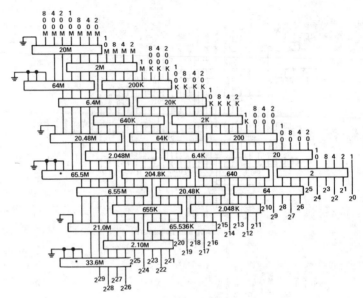

**9-DECADE-BCD-TO-BINARY CONVERTER**

*SN54184A/SN74184A can be used.
$K = 10^3$, $M = 10^6$

### TYPICAL APPLICATION DATA
### SN54S485A, SN74S485A

**6-BIT-BINARY-TO-BCD CONVERTER**

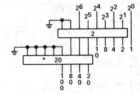

**7-BIT-BINARY-TO-BCD CONVERTER**

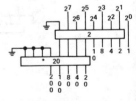

**8-BIT-BINARY-TO-BCD CONVERTER**

*SN54185A/SN74185A can be used.
$K = 10^3$, $M = 10^6$

**TEXAS INSTRUMENTS**

## TYPICAL APPLICATION DATA
### SN54S485A, SN74S485A

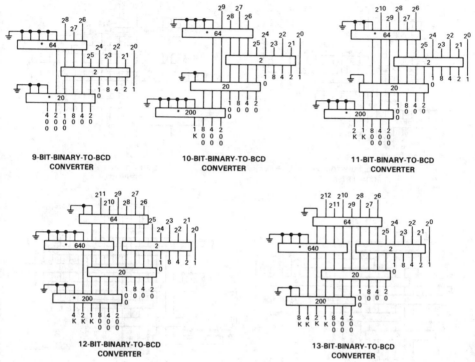

9-BIT-BINARY-TO-BCD
CONVERTER

10-BIT-BINARY-TO-BCD
CONVERTER

11-BIT-BINARY-TO-BCD
CONVERTER

12-BIT-BINARY-TO-BCD
CONVERTER

13-BIT-BINARY-TO-BCD
CONVERTER

*SN54185A/SN74185A can be used.
$K = 10^3$, $M = 10^6$

5

RAMs

### TYPICAL APPLICATION DATA
### SN54S485A, SN74S485A

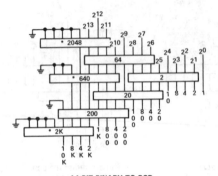

**14-BIT-BINARY-TO-BCD CONVERTER**

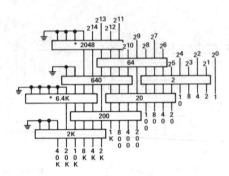

**15-BIT-BINARY-TO-BCD CONVERTER**

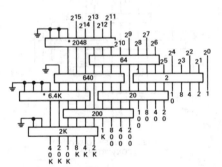

**16-BIT-BINARY-TO-BCD CONVERTER**

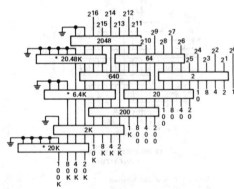

**17-BIT-BINARY-TO-BCD CONVERTER**

*SN54185A/SN74185A can be used.
$K = 10^3$, $M = 10^6$

5 RAMs

### TEXAS
### INSTRUMENTS

### TYPICAL APPLICATION DATA
### SN54S485A, SN74S485A

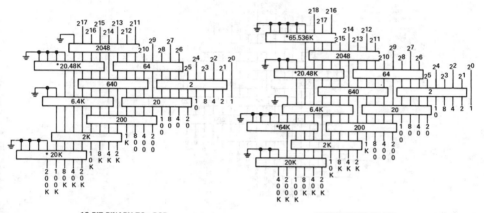

18-BIT-BINARY-TO—BCD
CONVERTER

19-BIT-BINARY-TO-BCD
CONVERTER

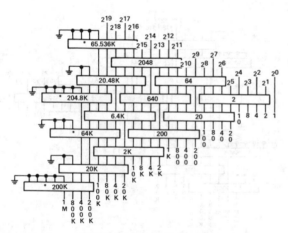

20-BIT-BINARY-TO-BCD CONVERTER

*SN54185A/SN74185A can be used.
$K = 10^3$, $M = 10^6$

5

RAMs

TEXAS
INSTRUMENTS

### TYPICAL APPLICATION DATA
### SN54S485A, SN74S485A

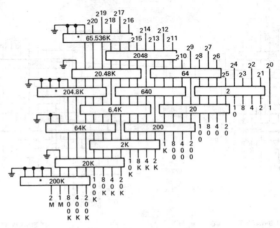

21-BIT-BINARY-TO-BCD CONVERTER

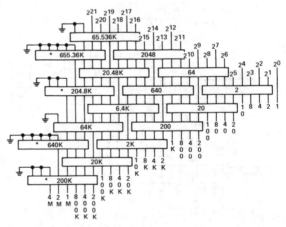

22-BIT-BINARY-TO-BCD CONVERTER

*SN54185A/SN74185A can be used.
$K = 10^3$, $M = 10^6$

TEXAS
INSTRUMENTS

## TYPICAL APPLICATION DATA
### SN54S485A, SN74S485A

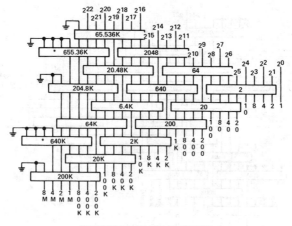

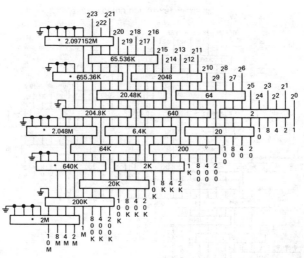

**23-BIT-BINARY-TO-BCD-CONVERTER**

**24-BIT-BINARY-TO-BCD CONVERTER**

*SN54185A/SN74185A can be used.
$K = 10^3$, $M = 10^6$

TEXAS
INSTRUMENTS

5
RAMs

### TYPICAL APPLICATION DATA
### SN54S485A, SN74S485A

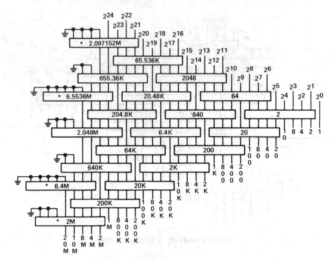

**25-BIT-BINARY-TO-BCD CONVERTER**

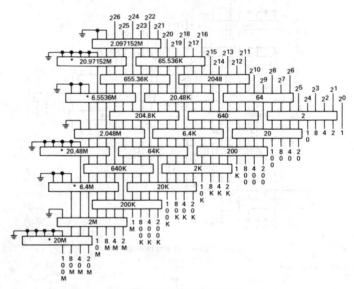

**26-BIT-BINARY-TO-BCD CONVERTER**

*SN54185A/SN74185A can be used.
$K = 10^3$, $M = 10^6$

TEXAS
INSTRUMENTS

## TYPICAL APPLICATION DATA
### SN54S485A, SN74S485A

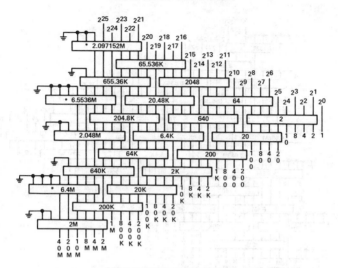

27-BIT-BINARY-TO-BCD CONVERTER

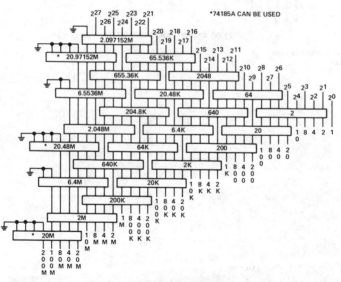

28-BIT-BINARY-TO-BCD CONVERTER

*SN54185A/SN74185A can be used.
$K = 10^3$, $M = 10^6$

TEXAS
INSTRUMENTS

## TYPICAL APPLICATION DATA
### SN54S485A, SN74S485A

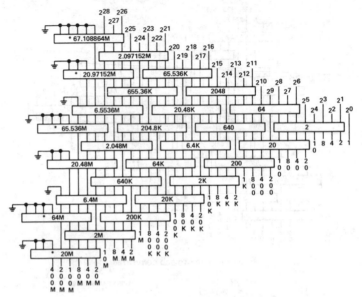

**29-BIT-BINARY-TO-BCD CONVERTER**

*SN54185A/SN74185A can be used.
$K = 10^3$, $M = 10^6$

**TEXAS**
**INSTRUMENTS**

## TYPICAL APPLICATION DATA
### SN54S485A, SN74S485A

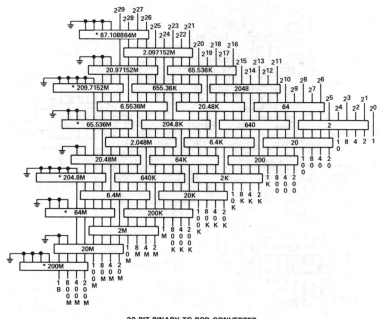

**30-BIT-BINARY-TO-BCD CONVERTER**

*SN54185A/SN74185A can be used.
$K = 10^3$, $M = 10^6$

**TEXAS INSTRUMENTS**

### TYPICAL APPLICATION DATA
### SN54S485A, SN74S485A

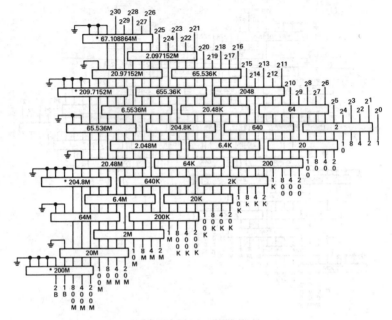

**31-BIT-BINARY-TO-BCD CONVERTER**

*SN54185A/SN74185A can be used.
$K = 10^3$, $M = 10^6$

TEXAS
INSTRUMENTS

## TYPICAL APPLICATION DATA
### SN54S485A, SN74S485A

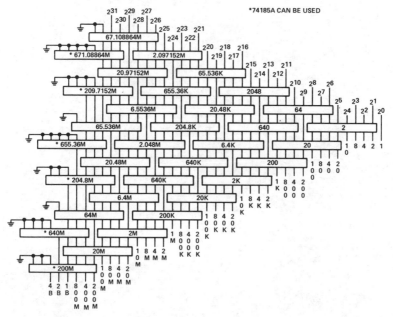

**32-BIT-BINARY-TO-BCD CONVERTER**

*SN54185A/SN74185A can be used.
$K = 10^3$, $M = 10^6$

RAMs

General Information **1**

Functional Index **2**

Field-Programmable Logic **3**

PROMs **4**

RAMs and Memory-Based
Code Converters **5**

Designing with Texas Instruments
Field-Programmable Logic **6**

Mechanical Data **7**

# Designing with Texas Instruments Field-Programmable Logic

## Robert K. Breuninger and Loren E. Schiele

### Contributors
**Bob Gruebel, Renee Tanaka, Jim Ptasinski**

**TEXAS INSTRUMENTS**

Applications

6

# Contents

® PAL is a registered trademark of Monolithic Memories Inc.

**Applications**

**6**

# List of Illustrations

# List of Tables

Applications

6

## INTRODUCTION

The purpose of this application report is to provide the first time user of field-programmable logic with a basic understanding of this new and powerful technology. The term "Field-Programmable Logic" refers to any device supplied with an uncommitted logic array, which the user programs to his own specific function. The most common, and widely known field-programmable logic family is the PROM, or Programmable Read-Only Memory. Relatively new entries into this expanding family of devices are the PAL® and FPLA. This report will primarily concentrate on the PAL family of programmable logic.

## FIELD-PROGRAMMABLE LOGIC ADVANTAGES

Field-programmable logic offers many advantages to the system designer who presently is using several standard catalog SSI and MSI functions. Listed below are just a few of the benefits which are achievable when using programmable logic.

1. Package Count Reduction: typically, 3 to 6 MSI/SSI functions can be replaced with one PAL or FPLA.
2. PC Board Area Reduced: Fewer devices consume less PC board space. This results in lower PC board cost.
3. Circuit Flexibility: Programmability allows for minor circuit changes without changing PC boards.
4. Improved Reliability: With fewer PC interconnects, overall system reliability increases.
5. Shorter Design Cycle: When compared with standard-cell or gate-array approaches, custom functions can be implemented much more quickly.

The PAL and FPLA, will fill the gap between standard logic and large scale integration. The versatility of these devices provide a very powerful tool for the system designer.

## PAL AND FPLA SYMBOLOGY

In order to keep PAL and FPLA logic easy to understand and use, a special convention has been adopted. Figure 1 is the representation for a 3-input AND gate. Note that only one line is shown as the input to the AND gate. This line is commonly refered to as the product line. The inputs are shown as vertical lines, and at the intersection of these lines are the programmable fuses.

An X represents an intact fuse. This makes that input, part of the product term. No X represents a blown fuse. This means that input will not be part of the product term (in Figure 1, input B is not part of the product term). A dot at the intersection of any line represents a hard wire connection.

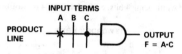

**Figure 1. Basic Symbology**

In Figure 2, we will extend the symbology to develop a simple 2-input programmable AND array feeding an OR gate. Notice that buffers have been added to the inputs, which provide both true and complement outputs to the product lines. The intersection of the input terms form a $4 \times 3$ programmable AND array. From the above symbology, we can see that the output of the OR gate is programmed to the following equation, $A\overline{B} + \overline{A}B$. Note that the bottom AND gate has an X marked inside the gate symbol. This means that all fuses are left intact, which results in that product line not having any effect on the sum term. In other words, the output of the AND gate will be a logic 0. **When all the fuses are blown on a product line, the output of the AND gate will always be a logic 1. This has the effect of locking up the output of the OR gate to a logic level 1.**

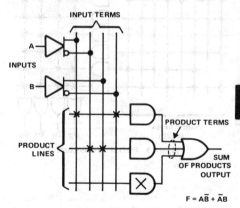

$$F = A\overline{B} + \overline{A}B$$

**Figure 2. Basic Symbology Example**

## FAMILY ARCHITECTURES

As stated before, the PROM was the first widely used programmable logic family. Its basic architecture is an input decoder configured from AND gates, combined with a programmable OR matrix on the outputs. As shown in Figure 3, this allows every output to be programmed individually from every possible input combination. In this example, a PROM with 4 inputs has $2^4$, or 16 possible input combinations. With the output word width being 4 bits, each of the $16 \times 4$ bit words can be programmed individually. Applications such as data storage tables, character generators, and code converters, are just a few design examples which are ideally suited for the PROM. In general, any application which requires every input combination to be programmable, is a good candidate for a PROM. However, PROMs have difficulty accommodating large numbers of input variables. Eventually, the size of the fuse matrix will become prohibitive because for each input variable added, the size of the fuse matrix doubles. Currently, manufacturers are not producing PROMs with over 13 inputs.

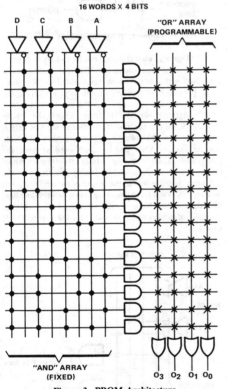

**16 WORDS X 4 BITS**

"OR" ARRAY (PROGRAMMABLE)

D   C   B   A

"AND" ARRAY (FIXED)

$O_3$  $O_2$  $O_1$  $O_0$

**Figure 3. PROM Architecture**

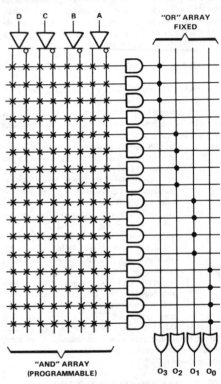

D   C   B   A

"OR" ARRAY FIXED

"AND" ARRAY (PROGRAMMABLE)

$O_3$  $O_2$  $O_1$  $O_0$

**Figure 4. PAL Architecture**

To overcome the limitation of a restricted number of inputs, the PAL utilizes a slightly different architecture as shown in Figure 4. The same AND-OR implementation is used as with PROMs, but now the input AND array is programmable instead of the output OR array. This has the effect of restricting the output OR array to a fixed number of input AND terms. The trade-off is that now, every output is not programmable from every input combination, but more inputs can be added without doubling the size of the fuse matrix. For example, If we were to expand the inputs on the PAL shown in Figure 4, to 10, and on the PROM in Figure 3, to 10. We would see that the fuse matrix required for the PAL would be $20 \times 16$ (320 fuses) vs $4 \times 1024$ (4096 fuses for the PROM). **It is important to realize that not every application requires every output be programmable from every input combination. This is what makes the PAL a viable product family.**

The FPLA goes one step further in offering both a programmable AND array, and a programmable OR array (Figure 5). This feature makes the FPLA the most versatile device of the three, but usually impractical in most low complexity applications.

All three field-programmable logic approaches discussed have their own unique advantages and limitations. The best choice depends on the complexity of the function being implemented and the current cost of the devices themselves. It is important to realize, that a circuit solution may exist from more than one of these logic families.

## PAL OPTIONS

Figure 6 shows the logic diagram of the popular TIBPAL16L8. Its basic architecture is the same as discussed in the previous section, but with the addition of some special circuit features. First notice that the PAL has 10 simple inputs. In addition, 6 of the outputs operate as I/O ports. This allows feedback into the AND array. One AND gate in each product term controls each 3-state output. The architecture used in this PAL makes it very useful in generating all sorts of combinational logic.

Another important feature about the logic diagram, and all other block diagrams supplied from individual datasheets, are that there are no X's marked at every fuse location. From the previous convention, we stated that everywhere there was a intact fuse, there was an X. However, in order to make the logic diagram useful when generating specific functions, it is supplied with no X's. This allows the user to insert the X's wherever an intact fuse is desired.

The basic concept of the TIBPAL16L8 can be expanded further to include D-type flip-flops on the outputs. An example of this is shown in Figure 7 with the TIBPAL16R8. This added feature allows the device to be configured as a counter, simple storage register, or similar clocked function.

Circuit variations which are available on other members of the TI PAL and FPLA family are explained below.

### Polarity Fuse

The polarity of the output can be selected via the fuse shown in Figure 8.

### Input Registers

On PALs equipped with this special feature, the option of having D-type input registers is fuse programmable. Figure 9 shows an example of this type of input. If the fuse is left intact, data enters on a low-high transition of the clock. If the fuse is blown, the register becomes permanently transparent and is equivalent to a normal input buffer.

### Input Latches

On PALs equipped with this special feature, the option of having input latches is fuse programmable.

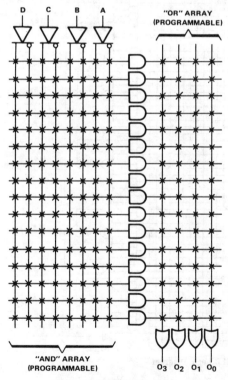

**Figure 5. FPLA Architecture**

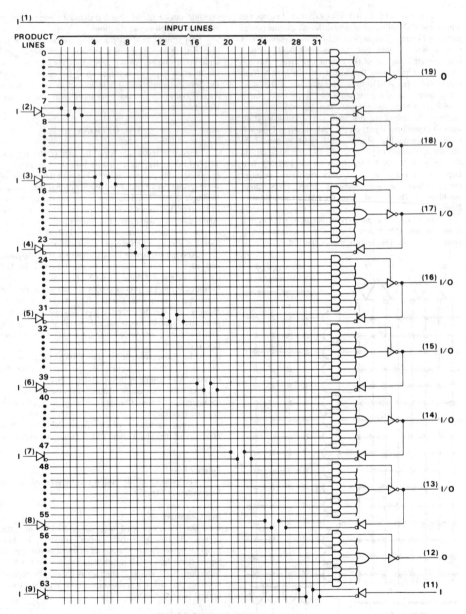

Figure 6. TIBPAL16L8 Logic Diagram

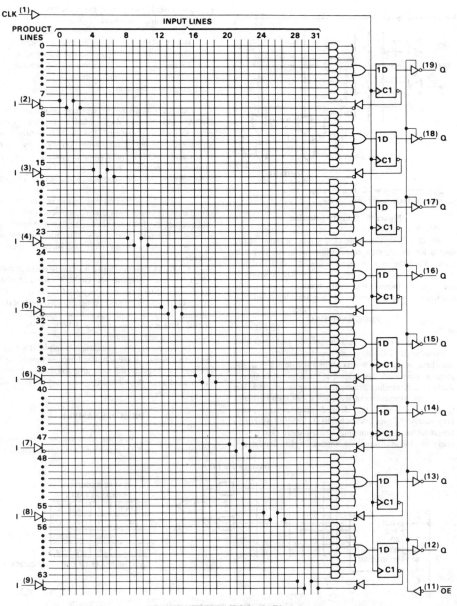

Figure 7. TIBPAL16R8 Logic Diagram

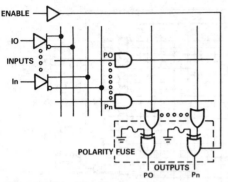

ENABLE

IO
INPUTS
In

PO
Pn

POLARITY FUSE

OUTPUTS
PO        Pn

INTACT: OUTPUT = $\overline{P0 + P1 + ... + Pn}$
BLOWN: OUTPUT = $\overline{\overline{P0} \cdot \overline{P1} \cdot ... \cdot \overline{Pn}}$

**Figure 8. Polarity Selection**

Figure 10 shows an example of this type of input. If the fuse is left intact, data enters while the control input is high. When the control input is low, the data that was present when the control input went low will be saved. If the fuse is blown, the latch becomes permanently transparent, and is equivalent to a normal input buffer.

## PROGRAMMING

Notice in Figure 7, that the product and input lines are numbered. This allows any specific fuse to be located anywhere in the fuse matrix. When the device is in the programming mode (as defined in the device data sheet), the individual product and input lines can be selected. The fuse at the intersection of these lines, can then be blown (programmed) with the defined programming pulse. Fortunately, the user seldom has to get involved with these actual details of programming, because there exist several commercially available programmers which handle this

function. Listed below are some of the manufacturers of this programming equipment.*

| | |
|---|---|
| Citel | Storey Systems |
| DATA I/O | Structured Design |
| Digelec | Sunrise Electronics |
| Kontron | Valley Data Science |
| Wavetec | Varix |
| Stag Micro Systems | |

At Texas Instruments, we have coordinated with DATA I/O using their Model 19 for device characterization. Currently, DATA I/O, Sunrise, and Structured Design have been certified by Texas Instruments. Other programmers are now in the certification process. For a current list of certified programmers, please contact your local TI sales representative.

It should now be obvious to the reader, that the actual blowing of the fuses is not a problem. Instead, the real question is what fuses need to be blown to generate a particular function. Fortunately, this problem has also been greatly simplified by recent advances in computer software.

DATA I/O has developed a software package called ABEL™. Also available is CUPL™, from Assisted Technology. Both have been designed to be compatible with several different types of programmers. Both of these software packages greatly extend the capabilities of the original PALASM™ program, and both can be run on most professional computers.

Before proceeding to a design example, it would be instructive to look at the simplified process flow of a PAL (Figure 11). This should help give the reader a better understanding of the basic steps necessary to generate a working device.

## DESIGN EXAMPLE

The easiest way to demonstrate the unique capabilities of the PAL is through a design example. It is

**REGISTER FUSE INTACT**

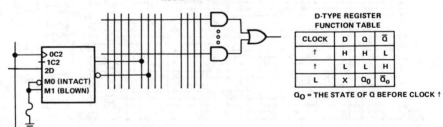

0C2
1C2
2D
M0 (INTACT)
M1 (BLOWN)

**D-TYPE REGISTER
FUNCTION TABLE**

| CLOCK | D | Q | $\overline{Q}$ |
|---|---|---|---|
| ↑ | H | H | L |
| ↑ | L | L | H |
| L | X | $Q_0$ | $\overline{Q}_0$ |

$Q_0$ = THE STATE OF Q BEFORE CLOCK ↑

**Figure 9. Input Register Selection**

ABEL™ is a trademark of DATA I/O.
CUPL™ is a trademark of Assisted Technology, Inc.
PALASM™ is a trademark of Monolithic Memories Inc.

LATCH FUSE INTACT

**TRANSPARENT LATCH FUNCTION TABLE**

| ENABLE | D | O | $\overline{Q}$ |
|--------|---|---|----|
| H | L | L | H |
| H | H | H | L |
| L | X | $Q_0$ | $\overline{Q}_0$ |

$Q_0$ = THE LEVEL OF Q BEFORE ENABLE ↓

**Figure 10. Input Latch Selection**

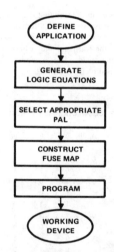

**Figure 11. PAL Process Flow Diagram**

hoped that through this example the reader will gain the basic understanding needed when applying the PAL in his own application. In some cases, this goal may only be to reduce existing logic, but the overall approach will be the same.

### EXAMPLE REQUIREMENTS

It is desired to generate a 4-bit binary counter which is fed by one of four clocks. There are two lines available for selecting the clocks, SEL1 and SEL0. Table 1 shows the required input for the selection of the clocks. In addition, it is desired that the counter be able to switch from binary to decade count. This feature is controlled by an input called BD. When BD is high, the counter should count in binary. When low, the counter should count in decade.

Figure 12 shows how this example could be implemented if standard data book functions were used.

**Table 1. Clock Selection**

| SEL1 | SEL0 | OUTPUT |
|------|------|--------|
| 0 | 0 | CLKA |
| 0 | 1 | CLKB |
| 1 | 0 | CLKC |
| 1 | 1 | CLKD |

As can be seen, three MSI functions are required. The 'LS162 is used to generate the 4-bit counter while the clock selection is handled by the 'LS253. The 'LS688 is an 8-bit comparator which is used for selecting either the binary or decade count. In this example, only five of the eight comparator inputs are used. Four are used for comparing the counter outputs, while the other is used for the BD input. The comparator is hard-wired to go low whenever the BD input is low and the counter output is "9". The $\overline{P=Q}$ output is then fed back to the synchronous clear input on the 'LS162. This will reset the counter to zero whenever this condition occurs.

### PAL IMPLEMENTATION

As stated before, the problem in programming a PAL is not in blowing the fuses, but rather what fuses need to be blown to generate a particular function. Fortunately, this problem has been greatly simplified by computer software, but before we examine these techniques, it is beneficial to explore the methods used in generating the logic equations. This will help develop an understanding, and appreciation for these advanced software packages.

From digital logic theory, we know that most any type of logic can be implemented in either AND-OR-INVERT or AND-NOR form. This is the basic concept used in the PAL and FPLA. This allows classical techniques, such as Karnaugh Maps[1] to be used in generating specific logic functions. As with the separate component example above, it is easier to break it into separate functions. The first one that we will look at is the clock selector, but remember that the overall goal will be to reduce this design example into one PAL.

**Applications**

**6**

6-13

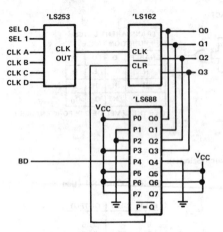

Figure 12. Counter Implementation With Standard Logic

## PAL SELECTION

Before proceeding with the design for the clock selector, the first question which needs to be addressed is which PAL to use. As discussed earlier, there are several different types of output architectures. Looking at our example, we can see that four flip-flops with feedback will be required in the 4-bit counter, plus input clock and clear lines. In addition, seven inputs plus two simple outputs will be required in the clock selector and comparator. With this information in hand, we can see that the TIBPAL16R4 (Figure 13) will handle our application.

## CLOCK SELECTOR DETAILS

The first step in determining the logic equation for the clock selector is to generate a function table with all the possible input combinations. This is shown in Table 2. From this table, the Karnaugh map can be generated and is shown in Figure 14. The minimized equation for CLKOUT comes directly from this.

### Table 2. Function Table

| SEL1 | SEL0 | CLKA | CLKB | CLKC | CLKD | CLKOUT | | SEL1 | SEL0 | CLKA | CLKB | CLKC | CLKD | CLKOUT |
|---|---|---|---|---|---|---|---|---|---|---|---|---|---|---|
| 0 | 0 | 0 | 0 | 0 | 0 | 0 | | 1 | 0 | 0 | 0 | 0 | 0 | 0 |
| 0 | 0 | 0 | 0 | 0 | 1 | 0 | | 1 | 0 | 0 | 0 | 0 | 1 | 0 |
| 0 | 0 | 0 | 0 | 1 | 0 | 0 | | 1 | 0 | 0 | 0 | 1 | 0 | 1 |
| 0 | 0 | 0 | 0 | 1 | 1 | 0 | | 1 | 0 | 0 | 0 | 1 | 1 | 1 |
| 0 | 0 | 0 | 1 | 0 | 0 | 0 | | 1 | 0 | 0 | 1 | 0 | 0 | 0 |
| 0 | 0 | 0 | 1 | 0 | 1 | 0 | | 1 | 0 | 0 | 1 | 0 | 1 | 0 |
| 0 | 0 | 0 | 1 | 1 | 0 | 0 | | 1 | 0 | 0 | 1 | 1 | 0 | 1 |
| 0 | 0 | 0 | 1 | 1 | 1 | 0 | | 1 | 0 | 0 | 1 | 1 | 1 | 1 |
| 0 | 0 | 1 | 0 | 0 | 0 | 1 | | 1 | 0 | 1 | 0 | 0 | 0 | 0 |
| 0 | 0 | 1 | 0 | 0 | 1 | 1 | | 1 | 0 | 1 | 0 | 0 | 1 | 0 |
| 0 | 0 | 1 | 0 | 1 | 0 | 1 | | 1 | 0 | 1 | 0 | 1 | 0 | 1 |
| 0 | 0 | 1 | 0 | 1 | 1 | 1 | | 1 | 0 | 1 | 0 | 1 | 1 | 1 |
| 0 | 0 | 1 | 1 | 0 | 0 | 1 | | 1 | 0 | 1 | 1 | 0 | 0 | 0 |
| 0 | 0 | 1 | 1 | 0 | 1 | 1 | | 1 | 0 | 1 | 1 | 0 | 1 | 0 |
| 0 | 0 | 1 | 1 | 1 | 0 | 1 | | 1 | 0 | 1 | 1 | 1 | 0 | 1 |
| 0 | 0 | 1 | 1 | 1 | 1 | 1 | | 1 | 0 | 1 | 1 | 1 | 1 | 1 |
| 0 | 1 | 0 | 0 | 0 | 0 | 0 | | 1 | 1 | 0 | 0 | 0 | 0 | 0 |
| 0 | 1 | 0 | 0 | 0 | 1 | 0 | | 1 | 1 | 0 | 0 | 0 | 1 | 1 |
| 0 | 1 | 0 | 0 | 1 | 0 | 0 | | 1 | 1 | 0 | 0 | 1 | 0 | 0 |
| 0 | 1 | 0 | 0 | 1 | 1 | 0 | | 1 | 1 | 0 | 0 | 1 | 1 | 1 |
| 0 | 1 | 0 | 1 | 0 | 0 | 1 | | 1 | 1 | 0 | 1 | 0 | 0 | 0 |
| 0 | 1 | 0 | 1 | 0 | 1 | 1 | | 1 | 1 | 0 | 1 | 0 | 1 | 1 |
| 0 | 1 | 0 | 1 | 1 | 0 | 1 | | 1 | 1 | 0 | 1 | 1 | 0 | 0 |
| 0 | 1 | 0 | 1 | 1 | 1 | 1 | | 1 | 1 | 0 | 1 | 1 | 1 | 1 |
| 0 | 1 | 1 | 0 | 0 | 0 | 0 | | 1 | 1 | 1 | 0 | 0 | 0 | 0 |
| 0 | 1 | 1 | 0 | 0 | 1 | 0 | | 1 | 1 | 1 | 0 | 0 | 1 | 1 |
| 0 | 1 | 1 | 0 | 1 | 0 | 0 | | 1 | 1 | 1 | 0 | 1 | 0 | 0 |
| 0 | 1 | 1 | 0 | 1 | 1 | 0 | | 1 | 1 | 1 | 0 | 1 | 1 | 1 |
| 0 | 1 | 1 | 1 | 0 | 0 | 1 | | 1 | 1 | 1 | 1 | 0 | 0 | 0 |
| 0 | 1 | 1 | 1 | 0 | 1 | 1 | | 1 | 1 | 1 | 1 | 0 | 1 | 1 |
| 0 | 1 | 1 | 1 | 1 | 0 | 1 | | 1 | 1 | 1 | 1 | 1 | 0 | 0 |
| 0 | 1 | 1 | 1 | 1 | 1 | 1 | | 1 | 1 | 1 | 1 | 1 | 1 | 1 |

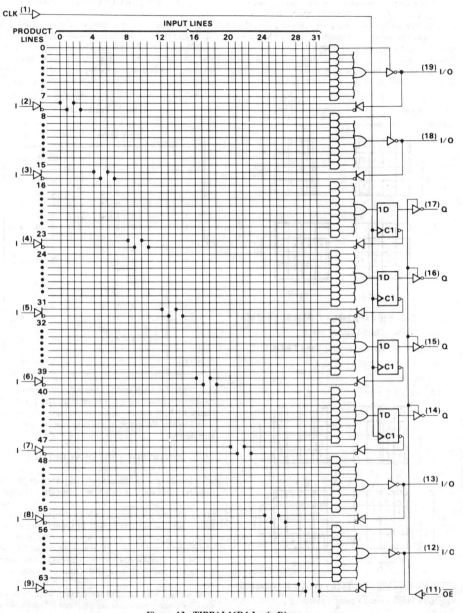

Figure 13. TIBPAL16R4 Logic Diagram

It is important to notice that the equation derived from the Karnaugh map is stated in AND-OR notation. The PAL that we have selected is implemented in AND-NOR logic. This means we either have to do DeMorgan's theorem on the equation, or solve the inverse of the Karnaugh map. Figure 15 shows the inverse of the Karnaugh map and the resulting equation. This equation can be easily implemented in the TIBPAL16R4.

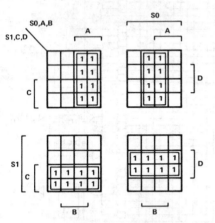

CLKOUT = $\overline{S1S0}A$**XXX** + $\overline{S1S0}AB$**XX** + $S1\overline{S0}$**XX**C**X** + $S1S0A$**XXX**D

CLKOUT = $\overline{S1S0}A$ + $\overline{S1}S0B$ + $S1\overline{S0}C$ + $S1S0D$

**Figure 14. Karnaugh Map for CLKOUT**

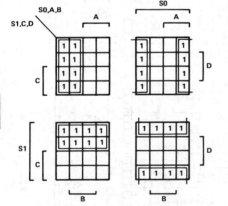

$\overline{\text{CLKOUT}}$ = $\overline{S1S0}A$**XXX** + $\overline{S1}S0AB$**XX** + $S1\overline{S0}$**XX**C**X** + $S1S0A$**XXX**D

$\overline{\text{CLKOUT}}$ = $\overline{S1S0A}$ + $\overline{S1S0B}$ + $\overline{S1S0C}$ + $\overline{S1S0D}$

**Figure 15. Karnaugh Map for $\overline{\text{CLKOUT}}$**

## 4-BIT BINARY COUNTER DETAILS

The same basic procedure used in determining the equations for the clock selector, is used in determining the equations for the 4-bit counter. The only difference is that now we are dealing with a present state, next state situation. This means a D-type flip-flop will be required in actual circuit implementation. As before, the truth table is generated first, and is shown in Table 3.

**Table 3. Truth Table**

| | PRESENT STATE | | | | NEXT STATE | | | |
|---|---|---|---|---|---|---|---|---|
| CLR | Q3 | Q2 | Q1 | Q0 | Q3 | Q2 | Q1 | Q0 |
| 0 | X | X | X | X | 0 | 0 | 0 | 0 |
| 1 | 0 | 0 | 0 | 0 | 0 | 0 | 0 | 1 |
| 1 | 0 | 0 | 0 | 1 | 0 | 0 | 1 | 0 |
| 1 | 0 | 0 | 1 | 0 | 0 | 0 | 1 | 1 |
| 1 | 0 | 0 | 1 | 1 | 0 | 1 | 0 | 0 |
| 1 | 0 | 1 | 0 | 0 | 0 | 1 | 0 | 1 |
| 1 | 0 | 1 | 0 | 1 | 0 | 1 | 1 | 0 |
| 1 | 0 | 1 | 1 | 0 | 0 | 1 | 1 | 1 |
| 1 | 0 | 1 | 1 | 1 | 1 | 0 | 0 | 0 |
| 1 | 1 | 0 | 0 | 0 | 1 | 0 | 0 | 1 |
| 1 | 1 | 0 | 0 | 1 | 1 | 0 | 1 | 0 |
| 1 | 1 | 0 | 1 | 0 | 1 | 0 | 1 | 1 |
| 1 | 1 | 0 | 1 | 1 | 1 | 1 | 0 | 0 |
| 1 | 1 | 1 | 0 | 0 | 1 | 1 | 0 | 1 |
| 1 | 1 | 1 | 0 | 1 | 1 | 1 | 1 | 0 |
| 1 | 1 | 1 | 1 | 0 | 1 | 1 | 1 | 1 |
| 1 | 1 | 1 | 1 | 1 | 0 | 0 | 0 | 0 |

From the truth table, the equations for each output can be derived from the Karnaugh map. This is shown in Figure 16. Note that the inverse of the truth table is being solved so that the equation will come out in AND-NOR logic form.

## BINARY/DECADE COUNT DETAILS

Recalling from the example requirements that the counter should count in decade whenever the BD input is low, we can again generate a truth table for this function (Table 4). Since the counter is already designed to count in binary, we can use this feature to simplify our design. What we desire is a circuit whose output goes low, whenever the BD input is equal to a logic level "0", and the counter output is equal to "9". This output can then be fed back to the CLR input of the counter so that it will reset whenever the BD input is low. Whenever the BD input is high, the output of the circuit should be a high since the counter will automatically count in binary. Notice that $\overline{Q}$ shown in the truth table is the function we desire.

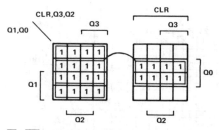

$\overline{Q0} = \overline{CLR}\cdot\overline{Q3}\cdot\overline{Q2}\cdot\overline{Q1}\cdot\overline{Q0} + \overline{CLR}\cdot\overline{Q3}\cdot\overline{Q2}\cdot\overline{Q1}\cdot Q0$

$\overline{Q0} = \overline{CLR} + Q0$

**(a) KARNAUGH MAP FOR $\overline{Q0}$**

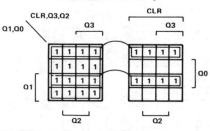

$\overline{Q1} = \overline{CLR}\cdot\overline{Q3}\cdot\overline{Q2}\cdot\overline{Q1}\cdot\overline{Q0} + \overline{CLR}\cdot\overline{Q3}\cdot\overline{Q2}\cdot\overline{Q1}\cdot\overline{Q0} + \overline{CLR}\cdot\overline{Q3}\cdot\overline{Q2}\cdot Q1\cdot Q0$

$\overline{Q1} = \overline{CLR} + \overline{Q1}\cdot\overline{Q0} + Q1\cdot Q0$

**(b) KARNAUGH MAP FOR $\overline{Q1}$**

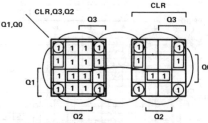

$\overline{Q2} = \overline{CLR}\cdot\overline{Q3}\cdot\overline{Q2}\cdot\overline{Q1}\cdot\overline{Q0} + \overline{CLR}\cdot\overline{Q3}\cdot\overline{Q2}\cdot\overline{Q1}\cdot\overline{Q0} + \overline{CLR}\cdot\overline{Q3}\cdot Q2\cdot Q1\cdot Q0 + \overline{CLR}\cdot\overline{Q3}\cdot\overline{Q2}\cdot\overline{Q1}\cdot\overline{Q0}$

$\overline{Q2} = \overline{CLR} + \overline{Q2}\cdot\overline{Q1} + Q2\cdot Q1\cdot Q0 + \overline{Q2}\cdot\overline{Q0}$

**(c) KARNAUGH MAP FOR $\overline{Q2}$**

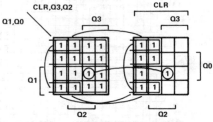

$\overline{Q3} = \overline{CLR}\cdot\overline{Q3}\cdot\overline{Q2}\cdot\overline{Q1}\cdot\overline{Q0} + \overline{CLR}\cdot\overline{Q3}\cdot\overline{Q2}\cdot\overline{Q1}\cdot\overline{Q0} + \overline{CLR}\cdot\overline{Q3}\cdot\overline{Q2}\cdot\overline{Q1}\cdot\overline{Q0} + \overline{CLR}\cdot Q3\cdot Q2\cdot Q1\cdot Q0$

$\overline{Q3} = \overline{CLR} + \overline{Q3}\cdot\overline{Q2} + \overline{Q3}\cdot\overline{Q1} + \overline{Q3}\cdot\overline{Q0} + Q3\cdot Q2\cdot Q1\cdot Q0$

**(d) KARNAUGH MAP FOR $\overline{Q3}$**

**Figure 16. Karnaugh Maps**

In this particular example, a Karnaugh map is not required because the equation cannot be further simplified. The resulting equation is given below.

$$\overline{BD\ OUT} = \overline{BD}\cdot Q3\cdot\overline{Q2}\cdot Q1\cdot Q0$$

**Table 4. Truth Table**

| BD | Q3 | Q2 | Q1 | Q0 | Q | $\overline{Q}$ | BD | Q3 | Q2 | Q1 | Q0 | Q | $\overline{Q}$ |
|----|----|----|----|----|---|---|----|----|----|----|----|---|---|
| 0 | 0 | 0 | 0 | 0 | 0 | 1 | 1 | 0 | 0 | 0 | 0 | 0 | 1 |
| 0 | 0 | 0 | 0 | 1 | 0 | 1 | 1 | 0 | 0 | 0 | 1 | 0 | 1 |
| 0 | 0 | 0 | 1 | 0 | 0 | 1 | 1 | 0 | 0 | 1 | 0 | 0 | 1 |
| 0 | 0 | 0 | 1 | 1 | 0 | 1 | 1 | 0 | 0 | 1 | 1 | 0 | 1 |
| 0 | 0 | 1 | 0 | 0 | 0 | 1 | 1 | 0 | 1 | 0 | 0 | 0 | 1 |
| 0 | 0 | 1 | 0 | 1 | 0 | 1 | 1 | 0 | 1 | 0 | 1 | 0 | 1 |
| 0 | 0 | 1 | 1 | 0 | 0 | 1 | 1 | 0 | 1 | 1 | 0 | 0 | 1 |
| 0 | 0 | 1 | 1 | 1 | 0 | 1 | 1 | 0 | 1 | 1 | 1 | 0 | 1 |
| 0 | 1 | 0 | 0 | 0 | 0 | 1 | 1 | 1 | 0 | 0 | 0 | 0 | 1 |
| 0 | 1 | 0 | 0 | 1 | 1 | 0 | 1 | 1 | 0 | 0 | 1 | 0 | 1 |
| 0 | 1 | 0 | 1 | 0 | 0 | 1 | 1 | 1 | 0 | 1 | 0 | 0 | 1 |
| 0 | 1 | 0 | 1 | 1 | 0 | 1 | 1 | 1 | 0 | 1 | 1 | 0 | 1 |
| 0 | 1 | 1 | 0 | 0 | 0 | 1 | 1 | 1 | 1 | 0 | 0 | 0 | 1 |
| 0 | 1 | 1 | 0 | 1 | 0 | 1 | 1 | 1 | 1 | 0 | 1 | 0 | 1 |
| 0 | 1 | 1 | 1 | 0 | 0 | 1 | 1 | 1 | 1 | 1 | 0 | 0 | 1 |
| 0 | 1 | 1 | 1 | 1 | 0 | 1 | 1 | 1 | 1 | 1 | 1 | 0 | 1 |

## FUSE MAP DETAILS

Now that the logic equations have been defined, the next step will be to specify which fuses need to be blown. Before we do this however, we first need to label the input and output pins on the TIBPAL16R4. By using Figure 12 as a guide, we can make the following pin assignments in Figure 17.

PIN

| | |
|---|---|
| 1 CLK | 20 VCC |
| 2 SEL0 | 19 CLKOUT |
| 3 SEL1 | 18 NC |
| 4 CLKA | 17 Q0 |
| 5 CLKB | 16 Q1 |
| 6 CLKC | 15 Q2 |
| 7 CLKD | 14 Q3 |
| 8 CLR | 13 NC |
| 9 BD | 12 BD OUT |
| 10 GND | 11 OE |

With this information defined, we now need to insert the logic equations into the logic diagram as shown in Figure 17.

**Applications**

**6**

6-17

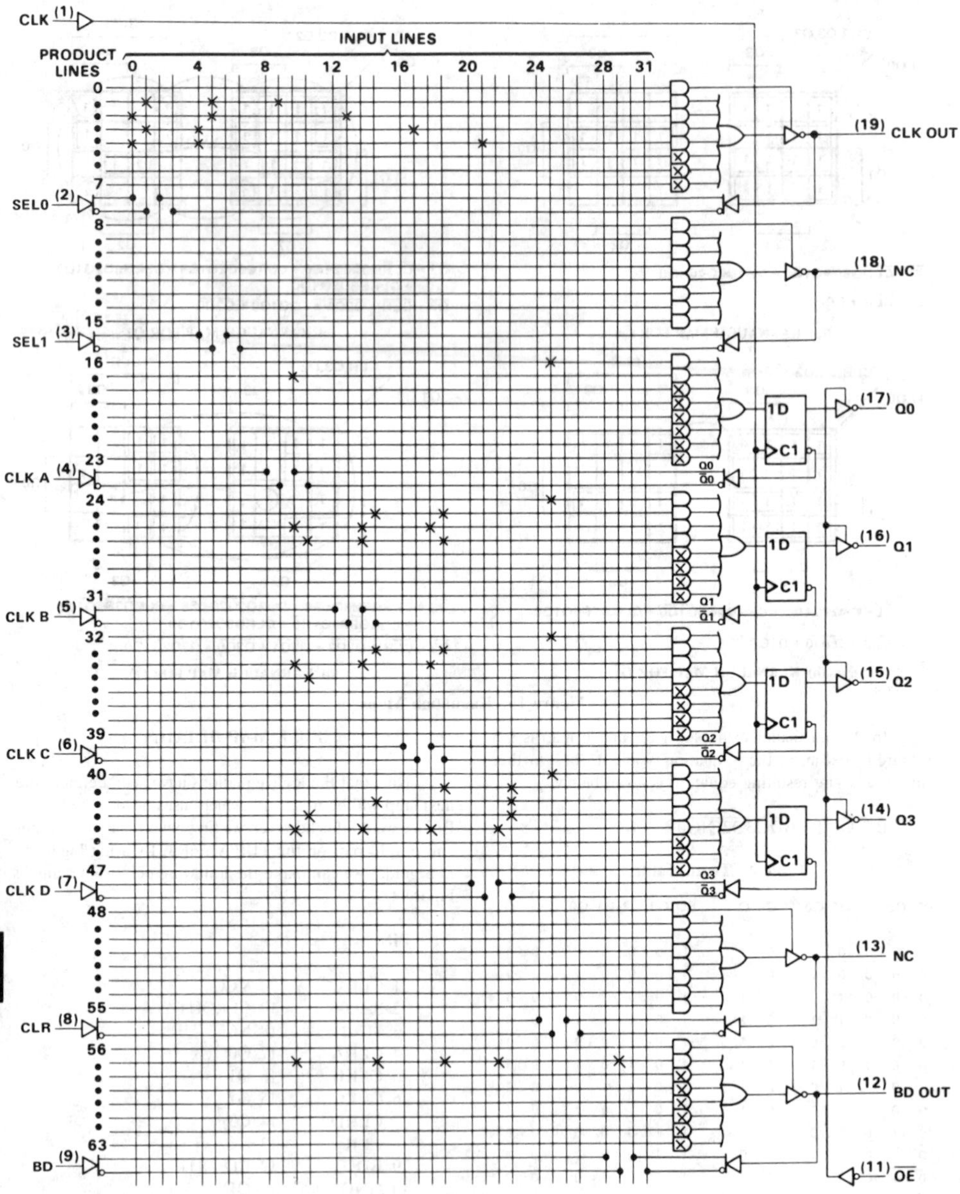

Figure 17. Programmed TIBPAL16R4

It is now probably obvious to the reader, that inserting the logic equations into the logic diagram is a tedious operation. Fortunately, a computer program called PALASM will perform this task automatically. All that is required is telling the program which device has been selected, and defining the input and output pins with their appropriate logic equations (Figure 18). The program will then generate a fuse map (Figure 19) for the device selected. Notice that the fuse map looks very similar to the block diagram (Figure 17) which we have just completed by hand. In addition, this information can now be down loaded into the selected device programmer.

```
DEVICE TYPE 16R4


PIN LIST NAMES =
PIN NUMBER =   1      PIN NAME = CLK
PIN NUMBER =   2      PIN NAME = SEL0
PIN NUMBER =   3      PIN NAME = SEL1
PIN NUMBER =   4      PIN NAME = CLKA
PIN NUMBER =   5      PIN NAME = CLKB
PIN NUMBER =   6      PIN NAME = CLKC
PIN NUMBER =   7      PIN NAME = CLKD
PIN NUMBER =   8      PIN NAME = CLR
PIN NUMBER =   9      PIN NAME = BD
PIN NUMBER =  10      PIN NAME = GND
PIN NUMBER =  11      PIN NAME = /OE
PIN NUMBER =  12      PIN NAME = BDOUT
PIN NUMBER =  13      PIN NAME = NC
PIN NUMBER =  14      PIN NAME = Q3
PIN NUMBER =  15      PIN NAME = Q2
PIN NUMBER =  16      PIN NAME = Q1
PIN NUMBER =  17      PIN NAME = Q0
PIN NUMBER =  18      PIN NAME = NC
PIN NUMBER =  19      PIN NAME = CLKOUT
PIN NUMBER =  20      PIN NAME = VCC


EXPRESSIONS  AND DESCRIPTION =
EXPRESSION[ 1] =
/CLKOUT=/SEL1*/SEL0*/CLKA +/SEL1*SEL0*/CLKB +SEL1*/SEL0*/CLKC +SEL1*SEL0*/CLKD


EXPRESSION[ 2] =
/Q0=/CLR +Q0


EXPRESSION[ 3] =
/Q1=/CLR +/Q1*/Q0 +Q1*Q0


EXPRESSION[ 4] =
/Q2=/CLR +/Q2*/Q1 +Q2*Q1*Q0 +/Q2*/Q0


EXPRESSION[ 5] =
/Q3=/CLR +/Q3*/Q2 +/Q3*/Q1 +/Q3*/Q0 +Q3*Q2*Q1*Q0


EXPRESSION[ 6] =
/BDOUT=/BD*Q3*/Q2*/Q1*Q0
```

**Figure 18. Pin ID and Logic Equations**

Applications

6

```
                  0000 0000 0011 1111 1111 2222 2222 2233
                  0123 4567 8901 2343 6789 0123 4567 8901
         /CLKOUT  =
                  ---- ---- ---- ---- ---- ---- ---- ----   0 -
                  -X-- -X-- -X-- ---- ---- ---- ---- ----   1 - /SEL1*/SEL0*/CLKA+
                  X--- -X-- ---- -X-- ---- ---- ---- ----   2 - /SEL1*SEL0*/CLKB+
                  -X-- X--- ---- ---- -X-- ---- ---- ----   3 - SEL1*/SEL0*/CLKC+
                  X--- X--- ---- ---- ---- -X-- ---- ----   4 - SEL1*SEL0*/CLKD
                  XXXX XXXX XXXX XXXX XXXX XXXX XXXX XXXX   5 -
                  XXXX XXXX XXXX XXXX XXXX XXXX XXXX XXXX   6 -
                  XXXX XXXX XXXX XXXX XXXX XXXX XXXX XXXX   7 -
                  =
                  XXXX XXXX XXXX XXXX XXXX XXXX XXXX XXXX   8 -
                  XXXX XXXX XXXX XXXX XXXX XXXX XXXX XXXX   9 -
                  XXXX XXXX XXXX XXXX XXXX XXXX XXXX XXXX  10 -
                  XXXX XXXX XXXX XXXX XXXX XXXX XXXX XXXX  11 -
                  XXXX XXXX XXXX XXXX XXXX XXXX XXXX XXXX  12 -
                  XXXX XXXX XXXX XXXX XXXX XXXX XXXX XXXX  13 -
                  XXXX XXXX XXXX XXXX XXXX XXXX XXXX XXXX  14 -
                  XXXX XXXX XXXX XXXX XXXX XXXX XXXX XXXX  15 -
         /Q0      =
                  ---- ---- ---- ---- ---- ---- -X-- ----  16 - /CLR+
                  ---- ---- --X- ---- ---- ---- ---- ----  17 - Q0
                  XXXX XXXX XXXX XXXX XXXX XXXX XXXX XXXX  18 -
                  XXXX XXXX XXXX XXXX XXXX XXXX XXXX XXXX  19 -
                  XXXX XXXX XXXX XXXX XXXX XXXX XXXX XXXX  20 -
                  XXXX XXXX XXXX XXXX XXXX XXXX XXXX XXXX  21 -
                  XXXX XXXX XXXX XXXX XXXX XXXX XXXX XXXX  22 -
                  XXXX XXXX XXXX XXXX XXXX XXXX XXXX XXXX  23 -
         /Q1      =
                  ---- ---- ---- ---- ---- ---- -X-- ----  24 - /CLR+
                  ---- ---- ---X ---X ---- ---- ---- ----  25 - /Q1*/Q0+
                  ---- ---- --X- --X- ---- ---- ---- ----  26 - Q1*Q0
                  XXXX XXXX XXXX XXXX XXXX XXXX XXXX XXXX  27 -
                  XXXX XXXX XXXX XXXX XXXX XXXX XXXX XXXX  28 -
                  XXXX XXXX XXXX XXXX XXXX XXXX XXXX XXXX  29 -
                  XXXX XXXX XXXX XXXX XXXX XXXX XXXX XXXX  30 -
                  XXXX XXXX XXXX XXXX XXXX XXXX XXXX XXXX  31 -
         /Q2      =
                  ---- ---- ---- ---- ---- ---- -X-- ----  32 - /CLR+
                  ---- ---- ---X ---X ---- ---- ---- ----  33 - /Q2*/Q1+
                  ---- ---- --X- --X- --X- ---- ---- ----  34 - Q2*Q1*Q0+
                  ---- ---- --X- ---X ---X ---- ---- ----  35 - /Q2*/Q0
                  XXXX XXXX XXXX XXXX XXXX XXXX XXXX XXXX  36 -
                  XXXX XXXX XXXX XXXX XXXX XXXX XXXX XXXX  37 -
                  XXXX XXXX XXXX XXXX XXXX XXXX XXXX XXXX  38 -
                  XXXX XXXX XXXX XXXX XXXX XXXX XXXX XXXX  39 -
         /Q3      =
                  ---- ---- ---- ---- ---- ---- -X-- ----  40 - /CLR+
                  ---- ---- ---- ---- ---X ---X ---- ----  41 - /Q3*/Q2+
                  ---- ---- ---X ---- ---X ---- ---- ----  42 - /Q3*/Q1+
                  ---- ---- --X- ---- ---- ---X ---- ----  43 - /Q3*/Q0+
                  ---- ---- --X- --X- --X- --X- ---- ----  44 - Q3*Q2*Q1*Q0
                  XXXX XXXX XXXX XXXX XXXX XXXX XXXX XXXX  45 -
                  XXXX XXXX XXXX XXXX XXXX XXXX XXXX XXXX  46 -
                  XXXX XXXX XXXX XXXX XXXX XXXX XXXX XXXX  47 -
                  =
                  XXXX XXXX XXXX XXXX XXXX XXXX XXXX XXXX  48 -
                  XXXX XXXX XXXX XXXX XXXX XXXX XXXX XXXX  49 -
                  XXXX XXXX XXXX XXXX XXXX XXXX XXXX XXXX  50 -
                  XXXX XXXX XXXX XXXX XXXX XXXX XXXX XXXX  51 -
                  XXXX XXXX XXXX XXXX XXXX XXXX XXXX XXXX  52 -
                  XXXX XXXX XXXX XXXX XXXX XXXX XXXX XXXX  53 -
                  XXXX XXXX XXXX XXXX XXXX XXXX XXXX XXXX  54 -
                  XXXX XXXX XXXX XXXX XXXX XXXX XXXX XXXX  55 -
         /BDOUT   =
                  ---- ---- ---- ---- ---- ---- ---- ----  56 -
                  ---- ---- --X- ---X ---X --X- ---- -X--  57 - /BD*Q3*/Q2*/Q1*Q0
                  XXXX XXXX XXXX XXXX XXXX XXXX XXXX XXXX  58 -
                  XXXX XXXX XXXX XXXX XXXX XXXX XXXX XXXX  59 -
                  XXXX XXXX XXXX XXXX XXXX XXXX XXXX XXXX  60 -
                  XXXX XXXX XXXX XXXX XXXX XXXX XXXX XXXX  61 -
                  XXXX XXXX XXXX XXXX XXXX XXXX XXXX XXXX  62 -
                  XXXX XXXX XXXX XXXX XXXX XXXX XXXX XXXX  63 -
```

**Figure 19. Fuse Map**

## ADVANCED SOFTWARE

PALASM, while extremely useful in generating the fuse map, does little to help formulate the logic equations. This is what the new software packages such as ABEL and CUPL address. They not only generate the fuse map, but they also help in developing the logic equations. In most cases, they can generate the logic equations from simply providing the program with either a truth table or state diagram. In addition, they can test the logic equations against a set of test vectors. This helps ensure the designer gets the desired function.

These are only a few of the features available on these new advanced software packages. We recommend that the reader contact the specific manufacturers themselves to obtain the latest information available. For your convenience, at the end of this application note we have included the addresses and phone numbers for many of these programming and software companies.

As an example, we will approach our previous design utilizing DATA I/O's ABEL package. The purpose here is not to teach the reader how to use ABEL, but rather to give them a basic overview of this powerful software package. Figure 20 shows the source file required by ABEL. Note that the 4-bit counter has been described with a state diagram table. When the ABEL program is complied, the logic equations will be generated from this. The equations for CLK OUT and BD OUT have been given in their final form to demonstrate how ABEL would handle these. Also notice that test vectors are included for checking the logic equations. This is especially important when only the logic equations has been given.

Figure 21 shows some of the output documentation generated by the program. Notice that the equations generated for the counter, match the the ones generated by the Karnaugh maps. A pinout for the device has also been generated and displayed. The fuse map for the device has not been shown, but looks very similar to the one in Figure 19. As with the PALASM program, this information can be down loaded into the device programmer.

## PERFORMANCE

Up to this point, nothing has been said about the performance of these devices. The Standard High Speed PAL (indicated by an "A" after the device number) offered by TI has a maximum propagation of 25 ns from input to output, and 35 MHz $f_{max}$. Also available is a new, higher speed family of devices called TIBPALs. These devices are functionally equivalent with the current family and offer a maximum propagation delay of 15 ns from input to output. They are also rated at 50 MHz $f_{max}$. The higher speeds on these devices make them compatible with most high-speed logic families. This allows them to be designed into more critical speed path applications.

Applications

6

```
module BD_COUNT flag '-r2'
title '4-bit binary/decade counter'

      IC1   device 'P16R4';

"  pin assignments and constant declarations
    CLK_IN SEL0 SEL1,CLKA      pin  1,2,3,4;
    CLKB,CLKC,CLKD             pin  5,6,7;
    CLR,BD_IN,OE               pin  8,9,11;
    BD_OUT,CLK_OUT             pin  12,19;
    Q3,Q2,Q1,Q0                pin  14,15,16,17;
    CK, L, H, X, Z      =      .C. , 0 , 1 , .X. , .Z.;
    OUTPUT              =      [Q3,Q2,Q1,Q0];

"  counter states
    S0=^b0000;   S4=^b0100;   S8=^b1000;    S12=^b1100;
    S1=^b0001;   S5=^b0101;   S9=^b1001;    S13=^b1101;
    S2=^b0010;   S6=^b0110;   S10=^b1010;   S14=^b1110;
    S3=^b0011;   S7=^b0111;   S11=^b1011;   S15=^b1111;

equations
"  clock selector
    CLK_OUT = CLKA & !SEL0 & !SEL1 # CLKB & !SEL1 & SEL0
            # CLKC & SEL1 & !SEL0 # CLKD & SEL1 & SEL0;

"  count nine indicator for decade counting
    BD_OUT  = !(!BD_IN & Q3 & !Q2 & !Q1 & Q0);

state_diagram [Q3,Q2,Q1,Q0]
    State  S0:   IF CLR == 0 THEN S0 ELSE  S1;
    State  S1:   IF CLR == 0 THEN S0 ELSE  S2;
    State  S2:   IF CLR == 0 THEN S0 ELSE  S3;
    State  S3:   IF CLR == 0 THEN S0 ELSE  S4;
    State  S4:   IF CLR == 0 THEN S0 ELSE  S5;
    State  S5:   IF CLR == 0 THEN S0 ELSE  S6;
    State  S6:   IF CLR == 0 THEN S0 ELSE  S7;
    State  S7:   IF CLR == 0 THEN S0 ELSE  S8;
    State  S8:   IF CLR == 0 THEN S0 ELSE  S9;
    State  S9:   IF CLR == 0 THEN S0 ELSE  S10;
    State  S10:  IF CLR == 0 THEN S0 ELSE  S11;
    State  S11:  IF CLR == 0 THEN S0 ELSE  S12;
    State  S12:  IF CLR == 0 THEN S0 ELSE  S13;
    State  S13:  IF CLR == 0 THEN S0 ELSE  S14;
    State  S14:  IF CLR == 0 THEN S0 ELSE  S15;
    State  S15:  IF CLR == 0 THEN S0 ELSE  S0;

test_vectors    'clock selector'
    ([CLKA, CLKB, CLKC, CLKD, SEL1, SEL0] -> CLK_OUT)
    [ L  ,  X  ,  X  ,  X  ,  L,   L ] ->    L;
    [ H  ,  X  ,  X  ,  X  ,  L,   L ] ->    H;
    [ X  ,  L  ,  X  ,  X  ,  L,   H ] ->    L;
    [ X  ,  H  ,  X  ,  X  ,  L,   H ] ->    H;
    [ X  ,  X  ,  L  ,  X  ,  H,   L ] ->    L;
    [ X  ,  X  ,  H  ,  X  ,  H,   L ] ->    H;
    [ X  ,  X  ,  X  ,  L  ,  H,   H ] ->    L;
    [ X  ,  X  ,  X  ,  H  ,  H,   H ] ->    H;

test_vectors    'counter'
    ([CLK_IN, OE, CLR, BD_IN] -> [OUTPUT, BD_OUT])
    [  CK,  L ,  L ,   X  ] -> [  S0,   H ];
    [  CK,  L ,  H ,   X  ] -> [  S1,   H ];
    [  CK,  L ,  H ,   X  ] -> [  S2,   H ];
    [  CK,  L ,  H ,   X  ] -> [  S3,   H ];
    [  CK,  L ,  H ,   X  ] -> [  S4,   H ];
    [  CK,  L ,  H ,   X  ] -> [  S5,   H ];
    [  CK,  L ,  H ,   X  ] -> [  S6,   H ];
    [  CK,  L ,  H ,   X  ] -> [  S7,   H ];
    [  CK,  L ,  H ,   X  ] -> [  S8,   H ];
    [  CK,  L ,  H ,   L  ] -> [  S9,   L ];
    [  CK,  L ,  H ,   X  ] -> [ S10,   H ];
    [  CK,  L ,  H ,   X  ] -> [ S11,   H ];
    [  CK,  L ,  H ,   X  ] -> [ S12,   H ];
    [  CK,  L ,  H ,   X  ] -> [ S13,   H ];
    [  CK,  L ,  H ,   X  ] -> [ S14,   H ];
    [  CK,  L ,  H ,   H  ] -> [ S15,   H ];
    [  CK,  L ,  H ,   X  ] -> [  S0,   H ];
    [  X ,  H ,  X ,   X  ] -> [  Z ,   H ];
end BD_COUNT
```

**Figure 20.  Source File for ABEL**

```
ABEL(tm) Version  1.00  - Document Generator
4-bit binary/decade counter

Equations for Module BD_COUNT

Device IC1


    Reduced Equations:

        CLK_OUT = !((SEL1 & SEL0 & !CLKD
                  # (SEL1 & !SEL0 & !CLKC
                  # (!SEL1 & SEL0 & !CLKB
                  # !SEL1 & !SEL0 & !CLKA))));


        BD_OUT = !(Q3 & !Q2 & !Q1 & Q0 & !BD_IN);

        Q3 := !((Q3 & Q2 & Q1 & Q0
              # (!Q3 & !Q2
              # (!Q3 & !Q1
              # (!Q3 & !Q0
              # !CLR)))));


        Q2 := !((Q2 & Q1 & Q0 # (!Q2 & !Q1 # (!Q2 & !Q0 # !CLR))));

        Q1 := !((Q1 & Q0 # (!Q1 & !Q0 # !CLR)));

        Q0 := !((Q0 # !CLR));
```

```
ABEL(tm) Version  1.00  - Document Generator
4-bit binary/decade counter

Chip diagram for Module BD_COUNT

Device IC1
```

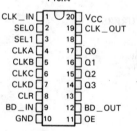

```
end of module BD_COUNT
```

**Figure 21. ABEL Output Documentation**

## ADDRESS FOR PROGRAMMING AND SOFTWARE MANUFACTURERS*

### HARDWARE MANUFACTURERS

Citel
3060 Raymond St.
Santa Clara, CA 95050
(408) 727-6562

DATA I/O
10525 Willows Rd.
Redmond, WA 98052
(206) 881-6444

DIGITAL MEDIA
3178 Gibralter Ave.
Costa Mesa, CA 92626
(714) 751-1373

Kontron Electronics
630 Price Avenue
Redwood City, CA 94063
(415) 361-1012

Stag Micro Systems
528-5 Weddell Drive
Sunnyvale, CA 94086
(408) 745-1991

Storey Systems
3201 N. Hwy 67, Suite H
Mesquite, Tx 75150
(214) 270-4135

Structured Design
1700 Wyatt Dr., Suite 7
Santa Clara, CA 95054
(408) 988-0725

Sunrise Electronics
524 S. Vermont Avenue
Glendora, CA 91740
(213) 914-1926

Valley Data Sciences
2426 Charleston Rd.
Mountain View, CA 94043
(415) 968-2900

Varix
1210 Campbell Rd.
Richardson, TX 75081
(214) 437-0777

Wavetec/Digelec
586 Weddel Dr., Suite 1
Sunnyvale, CA 94089
(408) 745-0722

### SOFTWARE MANUFACTURERS

Assisted Technologies (CUPL)
2381 Zanker Road, Suite 150
Santa Clara, CA 95050
(408) 942-8787

DATA I/O (ABEL)
10525 Willows Rd.
Redmond, WA 98052
(206) 881-6444

*Texas Instruments does not endorse or warrant the suppliers referenced.

### Reference

1. H. Troy Nagle, Jr., B.D. Carroll, and David Irwin, *An Introduction to Computer Logic*. New Jersey: Prentice-Hall, Inc., 1975.

**Applications**

**6**

## DW plastic dual-in-line packages

Each of these dual-in-line packages consists of a circuit mounted on a lead frame and encapsulated within a plastic compound. The compound will withstand soldering temperature with no deformation, and circuit performance characteristics will remain stable when operated in high-humidity conditions. Leads require no additional cleaning or processing when used in soldered assembly.

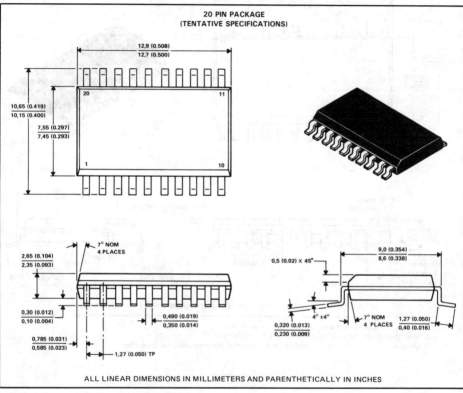

**20 PIN PACKAGE**
**(TENTATIVE SPECIFICATIONS)**

ALL LINEAR DIMENSIONS IN MILLIMETERS AND PARENTHETICALLY IN INCHES

NOTES:  A. Body dimensions do not include mold flash or protrusion.
  B. Mold flash or protrusion shall not exceed 0,15 (0.006).
  C. Leads are within 0,25 (0.010) radius of true position at maximum material dimension.

**Mechanical Data**

**7**

TEXAS
INSTRUMENTS

## MECHANICAL DATA

### DW plastic dual-in-line packages (continued)

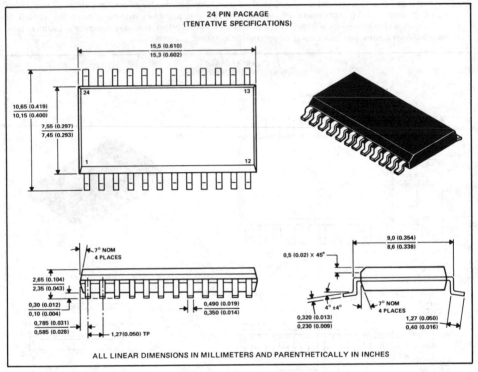

**24 PIN PACKAGE**
**(TENTATIVE SPECIFICATIONS)**

ALL LINEAR DIMENSIONS IN MILLIMETERS AND PARENTHETICALLY IN INCHES

NOTES: A. Body dimensions do not include mold flash or protrusion.
B. Mold flash or protrusion shall not exceed 0,15 (0.006).
C. Leads are within 0,25 (0.010) radius of true position at maximum material dimension.

**TEXAS**
**INSTRUMENTS**

### FK ceramic chip carrier packages

Each of these hermetically sealed chip carrier packages has a three-layer ceramic base with a metal lid and braze seal. The packages are intended for surface mounting on solder lands on 1,27 (0.050-inch) centers. Terminals require no additional cleaning or processing when used in soldered assembly.

FK package terminal assignments conform to JEDEC Standards 1 and 2.

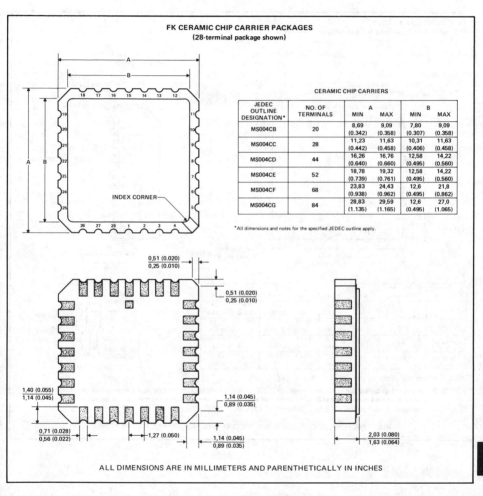

**FK CERAMIC CHIP CARRIER PACKAGES**
(28-terminal package shown)

CERAMIC CHIP CARRIERS

| JEDEC OUTLINE DESIGNATION* | NO. OF TERMINALS | A | | B | |
|---|---|---|---|---|---|
| | | MIN | MAX | MIN | MAX |
| MS004CB | 20 | 8,69 (0.342) | 9,09 (0.358) | 7,80 (0.307) | 9,09 (0.358) |
| MS004CC | 28 | 11,23 (0.442) | 11,63 (0.458) | 10,31 (0.406) | 11,63 (0.458) |
| MS004CD | 44 | 16,26 (0.640) | 16,76 (0.660) | 12,58 (0.495) | 14,22 (0.560) |
| MS004CE | 52 | 18,78 (0.739) | 19,32 (0.761) | 12,58 (0.495) | 14,22 (0.560) |
| MS004CF | 68 | 23,83 (0.938) | 24,43 (0.962) | 12,6 (0.495) | 21,8 (0.862) |
| MS004CG | 84 | 28,83 (1.135) | 29,59 (1.165) | 12,6 (0.495) | 27,0 (1.065) |

*All dimensions and notes for the specified JEDEC outline apply.

INDEX CORNER

0,51 (0.020) / 0,25 (0.010)

0,51 (0.020) / 0,25 (0.010)

1,40 (0.055) / 1,14 (0.045)

1,14 (0.045) / 0,89 (0.035)

0,71 (0.028) / 0,56 (0.022)

1,27 (0.050)

1,14 (0.045) / 0,89 (0.035)

2,03 (0.080) / 1,63 (0.064)

ALL DIMENSIONS ARE IN MILLIMETERS AND PARENTHETICALLY IN INCHES

**TEXAS INSTRUMENTS**

Mechanical Data

7

# MECHANICAL DATA

## FN plastic chip carrier package

Each of these chip carrier packages consists of a circuit mounted on a lead frame and encapsulated within an electrically nonconductive plastic compound. the compound withstands soldering temperatures with no deformation, and circuit performance characteristics remain stable when the devices are operated in high-humidity conditions. The packages are intended for surface mounting on solder lands on 1,27-mm (0.050-inch) centers. Leads require no additional cleaning or processing when used in soldered assembly.

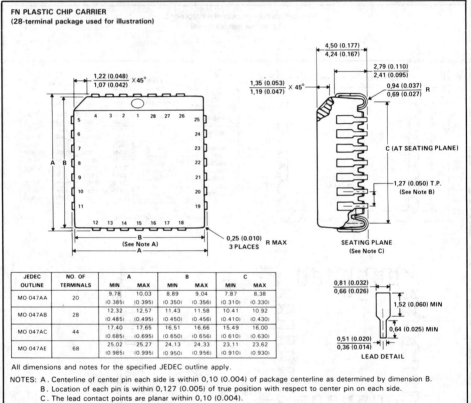

**FN PLASTIC CHIP CARRIER**
(28-terminal package used for illustration)

| JEDEC OUTLINE | NO. OF TERMINALS | A MIN | A MAX | B MIN | B MAX | C MIN | C MAX |
|---|---|---|---|---|---|---|---|
| MO-047AA | 20 | 9.78 (0.385) | 10.03 (0.395) | 8.89 (0.350) | 9.04 (0.356) | 7.87 (0.310) | 8.38 (0.330) |
| MO-047AB | 28 | 12.32 (0.485) | 12.57 (0.495) | 11.43 (0.450) | 11.58 (0.456) | 10.41 (0.410) | 10.92 (0.430) |
| MO-047AC | 44 | 17.40 (0.685) | 17.65 (0.695) | 16.51 (0.650) | 16.66 (0.656) | 15.49 (0.610) | 16.00 (0.630) |
| MO-047AE | 68 | 25.02 (0.985) | 25.27 (0.995) | 24.13 (0.950) | 24.33 (0.956) | 23.11 (0.910) | 23.62 (0.930) |

All dimensions and notes for the specified JEDEC outline apply.

NOTES: A. Centerline of center pin each side is within 0,10 (0.004) of package centerline as determined by dimension B.
B. Location of each pin is within 0,127 (0.005) of true position with respect to center pin on each side.
C. The lead contact points are planar within 0,10 (0.004).

ALL LINEAR DIMENSIONS ARE IN MILLIMETERS AND PARENTHETICALLY IN INCHES

**Mechanical Data**

**7**

TEXAS
INSTRUMENTS

## J ceramic dual-in-line packages (including JD, JT, and JW)

Each of these hermetically sealed dual-in-line packages consists of a ceramic base, ceramic cap, and a lead frame. Hermetic sealing is accomplished with glass. The packages are intended for insertion in mounting-hole rows on 7,62 (0.300) or 15,24 (0.600) centers. Once the leads are compressed and inserted sufficient tension is provided to secure the package in the board during soldering. Tin-plated ("bright-dipped") leads require no additional cleaning or processing when used in soldered assembly.

NOTE:  For the 14-, 16-, and 20-pin packages, the letter J is used by itself since these packages are available only in the 7,62 (0.300) row spacing. For the 24-pin packages, if no second letter or row spacing is specified, the package is assumed to have 15,24 (0.600) row spacing.

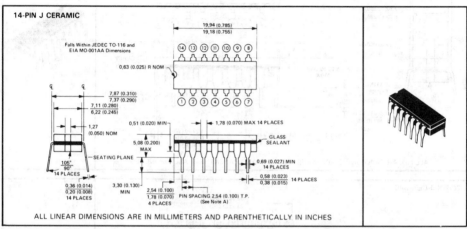

**14-PIN J CERAMIC**

Falls Within JEDEC TO-116 and EIA MO-001AA Dimensions

ALL LINEAR DIMENSIONS ARE IN MILLIMETERS AND PARENTHETICALLY IN INCHES

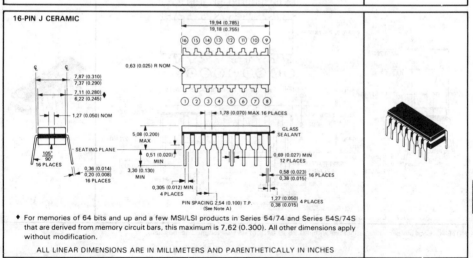

**16-PIN J CERAMIC**

♦ For memories of 64 bits and up and a few MSI/LSI products in Series 54/74 and Series 54S/74S that are derived from memory circuit bars, this maximum is 7,62 (0.300). All other dimensions apply without modification.

ALL LINEAR DIMENSIONS ARE IN MILLIMETERS AND PARENTHETICALLY IN INCHES

NOTE A:  Each pin centerline is located within 0,25 (0.010) of its true longitudinal position.

**TEXAS INSTRUMENTS**

**Mechanical Data**

7

## MECHANICAL DATA

### J ceramic dual-in-line packages (continued)

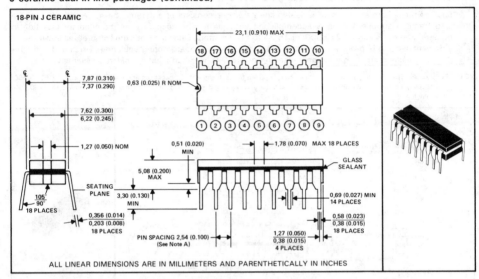

**18-PIN J CERAMIC**

ALL LINEAR DIMENSIONS ARE IN MILLIMETERS AND PARENTHETICALLY IN INCHES

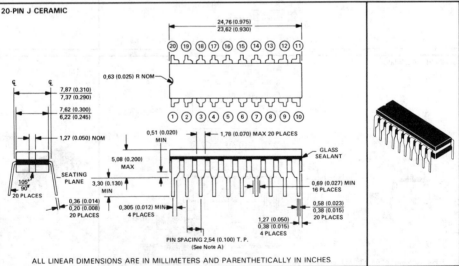

**20-PIN J CERAMIC**

ALL LINEAR DIMENSIONS ARE IN MILLIMETERS AND PARENTHETICALLY IN INCHES

NOTE A: Each pin centerline is located within 0,25 (0.010) of its true longitudinal position.

TEXAS
INSTRUMENTS

## J ceramic dual-in-line packages (continued)

### 24-PIN JT CERAMIC, 0.300-INCH ROW SPACING

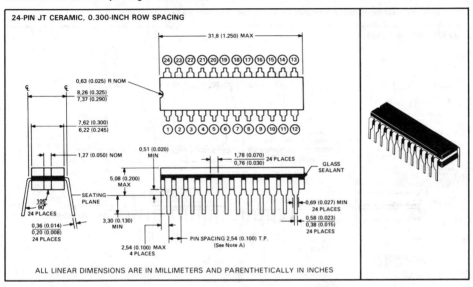

ALL LINEAR DIMENSIONS ARE IN MILLIMETERS AND PARENTHETICALLY IN INCHES

### 24-PIN JW CERAMIC

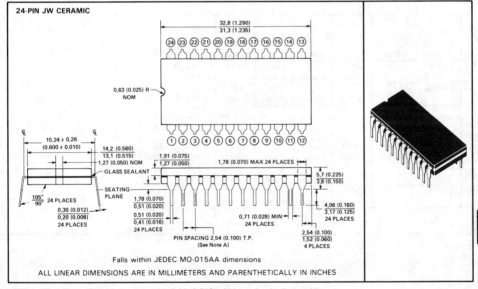

Falls within JEDEC MO-015AA dimensions

ALL LINEAR DIMENSIONS ARE IN MILLIMETERS AND PARENTHETICALLY IN INCHES

NOTE A: Each pin centerline is located within 0,25 (0.010) of its true longitudinal position.

Mechanical Data

7

### J ceramic dual-in-line packages (continued)

This is a hermetically sealed ceramic package with a metal cap and side-brazed tin-plated leads.

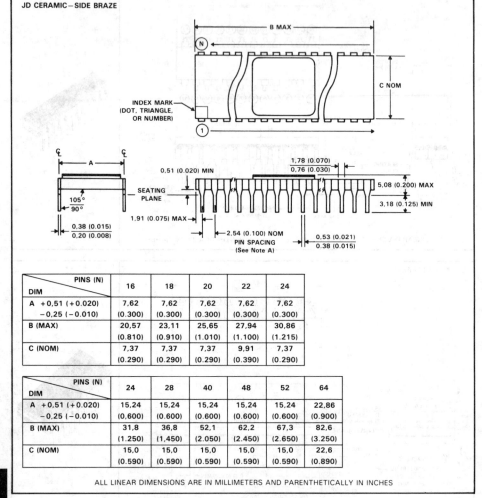

| DIM \ PINS (N) | 16 | 18 | 20 | 22 | 24 |
|---|---|---|---|---|---|
| A  +0,51 (+0.020) | 7,62 | 7,62 | 7,62 | 7,62 | 7,62 |
|     −0,25 (−0.010) | (0.300) | (0.300) | (0.300) | (0.300) | (0.300) |
| B (MAX) | 20,57 | 23,11 | 25,65 | 27,94 | 30,86 |
|  | (0.810) | (0.910) | (1.010) | (1.100) | (1.215) |
| C (NOM) | 7,37 | 7,37 | 7,37 | 9,91 | 7,37 |
|  | (0.290) | (0.290) | (0.290) | (0.390) | (0.290) |

| DIM \ PINS (N) | 24 | 28 | 40 | 48 | 52 | 64 |
|---|---|---|---|---|---|---|
| A  +0,51 (+0.020) | 15,24 | 15,24 | 15,24 | 15,24 | 15,24 | 22,86 |
|     −0,25 (−0.010) | (0.600) | (0.600) | (0.600) | (0.600) | (0.600) | (0.900) |
| B (MAX) | 31,8 | 36,8 | 52,1 | 62,2 | 67,3 | 82,6 |
|  | (1.250) | (1.450) | (2.050) | (2.450) | (2.650) | (3.250) |
| C (NOM) | 15,0 | 15,0 | 15,0 | 15,0 | 15,0 | 22,6 |
|  | (0.590) | (0.590) | (0.590) | (0.590) | (0.590) | (0.890) |

ALL LINEAR DIMENSIONS ARE IN MILLIMETERS AND PARENTHETICALLY IN INCHES

NOTE A: Each pin centerline is located within 0,25 (0.010) of its true longitudinal position.

Mechanical Data

7

TEXAS
INSTRUMENTS

## N plastic dual-in-line packages (including NT and NW)

Each of these dual-in-line packages consists of a circuit mounted on a lead frame and encapsulated within an electrically nonconductive plastic compound. The compound will withstand soldering temperature with no deformation, and circuit performance characteristics will remain stable when operated in high-humidity conditions. The packages are intended for insertion in mounting-hole rows on 7,62 (0.300), 15,24 (0.600), or 22,86 (0.900) centers. Once the leads are compressed and inserted, sufficient tension is provided to secure the package in the board during soldering. Leads require no additional cleaning or processing when used in soldered assembly.

NOTE: For all except 24-pin packages, the letter N is used by itself since only the 24-pin package is available in more than one row-spacing. For the 24-pin package, the 7,62 (0.300) version is designated NT; the 15,24 (0.600) version is designated NW. If no second letter or row-spacing is specified, the package is assumed to have 15,24 (0.600) row-spacing.

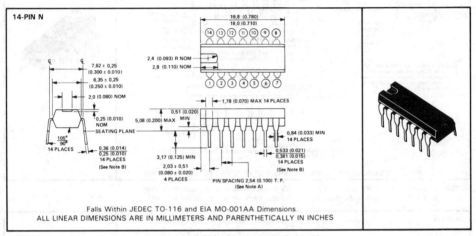

**14-PIN N**

Falls Within JEDEC TO-116 and EIA MO-001AA Dimensions
ALL LINEAR DIMENSIONS ARE IN MILLIMETERS AND PARENTHETICALLY IN INCHES

NOTES: A. Each pin centerline is located within 0,25 (0.010) of its true longitudinal position.
B. For solder-dipped leads, this dimension applies from the lead tip to the standoff.

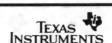

Mechanical Data

7

## MECHANICAL DATA

### N plastic dual-in-line packages (continued)

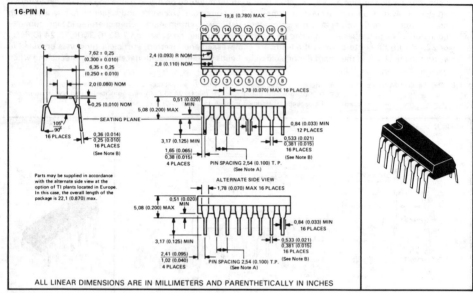

**16-PIN N**

ALL LINEAR DIMENSIONS ARE IN MILLIMETERS AND PARENTHETICALLY IN INCHES

NOTES: A. Each pin centerline is located within 0,25 (0.010) of its true longitudinal position.
B. For solder-dipped leads, this dimension applies from the lead tip to the standoff.

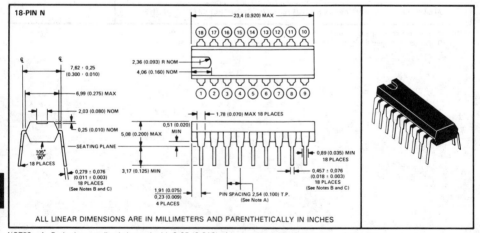

**18-PIN N**

ALL LINEAR DIMENSIONS ARE IN MILLIMETERS AND PARENTHETICALLY IN INCHES

NOTES: A. Each pin centerline is located with 0,25 (0.010) of its true longitudinal position.
B. This dimension does not apply for solder-dipped leads.
C. When solder-dipped leads are specified, dipped area of the lead extends from the lead tip to at least 0,51 (0.020) above seating plane.

TEXAS INSTRUMENTS

## N plastic dual-in-line packages (continued)

**20-PIN N**

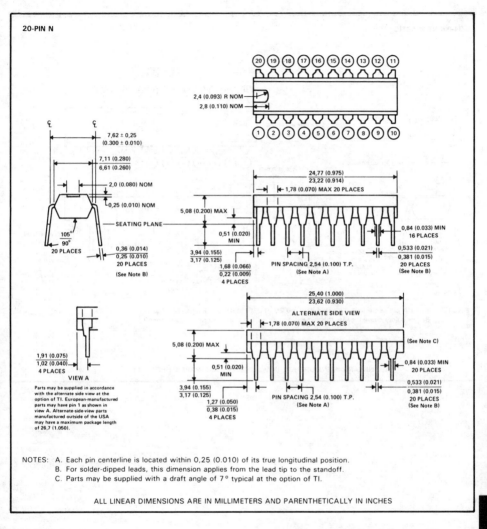

NOTES: A. Each pin centerline is located within 0,25 (0.010) of its true longitudinal position.
B. For solder-dipped leads, this dimension applies from the lead tip to the standoff.
C. Parts may be supplied with a draft angle of 7° typical at the option of TI.

ALL LINEAR DIMENSIONS ARE IN MILLIMETERS AND PARENTHETICALLY IN INCHES

Parts may be supplied in accordance with the alternate side view at the option of TI. European-manufactured parts may have pin 1 as shown in view A. Alternate-side-view parts manufactured outside of the USA may have a maximum package length of 26,7 (1.050).

## N plastic dual-in-line packages (continued)

**24-PIN NT PLASTIC**

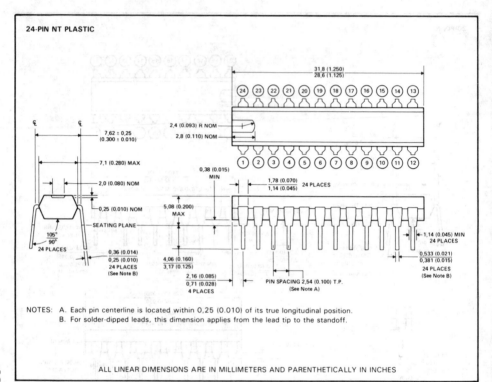

NOTES: A. Each pin centerline is located within 0,25 (0.010) of its true longitudinal position.
B. For solder-dipped leads, this dimension applies from the lead tip to the standoff.

ALL LINEAR DIMENSIONS ARE IN MILLIMETERS AND PARENTHETICALLY IN INCHES

Mechanical Data

7

**TEXAS**
**INSTRUMENTS**

## N plastic dual-in-line packages (continued)

**24-PIN NW PLASTIC**

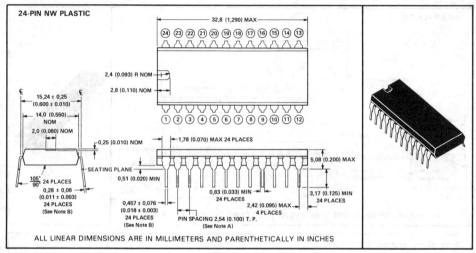

ALL LINEAR DIMENSIONS ARE IN MILLIMETERS AND PARENTHETICALLY IN INCHES

**28-PIN N PLASTIC**

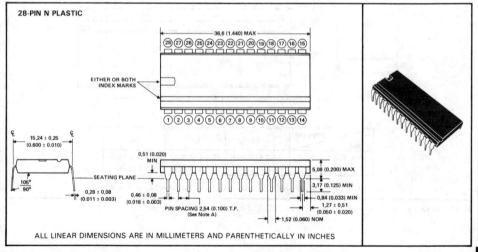

ALL LINEAR DIMENSIONS ARE IN MILLIMETERS AND PARENTHETICALLY IN INCHES

NOTES: A. Each pin centerline is located within 0,25 (0.010) of its true longitudinal position.
B. For solder-dipped leads, this dimension applies from the lead tip to the standoff.

**TEXAS INSTRUMENTS**

Mechanical Data

7

# MECHANICAL DATA

## N plastic dual-in-line packages (continued)

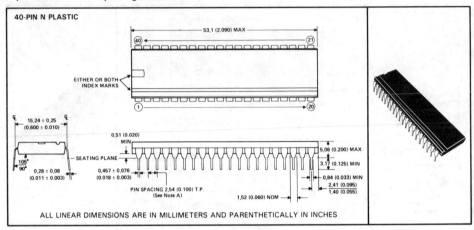

40-PIN N PLASTIC

ALL LINEAR DIMENSIONS ARE IN MILLIMETERS AND PARENTHETICALLY IN INCHES

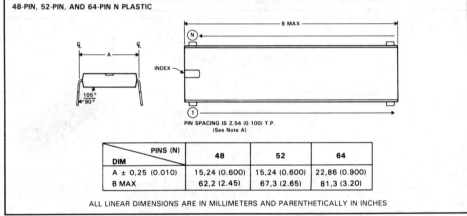

48-PIN, 52-PIN, AND 64-PIN N PLASTIC

PIN SPACING IS 2,54 (0.100) T.P.
(See Note A)

| DIM \ PINS (N) | 48 | 52 | 64 |
|---|---|---|---|
| A ± 0,25 (0.010) | 15,24 (0.600) | 15,24 (0.600) | 22,86 (0.900) |
| B MAX | 62,2 (2.45) | 67,3 (2.65) | 81,3 (3.20) |

ALL LINEAR DIMENSIONS ARE IN MILLIMETERS AND PARENTHETICALLY IN INCHES

NOTE: A. Each pin centerline is located within 0,25 (0.010) of its true longitudinal position.

Mechanical Data

7

TEXAS
INSTRUMENTS